Nissan Bluebird Owners Workshop Manual

Jeremy Churchill

Models covered
All T12 & T72 Nissan Bluebird Saloons & Hatchbacks;
1598 cc, 1796 cc, 1809 cc & 1974 cc

Does not cover U11 range, Estate or Diesel engine models

(1473-11S1)

ABCDE
FGHJJ
KLMNO
PQR

Haynes
THE BOOK ®

Haynes Publishing Group
Sparkford Nr Yeovil
Somerset BA22 7JJ England

Haynes Publications, Inc
861 Lawrence Drive
Newbury Park
California 91320 USA

Acknowledgements

Thanks are due to the Champion Sparking Plug Company Limited who supplied the illustrations showing spark plug conditions, and to Duckhams Oils, who provided lubrication data. Certain illustrations are the copyright of the Nissan Motor Company Limited of Japan and are used with their permission. Thanks are also due to Sykes-Pickavant Limited, who provided some of the workshop tools, and to all those people at Sparkford who helped in the production of this manual.

© Haynes Publishing Group 1990

A book in the **Haynes Owners Workshop Manual Series**

Printed by J. H. Haynes & Co. Ltd, Sparkford, Nr Yeovil, Somerset BA22 7JJ, England

ISBN 1 85010 473 5

British Library Cataloguing in Publication Data
Churchill, Jeremy *1954–*
    Nissan Bluebird ('86 to '90) owners workshop manual.
    1. Cars. Maintenance & repair
    I. Title   II. Series
    629.28722
    ISBN 1-85010-473-5

Contents

Nissan Bluebird 2.0i GSX

Nissan Bluebird Premium

Nissan Bluebird 1.8 Turbo ZX

About this manual

Its aim

The aim of this manual is to help you get the best value from your vehicle. It can do so in several ways. It can help you decide what work must be done (even should you choose to get it done by a garage), provide information on routine maintenance and servicing, and give a logical course of action and diagnosis when random faults occur. However, it is hoped that you will use the manual by tackling the work yourself. On simpler jobs it may even be quicker than booking the car into a garage and going there twice, to leave and collect it. Perhaps most important, a lot of money can be saved by avoiding the costs a garage must charge to cover its labour and overheads.

The manual has drawings and descriptions to show the function of the various components so that their layout can be understood. Then the tasks are described and photographed in a step-by-step sequence so that even a novice can do the work.

Its arrangement

The manual is divided into 12 Chapters, each covering a logical sub-division of the vehicle. The Chapters are each divided into Sections, numbered with single figures, eg 5; and the Sections into paragraphs (or sub-sections), with decimal numbers following on from the Section they are in, eg 5.1, 5.2, 5.3 etc.

It is freely illustrated, especially in those parts where there is a detailed sequence of operations to be carried out. There are two forms of illustration, figures and photographs. The figures are numbered in sequence with decimal numbers, according to their position in the Chapter – eg Fig. 6.4 is the fourth drawing/illustration in Chapter 6. Photographs carry the same number (either individually or in related groups) as the Section or sub-section to which they relate.

There is an alphabetical index at the back of the manual as well as a contents list at the front. Each Chapter is also preceded by its own individual contents list.

References to the 'left' or 'right' of the vehicle are in the sense of a person in the driver's seat facing forwards.

Unless otherwise stated, nuts and bolts are removed by turning anti-clockwise, and tightened by turning clockwise.

Vehicle manufacturers continually make changes to specifications and recommendations, and these, when notified, are incorporated into our manuals at the earliest opportunity.

Whilst every care is taken to ensure that the information in this manual is correct, no liability can be accepted by the authors or publishers for loss, damage or injury caused by any errors in, or omissions from, the information given.

Project vehicles

The main project vehicle used in the preparation of this manual, and appearing in the majority of the photographic sequences, was a 1989 Nissan Bluebird 2.0i GSX Saloon. Additional work was carried out and photographed on a 1989 Nissan Bluebird Turbo ZX Hatchback and a 1989 Nissan Bluebird 1.6 Premium Hatchback.

Introduction to the Nissan T12 and T72 Bluebird series

Introduced early in 1986, the models covered in this manual are the result of extensive refinement of the earlier U11 series Bluebird. Considerable development work was carried out in Europe to produce a car more suited to European tastes, particularly in the areas of handling and ride. The main distinguishing features from the U11 series are the narrower radiator grille and sloping bonnet line, coupled with a longer body and high-level boot line.

The Japanese-built T12 models formed the bulk of sales throughout 1986/7 until replaced by the UK-built T72 models during 1987. The T72 models are built by Nissan Motor Manufacturing (UK) Limited in their factory in Washington, Tyne and Wear.

The first cars were Saloon models, assembled from kits supplied by Japan in July 1986; Hatchback models came on stream in January 1987. At first 80% of the content of each car was Japanese, but this rapidly fell, and by October 1987 60% of each car's components was being obtained from suppliers within the EC. Since the opening of a press shop (to produce body panels) and an engine assembly shop during 1988, local content has risen to more than 70%.

The T12 and T72 Bluebirds are powered by the CA-series overhead camshaft engine, available in 1.6, 1.8 and 2.0 litre carburettor, 2.0 litre fuel-injected or 1.8 litre fuel-injected, turbocharged forms. The engine is mounted transversely at the front and drives either a five-speed manual or a four-speed automatic transaxle. Steering is by rack and pinion (power-assisted on most models) and suspension is by MacPherson strut at front and rear with anti-roll bars and transverse and trailing links.

A wide range of models is offered, in both Saloons and Hatchback form, to appeal to the fleet user as well as the private motorist. All versions of this straightforward, conventionally-engineered car are characterised by a high level of standard equipment.

General dimensions, weights and capacities

Dimensions

Overall length:

Saloon – early models	4405 mm (173.4 in)
Saloon – later models	4460 mm (175.6 in)
Hatchback – early models	4365 mm (171.9 in)
Hatchback – later models	4410 mm (173.6 in)
Overall width	1690 mm (66.5 in)
Overall height	1395 mm (54.9 in)
Wheelbase	2550 mm (100.4 in)
Track – front and rear	1460 mm (57.5 in)
Minimum ground clearance	150 mm (5.9 in)
Turning circle	10.0 m (32.8 ft)

Weights

Kerb weight:

	Saloon	Hatchback
1.6 L, LS, Premium	1120 kg (2469 lb)	1130 kg (2491 lb)
1.6 LX	1130 kg (2491 lb)	1140 kg (2513 lb)
1.8 LX 1.8 GS (manual)	1160 kg (2557 lb)	1170 kg (2579 lb)
1.8 SLX (manual)	1170 kg (2579 lb)	1180 kg (2601 lb)
2.0 SLX, 2.0 and 2.0i GSX (manual)	1175 kg (2590 lb)	1185 kg (2612 lb)
2.0i Executive (manual)	1300 kg (2867 lb)	Not available
1.8 SGX (manual)	1180 kg (2601 lb)	1190 kg (2623 lb)
2.0 SGX (manual)	1185 kg (2617 lb)	1195 kg (2634 lb)
1.8 GS (automatic)	1195 kg (2634 lb)	1205 kg (2656 lb)
1.8 SLX (automatic)	1205 kg (2656 lb)	1215 kg (2679 lb)
2.0 SLX, 2.0 and 2.0i GSX (automatic)	1210 kg (2668 lb)	1220 kg (2690 lb)
1.8 SGX (automatic), Turbo ZX	1215 kg (2679 lb)	1225 kg (2701 lb)
2.0 SGX (automatic)	1220 kg (2690 lb)	1230 kg (2712 lb)

Note: *Kerb weight is defined as the car unladen but with full fuel tank, coolant and lubricants and the spare wheel, jack, tools and mats in their correct positions*

Maximum towing weight:

Braked trailer	1200 kg (2646 lb)
Unbraked trailer	600 kg (1323 lb)

Note: *For all other weights, see vehicle identification plate*

Capacities (approximate)

Fuel tank	60 litres (13.2 Imp gals)	
Engine oil:	**At oil change**	**At oil and filter change**
2.0 litre fuel injection	3.4 litres (6.0 Imp pints)	3.8 litres (6.7 Imp pints)
All other models	3.2 litres (5.6 Imp pints)	3.6 litres (6.3 Imp pints)
Cooling system (total):		
Vertical-flow radiator – carburettor models	8.1 litres (14.3 Imp pints)	
Vertical-flow radiator – Turbo models	8.6 litres (15.1 Imp pints)	
Crossflow radiator – manual transmission	7.6 litres (13.4 Imp pints)	
Crossflow radiator – automatic transmission	7.5 litres (13.2 Imp pints)	
Manual transmission:		
1.6 litre models up to February 1987	2.7 litres (4.8 Imp pints)	
All other 1.6 litre models	2.8 litres (4.9 Imp pints)	
1.8 and 2.0 litre models	4.7 litres (8.3 Imp pints)	
Automatic transmission	6.8 litres (12.0 Imp pints)	
Power-assisted steering system	0.9 litre (1.6 Imp pints)	

Jacking, towing and wheel changing

Changing roadwheels

With the car parked on firm, level ground, apply the handbrake firmly and select first gear or reverse gear (manual) or the 'P' position (automatic). Ask any passengers to get out of the car and stay clear, then remove the jack, tools and spare wheel from the luggage compartment (photo).

Remove the roadwheel trim (where fitted) and slacken the roadwheel nuts through half to 1 turn each, working in a diagonal sequence. Using chalk or similar, mark the relationship of the wheel to any one of the studs.

Place chocks at the front and rear of the wheel diagonally opposite the one to be removed, then engage the jack in the jacking point nearest the wheel to be removed and jack up the car. Ensure the jack base rests on a firm surface.

Unscrew the roadwheel nuts and remove the wheel. Check that the stud threads and wheel-to-hub mating surfaces are clean and undamaged. If light alloy roadwheels are fitted, apply a thin smear of anti-seize compound (such as Holt Lloyd's Copaslip) to the mating surfaces to prevent the formation of corrosion. The stud threads should be cleaned with a brass wire brush if rusty, and the nuts should be refitted dry. In severe cases it is permissible to apply a very thin smear of anti-seize compound to the stud threads. Clean the inside of the roadwheel.

On refitting, align the marks made on removal (if the same wheel is being refitted) and refit the nuts with their tapered surfaces against the wheel. Tighten by hand as much as possible so that the wheel is correctly positioned.

Lower the car to the ground, remove the jack and tighten the nuts, (working in progressive stages and in a diagonal sequence) to the specified torque setting (photo). If a torque wrench is not available, have the tightness of the nuts checked as soon as possible, **especially** where light alloy roadwheels are fitted (photo). Check the tyre pressure.

Note: *If light alloy roadwheels are fitted, use a torque wrench to recheck the tightness of the roadwheel nuts 600 miles (1000 km) after the wheel is refitted.*

Refit the roadwheel trim (where fitted) remove the chocks and stow

Jack supplied with car

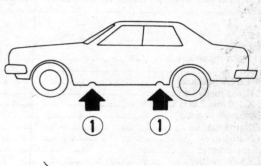

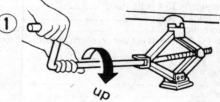

Using the car's jack

Roadwheel nuts should be tightened to specified torque setting

Front towing hook

Rear towing hook (Hatchback)

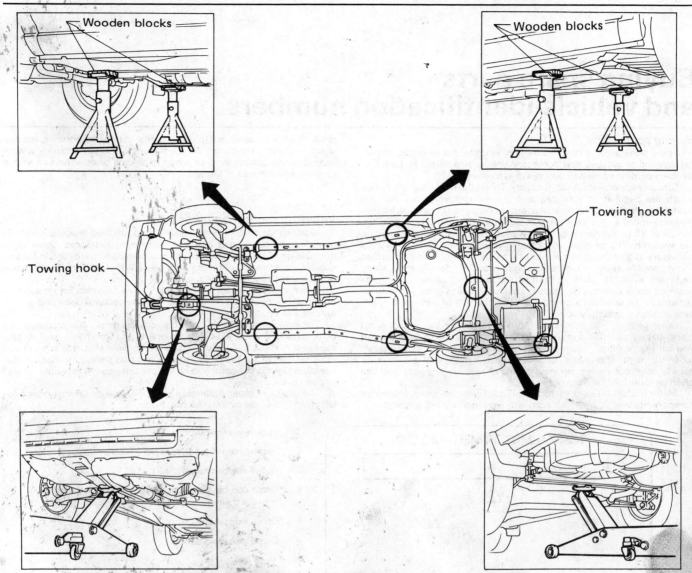

Workshop jacking points, axle stand locations and towing hook locations

the jack and tools. If a new roadwheel has been fitted, have it balanced as soon as possible.

Servicing

Note: *Never work underneath a car that is supported only by the car jack supplied; these are intended only for changing roadwheels at the roadside (see above). The car must always be supported by axle stands during servicing work.*

When raising the car for servicing work, preferably use a trolley or hydraulic jack with a wooden block as an insulator to prevent damage to the underbody. Place the jack under a structural member at the points indicated, never raise the car by jacking up under the engine sump or transmission casing. If both front or rear wheels are to be raised, jack up one side first and securely support it on an axle stand before raising the other side.

To avoid repetition, the procedures for raising the car in order to carry out work under it is not included before each relevant operation described in this manual.

It is to be preferred and is certainly recommended that the car is positioned over an inspection pit or raised on a lift. When such equipment is not available, use ramps or jack up the car as previously described, but always supplement the lifting device with axle stands.

Towing

Towing hooks are provided at both front and rear of the car (photos). The rear towing hook should be used only for emergency towing of another vehicle; for trailer towing a properly fitted towing bracket is required. Two tie-down hooks are provided at the front of the front wing inner panels, but these are **not** strong enough to be used for towing purposes.

If the car is to be towed, arrange it so that the front wheels are clear of the ground and check that the handbrake is released. If the car must be towed with the rear wheels clear of the ground, use a towing dolly to keep the front wheels off the ground as well. This is especially important with automatic transmission models, where serious (and expensive) damage can be caused to the transmission if the front wheels are on the ground when the car is towed.

If the car must be towed with all four wheels on the ground, automatic transmission models must not be towed for more than 40 miles (65 km) or faster than 30 mph (50 km/h), and position 'N' must be selected. On all models, insert the ignition key and turn to the 'On' position to unlock the steering and to allow the use of lights, direction indicators and horn. Expect to apply greater than normal pressure to the brake pedal, as servo assistance will not be available.

Buying spare parts and vehicle identification numbers

Buying spare parts

Spare parts are available from many sources, for example, Nissan garages, other garages and accessory shops, and motor factors. Our advice regarding spare part sources is as follows.

Officially appointed Nissan garages – This is the best source for parts which are peculiar to your car, and are not generally available (eg complete cylinder heads, internal gearbox components, badges, interior trim etc). It is also the only place at which you should buy parts if the vehicle is still under warranty – non-Nissan components may invalidate the warranty. To be sure of obtaining the correct parts, it will be necessary to give the storeman your car's vehicle identification number, and if possible, take the old part along for positive identification. Many parts are available under a factory exchange scheme – any parts returned should always be clean. It obviously makes good sense to go straight to the specialists on your car for this type of part, as they are best equipped to supply you.

Other garages and accessory shops – These are often very good places to buy materials and components needed for the maintenance of you car (eg oil filters, spark plugs, bulbs, drivebelts, oils and greases, touch-up paint, filler paste, etc). They also sell general accessories, usually have convenient opening hours, charge lower prices and can often be found not far from home.

Motor factors – Good factors will stock all the more important components which wear out comparatively quickly (eg exhaust systems, brake pads, seals and hydraulic parts, clutch components, bearing shells, pistons, valves etc). Motor factors will often provide new or reconditioned components on a part exchange basis – this can save a considerable amount of money.

Vehicle identification numbers

Modifications are a continuing and unpublicised process in vehicle manufacture, quite apart from the major model changes. Spare parts manuals and lists are compiled upon a numerical basis, the individual vehicle identification numbers being essential to correct identification of the component concerned.

When ordering spare parts, always give as much information as possible. Quote the car model, year of manufacture, body and engine numbers as appropriate.

The vehicle identification number (chassis number) is stamped on a plate attached to the engine compartment bulkhead and is also stamped into the bulkhead itself (photos). Note that this will tell you whether the car is a T12 or T72 model, and that the plate includes gross vehicle weight, gross combination weight and gross axle weight, as well as paint codes.

The engine number is stamped into a flat, raised, surface on the front left-hand end of the cylinder block (photo).

1 Type approval number

2 Vehicle identification number (chassis number)

3 Gross vehicle weight

4 Gross combination weight – gross vehicle weight + gross trailing capacity (weight)

5 Gross axle weight (Front)

6 Gross axle weight (Rear)

7 Type

8 Body colour code

9 Trim colour code

10 Model

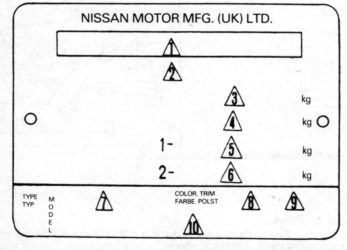

Vehicle identification plate information

Location of vehicle identification plate

Location of vehicle identification (chassis) number

Location of engine number

General repair procedures

Whenever servicing, repair or overhaul work is carried out on the car or its components, it is necessary to observe the following procedures and instructions. This will assist in carrying out the operation efficiently and to a professional standard of workmanship.

Joint mating faces and gaskets

Where a gasket is used between the mating faces of two components, ensure that it is renewed on reassembly, and fit it dry unless otherwise stated in the repair procedure. Make sure that the mating faces are clean and dry with all traces of old gasket removed. When cleaning a joint face, use a tool which is not likely to score or damage the face, and remove any burrs or nicks with an oilstone or fine file.

Make sure that tapped holes are cleaned with a pipe cleaner, and keep them free of jointing compound if this is being used unless specifically instructed otherwise.

Ensure that all orifices, channels or pipes are clear and blow through them, preferably using compressed air.

Oil seals

Whenever an oil seal is removed from its working location, either individually or as part of an assembly, it should be renewed.

The very fine sealing lip of the seal is easily damaged and will not seal if the surface it contacts is not completely clean and free from scratches, nicks or grooves. If the original sealing surface of the component cannot be restored, the component should be renewed.

Protect the lips of the seal from any surface which may damage them in the course of fitting. Use tape or a conical sleeve where possible. Lubricate the seal lips with oil before fitting and, on dual lipped seals, fill the space between the lips with grease.

Unless otherwise stated, oil seals must be fitted with their sealing lips toward the lubricant to be sealed.

Use a tubular drift or block of wood of the appropriate size to install the seal and, if the seal housing is shouldered, drive the seal down to the shoulder. If the seal housing is unshouldered, the seal should be fitted with its face flush with the housing top face.

Screw threads and fastenings

Always ensure that a blind tapped hole is completely free from oil, grease, water or other fluid before installing the bolt or stud. Failure to do this could cause the housing to crack due to the hydraulic action of the bolt or stud as it is screwed in.

When tightening a castellated nut to accept a split pin, tighten the nut to the specified torque, where applicable, and then tighten further to the next split pin hole. Never slacken the nut to align a split pin hole unless stated in the repair procedure.

When checking or retightening a nut or bolt to a specified torque setting, slacken the nut or bolt by a quarter of a turn, and then retighten to the specified setting.

Locknuts, locktabs and washers

Any fastening which will rotate against a component or housing in the course of tightening should always have a washer between it and the relevant component or housing.

Spring or split washers should always be renewed when they are used to lock a critical component such as a big-end bearing retaining nut or bolt.

Locktabs which are folded over to retain a nut or bolt should always be renewed.

Self-locking nuts can be reused in non-critical areas, providing resistance can be felt when the locking portion passes over the bolt or stud thread.

Split pins must always be replaced with new ones of the correct size for the hole.

Special tools

Some repair procedures in this manual entail the use of special tools such as a press, two or three-legged pullers, spring compressors etc. Wherever possible, suitable readily available alternatives to the manufacturer's special tools are described, and are shown in use. In some instances, where no alternative is possible, it has been necessary to resort to the use of a manufacturer's tool and this has been done for reasons of safety as well as the efficient completion of the repair operation. Unless you are highly skilled and have a thorough understanding of the procedure described, never attempt to bypass the use of any special tool when the procedure described specifies its use. Not only is there a very great risk of personal injury, but expensive damage could be caused to the components involved.

Tools and working facilities

Introduction

A selection of good tools is a fundamental requirement for anyone contemplating the maintenance and repair of a motor vehicle. For the owner who does not possess any, their purchase will prove a considerable expense, offsetting some of the savings made by doing-it-yourself. However, provided that the tools purchased meet the relevant national safety standards and are of good quality, they will last for many years and prove an extremely worthwhile investment.

To help the average owner to decide which tools are needed to carry out the various tasks detailed in this manual, we have compiled three lists of tools under the following headings: *Maintenance and minor repair, Repair and overhaul,* and *Special.* The newcomer to practical mechanics should start off with the *Maintenance and minor repair* tool kit and confine himself to the simpler jobs around the vehicle. Then, as his confidence and experience grow, he can undertake more difficult tasks, buying extra tools as, and when, they are needed. In this way, a *Maintenance and minor repair* tool kit can be built-up into a *Repair and overhaul* tool kit over a considerable period of time without any major cash outlays. The experienced do-it-yourselfer will have a tool kit good enough for most repair and overhaul procedures and will add tools from the *Special* category when he feels the expense is justified by the amount of use to which these tools will be put.

It is obviously not possible to cover the subject of tools fully here. For those who wish to learn more about tools and their use there is a book entitled *How to Choose and Use Car Tools* available from the publishers of this manual.

Maintenance and minor repair tool kit

The tools given in this list should be considered as a minimum requirement if routine maintenance, servicing and minor repair operations are to be undertaken. We recommend the purchase of combination spanners (ring one end, open-ended the other); although more expensive than open-ended ones, they do give the advantages of both types of spanner.

Combination spanners - 10, 11, 12, 13, 14 & 17 mm
Adjustable spanner - 9 inch
Transmission drain plug key
Spark plug spanner (with rubber insert)
Spark plug gap adjustment tool
Set of feeler gauges
Brake bleed nipple spanner
Screwdriver - 4 in long x $\frac{1}{4}$ in dia (flat blade)
Screwdriver - 4 in long x $\frac{1}{4}$ in dia (cross blade)
Combination pliers - 6 inch
Hacksaw (junior)
Tyre pump
Tyre pressure gauge
Oil can
Fine emery cloth (1 sheet)
Wire brush (small)
Funnel (medium size)

Repair and overhaul tool kit

These tools are virtually essential for anyone undertaking any major repairs to a motor vehicle, and are additional to those given in the *Maintenance and minor repair* list. Included in this list is a comprehensive set of sockets. Although these are expensive they will be found invaluable as they are so versatile - particularly if various drives are included in the set. We recommend the $\frac{1}{2}$ in square-drive type, as this can be used with most proprietary torque wrenches. If you cannot afford a socket set, even bought piecemeal, then inexpensive tubular box spanners are a useful alternative.

The tools in this list will occasionally need to be supplemented by tools from the *Special* list.

Sockets (or box spanners) to cover range in previous list
Reversible ratchet drive (for use with sockets)
Extension piece, 10 inch (for use with sockets)
Universal joint (for use with sockets)
Torque wrench (for use with sockets)
'Mole' wrench - 8 inch
Ball pein hammer
Soft-faced hammer, plastic or rubber
Screwdriver - 6 in long x $\frac{5}{16}$ in dia (flat blade)
Screwdriver - 2 in long x $\frac{5}{16}$ in square (flat blade)
Screwdriver - 1$\frac{1}{2}$ in long x $\frac{1}{4}$ in dia (cross blade)
Screwdriver - 3 in long x $\frac{1}{8}$ in dia (electricians)
Pliers - electricians side cutters
Pliers - needle nosed
Pliers - circlip (internal and external)
Cold chisel - $\frac{1}{2}$ inch
Scriber
Scraper
Centre punch
Pin punch
Hacksaw
Valve grinding tool
Steel rule/straight-edge
Allen keys (inc. splined/Torx type if necessary)
Selection of files
Wire brush (large)
Axle-stands
Jack (strong trolley or hydraulic type)

Special tools

The tools in this list are those which are not used regularly, are expensive to buy, or which need to be used in accordance with their manufacturers' instructions. Unless relatively difficult mechanical jobs are undertaken frequently, it will not be economic to buy many of these tools. Where this is the case, you could consider clubbing together with friends (or joining a motorists' club) to make a joint purchase, or borrowing the tools against a deposit from a local garage or tool hire specialist.

The following list contains only those tools and instruments freely available to the public, and not those special tools produced by the vehicle manufacturer specifically for its dealer network. You will find occasional references to these manufacturers' special tools in the text of this manual. Generally, an alternative method of doing the job without the vehicle manufacturers' special tool is given. However, sometimes, there is no alternative to using them. Where this is the case and the relevant tool cannot be bought or borrowed, you will have to entrust the work to a franchised garage.

> *Valve spring compressor (where applicable)*
> *Piston ring compressor*
> *Balljoint separator*
> *Universal hub/bearing puller*
> *Impact screwdriver*
> *Micrometer and/or vernier gauge*
> *Dial gauge*
> *Stroboscopic timing light*
> *Tachometer*
> *Universal electrical multi-meter*
> *Cylinder compression gauge*
> *Lifting tackle*
> *Trolley jack*
> *Light with extension lead*

Buying tools

For practically all tools, a tool factor is the best source since he will have a very comprehensive range compared with the average garage or accessory shop. Having said that, accessory shops often offer excellent quality tools at discount prices, so it pays to shop around.

There are plenty of good tools around at reasonable prices, but always aim to purchase items which meet the relevant national safety standards. If in doubt, ask the proprietor or manager of the shop for advice before making a purchase.

Care and maintenance of tools

Having purchased a reasonable tool kit, it is necessary to keep the tools in a clean serviceable condition. After use, always wipe off any dirt, grease and metal particles using a clean, dry cloth, before putting the tools away. Never leave them lying around after they have been used. A simple tool rack on the garage or workshop wall, for items such as screwdrivers and pliers is a good idea. Store all normal wrenches and sockets in a metal box. Any measuring instruments, gauges, meters, etc, must be carefully stored where they cannot be damaged or become rusty.

Take a little care when tools are used. Hammer heads inevitably become marked and screwdrivers lose the keen edge on their blades from time to time. A little timely attention with emery cloth or a file will soon restore items like this to a good serviceable finish.

Working facilities

Not to be forgotten when discussing tools, is the workshop itself. If anything more than routine maintenance is to be carried out, some form of suitable working area becomes essential.

It is appreciated that many an owner mechanic is forced by circumstances to remove an engine or similar item, without the benefit of a garage or workshop. Having done this, any repairs should always be done under the cover of a roof.

Wherever possible, any dismantling should be done on a clean, flat workbench or table at a suitable working height.

Any workbench needs a vice: one with a jaw opening of 4 in (100 mm) is suitable for most jobs. As mentioned previously, some clean dry storage space is also required for tools, as well as for lubricants, cleaning fluids, touch-up paints and so on, which become necessary.

Another item which may be required, and which has a much more general usage, is an electric drill with a chuck capacity of at least $\frac{5}{16}$in (8 mm). This, together with a good range of twist drills, is virtually essential for fitting accessories such as mirrors and reversing lights.

Last, but not least, always keep a supply of old newspapers and clean, lint-free rags available, and try to keep any working area as clean as possible.

Spanner jaw gap comparison table

Jaw gap (in)	Spanner size
0.250	$\frac{1}{4}$ in AF
0.276	7 mm
0.313	$\frac{5}{16}$ in AF
0.315	8 mm
0.344	$\frac{11}{32}$ in AF; $\frac{1}{8}$ in Whitworth
0.354	9 mm
0.375	$\frac{3}{8}$ in AF
0.394	10 mm
0.433	11 mm
0.438	$\frac{7}{16}$ in AF
0.445	$\frac{3}{16}$ in Whitworth; $\frac{1}{4}$ in BSF
0.472	12 mm
0.500	$\frac{1}{2}$ in AF
0.512	13 mm
0.525	1/4 in Whitworth; $\frac{5}{16}$ in BSF
0.551	14 mm
0.563	$\frac{9}{16}$ in AF
0.591	15 mm
0.600	$\frac{5}{16}$ in Whitworth; $\frac{3}{8}$ in BSF
0.625	$\frac{5}{8}$ in AF
0.630	16 mm
0.669	17 mm
0.686	$\frac{11}{16}$ in AF
0.709	18 mm
0.71	$\frac{3}{8}$ in Whitworth; $\frac{7}{16}$ in BSF
0.748	19 mm
0.750	$\frac{3}{4}$ in AF
0.813	$\frac{13}{16}$ in AF
0.820	$\frac{7}{16}$ in Whitworth; $\frac{1}{2}$ in BSF
0.866	22 mm
0.875	$\frac{7}{8}$ in AF
0.920	$\frac{1}{2}$ in Whitworth; $\frac{9}{16}$ in BSF
0.938	$\frac{15}{16}$ in AF
0.945	24 mm
1.000	1 in AF
1.010	$\frac{9}{16}$ in Whitworth; $\frac{5}{8}$ in BSF
1.024	26 mm
1.063	$1\frac{1}{16}$ in AF; 27 mm
1.100	$\frac{5}{8}$ in Whitworth; $\frac{11}{16}$ in BSF
1.125	$1\frac{1}{8}$ in AF
1.181	30 mm
1.200	$\frac{11}{16}$ in Whitworth; $\frac{3}{4}$ in BSF
1.250	$1\frac{1}{4}$ in AF
1.260	32 mm
1.300	$\frac{3}{4}$ in Whitworth; $\frac{7}{8}$ in BSF
1.313	$1\frac{5}{16}$ in AF
1.390	$\frac{13}{16}$ in Whitworth; $\frac{15}{16}$ in BSF
1.417	36 mm
1.438	$1\frac{7}{16}$ in AF
1.480	$\frac{7}{8}$ in Whitworth; 1 in BSF
1.500	$1\frac{1}{2}$ in AF
1.575	40 mm; $1\frac{5}{8}$ in Whitworth
1.614	41 mm
1.625	$1\frac{5}{8}$ in AF
1.670	1 in Whitworth; $1\frac{1}{8}$ in BSF
1.688	$1\frac{11}{16}$ in AF
1.811	46 mm
1.813	$1\frac{13}{16}$ in AF
1.860	$1\frac{1}{8}$ in Whitworth; $1\frac{1}{4}$ in BSF
1.875	$1\frac{7}{8}$ in AF
1.969	50 mm
2.000	2 in AF
2.050	$1\frac{1}{4}$ in Whitworth; $1\frac{3}{8}$ in BSF
2.165	55 mm
2.362	60 mm

Safety first!

Professional motor mechanics are trained in safe working procedures. However enthusiastic you may be about getting on with the job in hand, do take the time to ensure that your safety is not put at risk. A moment's lack of attention can result in an accident, as can failure to observe certain elementary precautions.

There will always be new ways of having accidents, and the following points do not pretend to be a comprehensive list of all dangers; they are intended rather to make you aware of the risks and to encourage a safety-conscious approach to all work you carry out on your vehicle.

Essential DOs and DON'Ts

DON'T rely on a single jack when working underneath the vehicle. Always use reliable additional means of support, such as axle stands, securely placed under a part of the vehicle that you know will not give way.

DON'T attempt to loosen or tighten high-torque nuts (e.g. wheel hub nuts) while the vehicle is on a jack; it may be pulled off.

DON'T start the engine without first ascertaining that the transmission is in neutral (or 'Park' where applicable) and the parking brake applied.

DON'T suddenly remove the filler cap from a hot cooling system – cover it with a cloth and release the pressure gradually first, or you may get scalded by escaping coolant.

DON'T attempt to drain oil until you are sure it has cooled sufficiently to avoid scalding you.

DON'T grasp any part of the engine, exhaust or catalytic converter without first ascertaining that it is sufficiently cool to avoid burning you.

DON'T allow brake fluid or antifreeze to contact vehicle paintwork.

DON'T syphon toxic liquids such as fuel, brake fluid or antifreeze by mouth, or allow them to remain on your skin.

DON'T inhale dust – it may be injurious to health (see *Asbestos* below).

DON'T allow any spilt oil or grease to remain on the floor – wipe it up straight away, before someone slips on it.

DON'T use ill-fitting spanners or other tools which may slip and cause injury.

DON'T attempt to lift a heavy component which may be beyond your capability – get assistance.

DON'T rush to finish a job, or take unverified short cuts.

DON'T allow children or animals in or around an unattended vehicle.

DO wear eye-protection when using power tools such as drill, sander, bench grinder etc, and when working under the vehicle.

DO use a barrier cream on your hands prior to undertaking dirty jobs – it will protect your skin from infection as well as making the dirt easier to remove afterwards; but make sure your hands aren't left slippery. Note that long-term contact with used engine oil can be a health hazard.

DO keep loose clothing (cuffs, tie etc) and long hair well out of the way of moving mechanical parts.

DO remove rings, wristwatch etc, before working on the vehicle – especially the electrical system.

DO ensure that any lifting tackle used has a safe working load rating adequate for the job.

DO keep your work area tidy – it is only too easy to fall over articles left lying around.

DO get someone to check periodically that all is well, when working alone on the vehicle.

DO carry out work in a logical sequence and check that everything is correctly assembled and tightened afterwards.

DO remember that your vehicle's safety affects that of yourself and others. If in doubt on any point, get specialist advice.

IF, in spite of following these precautions, you are unfortunate enough to injure yourself, seek medical attention as soon as possible.

Asbestos

Certain friction, insulating, sealing, and other products – such as brake linings, brake bands, clutch linings, torque converters, gaskets, etc – contain asbestos. *Extreme care must be taken to avoid inhalation of dust from such products since it is hazardous to health.* If in doubt, assume that they *do* contain asbestos.

Fire

Remember at all times that petrol (gasoline) is highly flammable. Never smoke, or have any kind of naked flame around, when working on the vehicle. But the risk does not end there – a spark caused by an electrical short-circuit, by two metal surfaces contacting each other, by careless use of tools, or even by static electricity built up in your body under certain conditions, can ignite petrol vapour, which in a confined space is highly explosive.

Always disconnect the battery earth (ground) terminal before working on any part of the fuel or electrical system, and never risk spilling fuel on to a hot engine or exhaust.

It is recommended that a fire extinguisher of a type suitable for fuel and electrical fires is kept handy in the garage or workplace at all times. Never try to extinguish a fuel or electrical fire with water.

Note: *Any reference to a 'torch' appearing in this manual should always be taken to mean a hand-held battery-operated electric lamp or flashlight. It does NOT mean a welding/gas torch or blowlamp.*

Fumes

Certain fumes are highly toxic and can quickly cause unconsciousness and even death if inhaled to any extent. Petrol (gasoline) vapour comes into this category, as do the vapours from certain solvents such as trichloroethylene. Any draining or pouring of such volatile fluids should be done in a well ventilated area.

When using cleaning fluids and solvents, read the instructions carefully. Never use materials from unmarked containers – they may give off poisonous vapours.

Never run the engine of a motor vehicle in an enclosed space such as a garage. Exhaust fumes contain carbon monoxide which is extremely poisonous; if you need to run the engine, always do so in the open air or at least have the rear of the vehicle outside the workplace.

If you are fortunate enough to have the use of an inspection pit, never drain or pour petrol, and never run the engine, while the vehicle is standing over it; the fumes, being heavier than air, will concentrate in the pit with possibly lethal results.

The battery

Never cause a spark, or allow a naked light, near the vehicle's battery. It will normally be giving off a certain amount of hydrogen gas, which is highly explosive.

Always disconnect the battery earth (ground) terminal before working on the fuel or electrical systems.

If possible, loosen the filler plugs or cover when charging the battery from an external source. Do not charge at an excessive rate or the battery may burst.

Take care when topping up and when carrying the battery. The acid electrolyte, even when diluted, is very corrosive and should not be allowed to contact the eyes or skin.

If you ever need to prepare electrolyte yourself, always add the acid slowly to the water, and never the other way round. Protect against splashes by wearing rubber gloves and goggles.

When jump starting a car using a booster battery, for negative earth (ground) vehicles, connect the jump leads in the following sequence: First connect one jump lead between the positive (+) terminals of the two batteries. Then connect the other jump lead first to the negative (–) terminal of the booster battery, and then to a good earthing (ground) point on the vehicle to be started, at least 18 in (45 cm) from the battery if possible. Ensure that hands and jump leads are clear of any moving parts, and that the two vehicles do not touch. Disconnect the leads in the reverse order.

Mains electricity and electrical equipment

When using an electric power tool, inspection light etc, always ensure that the appliance is correctly connected to its plug and that, where necessary, it is properly earthed (grounded). Do not use such appliances in damp conditions and, again, beware of creating a spark or applying excessive heat in the vicinity of fuel or fuel vapour. Also ensure that the appliances meet the relevant national safety standards.

Ignition HT voltage

A severe electric shock can result from touching certain parts of the ignition system, such as the HT leads, when the engine is running or being cranked, particularly if components are damp or the insulation is defective. Where an electronic ignition system is fitted, the HT voltage is much higher and could prove fatal.

Conversion factors

Length (distance)

Inches (in)	X	25.4	=	Millimetres (mm)	X	0.0394	= Inches (in)
Feet (ft)	X	0.305	=	Metres (m)	X	3.281	= Feet (ft)
Miles	X	1.609	=	Kilometres (km)	X	0.621	= Miles

Volume (capacity)

Cubic inches (cu in; in³)	X	16.387	=	Cubic centimetres (cc; cm³)	X	0.061	= Cubic inches (cu in; in³)
Imperial pints (Imp pt)	X	0.568	=	Litres (l)	X	1.76	= Imperial pints (Imp pt)
Imperial quarts (Imp qt)	X	1.137	=	Litres (l)	X	0.88	= Imperial quarts (Imp qt)
Imperial quarts (Imp qt)	X	1.201	=	US quarts (US qt)	X	0.833	= Imperial quarts (Imp qt)
US quarts (US qt)	X	0.946	=	Litres (l)	X	1.057	= US quarts (US qt)
Imperial gallons (Imp gal)	X	4.546	=	Litres (l)	X	0.22	= Imperial gallons (Imp gal)
Imperial gallons (Imp gal)	X	1.201	=	US gallons (US gal)	X	0.833	= Imperial gallons (Imp gal)
US gallons (US gal)	X	3.785	=	Litres (l)	X	0.264	= US gallons (US gal)

Mass (weight)

Ounces (oz)	X	28.35	=	Grams (g)	X	0.035	= Ounces (oz)
Pounds (lb)	X	0.454	=	Kilograms (kg)	X	2.205	= Pounds (lb)

Force

Ounces-force (ozf; oz)	X	0.278	=	Newtons (N)	X	3.6	= Ounces-force (ozf; oz)
Pounds-force (lbf; lb)	X	4.448	=	Newtons (N)	X	0.225	= Pounds-force (lbf; lb)
Newtons (N)	X	0.1	=	Kilograms-force (kgf; kg)	X	9.81	= Newtons (N)

Pressure

Pounds-force per square inch (psi; lbf/in²; lb/in²)	X	0.070	=	Kilograms-force per square centimetre (kgf/cm²; kg/cm²)	X	14.223	= Pounds-force per square inch (psi; lbf/in²; lb/in²)
Pounds-force per square inch (psi; lbf/in²; lb/in²)	X	0.068	=	Atmospheres (atm)	X	14.696	= Pounds-force per square inch (psi; lbf/in²; lb/in²)
Pounds-force per square inch (psi; lbf/in²; lb/in²)	X	0.069	=	Bars	X	14.5	= Pounds-force per square inch (psi; lbf/in²; lb/in²)
Pounds-force per square inch (psi; lbf/in²; lb/in²)	X	6.895	=	Kilopascals (kPa)	X	0.145	= Pounds-force per square inch (psi; lbf/in²; lb/in²)
Kilopascals (kPa)	X	0.01	=	Kilograms-force per square centimetre (kgf/cm²; kg/cm²)	X	98.1	= Kilopascals (kPa)
Millibar (mbar)	X	100	=	Pascals (Pa)	X	0.01	= Millibar (mbar)
Millibar (mbar)	X	0.0145	=	Pounds-force per square inch (psi; lbf/in²; lb/in²)	X	68.947	= Millibar (mbar)
Millibar (mbar)	X	0.75	=	Millimetres of mercury (mmHg)	X	1.333	= Millibar (mbar)
Millibar (mbar)	X	0.401	=	Inches of water (inH₂O)	X	2.491	= Millibar (mbar)
Millimetres of mercury (mmHg)	X	0.535	=	Inches of water (inH₂O)	X	1.868	= Millimetres of mercury (mmHg)
Inches of water (inH₂O)	X	0.036	=	Pounds-force per square inch (psi; lbf/in²; lb/in²)	X	27.68	= Inches of water (inH₂O)

Torque (moment of force)

Pounds-force inches (lbf in; lb in)	X	1.152	=	Kilograms-force centimetre (kgf cm; kg cm)	X	0.868	= Pounds-force inches (lbf in; lb in)
Pounds-force inches (lbf in; lb in)	X	0.113	=	Newton metres (Nm)	X	8.85	= Pounds-force inches (lbf in; lb in)
Pounds-force inches (lbf in; lb in)	X	0.083	=	Pounds-force feet (lbf ft; lb ft)	X	12	= Pounds-force inches (lbf in; lb in)
Pounds-force feet (lbf ft; lb ft)	X	0.138	=	Kilograms-force metres (kgf m; kg m)	X	7.233	= Pounds-force feet (lbf ft; lb ft)
Pounds-force feet (lbf ft; lb ft)	X	1.356	=	Newton metres (Nm)	X	0.738	= Pounds-force feet (lbf ft; lb ft)
Newton metres (Nm)	X	0.102	=	Kilograms-force metres (kgf m; kg m)	X	9.804	= Newton metres (Nm)

Power

Horsepower (hp)	X	745.7	=	Watts (W)	X	0.0013	= Horsepower (hp)

Velocity (speed)

Miles per hour (miles/hr; mph)	X	1.609	=	Kilometres per hour (km/hr; kph)	X	0.621	= Miles per hour (miles/hr; mph)

Fuel consumption*

Miles per gallon, Imperial (mpg)	X	0.354	=	Kilometres per litre (km/l)	X	2.825	= Miles per gallon, Imperial (mpg)
Miles per gallon, US (mpg)	X	0.425	=	Kilometres per litre (km/l)	X	2.352	= Miles per gallon, US (mpg)

Temperature

Degrees Fahrenheit = (°C x 1.8) + 32   Degrees Celsius (Degrees Centigrade; °C) = (°F - 32) x 0.56

*It is common practice to convert from miles per gallon (mpg) to litres/100 kilometres (l/100km), where mpg (Imperial) x l/100 km = 282 and mpg (US) x l/100 km = 235

Routine maintenance

Maintenance is essential for ensuring safety, and desirable for the purpose of getting the best in terms of performance and economy from your car. Over the years, the need for periodic lubrication has been greatly reduced, if not totally eliminated. This has unfortunately tended to lead some owners to think that because no such action is required the items no longer exist, or will last forever. This is certainly not the case; it is essential to carry out regular visual examination as comprehensively as possible, in order to spot any potential defects at an early stage before they develop into major expensive repairs.

The following service schedules are a list of the maintenance requirements, and the intervals at which they should be carried out, as recommended by the manufacturers. Where applicable, these procedures are covered in greater detail throughout this manual, near the beginning of each chapter.

Weekly, or before any long journey

Referring to the relevant Chapters of this manual, check the levels of engine oil (Chapter 1), coolant (Chapter 2), clutch hydraulic fluid (1.8 and 2.0 litre models only – Chapter 5), automatic transmission fluid, if applicable (Chapter 7), brake hydraulic fluid (Chapter 9), power-assisted steering fluid, if applicable (Chapter 10) and washer fluid (Chapter 12). Check the tyre pressures, and the tyre treads for wear or damage (Chapter 10), check the operation of the wipers and of all electrical equipment (Chapter 12) and clean the windows and all lamp lenses.

Every 3000 miles/5000 km or 6 months – whichever occurs first

Engine (Chapter 1)
Change the engine oil – T12 Turbo models

Every 4500 miles/7500 km or 6 months – whichever occurs first

Engine (Chapter 1)
Change the engine oil and filter – T72 Turbo models

Every 6000 miles/10 000 km (T12), 9000 miles/15 000 km (T72) or 6 months – whichever occurs first

Engine (Chapter 1)
Change the engine oil and filter – all models

Fuel, exhaust and emission control systems (Chapter 3)
Check idling speed and mixture
Check the exhaust system for leaks and security

Ignition system (Chapter 4)
Check the ignition timing
Check the spark plugs – T12 models
Renew the spark plugs – T72 models

Clutch (Chapter 5)
Check the clutch hydraulic fluid level and check the system for leaks – 1.8 and 2.0 litre models
Make a general check of the clutch system – all models
Check the clutch operation and adjustment

Manual transmission (Chapter 6)
Check for oil leaks
Check the transmission oil level

Automatic transmission (Chapter 7)
Check for fluid leaks
Check the transmission fluid

Braking system (Chapter 9)
Check the brake hydraulic fluid level and check the system for leaks
Make a general check of the brake system
Check the brake pedal operation and adjustment
Check the handbrake operation and adjustment
Check the brake pads and discs

Suspension and steering (Chapter 10)
Check the power-assisted steering system fluid lines for leaks

Bodywork and fittings (Chapter 11)
Lubricate the hinges, locks and door latches

Every 12 000 miles/20 000 km (T12), 18 000 miles/30 000 km (T72) or annually – whichever occurs first

In addition to the operations listed above, carry out the following:

Engine (Chapter 1)
Check the valve clearances

Cooling system (Chapter 2)
Check the condition and adjustment of all drivebelts
Make a general check of the cooling system

Fuel, exhaust and emission control system (Chapter 3)
Check the air cleaner automatic temperature control – carburettor models
Check the crankcase ventilation system
Check the engine breather and vacuum hoses
Renew the fuel filter – T72 models

Ignition system (Chapter 4)
Renew the spark plugs – T12 models

Driveshafts (Chapter 8)
Check the driveshafts, joints and driveshaft nuts

Braking system (Chapter 9)
Check the brake shoes and drums
Renew the brake hydraulic fluid – T72 models

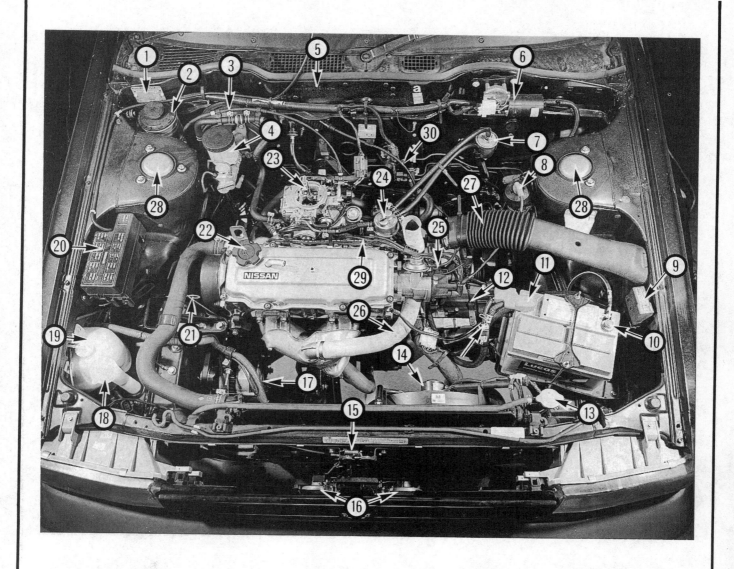

Engine and underbonnet component locations (carburettor engine, air cleaner removed)

1 Vehicle identification plate
2 Power-assisted steering fluid reservoir
3 Brake vacuum servo unit
4 Brake master cylinder
5 Chassis number
6 Windscreen wiper motor
7 Fuel filter
8 Ignition HT coil
9 Fusible links
10 Battery negative terminal

11 Battery positive terminal
12 Clutch cable adjuster unit
13 Radiator cap
14 Electric cooling fan
15 Bonnet lock
16 Horns
17 Alternator
18 Washer fluid reservoir
19 Cooling system expansion tank
20 Relay holder

21 Engine oil level dipstick
22 Engine oil filler cap
23 Carburettor
24 Fuel pump
25 Distributor
26 Warm air intake hose
27 Air intake flexible duct
28 Front suspension strut top mounting
29 Spark plug HT leads
30 Speedometer cable

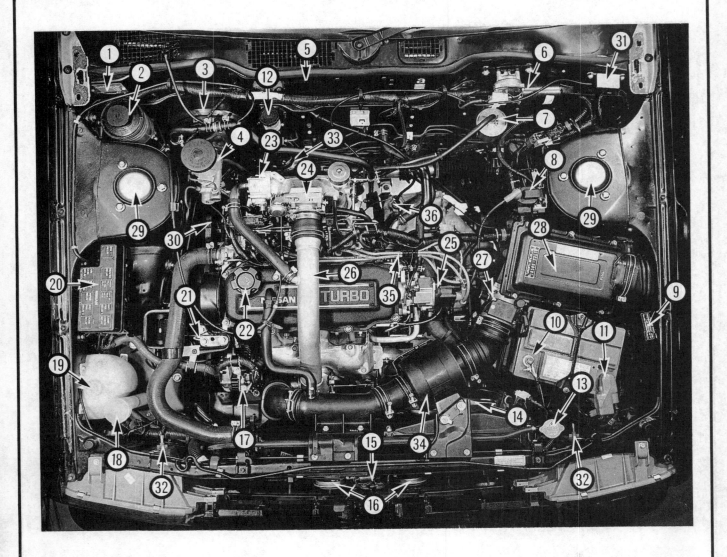

Engine and underbonnet component locations (Turbo)

1 Vehicle identification plate	13 Radiator cap	25 Distributor/crank angle sensor
2 Power-assisted steering fluid reservoir	14 Electronic cooling fan	26 Air intake tube
3 Brake vacuum servo unit	15 Bonnet lock	27 Airflow meter
4 Brake master cylinder	16 Horns	28 Air cleaner
5 Chassis number	17 Alternator	29 Front suspension strut top mounting
6 Windscreen wiper motor	18 Washer fluid reservoir	30 Power-assisted steering pump
7 Fuel filter	19 Cooling system expansion tank	31 Boost sensor
8 Ignition HT coil	20 Relay holder	32 Headlamp beam adjuster
9 Fusible links	21 Engine oil level dipstick	33 Steering gear
10 Battery negative terminal	22 Engine oil filler cap	34 Resonator assembly
11 Battery positive terminal	23 IAA unit	35 Spark plug HT leads
12 Clutch master cylinder	24 Throttle chamber	36 Speedometer pinion assembly

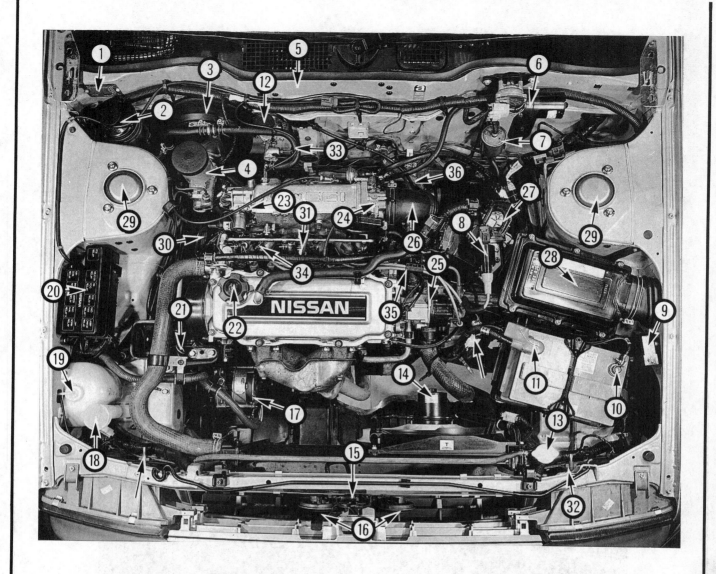

Engine and underbonnet component locations (2.0i GSX)

1	Vehicle identification plate
2	Power-assisted steering fluid reservoir
3	Brake vacuum servo unit
4	Brake master cylinder
5	Chassis number
6	Windscreen wiper motor
7	Fuel filter
8	Ignition (HT) coil
9	Fusible links
10	Battery negative terminal
11	Battery positive terminal
12	Clutch master cylinder
13	Radiator cap
14	Electric cooling fan
15	Bonnet lock
16	Horns
17	Alternator
18	Washer fluid reservoir
19	Cooling system expansion tank
20	Relay holder
21	Engine oil level dipstick
22	Engine oil filler cap
23	IAA unit
24	Throttle chamber
25	Distributor/crank angle sensor
26	Air intake duct
27	Airflow meter
28	Air cleaner
29	Front suspension strut top mounting
30	Power-assisted steering pump
31	Pressure regulator/fuel rail asssembly
32	Headlamp beam adjuster
33	Econometer vacuum hose
34	PCV valve
35	Spark plug (HT) leads
36	Speedometer cable

Front underbody view (undershields and underwing shields removed)

1 Engine oil drain plug
2 Transmission oil drain plug
3 Tie-down hooks
4 Towing hooks
5 Alternator
6 Engine mounting longitudinal member
7 Radiator

8 Electric cooling fan
9 Front suspension lower arm
10 Brake caliper
11 Anti-roll bar
12 Steering track rod
13 Oil pressure switch
14 Driveshaft

15 Gear position switch
16 Radiator bottom hose
17 Power-assisted steering pump pivot bolt
18 Gearchange support rod
19 Gearchange control rod
20 Front suspension lower arm mounting plate

Rear underbody view

1 Exhaust system rear section	6 Rear suspension rear (adjustable) transverse link	11 Fuel filler tube
2 Fuel tank	7 Spare wheel well	12 Fuel tank breather tubes
3 Rear anti-roll bar	8 Rear suspension trailing link	13 Rear suspension strut
4 Rear suspension crossmember	9 Handbrake cable	14 Towing hooks
5 Rear suspension front transverse link	10 Fuel hose	

Suspension and steering (Chapter 10)
  Check the steering gear and linkage
  Check the suspension, roadwheels and tyres

Bodywork and fittings (Chapter 11)
  Check the seat belts
  Check the bodywork and underframe

Every 24 000 miles/40 000 km (T12), 36 000 miles/60 000 km (T72) or 2 years – whichever occurs first

In addition to the operations listed in the previous services, carry out the following:

Cooling system (Chapter 2)
  Renew the coolant

Fuel, exhaust and emission control systems (Chapter 3)
  Make a general check of the fuel system
  Renew the air cleaner filter element
  Renew the fuel filter – T12 models
  Renew the PCV filter – T72 carburettor-engined models

Ignition system (Chapter 4)
  Check the distributor cap and spark plug (HT) leads

Braking system (Chapter 9)
  Check the vacuum servo unit hose, connections and check valve
  Renew the brake hydraulic fluid – T12 models

Every 60 000 miles/100 000 km

In addition to the operations listed in the 12 000 mile service, carry out the following:

Engine (Chapter 1)
  Renew the timing belt, irrespective of its apparent condition

Note: Engine oil and filter change – T12 carburettor-engined models *Intervals shown apply to use of non-genuine filter elements. If genuine Nissan Premium filter is used intervals can be extended to 12 000 miles after first 6000 and 12 000 mile services*
Engine oil and filter change – T72 models (except Turbo) – *If any filter other than genuine Nissan Premium is used, change the engine oil and filter every 6000 miles or 6 months, whichever occurs first.*
Transmission oil/fluid renewal *– No normal interval is specified, but under severe use (towing a trailer or caravan or travelling over poor road surfaces or in poor conditions) the oil or fluid should be renewed every 24 000 miles or 2 years on T12 models, or 18 000 miles or annually on T72, whichever occurs first.*
General *– Under severe use, some checks are to be carried out twice as often. See the owner's manual or a Nissan dealer for details.*

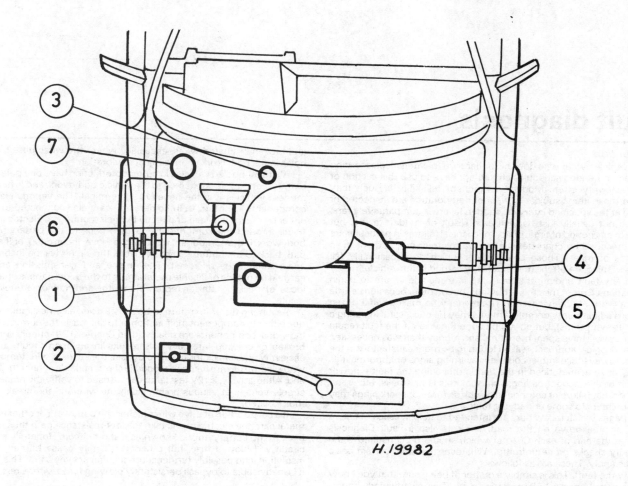

H.19982

Recommended lubricants and fluids

Component or system	Lubricant type/specification	Duckhams recommendation
Engine (1)	Multigrade engine oil, to API SF or SG, viscosity range SAE 10W/30 to 20W/50	Duckhams QXR, Hypergrade, or 10W/40 Motor Oil
Cooling system (2)	Ethylene glycol-based antifreeze, with corrosion inhibitors	Duckhams Universal Antifreeze and Summer Coolant
Clutch hydraulic system (3)	Hydraulic fluid to FMVSS 116, DOT 3 or 4	Duckhams Universal Brake and Clutch Fluid
Manual transmission (4)	Gear oil to API GL-4, viscosity SAE 80 to 90	Duckhams Hypoid 80
Automatic transmission (5)	Dexron II type ATF	Duckhams D-Matic
Brake hydraulic system (6)	Hydraulic fluid to FMVSS 116, DOT 3 or 4	Duckhams Universal Brake and Clutch Fluid
Power steering system (7)	Dexron II type ATF	Duckhams D-Matic
General greasing	Multi-purpose lithium-based grease	Duckhams LB 10

Fault diagnosis

Introduction

The vehicle owner who does his or her own maintenance according to the recommended schedules should not have to use this section of the manual very often. Modern component reliability is such that, provided those items subject to wear or deterioration are inspected or renewed at the specified intervals, sudden failure is comparatively rare. Faults do not usually just happen as a result of sudden failure, but develop over a period of time. Major mechanical failures in particular are usually preceded by characteristic symptoms over hundreds or even thousands of miles. Those components which do occasionally fail without warning are often small and easily carried in the vehicle.

With any fault finding, the first step is to decide where to begin investigations. Sometimes this is obvious, but on other occasions a little detective work will be necessary. The owner who makes half a dozen haphazard adjustments or replacements may be successful in curing a fault (or its symptoms), but he will be none the wiser if the fault recurs and he may well have spent more time and money than was necessary. A calm and logical approach will be found to be more satisfactory in the long run. Always take into account any warning signs or abnormalities that may have been noticed in the period preceding the fault – power loss, high or low gauge readings, unusual noises or smells, etc – and remember that failure of components such as fuses or spark plugs may only be pointers to some underlying fault.

The pages which follow here are intended to help in cases of failure to start or breakdown on the road. There is also a Fault Diagnosis Section at the end of each Chapter which should be consulted if the preliminary checks prove unfruitful. Whatever the fault, certain basic principles apply. These are as follows:

Verify the fault. This is simply a matter of being sure that you know what the symptoms are before starting work. This is particularly important if you are investigating a fault for someone else who may not have described it very accurately.

Don't overlook the obvious. For example, if the vehicle won't start, is there petrol in the tank? (Don't take anyone else's word on this particular point, and don't trust the fuel gauge either!) If an electrical fault is indicated, look for loose or broken wires before digging out the test gear.

Cure the disease, not the symptom. Substituting a flat battery with a fully charged one will get you off the hard shoulder, but if the underlying cause is not attended to, the new battery will go the same way. Similarly, changing oil-fouled spark plugs for a new set will get you moving again, but remember that the reason for the fouling (if it wasn't simply an incorrect grade of plug) will have to be established and corrected.

Don't take anything for granted. Particularly, don't forget that a 'new' component may itself be defective (especially if it's been rattling round in the boot for months), and don't leave components out of a fault diagnosis sequence just because they are new or recently fitted. When you do finally diagnose a difficult fault, you'll probably realise that all the evidence was there from the start.

Electrical faults

Electrical faults can be more puzzling than straightforward mechanical failures, but they are no less susceptible to logical analysis if the basic principles of operation are understood. Vehicle electrical wiring exists in extremely unfavourable conditions – heat, vibration and chemical attack – and the first things to look for are loose or corroded connections and broken or chafed wires, especially where the wires pass through holes in the bodywork or are subject to vibration.

All metal-bodied vehicles in current production have one pole of the battery 'earthed', ie connected to the vehicle bodywork, and in nearly all modern vehicles it is the negative (–) terminal. The various electrical components – motors, bulb holders etc – are also connected to earth, either by means of a lead or directly by their mountings. Electric current flows through the component and then back to the battery via the bodywork. If the component mounting is loose or corroded, or if a good path back to the battery is not available, the circuit will be incomplete and malfunction will result. The engine and transmission are also earthed by means of flexible metal straps to the body; if these straps are loose or missing, starter motor, alternator and ignition trouble may result.

Assuming the earth return to be satisfactory, electrical faults will be due either to component malfunction or to defects in the current supply. Individual components are dealt with in Chapter 12. If supply wires are broken or cracked internally this results in an open-circuit, and the easiest way to check for this is to bypass the suspect wire temporarily with a length of wire having a crocodile clip or suitable connector at each end. Alternatively, a 12V test lamp can be used to verify the presence of supply voltage at various points along the wire and the break can be thus isolated.

If a bare portion of a live wire touches the bodywork or other earthed metal part, the electricity will take the low-resistance path thus formed back to the battery: this is known as a short-circuit. Hopefully a short-circuit will blow a fuse, but otherwise it may cause burning of the insulation (and possibly further short-circuits) or even a fire. This is why it is inadvisable to bypass persistently blowing fuses with wire.

Spares and tool kit

Most vehicles are supplied only with sufficient tools for wheel changing; the *Maintenance and minor repair* tool kit detailed in *Tools and working facilities*, with the addition of a hammer, is probably sufficient for those repairs that most motorists would consider attempting at the roadside. In addition a few items which can be fitted without too much trouble in the event of a breakdown should be carried. Experience and available space will modify the list below, but the following may save having to call on professional assistance:

Spark plugs, clean and correctly gapped
HT lead and suppressor cap – long enough to reach the plug furthest from the distributor
Distributor rotor arm
Drivebelt(s) – emergency type may suffice
Spare fuses
Set of principal light bulbs
Tin of radiator sealer and hose bandage
Exhaust bandage
Roll of insulating tape
Length of soft iron wire
Length of electrical flex
Torch or inspection lamp (can double as test lamp)
Battery jump leads
Tow-rope
Ignition water dispersant aerosol
Litre of engine oil
Sealed can of hydraulic fluid
Emergency windscreen
Worm drive clips

Carrying a few spares may save a long walk!

If spare fuel is carried, a can designed for the purpose should be used to minimise risks of leakage and collision damage. A first aid kit and a warning triangle, whilst not at present compulsory in the UK, are obviously sensible items to carry in addition to the above.

When touring abroad it may be advisable to carry additional spares which, even if you cannot fit them yourself, could save having to wait while parts are obtained. The items below may be worth considering:

Clutch (1.6 litre models only) and accelerator cables
Cylinder head gasket
Alternator brushes
Tyre valve core

One of the motoring organisations will be able to advise on availability of fuel etc in foreign countries.

Engine will not start

Engine fails to turn when starter operated

Flat battery (recharge, use jump leads, or push start)
Battery terminals loose or corroded
Battery earth to body defective
Engine earth strap loose or broken
Starter motor (or solenoid) wiring loose or broken
Automatic transmission selector in wrong position, or inhibitor switch faulty
Ignition/starter switch faulty
Major mechanical failure (seizure)
Starter or solenoid internal fault (see Chapter 12)

Starter motor turns engine slowly

Partially discharged battery (recharge, use jump leads, or push start)
Battery terminals loose or corroded
Battery earth to body defective
Engine earth strap loose
Starter motor (or solenoid) wiring loose
Starter motor internal fault (see Chapter 12)

Starter motor spins without turning engine

Flat battery
Starter motor pinion sticking on sleeve
Flywheel gear teeth damaged or worn
Starter motor mounting bolts loose

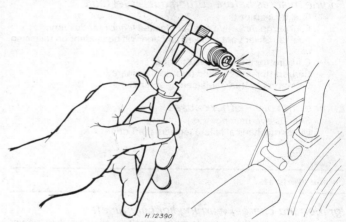

Crank engine and check for spark. Note use of insulated tool to hold plug lead

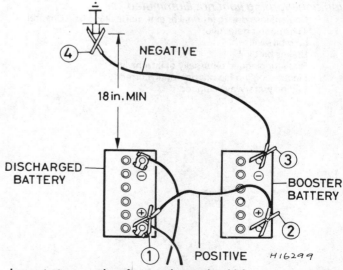

Jump start connections for negative earth vehicles – connect leads in order shown

Fault diagnosis

Engine turns normally but fails to start

Damp or dirty HT leads and distributor cap (crank engine and check for spark)
No fuel in tank (check for delivery at carburettor)
Excessive choke (hot engine) or insufficient choke (cold engine)
Fouled or incorrectly gapped spark plugs (remove, clean and regap)
Other ignition system fault (see Chapter 4)
Other fuel system fault (see Chapter 3)
Poor compression (see Chapter 1)
Major mechanical failure (eg camshaft drive)

Engine fires but will not run

Insufficient choke (cold engine)
Air leaks at carburettor or inlet manifold
Fuel starvation (see Chapter 3)
Other ignition fault (see Chapter 4)

Engine cuts out and will not restart

Engine cuts out suddenly – ignition fault

Loose or disconnected LT wires
Wet HT leads or distributor cap (after traversing water splash)
Coil failure (check for spark)
Other ignition fault (see Chapter 4)

Engine misfires before cutting out – fuel fault

Fuel tank empty
Fuel pump defective or filter blocked (check for delivery)
Fuel tank filler vent blocked (suction will be evident on releasing cap)
Carburettor needle valve sticking
Carburettor jets blocked (fuel contaminated)
Other fuel system fault (see Chapter 3)

Engine cuts out – other causes

Serious overheating
Major mechanical failure (eg camshaft drive)

Engine overheats

Ignition (no-charge) warning light illuminated

Slack or broken waterpump/drivebelt (models without power steering) – retension or renew (Chapter 2)

Ignition warning light not illuminated

Coolant loss due to internal or external leakage (see Chapter 2)
Thermostat defective
Low oil level
Brakes binding
Radiator clogged externally or internally
Electric cooling fan not operating correctly
Engine waterways clogged

Ignition timing incorrect or automatic advance malfunctioning
Mixture too weak

Note: *Do not add cold water to an overheated engine or damage may result*

Low engine oil pressure

Warning lamp illuminated with engine running

Oil level low or incorrect grade
Defective gauge or pressure switch
Wire to pressure switch earthed
Engine overheating
Oil filter clogged or pressure relief valve defective
Oil pressure regulator valve defective
Oil pick-up strainer clogged
Oil pump worn or mountings loose
Worn main or big-end bearings

Note: *Low oil pressure in a high-mileage engine at tickover is not necessarily a cause for concern. Sudden pressure loss at speed is far more significant. In any event, check the pressure switch before condemning the engine.*

Engine noises

Pre-ignition (pinking) on acceleration

Incorrect grade of fuel
Ignition timing incorrect
Distributor faulty or worn
Worn or maladjusted carburettor
Excessive carbon build-up in engine

Whistling or wheezing noises

Leaking vacuum hose
Leaking carburettor or manifold gasket
Blowing head gasket

Tapping or rattling

Incorrect valve clearances
Worn valve gear
Worn timing belt
Broken piston ring (ticking noise)

Knocking or thumping

Unintentional mechanical contact (eg fan blades)
Worn drivebelt
Peripheral component fault (alternator, water pump etc)
Worn big-end bearings (regular heavy knocking, perhaps less under load)
Worn main bearings (rumbling and knocking, perhaps worsening under load)
Piston slap (most noticeable when cold)

Chapter 1 Engine

Contents

Specifications

General

Engine type	Four-cylinder in-line overhead camshaft, transversely mounted

Engine designation and capacity:

	Code	Capacity
1.6 litre models	CA 16S	1598 cc (97.5 cu in)
1.8 litre carburettor models	CA 18NS	1796 cc (109.6 cu in)
1.8 litre turbocharged models	CA 18ET	1809 cc (110.4 cu in)
2.0 litre carburettor models	CA 20S	1974 cc (120.4 cu in)
2.0 litre fuel-injected models	CA 20E	1974 cc (120.4 cu in)

Engine dimensions:

	Bore	Stroke
CA 16S	78.0 mm (3.07 in)	83.6 mm (3.29 in)
CA 18NS	82.7 mm (3.26 in)	83.6 mm (3.29 in)
CA 18ET	83.0 mm (3.27 in)	83.6 mm (3.29 in)
CA 20S, CA 20E	84.5 mm (3.33 in)	88.0 mm (3.46 in)

Compression ratio:

CA 16S (up to engine number 190258 – July 1987)	9.0:1
CA 16S (from engine number 190259) & CA 18NS	9.6:1
CA 18ET	8.0:1
CA 20S, CA 20E	9.4:1
Firing order	1–3–4–2 (No. 1 at timing belt end of engine)
Direction of crankshaft rotation	Clockwise (viewed from right-hand side of car)

Compression pressure (at cranking speed, engine hot):

Standard:	
Turbo	1177 kPa (171 psi)
All other models	1196 kPa (173 psi)
Minimum:	
Turbo	883 kPa (128 psi)
All other models	902 kPa (131 psi)
Maximum difference between cylinders	98 kPa (14 psi)

Valve clearances

	Intake	Exhaust
Engine hot	0.30 mm (0.012 in)	0.30 mm (0.012 in)
Engine cold (coolant temperature up to 20°C – 68°F)	0.21 mm (0.008 in)	0.23 mm (0.009 in)

Note: *If clearances are checked when engine is cold, recheck them as soon as it is fully warmed up*

Valve springs

Standard free height:	
Outer	49.98 mm (1.9677 in)
Inner	44.10 mm (1.7362 in)

Camshaft

Journal diameter:	
Numbers 1 to 4	45.935 to 45.955 mm (1.8085 to 1.8093 in)
Number 5	45.915 to 45.935 mm (1.8077 to 1.8085 in)
Maximum journal to bearing clearance	0.10 mm (0.0039 in)
Maximum endfloat	0.20 mm (0.0079 in)
Lobe height:	
CA 16S	38.225 to 38.305 mm (1.5049 to 1.5081 in)
CA 18NS	Not available at time of writing
CA 18ET	38.391 to 38.471 mm (1.5115 to 1.5146 in)
CA 20S:	
Inlet	38.225 to 38.305 mm (1.5049 to 1.5081 in)
Exhaust	38.391 to 38.471 mm (1.5115 to 1.5146 in)
CA 20E	38.819 to 38.899 mm (1.5283 to 1.5315 in)
Maximum permissible lobe wear	0.20 mm (0.0079 in)

Cylinder head

Material	Light alloy
Maximum permissible distortion of gasket surface	0.1 mm (0.004 in)
Stem-to-guide clearance:	
Inlet	0.020 to 0.053 mm (0.0008 to 0.0021 in)
Exhaust	0.040 to 0.073 mm (0.0016 to 0.0029 in)
Wear limit	0.1 mm (0.004 in)
Valve face angle	45° 15' to 45° 45'
Valve seat angle	45°
Valve stem diameter:	
Inlet	6.965 to 6.980 mm (0.2742 to 0.2748 in)
Exhaust	6.945 to 6.960 mm (0.2734 to 0.2740 in)
Valve guide outside diameter	11.023 to 11.034 mm (0.4340 to 0.4344 in)
Interference fit of valve guide in cylinder head	0.027 to 0.059 mm (0.0011 to 0.0023 in)
Valve guide inside diameter (reamed)	7.000 to 7.018 mm (0.2756 to 0.2763 in)

Cylinder block/crankcase

Material	Cast iron
Maximum permissible distortion of gasket surface	0.1 mm (0.004 in)
Bore diameter:	
CA 16S	77.950 to 78.000 mm (3.0689 to 3.0709 in)
CA 18NS	Not available at time of writing
CA 18ET	83.000 to 83.050 mm (3.2677 to 3.2697 in)
CA 20S, CA 20E	84.500 to 84.550 mm (3.3268 to 3.3287 in)

Note: *Diameters sub-divided into 5 grades, identified by number stamped on block gasket surface*

Maximum permissible taper	0.02 mm (0.0008 in)
Maximum permissible ovality	0.02 mm (0.0008 in)

Pistons and rings

Skirt diameter – (20 mm above base of skirt):	
CA 16S	77.915 to 77.965 mm (3.0675 to 3.0695 in)
CA 18NS	82.665 to 82.715 mm (3.2545 to 3.2565 in)
CA 18ET	82.965 to 83.015 mm (3.2663 to 3.2683 in)
CA 20S, CA 20E	84.465 to 84.515 mm (3.3254 to 3.3274 in)

Note: *Diameters sub-divided into 5 grades, identified by number stamped in piston crown – should match cylinder block number*

Oversizes available:	
Early CA 18NS	0.30 mm (0.0118 in), 0.80 mm (0.0315 in)
Late CA 18NS, and all other models	0.50 mm (0.0197 in), 1.00 mm (0.0394 in)
Piston-to-cylinder bore clearance	0.025 to 0.045 mm (0.0010 to 0.0018 in)
Gudgeon pin outside diameter	19.995 to 20.000 mm (0.7872 to 0.7874 in)
Gudgeon pin to piston clearance	0.008 to 0.012 mm (0.0003 to 0.0005 in)
Interference fit of gudgeon pin in connecting rod	0.017 to 0.038 mm (0.0007 to 0.015 in)
Ring side clearance:	
Top	0.040 to 0.073 mm (0.0016 to 0.0029 in)
2nd	0.030 to 0.063 mm (0.0012 to 0.0025 in)
Wear limit	0.1 mm (0.004 in)
Ring end gap:	
Top:	
CA 16S	0.20 to 0.46 mm (0.0079 to 0.0181 in)
CA 18NS	Not available at time of writing
CA 18ET	0.19 to 0.42 mm (0.0075 to 0.0165 in)
CA 20S, CA 20E	0.25 to 0.51 mm (0.0098 to 0.0201 in)
Second:	
CA 16S	0.14 to 0.41 mm (0.0055 to 0.0161 in)
CA 18NS	Not available at time of writing
CA 18ET	0.15 to 0.41 mm (0.0059 to 0.0161 in)
CA 20S	0.25 to 0.51 mm (0.0098 to 0.0201 in)
CA 20E	0.15 to 0.31 mm (0.0059 to 0.0122 in)
Oil (side rail):	0.20 to 0.76 mm (0.0079 to 0.0299 in)
Maximum permissible endgap (all piston rings)	1.00 mm (0.0394 in)

Crankshaft

Number of main bearings	Five
Journal diameter	52.951 to 52.964 mm (2.0847 to 2.0852 in)
Crankpin diameter	44.961 to 44.974 mm (1.7701 to 1.7706 in)
Permitted taper of journal and crankpin	0.03 mm (0.0012 in) maximum
Permitted out of round of journal and crankpin	0.03 mm (0.0012 in) maximum
Crankshaft endfloat	0.3 mm (0.012 in) maximum
Main bearing running clearance (standard)	0.020 to 0.047 mm (0.0008 to 0.0019 in)
Wear limit	0.1 mm (0.004 in) maximum
Main bearing undersizes	0.25 mm (0.0098 in) 0.50 mm (0.0197 in)

Connecting rods

Rod side clearance	0.2 to 0.3 mm (0.008 to 0.012 in)
Wear limit	0.3 mm (0.012 in)
Connecting rod big-end bearing running clearance	0.1 mm (0.004 in) maximum
Big-end bearing undersize	0.08 mm (0.0031 in), 0.12 mm (0.0047 in), 0.25 mm (0.0098 in), 0.50 mm (0.020 in)

Flywheel

Permitted out of true	Less than 0.15 mm (0.0059 in)

Lubrication system

System pressure (at oil temperature of 77 to 83°C – 171 to 181°F):	
At idling speed	59 kPa (9 psi) minimum
At 3200 rpm	324 to 510 kPa (47 to 74 psi)
Oil filter	Champion C109
Oil type/specification	Multigrade engine oil, to API SF or SG, viscosity range SAE 10W/30 to 20W/50* (Duckhams QXR, Hypergrade, or 10W/40 Motor Oil)

*See owners handbook for full details

Oil pump clearances:	
Inner gear to crescent	0.12 to 0.23 mm (0.0047 to 0.0091 in)
Outer gear to crescent	0.21 to 0.32 mm (0.0083 to 0.0126 in)
Outer gear to body	0.11 to 0.20 mm (0.0043 to 0.0079 in)
Outer gear endfloat	0.05 to 0.11 mm (0.0020 to 0.0043 in)
Inner gear endfloat	0.05 to 0.09 mm (0.0020 to 0.0035 in)

Torque wrench settings

	Nm	lbf ft
Rocker cover screws	1 to 3	0.5 to 2
Rocker arm adjuster screw locknut	18 to 22	13 to 16
Rocker shaft bolts	18 to 22	13 to 16
Cylinder head left-hand cover bolts	6 to 10	4.5 to 7.5
Fuel pump cam/locate plate bolt	78 to 88	57.5 to 65
Camshaft toothed pulley bolt	78 to 88	57.5 to 65
Timing belt cover bolts	3 to 5	2 to 4
Cylinder head bolts (see Fig. 1.11):		
Stage 1	29	21.5
Stage 2	78	57.5
Stage 3	Loosen all bolts completely	Loosen all bolts completely
Stage 4	29	21.5
Stage 5	**Either** 74 to 83 **or** tighten through a further 83° to 88° (bolt 8), 75° to 80° (all other bolts) clockwise	**Either** 54.5 to 61 **or** tighten through a further 83° to 88° (bolt 8), 75° to 80° (all other bolts) clockwise
Timing belt tensioner bolts A and B	15 to 20	11 to 15
Crankshaft pulley bolt	123 to 132	90.5 to 97
Oil pump mounting bolt (large)	12 to 16	9 to 12
Oil pump mounting bolts (small)	6 to 7	4.5 to 5
Oil pick-up pipe and strainer bolts	10 to 14	7.5 to 10
Oil pump cover screws	4 to 5	3 to 4
Pressure regulator cap	39 to 49	29 to 36
Sump pan bolts:		
2.0 litre fuel injection models	7 to 8	5 to 6
All other models	5 to 7	4 to 5
Crankcase ventilation baffle plate bolt	4 to 6	3 to 4.5
Main bearing cap bolts	44 to 54	32.5 to 40
Connecting rod cap nuts	32 to 36	23.5 to 26.5
Crankshaft oil seal retainer bolts	4 to 6	3 to 4.5
Flywheel/driveplate bolts	98 to 108	72 to 79.5
Oil pressure switch	10 to 16	7.5 to 12
Oil cooler mounting nuts	20 to 25	15 to 18.5
Oil cooler-to-cover stud	29 to 39	21.5 to 29
Alternator (and air conditioning compressor) bracket-to-cylinder block/crankcase bolts	69 to 78	51 to 57.5
Engine front and rear mounting bracket-to-cylinder block/crankcase bolts	43 to 58	32 to 43

Torque wrench settings (continued)

	Nm	lbf ft
Engine oil (sump pan) drain plug	29 to 39	21.5 to 29
Engine mounting longitudinal member:		
2.0 litre fuel injection models:		
Front bolts	39 to 49	29 to 36
Rear bolts	49 to 59	36 to 43.5
All other models	39 to 49	29 to 36
Front mounting (buffer rod) top and bottom nuts	59 to 78	43.5 to 57.5
Rear mounting nuts	39 to 49	29 to 36
Rear (sub-mounting) top bolt and bottom nut	59 to 78	43.5 to 57.5
Rear (sub-mounting) adjusting bolts	39 to 49	29 to 36
Engine/transmission right-hand mounting:		
Cast bracket-to-engine bolts	Not available	Not available
Mounting insulator-to-cast bracket bolts	49 to 59	36 to 43.5
All other bolts and nuts	39 to 49	29 to 36
Engine/manual transmission left-hand mounting:		
Through-bolt retaining nut	39 to 49	29 to 36
Mounting-to-inner wing panel bolts	39 to 49	29 to 36
Mounting-to-transmission casing bolts (1.6 litre models)	49 to 59	36 to 43.5
Mounting-to-transmission casing bolts (1.8 and 2.0 litre models)	44 to 54	32.5 to 40
Engine/automatic transmission left-hand mounting:		
Through-bolt retaining nut	64 to 74	47 to 54.5
Mounting-to-transmission casing bolts	44 to 54	32.5 to 40
All other bolts and nuts	39 to 49	29 to 36

Note: *Only engine component fasteners are listed above – for all ancillary components (including engine-to-transmission fasteners) refer to the relevant Chapter of this Manual.*

1   General description

The engine is of four cylinder overhead cam type, mounted transversely at the front end of the car.

The cylinder head is of light alloy construction and the cylinder block/crankcase is of cast iron.

The crankshaft is of five main bearing type, whilst the belt-driven camshaft runs in a similar number of non-renewable bearings in the cylinder head.

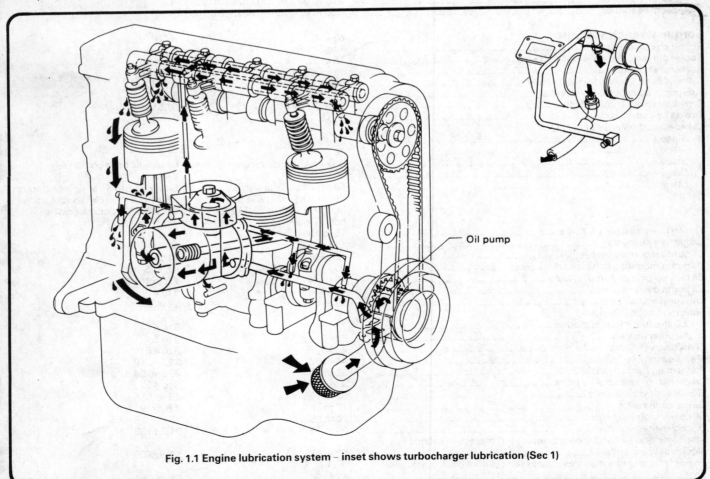

Oil pump

Fig. 1.1 Engine lubrication system – inset shows turbocharger lubrication (Sec 1)

2.5 Topping-up the engine oil

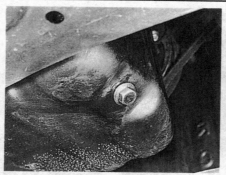
2.13 Engine oil drain plug in sump

2.15 Location of engine oil filter (seen from beneath)

The oil pump is mounted at the timing belt end of the crankshaft and supplies pressurised oil to all moving parts after the oil has first passed through an externally mounted full-flow cartridge type filter. An oil cooler, using coolant from the engine's cooling system (Chapter 2), is fitted to the rear of the cylinder block on turbo engine and 2.0 litre automatic transmission models.

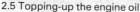

2 Routine maintenance

Carry out the following procedures at the intervals given in *'Routine maintenance'* at the beginning of this Manual.

Check the engine oil level
1 With the engine at normal operating temperature, park the car on level ground.
2 Switch off and wait two or three minutes to allow the oil to drain into the sump.
3 Withdraw the oil level dipstick from between the timing belt cover and the engine/transmission right-hand mounting, wipe it clean, reinsert it fully and withdraw it again.
4 The level should be between the 'L' and 'H' marks (Fig. 1.2).
5 If topping-up is necessary, add only good quality oil of the specified type through the oil filler in the rocker cover (photo).
6 Do not run the engine with the oil level below the 'L' mark or above the 'H' mark; either condition could cause engine damage.
7 Ensure that the oil filler cap and dipstick are securely refitted.

Change the engine oil and filter
8 Note that on T12 Turbo models the more frequent oil change interval calls for the renewal of the engine oil only; in all other cases the engine oil and filter are always renewed at the same time.
9 **Always** warm the engine up to normal operating temperature before changing the engine oil. This makes the operation quicker and

more effective but also requires care in handling hot oil and hot engine components if scalding is to be avoided.
10 It is useful, but not essential, to raise the front of the car and support it on axle stands.
11 Before starting work read the 'Safety First' section of this manual and note the danger of prolonged contact of the skin with used engine oil; use gloves or a good barrier cream before starting work and wash your hands carefully when finished.
12 Unscrew and remove the oil filler cap.
13 Position a suitable container beneath the engine and unscrew the sump drain plug (photo), keeping the hands clear of the hot oil.
14 Allow all the oil to drain, then clean the drain plug and refit it into the sump. Renew the washer if necessary.
15 Using a suitable oil filter wrench, unscrew the cartridge type oil filter (photo). Be prepared for some loss of oil as it is unscrewed.
16 If the old filter is found to be exceptionally tight and the wrench will not release it, drive a heavy screwdriver through the filter casing and use it as a lever to unscrew the filter.
17 Clean the filter mounting flange on the crankcase and smear a little oil on the rubber sealing ring of the new filter.
18 Screw the filter into position until the sealing ring seats firmly on the crankcase, then tighten it further through at least two-thirds of a turn using hand pressure only (Fig. 1.3).
19 Refill the engine with the correct amount of oil, refit the filler cap and start the engine.
20 As the engine warms up, check for oil leaks around the drain plug and filter seal; correct as required.
21 Stop the engine when it is fully warmed up and check the oil level (see above); top up if necessary.
Note: *When disposing of used engine oil, do not pour it down the drain – this is illegal and causes pollution. Your dealer or Local Authority may be able to dispose of it safely.*

Check the valve clearances
22 Refer to Section 4.

Renew the timing belt
23 Refer to Section 5.

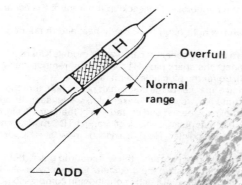
Fig. 1.2 Engine oil level dipstick markings (Sec 2)

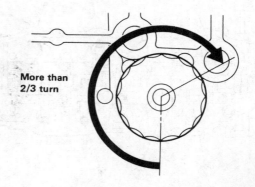
Fig. 1.3 Tightening engine oil filter (Sec 2)

4.4 Removing rocker cover

3 Major operations possible without removing engine from car

The following work can be carried out without having to remove the engine:

Valve clearances – adjustment
Timing belt – removal and refitting
Cylinder head – removal and refitting
Sump pan – removal and refitting
Oil pump – removal and refitting
Pistons and big-end bearings – renewal
Engine/transmission mountings – renewal

4 Valve clearances – adjustment

1   As a routine service operation, the valve clearances should be checked and adjusted while the engine is hot. After overhaul of the engine, the valve clearances will obviously have to be set cold initially and then re-set when the engine has been run to normal operating temperature.
2   Remove the air cleaner (carburettor models) or the turbocharger-to-throttle chamber air intake (inlet) duct (Turbo models) – Chapter 3.
3   Unclip and disconnect the spark plug (HT) leads, then remove the spark plugs (Chapter 4); cover the plug holes with rag.
4   Disconnect the breather hose, remove the securing screws and lift off the rocker cover (photo). While the rocker cover is off, clean its underside, removing all traces of sludge and dirt. Also inspect the gasket – it must be renewed if damaged or distorted. Note that Nissan recommend that the gasket be renewed as a matter of course whenever it is disturbed.

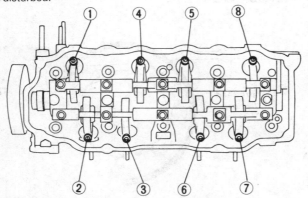

Fig. 1.4 Intake (inlet) and exhaust valve identification (Sec 4)

4.7 Adjusting valve clearances

5   To turn the crankshaft, either apply a spanner to the crankshaft pulley bolt and turn it clockwise, or (manual transmission only) select top gear and push the car forwards as required.
6   Turn the crankshaft clockwise until No 1 cylinder intake (inlet) valve has opened and closed again, then turn it slightly further until the crankshaft pulley's black and orange Top Dead Centre (TDC) mark aligns with the timing belt cover pointer. No 1 cylinder is now at TDC on the compression stroke and No 4 cylinder valves will be 'rocking' (intake (inlet) valve opening, exhaust valve closing).
7   Adjust the clearances on valve numbers '1, 2, 4 and 6 (Fig. 1.4). To do this, insert a feeler blade of the correct thickness between the end of the valve stem and the rocker arm. The blade should be a stiff sliding fit. If the clearance is incorrect, release the rocker arm adjuster screw locknut and turn the adjuster screw (photo). Once the clearance is correct, tighten the locknut without altering the position of the screw.
8   Having adjusted the clearances of the first four valves, turn the crankshaft forwards until No. 4 piston is at TDC on its compression stroke. No 1 cylinder valve will now be 'rocking'.
9   Adjust the clearances on valve numbers 3, 5, 7 and 8.
10   On completion, refit the rocker cover and breather hose, spark plugs and spark plug leads, and air cleaner or air ducting. Renew the rocker cover gasket if necessary and note that the smaller washers fit at the timing belt end of the rocker cover. **Do not** overtighten the rocker cover screws; this will merely distort the cover and make oil leaks more likely.

5 Timing belt and tensioner assembly – removal and refitting

Note: *A considerable amount of effort may be required to slacken the crankshaft pulley bolt; owners are advised to do this first, while the car is parked on firm, level ground, rather than when it is raised. See paragraph 9 below.*

1   Apply the handbrake, then jack up the front of the car and support on axle stands.
2   Remove the right-hand front roadwheel and the underwing shield (photo).
3   Remove the air cleaner on carburettor models (Chapter 3).
4   Disconnect the spark plug HT leads, then remove the spark plugs (Chapter 4). Cover the plug holes with rag.
5   Applying a spanner to the crankshaft pulley bolt, turn the crankshaft clockwise until No 1 cylinder intake (inlet) valve (seen through the oil filter aperture) has opened and closed again, then turn it slightly further until the crankshaft pulley's (black or orange) TDC mark aligns with the timing belt cover pointer. No 1 cylinder is now at TDC on the compression stroke.
6   Slacken, but do not remove, the water pump pulley bolts.
7   Remove (as applicable) the drivebelts for the power-assisted steering pump and the alternator or air conditioning compressor (Chapter 2).
8   Unbolt and remove the water pump pulley.

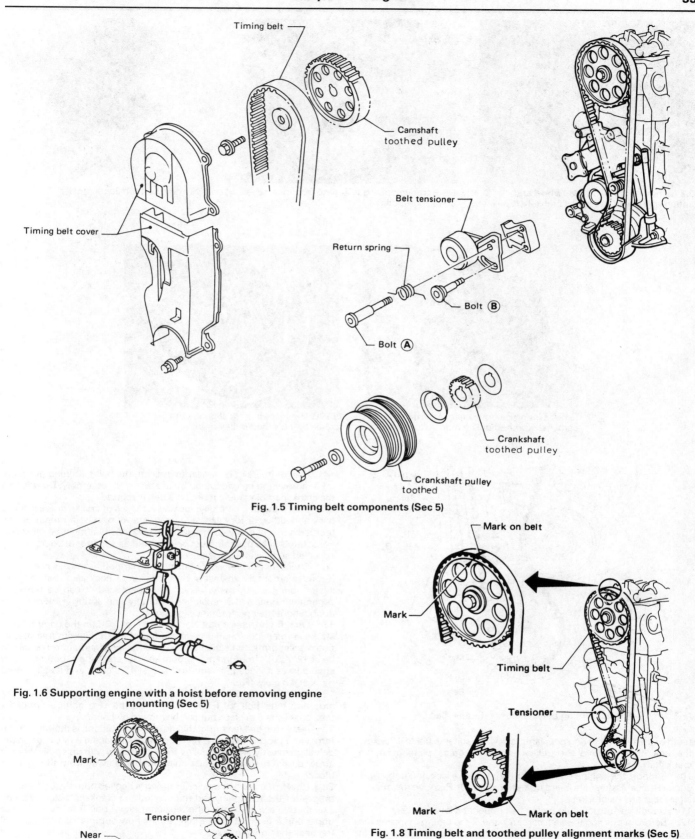

Fig. 1.5 Timing belt components (Sec 5)

Fig. 1.6 Supporting engine with a hoist before removing engine mounting (Sec 5)

Fig. 1.7 Timing belt toothed pulley alignment marks (Sec 5)

Fig. 1.8 Timing belt and toothed pulley alignment marks (Sec 5)

9   To slacken the crankshaft pulley bolt, the crankshaft must be held against rotation. On manual transmission models, select a gear and have an assistant apply the footbrake hard. On automatic transmission models, the bellhousing dust cover will have to be removed and the

5.2 Remove right-hand roadwheel and underwing shield to expose crankshaft pulley

5.9 Remove outer guide plate from behind crankshaft pulley

5.16 Timing belt tensioner

5.19A Timing belt mark aligned with camshaft toothed pulley mark

5.19B Timing belt mark aligned with crankshaft toothed pulley mark

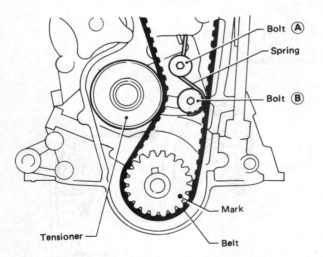

Bolt (A)
Spring
Bolt (B)
Mark
Tensioner
Belt

Fig. 1.9 Timing belt tensioner details (Sec 5)

teeth of the driveplate ring gear jammed with a suitable blade. Unscrew the bolt, then remove the pulley and outer guide plate from the crankshaft (photo).

10 Support the engine with a hoist (Fig. 1.6) or a jack and unbolt the engine/transmission right-hand mounting (Sec 10). Remove the mounting rubber and its bracket.

11 Unbolt and remove the timing belt upper and lower covers.

12 Before disturbing the belt, carefully check the timing marks on the toothed pulleys. The mark on the crankshaft toothed pulley should be at 4 o'clock, with its Woodruff key at 12 o'clock. The mark on the camshaft toothed pulley should also be at 12 o'clock (see Fig. 1.7). Note that the white lines on the timing belt may not line up with the timing marks.

13 Slacken the belt tensioner bolts A and B then push the tensioner pulley away from the belt (see Fig. 1.9).

14 Use white paint or similar to indicate the belt's running direction, then remove the belt, followed by the tensioner assembly. **Do not** turn the crankshaft or camshaft until the belt is refitted.

15 Check the belt carefully, looking for signs of cracks or wear on its back and sides, or for excessive wear, cracks or missing teeth on the toothed surface. If any such signs are found the belt must be renewed. For safety's sake the belt must be renewed as a matter of course at the specified service interval (see Section 2).

16 Check that the tensioner pulley spins smoothly and easily and that it moves smoothly against spring pressure. Check also that the tensioner spring is not rusty, distorted or damaged; it can be renewed separately. Renew the tensioner assembly and spring if there is any doubt about their performance (photo).

17 On refitting, check that No 1 piston is at TDC on the compression stroke ie the piston should be at the top of its stroke with free play at both rocker arms, the camshaft toothed pulley alignment mark should be at 12 o'clock from the pulley bolt, and the crankshaft toothed pulley should have its locating Woodruff key at 12 o'clock and its alignment mark at 4 o'clock (Fig. 1.7).

18 Refit the tensioner so that its spring is hooked correctly over the stop and over bolt 'B' (Fig. 1.9). Tighten the two bolts so that the tensioner is held in place but can be moved by hand.

19 Install the belt (ensuring that its running direction is the same as on removal, if the original belt is being refitted) so that the white lines on the belt align exactly with the pulley marks (photos). Where applicable the arrow on the timing belt must point outwards away from the cylinder block.

20 Check that the belt tensioner spring is hooked onto the bolt and the bracket of the tensioner, and then rotate the crankshaft clockwise by exactly two turns. Tighten the tensioner lower bolt B followed by the upper bolt A (Fig. 1.9). The timing belt is now automatically tensioned. Recheck the timing marks.

21 Refit the outer guide plate and the pulley to the crankshaft and tighten the bolt to the specified torque while holding the crankshaft against rotation as described in paragraph 9.

22 Refit the timing belt covers (photo).

23 Bolt the pulley onto the water pump.

6.6A Main earth cable at front of cylinder head ...

6.6B ... and at rear, on some models

6.19A Refitting carburettor and intake (inlet) manifold

6.19B Exhaust manifold and heat shield

6.20 New cylinder head gasket in position

24   Refit and tension the drivebelts (Chapter 2).
25   Refit the engine/transmission right-hand mounting, tightening the mounting bolts to the specified torque setting. Release the hoist or jack.
26   Refit the spark plugs, HT leads and air cleaner (where applicable).
27   Refit the underwing shield and the roadwheel, then lower the car to the ground.

6   Cylinder head – removal and refitting

1   Disconnect the battery (Chapter 12) and drain the cooling system (Chapter 2).
2   Remove the air cleaner and intake (inlet) ducting according to model (Chapter 3).
3   Disconnect the radiator top hose from the intake (inlet) manifold.
4   Disconnect the vacuum servo unit hose and other vacuum hoses from the intake (inlet) manifold.
5   Disconnect the accelerator cable (Chapter 3).

6   Unbolt the earth cables from the cylinder head (photos).
7   Remove the distributor if the head is to be dismantled (Chapter 4).
8   On carburettor models remove the fuel pump (Chapter 3).
9   On Turbo and 2.0 litre fuel injection models remove the fuel-injection system components (Chapter 3).
10   Disconnect the hot air hose from the exhaust manifold (carburettor models).
11   Unscrew the flange nuts and separate the exhaust downpipe from the manifold or turbocharger as applicable.
12   Disconnect the wiring from the coolant temperature gauge sensor and the carburettor or fuel-injection equipment (Chapter 3).
13   Remove the spark plugs, the rocker cover securing screws and the rocker cover.
14   Remove the timing belt with reference to Section 5.
15   If the cylinder head is to be dismantled, it is easier to slacken the camshaft toothed pulley bolt, the fuel pump cam/locating plate bolt and the rocker shaft bolts while the head is still bolted in place (see Section 17).

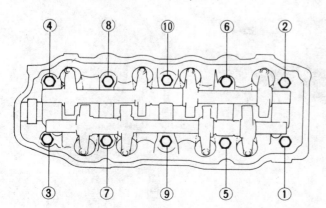

Fig. 1.10 Cylinder head bolt slackening sequence (Sec 6)

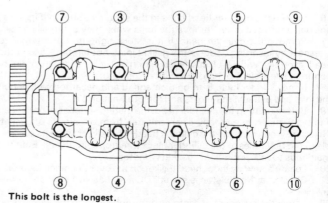

This bolt is the longest.

Fig. 1.11 Cylinder head bolt tightening sequence (Sec 6)

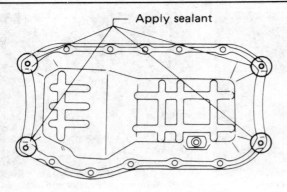

Apply sealant

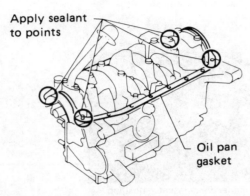

Apply sealant
to points

Oil pan
gasket

Fig. 1.12 Sump pan sealant application points – early models (Sec 7)

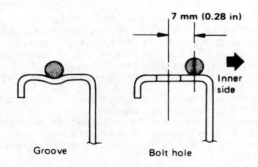

7 mm (0.28 in)

Inner
side

Groove   Bolt hole

Fig. 1.13 Sump pan sealant bead details – later models (Sec 7)

16   Loosen the cylinder head bolts in the sequence shown (Fig. 1.10), one half a turn at a time. Remove the bolts when they are totally slack.
17   Remove the cylinder head. If it is stuck tight, do not attempt to release it by inserting a tool in the gasket joint, but tap the sides of the head carefully with a plastic-faced hammer, or if using an ordinary hammer, use a block of hard wood as an insulator.
18   If the cylinder head is to be dismantled and decarbonised, unbolt the inlet and exhaust manifolds and refer to Section 17.
19   Before refitting the cylinder head, the mating surfaces of both head and block must be perfectly clean and free from old pieces of gasket. Take care when cleaning the cylinder head not to dig or score its surface. Clean the bolt holes in the cylinder block free from dirt and oil. Refit the manifolds together with new gaskets (photos).
20   Locate a new cylinder head gasket on the cylinder block (photo).
21   Check that No 1 piston is still at TDC and that No 1 cylinder valves are closed.
22   Lower the cylinder head into position and screw in the lightly oiled bolts. Make sure that each bolt is fitted with a washer.

23   Tighten the cylinder head bolts to the specified torque in the sequence shown (Fig. 1.11) and following the stages given in the Specifications.
24   Bolt the toothed pulley onto the camshaft (where applicable).
25   Refit the timing belt with reference to Section 5.
26   Adjust the valve clearances as described in Section 4.
27   Refit the spark plugs.
28   Reconnect the wiring, the exhaust downpipe, and the hot air hose.
29   Refit the fuel pump or fuel-injection components (Chapter 3).
30   Refit the distributor (Chapter 4) and the earth cables.
31   Reconnect the accelerator cable (Chapter 3), the vacuum servo unit hose and other vacuum hoses and the radiator top hose.
32   Refit the air cleaner or inlet ducting.
33   Fill the cooling system (Chapter 2) and reconnect the battery.
34   Run the engine to normal operating temperature, then recheck and if necessary adjust the valve clearances.
35   After 600 miles (1000 km), the cylinder head bolts should be re-tightened with the engine cold. To do this, remove the rocker cover, then using the same sequence as for tightening the bolts, loosen each bolt half a turn and re-tighten it to the specified final torque wrench setting.

7 Sump pan – removal and refitting

1   Apply the handbrake, then jack up the front of the car and support on axle stands.
2   Remove the engine compartment undershields (Chapter 1).
3   Unbolt the exhaust downpipe from the manifold or turbocharger (as applicable).
4   Release the exhaust system forward mountings and then pull the front of the system down as far as the flexible connection will allow.
5   Drain the engine oil (Section 2).
6   Unscrew the sump pan retaining bolts. Pull the pan downwards and remove it. If clearance is limited it will be necessary to unbolt the engine mountings from the longitudinal member and to unbolt the member so that it can be lowered sufficiently for the sump pan to be removed (Section 10).
7   On refitting, be careful to remove all traces of old gasket (early models) or sealant (later models) from the cylinder block/crankcase and sump pan mating surfaces.
8   On early models, stick a new gasket in position on the crankcase using a smear of sealant (photo), then apply additional sealant at the points indicated in Fig. 1.12.
9   On July 1986 on T12 models and all T72 models, apply a continuous bead of sealant 3.5 to 4.5 mm (0.14 to 0.18 in) wide all the way around the sump pan mating surface. The bead should run in the pan mating surface groove and to the inside of the bolt holes, as shown in Fig. 1.13. Fit new oil pump and oil seal retainer gaskets, then refit the sump pan

7.8 Fitting a new sump pan gasket – early models

7.10 Refitting the sump pan (engine removed)

8 Oil pump – removal and refitting

1   Remove the sump pan (Section 7).
2   Remove the timing belt and tensioner (Section 5).
3   Unbolt and remove the oil pick-up pipe and strainer.
4   Pull off the crankshaft toothed pulley. Remove the Woodruff key and inner guide plate.
5   Unbolt and remove the oil pump from the right-hand face of the crankcase. Discard the joint gasket.
6   The oil pump can be examined as described in Section 18 and renewed if worn.
7   Before refitting the oil pump, always renew the oil seal and grease the seal lips. Use a new joint gasket.
8   As the oil pump is offered into position, align the inner gear with the flats on the crankshaft. Tape the shoulder on the crankshaft to prevent damage to the oil seal lips during fitting of the pump. Remove the tape when the pump is in position (photos).
9   Fit the inner guide plate, crankshaft Woodruff key and toothed pulley so that its timing mark is visible (photos).
10   Refit the oil pick-up pipe and strainer together with a new gasket and tighten the bolts (photo).
11   Refit the tensioner and timing belt (Section 5).
12   Refit the sump pan (Section 7).

within 5 minutes of applying the sealant, but do not refill the engine with oil for at least 30 minutes.
10   Offer up the sump pan (photo) and screw in the bolts evenly in diagonal sequence.
11   Refit the engine mounting longitudinal member (if removed).
12   Reconnect the exhaust system and the engine compartment undershields.
13   Fit and tighten the drain plug and lower the car to the ground.
14   Fill the engine with oil and check carefully for oil leaks when the engine is restarted.

9 Pistons and big-end bearings – renewal

1   Remove the cylinder head (Section 6).
2   Remove the engine sump pan (Section 7).
3   Unbolt and remove the oil pick-up pipe and strainer.
4   Note that the connecting rod big-end cap and rod are numbered at adjacent points (photo). Number 1 is at the timing belt end of the engine.

8.8A Crankshaft shoulder taped for oil pump refitting

8.8B Refitting oil pump

8.9A Timing belt inner guide plate

8.9B Ensure timing mark is visible when refitting toothed pulley

8.10 Refitting oil pump pick-up pipe and strainer

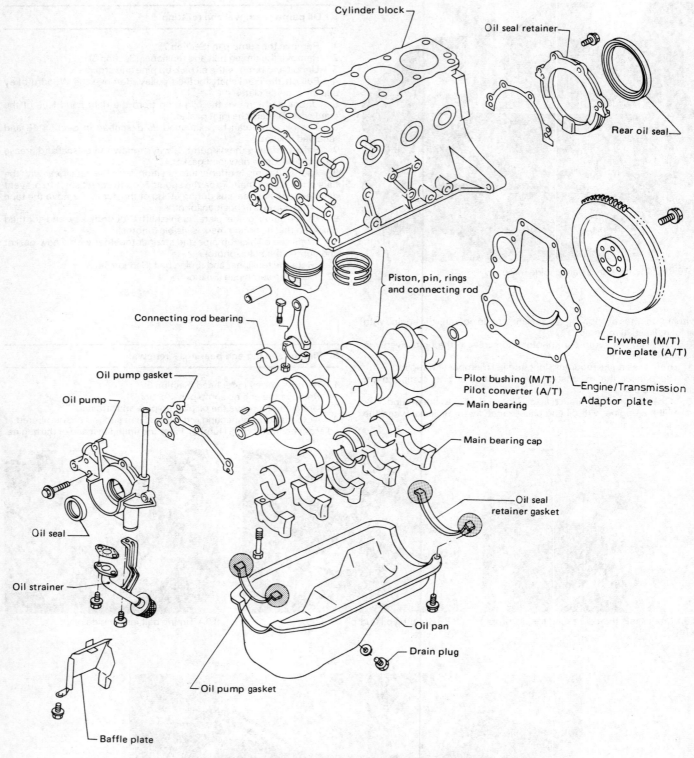

Fig. 1.14 Engine bottom end components (Secs 8, 9 and 16)

5   Feel the top of the cylinder bore for a wear ridge. If a thick one is felt then it should be removed using a ridge reamer or by careful scraping, in order to enable the piston rings to pass out of the bore during removal.
6   Unscrew the big-end cap nuts and take off the cap with the shell bearing.
7   Push the piston/rod assembly out of the top of the block.
8   If the bearing shells are to be used again, tape them to their original cap or rod.

9   Repeat the operations on the three remaining assemblies.
10   If the reason for removal of the piston/rod assemblies was to fit new piston rings to reduce oil consumption, then either standard or special proprietary rings may be fitted.
11   To remove a piston ring, slide three feeler blades behind the top ring and space them at equidistant points.
12   Remove the ring by pulling it off the top of the piston using a twisting motion.

9.4 Connecting rod and cap numbers refer to cylinder numbers

9.23A Insert piston/connecting rod into cylinder bore ...

9.23B ... so that piston crown mark is towards timing belt end

9.24 Driving piston into cylinder bore

9.26 Tightening connecting rod cap nut

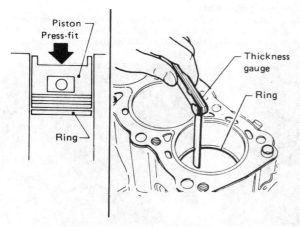

Fig. 1.15 Checking piston ring end gap (Sec 9)

13   Repeat on the remaining rings, always removing them from the crown of the piston.
14   Clean the piston ring grooves of carbon. A piece of broken piston ring is useful for this.
15   Make sure that the oil return holes at the base of the ring grooves are clear.
16   Push the piston rings down their cylinder bore one at a time using a piston and check the ring end gap using a feeler blade (Fig. 1.15). If not as specified, carefully grind the end of the ring.
17   Check each ring in its groove for side clearance again using a feeler blade (Fig. 1.16). If the clearance is too small then the piston grooves can be widened by your engine reconditioner or the ring width reduced by rubbing it on abrasive sheeting located on a very flat surface.
18   Fit the rings by reversing the removal operations. Stagger the ring gaps as shown in Fig. 1.18.
19   If new rings have been fitted, then to assist them to bed in rapidly, the hard glaze in the cylinder bores should be removed. Do this using a rotary type flap wheel in an electric drill or with fine glasspaper rubbed up and down at an angle to give a cross-hatch effect.
20   If new bearing shells are fitted, make sure that shells of the same size as the originals are used. The shells will be marked on their backs either standard or undersize.

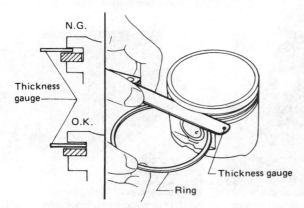

Fig. 1.16 Checking piston ring side clearance (Sec 9)

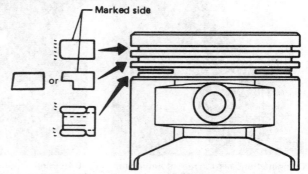

Fig. 1.17 Piston ring identification (Sec 9)

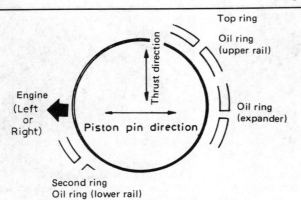

Fig. 1.18 Piston ring end gap location (Sec 9)

21　Fit the shells to caps and rods noting that the upper bearing shell has an oil hole which must align exactly with that of the connecting rod (Fig. 1.19).

22　Oil the piston rings liberally and fit a piston ring compressor.

23　Lower the rod of No 1 piston into its cylinder bore so that the compressor sits squarely on the surface of the block. Make sure that the mark on the piston crown is towards the timing belt end of the engine (photos).

24　Place the wooden handle of a hammer against the middle of the piston crown and then strike the head of the hammer with the hand to drive the piston with rings into the cylinder. The compressor will be released (photo).

25　Pull the rod down onto the crankshaft and fit the big-end cap (with shell) so that the matching numbers are adjacent.

26　Screw on the cap nuts (threads lightly oiled) and tighten to the specified torque wrench setting (photo).

27　Repeat the operations on the remaining pistons.

28　Fit the oil pick-up pipe and strainer, the sump pan and the cylinder head all as described earlier in this Chapter.

29　Fill the engine with oil.

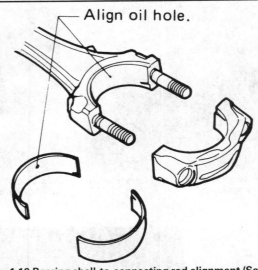

Fig. 1.19 Bearing shell-to-connecting rod alignment (Sec 9)

10　Engine/transmission mountings – renewal and adjustment

1　The mountings can be renewed provided the weight of the engine and transmission is taken on a hoist or jack (photos).

2　The component which incorporates the flexible insulator should be renewed if the rubber has become sticky or has perished or becomes deformed as the result of the weight of the power train.

3　Tighten the mountings in the following order:

(a)　*Right-hand mounting*
(b)　*Left-hand mounting*
(c)　*Rear (main) mounting*
(d)　*Remove the jack or hoist so that all engine/transmission weight is on the mountings, then tighten the bolts and nuts on the rear sub-mounting and the front buffer rod in the order shown in Fig. 1.21.*

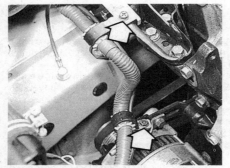

10.1A Unbolt wiring clamps (arrowed) and disconnect alternator wiring ...

10.1B ... before dismantling engine right-hand mounting

10.1C Engine/transmission rear sub-mounting (engine removed)

10.1D Engine/transmission rear mounting nut seen from below (see photo 12.31)

10.1E Engine mounting longitudinal member rear mountings (arrowed)

10.1F Engine mounting longitudinal member front mountings

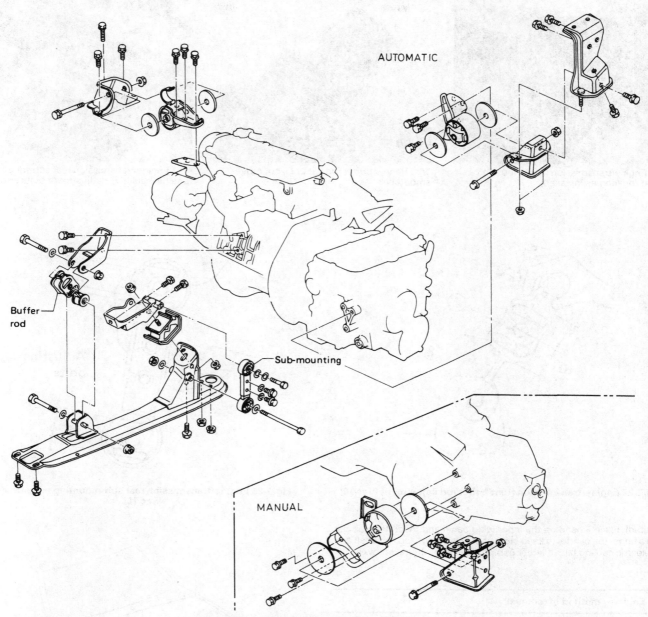

Fig. 1.20 Engine/transmission mountings (Sec 10)

Adjustment

4   If the engine vibrates excessively at idle speed, first check that all mountings are in good condition and securely fastened to the specified torque settings, then check the following.

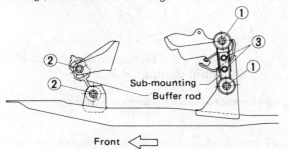

Fig. 1.21 Engine/transmission front and rear mounting tightening sequence (Sec 10)

5   With reference to Fig. 1.22 check that the front buffer rod (photo) distances A and B are equal and that the distance between bolts 1 and 2 is 100 mm (3.94 in). Slacken the mounting bolts and nuts and adjust if necessary.

6   Hold the upper end of the buffer rod and move it from front to rear and from side to side; it should move smoothly. If not, slacken bolts 1 and 2, then retighten them in the reverse order. If the rod still does not move smoothly, renew it (photo).

7   With reference to Fig. 1.23 check that the rear sub-mounting gaps A and B are equal when the engine is running at idle speed; on automatic models check gaps A with the transmission D position selected and check gaps B with the R position selected. If either pair of gaps is closed up, slacken the two adjusting bolts and alter the length of the sub-mounting until the adjustment is correct (photo).

8   If both front and rear mountings are correctly adjusted, check that the radiator does not vibrate when the engine is running at idle speed (D position selected for automatic transmission). If it does, check the radiator mountings and renew them if necessary (Chapter 2).

9   On automatic transmission models only, check that the dynamic dampers vibrate when the engine is running at idle speed (D position

10.5 Engine/transmission front mounting buffer rod (engine installed)

10.6 Renew buffer rod if it does not move smoothly

10.7 Engine/transmission rear sub-mounting (engine installed) – adjustment bolts arrowed

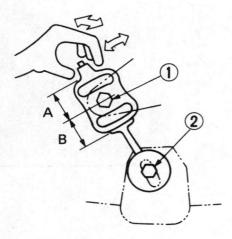

Fig. 1.22 Engine/transmission front buffer rod adjustment (Sec 10)

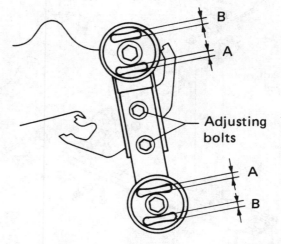

Fig. 1.23 Engine/transmission rear sub-mounting adjustment (Sec 10)

selected). Place a hand on the inner wing panel and touch the damper with a finger (be careful to keep clear of the alternator and drivebelt and the electric cooling fan). If either damper does not vibrate, renew it.

11 Engine – method of removal

The engine should be removed complete with transmission by lifting it out upwards from the engine compartment.

12 Engine/manual transmission – removal and separation

1   Park the car on firm, level ground, apply the handbrake, then remove the bonnet (Chapter 11).
2   On Turbo and 2.0 litre fuel injection models, relieve fuel system pressure (Chapter 3).
3   Disconnect the battery and remove it (Chapter 12), then unbolt the battery tray. Disconnect the wiring connector plugs in the positive (+) lead (photos).
4   If the engine is to be dismantled, drain the oil and remove the oil filter (Section 2).
5   Drain the transmission oil (Chapter 6).
6   Remove the engine compartment undershields and the underwing shields (Chapter 11).
7   On carburettor models, remove the air cleaner, the intake (inlet) flexible duct and the warm air intake (inlet) hose (Chapter 3).

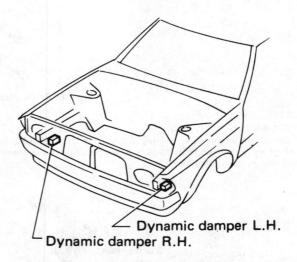

Fig. 1.24 Location of dynamic dampers – automatic transmission (Sec 10)

8   On Turbo models, remove the air cleaner, airflow meter and air intake (inlet) ducting. Be sure to pack the turbocharger intake with clean rag (Chapter 3).
9   On 2.0 litre fuel injection models, disconnect the wiring from the

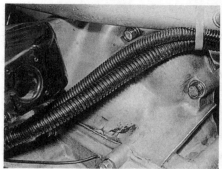

12.3A Engine/transmission wiring loom runs over bellhousing ...

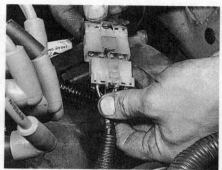

12.3B ... to connector plug next to battery

12.14 Disconnecting carburettor wiring

12.21 Power-assisted steering pump secured clear of engine

12.26 Unscrewing exhaust downpipe retaining nuts

12.28 Oil pressure switch wiring (switch end)

ignition system components and remove the air cleaner, airflow meter and air intake (inlet) duct (Chapter 3).

10   On all models, disconnect the accelerator cable (Chapter 3).

11   Making notes so that they can be correctly refitted, and taking precautions to prevent fuel spillage, disconnect the fuel feed and return hoses (Chapter 3).

12   Disconnect the alternator wiring (Chapter 12) and unbolt the wiring clamps from the engine mounting. Secure the wiring clear of the engine/transmission.

13   Disconnect, as applicable, the vacuum servo unit vacuum hose, econometer hose and boost sensor hose from the intake (inlet) manifold unions (Chapter 3).

14   On carburettor models, disconnect the distributor wiring and ignition HT coil lead (Chapter 4) and the carburettor wiring (Chapter 3) (photo).

15   On Turbo and 2.0 litre fuel injection models first make written notes as an aid to correct identification on reassembly, then disconnect the wiring for the distributor/crank angle sensor (Chapter 4) and all fuel injection system components (Chapter 3).

16   On all models, unbolt and disconnect the earth leads from the cylinder head left-hand end (front and rear on some models), the distributor/crank angle sensor and the transmission.

17   Disconnect the transmission wiring lead (Chapter 6), if separate from the (already disconnected) engine wiring harness.

18   Disconnect the speedometer drive cable (Chapter 12).

19   On 1.6 litre models, disconnect the clutch cable from the transmission (Chapter 5).

20   On 1.8 and 2.0 litre models, place a block of wood under the clutch pedal so that it cannot be depressed accidentally, then unbolt the clutch slave cylinder (and head shield, on Turbo models) from the front of the bellhousing. Remove the spring clip to release the hydraulic pipe and/or flexible hose from the transmission bracket, unbolt the bracket from the inner wing panel and secure the assembly clear of the engine/transmission, taking care not to twist or bend the hose or pipe.

21   Where fitted, remove the power-assisted steering pump drivebelt from the pump (Chapter 2), then undo the pump pivot bolt and adjuster lockbolt. Withdraw the pump without kinking or stretching the hoses and secure it to the bodywork, clear of the engine (photo).

22   Working as described in Chapter 2, drain the cooling system, remove the radiator top and bottom hoses, withdraw the radiator (complete with electric cooling fan) and disconnect the heater hoses from the engine/transmission.

23   On Executive models, remove the drivebelt from the air conditioning compressor pulley (Chapter 2), then unbolt the compressor from the mounting bracket and secure it to the body front panel, clear of the engine. Take care not to kink or stretch any of the air conditioning system hoses.

Note: *If the driveshafts are to be removed completely (see paragraph 25 below) the driveshaft nuts should be slackened while the front road-wheels are still on the ground – refer to Chapter 8, Section 3, paragraphs 1 to 5.*

24   Chock the rear wheels, jack up the front of the car and support it securely on axle stands.

25   Remove both driveshafts (Chapter 8) or carry out the abbreviated procedure outlined in Chapter 6, Section 7, paragraph 10.

26   Unscrew the retaining nuts securing the exhaust front downpipe to the exhaust manifold or turbocharger, as applicable (photo), unbolt the exhaust system front mounting from the bellhousing and pull the downpipe downwards as far as possible. Secure it clear of the engine/transmission.

27   Disconnect the gearchange control and support rods from the transmission (Chapter 6).

28   Disconnect the wiring from the starter motor and oil pressure switch (photo) if separate from the (already disconnected) engine wiring harness.

29   Make a careful check that all components which secure the engine/transmission to the body have been disconnected or removed.

30   Connect a hoist to the engine and take its weight.

31   Unbolt the four mountings (photo). Unbolt the left-hand mounting complete from the transmission casing.

32   Hoist the engine/transmission assembly carefully up and out of the engine compartment (photo).

33   Unbolt and remove the starter motor (Chapter 12).

34   Unscrew and remove the nuts and bolts connecting the transmission to the engine, noting the position of the engine/transmission stays (Chapter 6, Section 7).

12.31 With engine removed, rear mounting nut and locating dowel seen (arrowed)–also see photo 10.1d

12.32 Lifting the engine/transmission assembly from the engine compartment

12.35 Separating the transmission from the engine

14.1 Engine/transmission unit removed from car

35   Withdraw the transmission from the engine in a straight line, keeping it horizontal to prevent any damage to the clutch (photo).

13   Engine/automatic transmission – removal and separation

1   The operations required are very similar to those described in the preceding Section, but note the following differences.
2   Proceed as described in paragraphs 1 to 4 (where applicable).
3   Drain the transmission fluid, then slacken their clips and disconnect the two flexible hoses from the transmission fluid pipes. Note or label each hose to ensure that it is refitted correctly. Allow the hoses to drain into a container (Chapter 7).
4   Proceed as described in paragraphs 6 to 18 (as applicable) ignoring paragraph 8 and referring to Chapter 7, paragraph 17.
5   Ignore the references to the clutch (paragraphs 19 and 20); instead disconnect the kickdown and gear selector cables from the transmission (Chapter 7).
6   Proceed as described in paragraphs 21 to 24 (as applicable).
7   With reference to paragraph 25, note that the driveshafts must be removed completely on cars with automatic transmission – the shortcut mentioned is not feasible.
8   Proceed as described in paragraphs 26 to 33, ignoring paragraph 27.
9   With the engine/transmission removed, separate the assemblies in the following way.
10   Unbolt the dust cover from the bellhousing, noting the positions of the engine/transmission front and rear stays.
11   Mark the relationship of the torque converter to the driveplate with quick-drying paint and then unscrew the converter-to-driveplate mounting bolts. The crankshaft will have to be turned by means of the crankshaft pulley bolt to bring the bellhousing bolts into view in the bellhousing aperture.

12   Unscrew and remove the bolts connecting the bellhousing to the engine (Chapter 7, Section 15).
13   Withdraw the transmission from the engine, but keep the torque converter in full engagement with the oil pump, otherwise the fluid will spill from the torque converter.

14   Engine dismantling – general

1   It is best to mount the engine on a dismantling stand (photo) but if this is not available, stand the engine on a strong bench at a comfortable working height. Failing this, it will have to be stripped down on the floor, but at least place a sheet of hardboard down first.
2   Clean each component in paraffin (or similar safe cleaning agent) as it is removed.
3   Never immerse parts with oilways in paraffin (eg crankshaft and camshaft) unless you can be sure of removing all traces of solvent before reassembly (eg by using compressed air). To clean these parts, wipe down carefully with a paraffin dampened rag. Oilways can be cleaned out with wire. If an air line is available, all parts can be blown dry and the oilways blown through as an added precaution.
4   Re-use of old gaskets is false economy. To avoid the possibility of trouble after the engine has been reassembled **always** use new gaskets throughout.
5   Do not throw away the old gaskets, as sometimes it happens that an immediate replacement cannot be found and the old gasket is then very useful as a template. Hang up the gaskets as they are removed.
6   To strip the engine, it is best to work from the top down. When the stage is reached where the crankshaft must be removed, the engine can be turned on its side and all other work carried out with it in this position.
7   Wherever possible, refit nuts, bolts and washers finger tight from wherever they were removed. This helps to avoid loss and muddle. If they cannot be fitted, then arrange them in a sequence that ensures correct reassembly.
8   Make sure that you have a valve grinding tool, a valve spring compressor and a torque wrench as well as all the other tools and equipment required in the following Sections.

15   Engine ancillary components – removal

1   Before engine dismantling commences, remove the following ancillary components:

Alternator (Chapter 12)
Intake (inlet) manifold, carburettor and fuel pump, or fuel injection components (Chapter 3)
Distributor (Chapter 4) with cap and HT leads
Water pump and coolant return tube (Chapter 2)
Exhaust manifold and turbocharger (Chapter 3)
Clutch – if applicable (Chapter 5)
Crankcase ventilation oil separator (tap it out) (photo)

2   It is also recommended that the engine mounting brackets are removed. This will make the engine easier to handle (photos).

15.1 PCV oil separator and breather hoses

15.2A Engine front mounting bracket

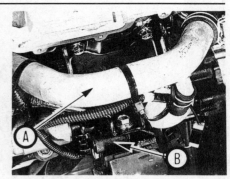

15.2B Coolant return tube (A) and engine rear mounting (B)

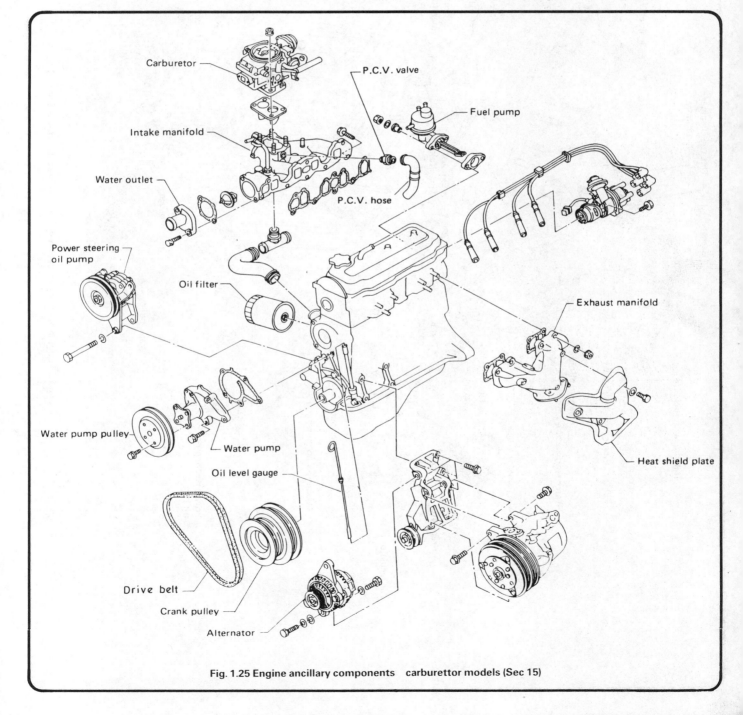

Fig. 1.25 Engine ancillary components   carburettor models (Sec 15)

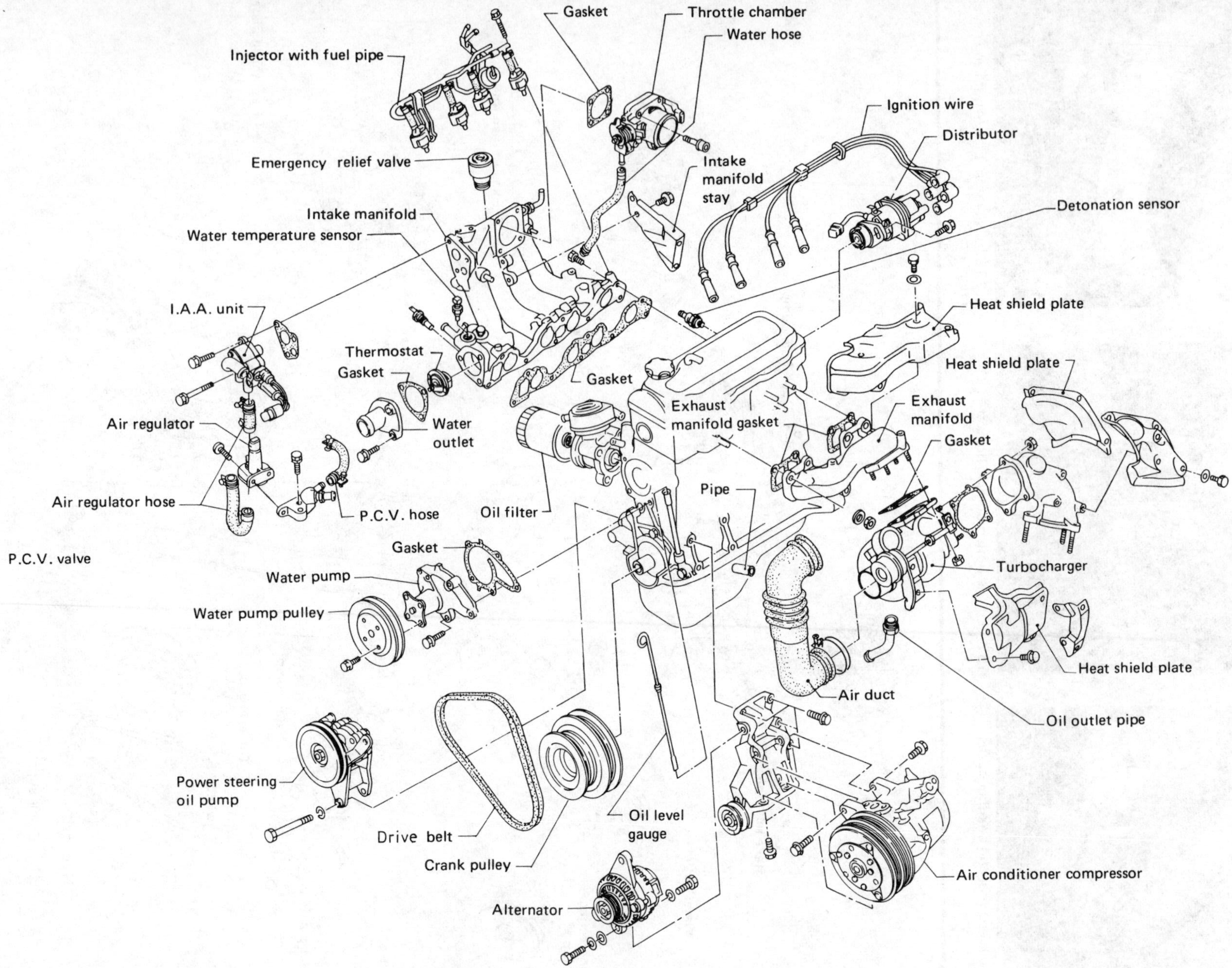

Fig. 1.26 Engine ancillary components – Turbo Executive models (Sec 15)

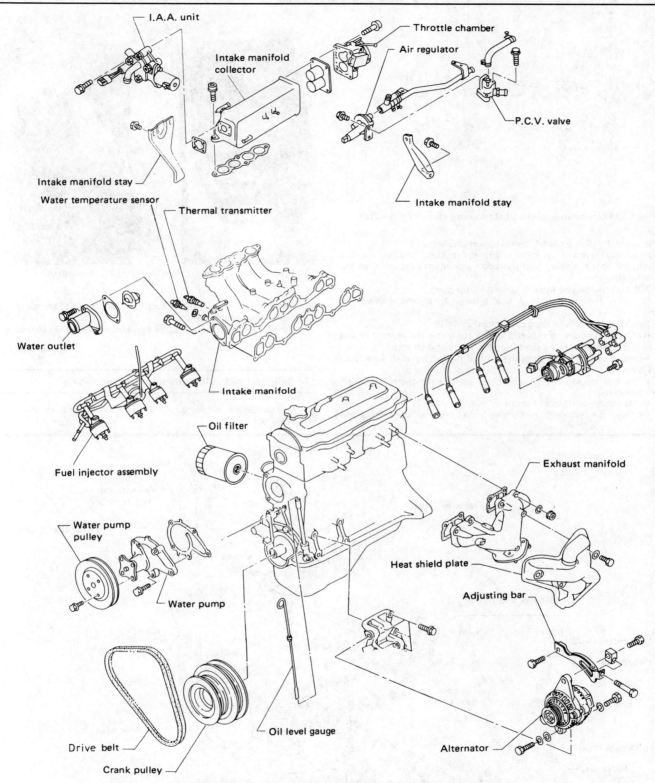

Fig. 1.27 Engine ancillary components – 2.0i GSX models (Sec 15)

16 Engine – complete dismantling

1   Unbolt the alternator and power steering pump adjuster and mounting brackets as applicable.
2   Unscrew and discard the oil filter.
3   Unscrew and remove the oil pressure switch.
4   Remove the timing belt with reference to Section 5.
5   Remove the cylinder head with reference to Section 6.
6   Turn the engine on its side.
7   Remove the sump pan and oil pump with reference to Sections 7 and 8.

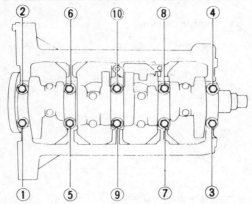

Fig. 1.28 Main bearing cap bolt slackening sequence (Sec 16)

8   Remove the pistons and big-end bearings (Section 9).
9   Unbolt and remove the flywheel/driveplate bolts and remove the flywheel/driveplate, having first marked its position in relation to the mounting flange.
10   Take off the engine/transmission adaptor plate.
11   Unscrew the crankshaft oil seal retainer bolts and remove the retainer.
12   Remove the main bearing cap bolts (Fig. 1.28).
13   Note the caps are numbered 1 to 5 from the timing end of the engine and the numbers are read from the same end (photo).
14   Remove the caps, tapping them off if necessary with a copper-faced hammer.
15   If the bearing shells are to be used again, keep them with their respective caps.
16   Lift the crankshaft from the crankcase.
17   Remove the remaining half shells from their crankcase seats and

16.13 Main bearing caps are identified by cast-in numbers

again keep them in their original sequence if they are to be refitted; note that these have oil grooves.
18   Unbolt and remove the baffle plate from inside the crankcase.

17   Cylinder head – dismantling and decarbonising

1   The manifolds will already have been removed from the cylinder head (see Section 15).

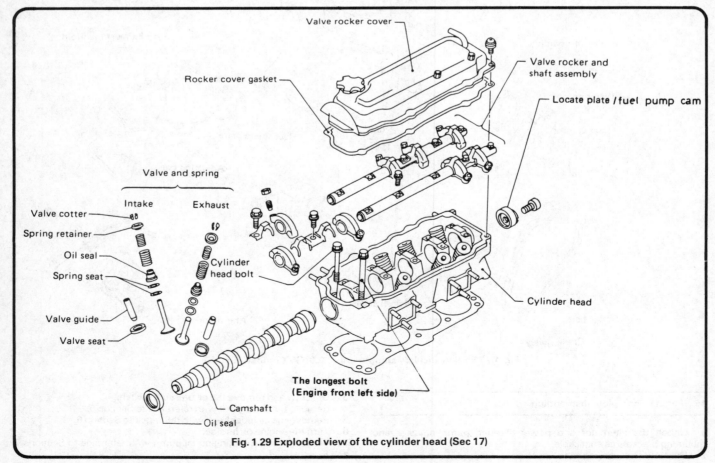

Fig. 1.29 Exploded view of the cylinder head (Sec 17)

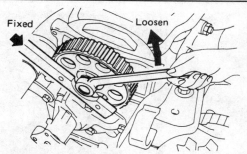

Fig. 1.30 Holding camshaft toothed pulley to prevent rotation (Sec 17)

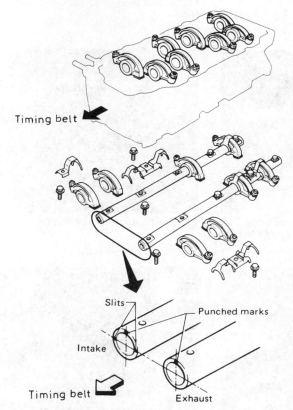

Fig. 1.32 Rocker assembly details (Sec 17)

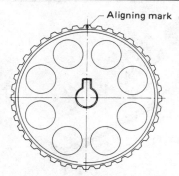

Fig. 1.31 Camshaft toothed pulley keyway and alignment marks (Sec 17)

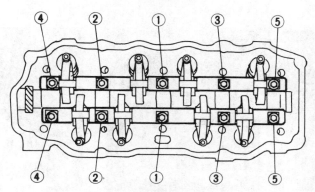

Fig. 1.33 Rocker shaft bolt tightening sequence (Sec 17)

2   Unscrew the bolts progressively, and in two stages, and lift the rocker assemblies from the cylinder head. Identify which way round the assemblies are located as this will aid refitting.

3   Remove the spark plugs.

4   Using a home-made tool (fabricated from a strip of metal and two bolts and nuts) hold the camshaft toothed pulley to prevent rotation (Fig. 1.30) while the camshaft toothed pulley bolt and fuel pump cam/locate plate bolt are unscrewed. Withdraw the toothed pulley and the fuel pump cam/locate plate.

5   Withdraw the camshaft and its oil seal, taking care not to damage the bearings as the cam lobes pass through.

6   The valves and their associated components should now be removed.

7   Owing to the depth of the cylinder head, a valve spring compressor having a long reach will be required.

8   If this is not available, temporarily refit the rocker shafts and then make up a lever with a fork at one end to compress the valve spring by using the underside of the shafts as a fulcrum point.

9   Compress the first valve springs, extract the split cotters. If the valve springs refuse to compress, do not apply excessive force, but remove the compressor and place the end of a piece of tubing on the valve spring retainer. Strike it a sharp blow to release the collets from the valve stem. Refit the compressor and resume operations, where-

upon the collets should come out.

10   Gently release the compressor, take off the spring retainer, the valve springs and both spring seats, then remove and discard the valve stem oil seal.

11   Remove the valve and keep it, with its associated components, in numbered sequence so that they can be refitted in their original position. A small box with divisions is useful for this purpose (photo).

12   Remove the remaining valves in a similar way.

13   Bearing in mind that the cylinder head is of light alloy construction and is easily damaged; use a blunt scraper or rotary wire brush to clean all traces of carbon deposits from the combustion spaces and the ports. The valve head, stems and valve guides should also be freed from any carbon deposits. Wash the combustion spaces and ports down with paraffin and scrape the cylinder head surface free of any foreign matter with the side of a steel rule, or a similar article.

14   If the engine is installed in the car, clean the pistons and the top of the cylinder bores. If the pistons are still in the block then it is essential that great care is taken to ensure that no carbon gets into the cylinder bores as this could scratch the cylinder walls or cause damage to the piston and rings. To ensure this does not happen, first turn the crankshaft so that two of the pistons are at the top of their bores. Stuff rag into the other two bores and seal them off with paper and masking tape. The waterways should also be covered with small pieces of masking tape to prevent particles of carbon entering the cooling system and damaging the coolant pump.

15   Press a little grease into the gap between the cylinder walls and the two pistons which are to be worked on. With a blunt scraper carefully scrape away the carbon from the piston crown, taking great care not to scratch the aluminium. Also scrape away the carbon from the surrounding lip of the cylinder wall. When all carbon has been removed, scrape away the grease which will now be contaminated with carbon particles, taking care not to press any into the bores. To assist prevention of carbon build-up the piston crown can be polished with a metal polish. Remove the rags or masking tape from the other two cylinders and turn the crankshaft so that the two pistons which were at the bottom are now at the top. Place rag or masking tape in the cylinders which have been decarbonised, and proceed as just described.

16   Examine the head of the valves for pitting and burning, especially the heads of the exhaust valves. The valve seatings should be examined at the same time. If the pitting on the valve and seat is very slight, the

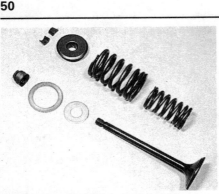

17.11 Components of one valve – keep assemblies marked and separate

17.27 Installing a valve

17.28A Refit inner and outer valve spring seats ...

17.28B ... followed by new valve stem oil seal

17.28C Outer valve springs painted ends (close-pitched coils) fit against cylinder head

17.28D Fitting valve spring retainer

17.29D Compressing a valve spring (split cotters arrowed)

17.34 Camshaft is located by fuel pump cam/locate plate

17.39 Arrow marks in rocker springs point to timing belt end

marks can be removed by grinding the seats and valves together with coarse, and then fine, valve grinding paste.

17   Where bad pitting has occurred to the valve seats it will be necessary to recut them and fit new valves. This latter job should be entrusted to the local agent or engineering works. In practice it is very seldom that the seats are so badly worn. Normally it is the valve that is too badly worn for refitting, and the owner can easily purchase a new set of valves and match them to the seats by valve grinding.

18   Valve grinding is carried out as follows. Smear a trace of coarse carborundum paste on the seat face and apply a suction grinder tool to the valve head. With a semi-rotary motion, grind the valve head to its seat, lifting the valve occasionally to redistribute the grinding paste. When a dull matt even surface is produced on both the valve seat and the valve, wipe off the paste and repeat the process with fine carborundum paste as before. A light spring placed under the valve head will greatly ease this operation. When a smooth unbroken ring of light grey matt finish is produced, on both valve and valve seat faces, the grinding operation is complete. Carefully clean away every trace of grinding

compound, take great care to leave none in the ports or in the valve guides. Clean the valves and valve seats with a paraffin soaked rag, then a clean rag, and finally, if an air line is available, blow the valves, valve guides and valve ports clean.

19   Check that all valve springs are intact. If any one is broken, all should be renewed. Check the free height of the springs against new ones. If some springs are not within specifications, renew them all. Springs suffer from fatigue and it is a good idea to renew them even if they look serviceable.

20   Check that the oil supply holes in the rocker arm studs are clear.

21   The cylinder head can be checked for warping either by placing it on a piece of plate glass or using a straight-edge and feeler blades. If there is any doubt or if its block face is corroded, have it re-faced by your dealer or motor engineering works.

22   Examine the camshaft bearings for wear, scoring or pitting. If evident, then the complete cylinder head will have to be renewed as the bearings are machined directly in it.

23   The camshaft itself should show no marks or scoring on the journal

cam lobe surfaces. Where evident, renew the camshaft or have it reprofiled by a specialist reconditioner.

24 Check the teeth of the camshaft toothed puller, renew if chipped or worn. The fuel pump cam/locate plate should not show any sign of scoring or grooving.

25 Test the valves in their guides for side to side rock. If this is anything more than almost imperceptible, new guides must be fitted. This is really a job for your dealer as the cylinder head must be warmed and the guide driven out towards the rocker cover side. New guides should be pressed in to protrude between 10.2 and 10.4 mm (0.402 and 0.409 in) above the cylinder head and then reamed to between 7.000 and 7.018 mm (0.2756 and 0.2763 in).

26 Obtain new valve stem oil seals.

27 Commence reassembly by oiling the stem of the first valve and pushing it into its guide (photo).

28 Fit the inner and outer spring seats, the stem oil seal and the inner and outer springs so that their closer coils are towards the cylinder head, and then fit the spring retainer (photos).

29 Compress the valve springs and locate the split cotters in the valve stem cut-out (photo).

30 Gently release the compressor, checking to see that the cotters are not displaced.

31 Fit the remaining valves in the same way.

32 Tap the end of each valve stem with a plastic or copper-faced hammer to settle the components.

33 Lubricate the camshaft bearings and insert the camshaft into the cylinder head.

34 Fit the fuel pump cam/locate plate and its bolt. Fit a new camshaft oil seal (photo).

35 Check that the camshaft toothed pulley dowel is in position at the end of the camshaft then refit the pulley and its bolt. Hold the pulley by the method used on removal and tighten the bolt to its specified torque wrench setting, then similarly tighten the fuel pump cam/locate plate bolt. Rotate the toothed pulley until the alignment mark on its rim is in the 12 o'clock position. No 1 cylinder cam lobe should be pointing downwards, towards the cylinder head.

36 Before refitting the rocker gear, check the shafts for wear and the rocker arms for general condition. Renew any worn components, but make sure when reassembling that they are kept in their original order.

37 The intake(inlet) rocker shaft is marked on one end with two slits (Fig. 1.32). This end of the shaft should be at the timing belt end. The exhaust rocker shaft is not slitted.

38 The punch marks on the ends of the shafts should be uppermost. These marks indicate the location of the rocker shaft oil holes.

39 Assemble each rocker shaft, ensuring that each arm and spring is refitted in its original position (photo).

40 Release the rocker arm adjuster screws fully and then bolt the rocker gear onto the cylinder head. Bolt the shafts down evenly in two or three stages (Fig. 1.33) and raise the cylinder head on wooden blocks while doing it as some of the valves will be forced open by the setting of the camshaft lobes.

41 Check that the camshaft toothed pulley is positioned so that No 1 cylinder will be at TDC on the compression stroke (paragraph 35). Refit the spark plugs.

18 Engine – examination and renovation

1 With the engine stripped and all parts thoroughly cleaned, every component should be examined for wear. The items listed in the Sections following should receive particular attention and where necessary be renewed or renovated.

2 Many measurements of engine components require accuracies down to tenths of a thousandth of an inch. It is advisable therefore to check your micrometer against a standard gauge occasionally to ensure that the instrument zero is set correctly.

3 If in doubt as to whether or not a particular component must be renewed, take into account not only the cost of the component, but the time and effort which will be required to renew it if it subsequently fails at an early date.

Cylinder block and crankcase

4 Examine the casting carefully for cracks, especially around the bolt holes and between the cylinders.

5 The cylinder bores must be checked for taper, ovality, scoring and scratching. Start by examining the top of the cylinder bores. If they are at all worn, a ridge will be felt on the thrust side. This ridge marks the upper limit of piston ring travel. The owner will have a good indication of bore wear prior to dismantling by the quantity of oil consumed and the emission of blue smoke from the exhaust especially when the engine is cold.

6 An internal micrometer or dial gauge can be used to check bore wear and taper against Specifications, but this is a pointless operation if the engine is obviously in need of reboring as indicated by excessive oil consumption.

7 Your engine reconditioner will be able to rebore the block for you and supply the correct oversize pistons to give the correct running clearance.

8 To rectify minor bore wear, it is possible to fit special oil control rings as described in Section 9.

9 A good way to test the condition of the engine is to carry out a check of the compression pressures (Section 25).

10 Some coolant passages within the cylinder block/crankcase are sealed by core (welch) plugs. If any of these is leaking or excessively rusty, drill a small hole in its centre and screw in a self-tapping screw. Use pliers to draw out the screw and plug, then carefully clean the aperture. Drive in the new plug using a suitably-sized socket as a drift.

Crankshaft and bearings

11 Examine the crankpin and main journal surfaces for signs of scoring or scratches, and check the ovality and taper of the crankpins and main journals. If the bearing surface dimensions do not fall within the tolerance ranges given in the Specifications at the beginning of this Chapter, the crankpins and/or main journals will have to be reground.

12 Big-end and crankpin wear is accompanied by distinct metallic knocking, particularly noticeable when the engine is pulling from low revs, and some loss of oil pressure.

13 Main bearing and main journal wear is accompanied by severe engine vibration rumble – getting progressively worse as engine revs increase – and again by loss of oil pressure.

14 If the crankshaft requires regrinding take it to an engine reconditioning specialist, who will machine it for you and supply the correct undersize bearing shells.

15 Inspect the big-end and main bearing shells for signs of general wear, scoring, pitting and scratches. The bearings should be matt grey in colour. With lead lithium bearings, should a trace of copper colour be noticed, the bearings are badly worn as the lead bearing material has worn away to expose the indium underlay. Renew the bearings if they

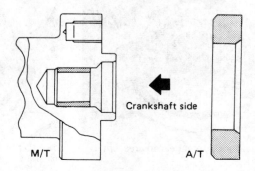

Fig. 1.34 Piston-to-connecting rod alignment (Sec 18)

Front mark (notch)   Oil hole   Cylinder No.

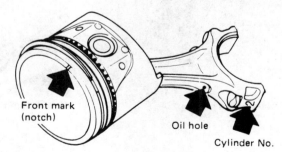

Crankshaft side

M/T   A/T

Fig. 1.35 Crankshaft spigot (pilot) bush fitting details (Sec 18)

are in this condition or if there are any signs of scoring or pitting. **You are strongly advised to renew the bearings – regardless of their condition at time of major overhaul. Refitting used bearings is a false economy.**

16　The undersizes available are designed to correspond with crankshaft regrind sizes. The bearings are in fact, slightly more than the stated undersize as running clearances have been allowed for during their manufacture.

17　Main and big-end bearing shells can be identified as to size by the marking on the back of the shell. Standard size bearing shells are marked STD or .00, undersize shells are marked with the undersize such as 0.020 u/s (photo).

Connecting rods

18　Check the alignment of the connecting rods visually. If you suspect distortion, have them checked by your dealer or engine reconditioner on the special jig which he will have.

19　The gudgeon pin is an interference fit in the connecting rod small-end and removal, refitting of the pin or changing a piston is a job best left to your dealer or engine reconditioner owing to the need for a press and jig and careful heating of the connecting rod.

Pistons and piston rings

20　If the engine is rebored then new oversize pistons with rings and gudgeon pins will be supplied. Have the supplier fit the new pistons to the rods making sure that the oil hole in the connecting rod is located as shown with reference to the front facing mark on the piston crown (Fig. 1.34).

21　Removal and refitting of the piston rings is covered in Section 9.

Flywheel

22　Check the clutch mating surface of the flywheel. If it is deeply scored (owing to failure to renew a worn driven plate), then it may be possible to have it surface ground; seek the advice of a Nissan dealer or engine reconditioner.

23　Where lots of tiny cracks are visible on the surface of the flywheel, then this will be due to overheating caused by slipping the clutch or riding the clutch pedal.

24　With a pre-engaged type of starter motor, it is rare to find the teeth of the flywheel starter ring gear damaged or worn, but if they are then the ring gear will have to be renewed.

25　To remove the ring gear, drill a hole between the roots of two teeth taking care not to damage the flywheel and then split the ring with a sharp cold chisel.

26　The new ring gear must be heated to between 180 and 220°C (356 and 428°F).

27　This is very hot so if you do not have facilities for obtaining these temperatures, leave the job to your dealer or engine reconditioner.

Driveplate (automatic transmission)

28　Should the starter ring gear on the driveplate require renewal., the removal and fitting procedure is the same as for the flywheel.

Spigot (pilot) bush

29　The spigot bush is pressed into the crankshaft clutch end to support the transmission input shaft (manual) or torque converter (automatic). If worn, the old bush must be pulled out using an internally-expanding puller. The new bush can be tapped into place using a suitably-sized socket as a drift.

Timing belt and tensioner

30　Refer to Section 5.

Oil pump

31　Extract the screws (impact driver), remove the cover and check the following clearances with a feeler blade and compare with the specified tolerances (photos).

> Inner gear to crescent
> Outer gear to crescent
> Outer gear to body

32　If these clearances are satisfactory, now measure the gear endfloat

18.17 Bearing shell marking

18.31A Removing oil pump cover

18.31B Measuring inner gear-to-crescent clearance

18.31C Measuring outer gear-to-crescent clearance

18.31D Measuring outer gear-to-body clearance

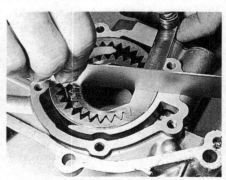

18.32 Measuring outer gear endfloat

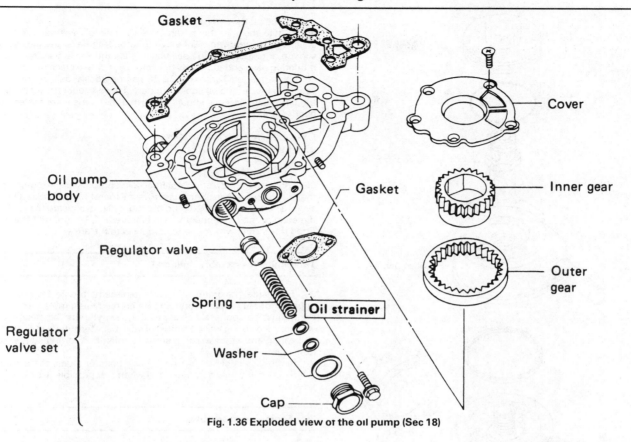

Fig. 1.36 Exploded view of the oil pump (Sec 18)

18.34A Remove pressure regulator cap – note sealing washer ...

18.34B ... to withdraw regulator spring and valve

18.34C Prising out oil pump oil seal

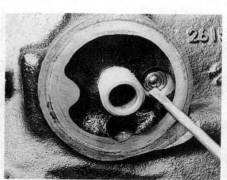

18.34D Oil seals should be renewed whenever they are disturbed

18.35 Checking oil pressure relief valve

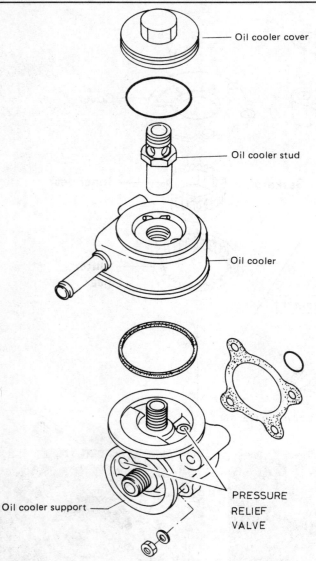

- Oil cooler cover
- Oil cooler stud
- Oil cooler
- Oil cooler support
- PRESSURE RELIEF VALVE

Fig. 1.37 Exploded view of oil cooler – 2.0 litre automatic and early Turbo models (Sec 18)

using a feeler blade and a straight edge across the pump body (photo). The endfloat must be within the specified tolerance.

33   If any of the clearances are outside those specified, renew the complete oil pump.

34   The pressure regulator components are seldom found to be faulty, but if they are, unscrew the cap and renew all the valve components.

Renew the pump oil seal (photos).

35   While the oil filter is removed at time of renewal, it is worth checking the pressure relief valve (photo). If there is any indication of scoring or chipping of the ball valve, prise the valve from the oil filter mounting base and tap a new one into place with a piece of tubing.

36   Note that on Turbo and 2.0 litre automatic models, there are two similar valves in the oil cooler support. These should be checked, and the oil cooler passages should be flushed out, whenever the engine is overhauled.

Cylinder head components
37   Refer to Section 17.

Oil seals and gaskets
38   It is recommended that all gaskets and oil seals are renewed at major engine overhaul. Sockets are useful for refitting oil seals. On most seals, an arrow is moulded onto the rubber lip to indicate the rotational direction of the component which it serves. Make sure that the seal is fitted the correct way round to comply with the arrow.

19 Engine reassembly – general

1   To ensure maximum life with minimum trouble from a rebuilt engine, not only must everything be correctly assembled, but everything must be spotlessly clean, all the oilways must be clear, locking washers and spring washers must always be fitted where indicated and all bearing and other working surfaces must be thoroughly lubricated during assembly.

2   Before assembly begins renew any bolts or studs, the threads of which are in any way damaged, and whenever possible use new spring washers.

20 Engine – reassembly

1   Have the block standing on a flat surface with the crankcase uppermost and thoroughly clean internally.

2   Bolt the baffle plate into the crankcase (photo).

3   Wipe out the crankcase bearing shell seats and locate the shells, with oil grooves, noting that the flanged one which controls crankshaft endfloat is the centre one (photo).

4   Oil the shells liberally and then lower the crankshaft into them, (photo).

5   Wipe out the bearing shell seats in the main bearing caps and locate the shells (photo).

6   Oil the journals and fit the caps in their numbered sequence (No 1 at timing belt end).

7   Screw in the cap bolts and tighten to the specified torque in the sequence shown in Fig. 1.38 (photo).

8   If new bearing shells have been fitted, then the crankshaft endfloat should be as specified, but it is worth checking at this stage. If the original shells are being used again then the endfloat should certainly be checked to ensure that wear on the centre bearing shell thrust flanges has not increased the crankshaft endfloat to the point where it is outside specified tolerance.

20.2 Crankcase ventilation baffle plate refitted to crankcase

20.3 Main bearing centre shell has thrust flanges – note oil groove

20.4 Refitting crankshaft to crankcase

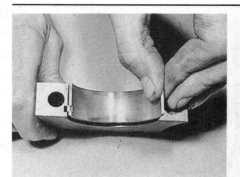
20.5 Fitting main bearing shell to cap

20.7 Tighten main bearing cap bolts in sequence shown to specified torque setting

20.9 Measuring crankshaft endfloat

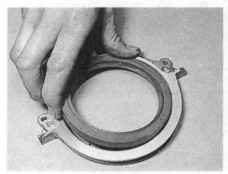
20.11A Fit a new oil seal to retainer ...

20.11B ... and refit retainer to crankcase – note new gasket

20.12 Locating engine/transmission adaptor plate on dowels

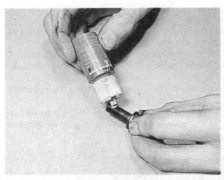
20.14A Apply thread-locking fluid to flywheel bolts

20.14B Use fabricated device shown to lock flywheel ...

20.14C ... while bolts are tightened to specified torque setting

9   To check the endfloat, tap the crankshaft fully in one direction and measure the gap between the thrust flange of the bearing shell and the machined face of the crankshaft (photo).

10   If the clearance is too large and the new shells have been fitted, suspect a fault in regrinding of the crankshaft.

11   Bolt the crankshaft oil seal retainer into position using a new oil seal and gasket (photos).

12   Locate the engine transmission adaptor plate on its dowels (photo).

13   Fit the flywheel onto its mounting flange.

14   Apply thread-locking fluid to the flywheel bolts, screw them in and tighten to the specified torque. Lock the flywheel teeth as shown (photos).

15   Fit the piston/connecting rods as described in Section 9.

16   Fit the oil pump and sump pan as described in Sections 8 and 7.

17   Refit the cylinder head as described in Section 6.

18   Refit the timing belt as described in Section 5.

19   Screw in the oil pressure switch (photo).

20   Fit a new oil filter with reference to Section 2.

21   Fit the alternator and power steering pump adjuster and mounting brackets and tighten the bolts.

---

21   Engine ancillary components – refitting

Reverse the procedures listed in Section 15.

---

22   Engine/manual transmission – reconnection and refitting

1   Reverse the procedure given in Section 12, but note the following points.

2   Tighten the engine/transmission mountings (Section 10).

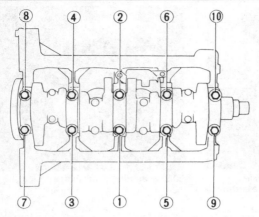

Fig. 1.38 Main bearing cap bolt tightening sequence (Sec 20)

3   Where necessary, for adjustment procedures refer to the relevant Chapters.
4   Fill the engine with oil (Section 2), and coolant (Chapter 2); do not forget to refill the transmission as well (Chapter 6).

23   Engine/automatic transmission – reconnection and refitting

1   Reverse the procedure given in Section 13, but note the following points.
2   Before commencing work, check that the torque converter is correctly engaged with the oil pump with reference to Chapter 7, Section 15.
3   Apply thread-locking fluid to the threads of the torque converter bolts and tighten them to the specified torque (Chapter 7).
4   Tighten the engine/transmission mountings (Section 10).
5   Adjust the kickdown cable and selector lever cable as described in Chapter 7. For other adjustment procedures, refer to the relevant Chapters.
6   Fill the engine with oil (Section 2), refill the transmission (Chapter 7) and the cooling system (Chapter 2).

24   Engine – initial start-up after overhaul

1   Make sure the battery is fully charged and that all lubricants, coolant and fuel are replenished.
2   If the fuel system has been dismantled it will require several revolutions of the engine on the starter motor to prime the system.
3   As soon as the engine fires and runs, keep it going at a fast tickover only (no faster), and bring it up to the normal working temperature.
4   As the engine warms up there will be odd smells and some smoke from parts getting hot and burning off oil deposits. The signs to look for are leaks of water or oil which will be obvious if serious. Check also the exhaust pipe and manifold connections, as these do not always 'find' an exact gastight position until the warmth and vibration have acted on them, and it is almost certain that they will need tightening further. This should be done, of course, with the engine stopped.
5   When normal running temperature has been reached adjust the engine idling speed, and check the ignition timing.
6   Stop the engine and wait a few minutes to see if any lubricant or coolant is dripping out when the engine is stationary.
7   Road test the car to check that the timing is correct and that the engine is giving the necessary smoothness and power. Do not race the engine – if new bearings and/or pistons have been fitted it should be treated as a new engine and run in at a reduced speed for the first 500 miles (800 km).
8   After 600 miles (1000 km), the cylinder head bolts should be retightened with the engine cold. To do this, remove the rocker cover, then using the same sequence as for tightening the bolts, loosen each bolt half a turn and retighten it to the specified final torque wrench setting.

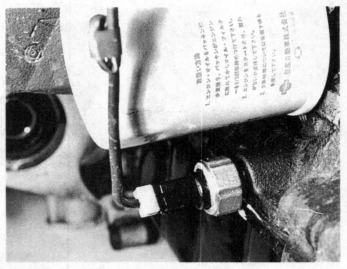

20.19 Do not forget to refit oil pressure switch

25   Compression test – description and interpretation

1   When engine performance is down, or if misfiring occurs which cannot be attributed to the ignition or fuel system, a compression test can provide diagnostic clues. If the test is performed regularly it can give warning of trouble before any other symptoms become apparent.
2   The engine must be fully warmed up to normal operating temperature, the battery must be fully charged and the spark plugs must be removed. The services of an assistant will also be required.
3   Disable the ignition system by disconnecting the distributor/crank angle sensor wiring at its connector plug, on carburettor-engined and Turbo models (photo). On 2.0 litre fuel injection models disconnect the ignition HT coil lead from the distributor/crank angle sensor cap and earth it safely. Also, on Turbo and 2.0 litre fuel injection models, remove the fuel pump fuse.
4   Fit the compression tester to No 1 spark plug hole. (The type of tester which screws into the spark plug hole is to be preferred.)
5   Have the assistant hold the throttle wide open and crank the engine on the starter. Record the highest reading obtained on the compression tester.
6   Repeat the test on the remaining cylinders, recording the pressure developed in each.
7   Desired pressures are given in the Specifications. If the pressure in any cylinder is low, introduce a teaspoonful of clean engine oil into the spark plug hole and repeat the test.

25.3 Disable ignition system before carrying out compression test

8   If the addition of oil temporarily improves the compression pressure, this indicates that bore or piston wear was responsible for the pressure loss. No improvement suggests that leaking or burnt valves, or a blown head gasket, may be to blame.

9   A low reading from two adjacent cylinders is almost certainly due to the head gasket between them having blown.

10   On completion of the test, refit the spark plugs and reconnect the ignition system and fuel pump.

26   Fault diagnosis – engine

Symptom	Reason(s)
Engine will not turn over when starter switch is operated	Flat battery Loose battery connections Loose connections at solenoid switch and/or starter motor Starter motor jammed Starter motor defective
Engine turns over normally but fails to fire and run	No spark at plugs No fuel reaching engine Too much fuel reaching engine (flooding)
Engine starts but runs unevenly and misfires	Ignition and/or fuel system fault Incorrect valve clearance Burnt out valves Blown cylinder head gasket Worn out piston rings Worn cylinder bores
Lack of power	Ignition and/or fuel system faults Incorrect valve clearance Burnt out valves Low cylinder compression
Excessive oil consumption	Oil leaks from crankshaft oil seals, camshaft oil seal, rocker cover gasket or sump gasket Worn piston rings or cylinder bores Worn valve guides and/or defective valve stem oil seals
Excessive mechanical noise from engine	Excessive valve clearances Worn crankshaft bearings Worn cylinder bores (piston slap)

Note: *This Section is not intended to be an exhaustive guide to fault diagnosis but summarises a few of the more common faults which may be encountered during a car's life. Consult a dealer for more specific advice.*

Chapter 2 Cooling system

Contents

Specifications

System type .... Pressurized, pump-assisted thermo-syphon, thermostatically controlled

Thermostat
Opens at... 88°C (190°F)
Fully open at .... 8 mm at 100°C (0.32 in at 212°F)

Pressure ratings
Radiator cap relief valve pressure .... 0.78 to 0.98 bar (11 to 14 psi)
System maximum test pressure:
    Vertical-flow radiator (T12 and early T72 models).................. 1.57 bar (23 psi)
    Crossflow radiator (later T72 models) .... 0.98 bar (14 psi)

Electric cooling fan thermostatic switch operating temperatures (see Section 12)

	Switches on at	Switches off at
Switch number 1 (all models)........................	90°C (194°F)	83°C (181°F)
Switch number 2 (where fitted).....................	100°C (212°F)	93°C (199°F)

Temperature sensors
Coolant temperature gauge sensor (thermal transmitter) resistances:
    At 60°C (140°F)... Approx 70 to 90 ohms
    At 100°C (212°F) .... Approx 21 to 24 ohms
Water temperature sensor resistances (Turbo and 2.0i GSX models):
    At –10°C (14°F).. 8.00 to 10.00 k ohm
    At 20°C (68°F).. 2.30 to 2.70 k ohm
    At 50°C (122°F).. 0.70 to 0.90 k ohm
    At 80°C (176°F).. 0.30 to 0.33 k ohm

Coolant
Antifreeze type .... Ethylene glycol-based antifreeze, with corrosion inhibitors (Duckhams Universal Antifreeze and Summer Coolant)
Water type .... Clean, soft water (soft tap water or clean rain water)
Mixture ratio required at varying ambient temperatures:
    Normal protection (down to –15°C/5°F).................... 30% antifreeze/70% water
    Full protection (down to –35°C/–31°F)..................... 50% antifreeze/50% water
Cooling system total capacity (including heater and expansion tank):
    Vertical-flow radiator, carburettor models .... 8.1 litres (14.3 Imp pints) approx
    Vertical-flow radiator, Turbo models .... 8.6 litres (15.1 Imp pints) approx
    Crossflow radiator, manual transmission .... 7.6 litres (13.4 Imp pints) approx
    Crossflow radiator, automatic transmission .... 7.5 litres (13.2 Imp pints) approx

Drivebelt deflection

Under pressure of 98N (22 lbf)

	Maximum	Adjust to	
		Used belt	New belt
Water pump and alternator (models without power-assisted steering) ..	15 mm (0.59 in)	8 to 10 mm (0.32 to 0.39 in)	7 to 9 mm (0.28 to 0.35 in)
Water pump and power-assisted steering pump	12.5 mm (0.49 in)	7 to 9 mm (0.28 to 0.35 in)	6 to 8 mm (0.24 to 0.32 in)
Alternator:			
Executive models	10 mm (0.39 in)	5 to 7 mm (0.20 to 0.28 in)	5 to 7 mm (0.20 to 0.28 in)
Other models up to December 1987..........................	12 mm (0.47 in)	6 to 8 mm (0.24 to 0.32 in)	5 to 7 mm (0.20 to 0.28 in)
Other models from January 1988................................	20 mm (0.79 in)	8 to 10 mm (0.32 to 0.39 in)	8 to 10 mm (0.32 to 0.39 in)
Air conditioning compressor	6 mm (0.24 in)	3 to 4 mm (0.12 to 0.16 in)	3 to 4 mm (0.12 to 0.16 in)

Torque wrench settings

	Nm	lbf ft
Thermostat housing cover bolts	18 to 22	13 to 16
Water pump pulley bolts	6 to 10	4.5 to 7.5
Water pump mounting bolts	16 to 20	12 to 15
Coolant temperature gauge sensor (thermal-transmitter):		
Early models	15 to 20	11 to 15
Later models	20 to 29	15 to 21.5
Water temperature (Turbo and 2.0 litre fuel injection models)..................	20 to 29	15 to 21.5
Radiator mounting bolts...	3.2 to 4.2	2.5 to 3
Main electric cooling fan mounting screws	6 to 10	4.5 to 7.5
Alternator:		
Drivebelt adjuster lockbolt	14 to 17	10 to 12.5
Pivot bolts..	43 to 58	32 to 43
Power-assisted steering pump:		
Drivebelt adjuster lockbolt	14 to 17	10 to 12.5
Pivot bolt..	31 to 42	23 to 31
Air conditioning compressor:		
Idler pulley locknut	26 to 36	19 to 26.5
Turbocharger coolant pipe banjo bolts	11 to 15	8 to 11

1 General description

The cooling system is of the pressurized, pump-assisted thermo-syphon type. The system consists of the radiator, water pump, thermostat, electric cooling fan(s), expansion tank and associated hoses.

The system functions as follows. Cold coolant in the radiator passes, via hoses and pipes, to the water pump, where it is pumped around the cylinder block and head passages. After cooling the cylinder bores, combustion surfaces and valve seats, the coolant reaches the manifold and thermostat, which is initially closed, and is diverted through a bypass hose back to the pump (Turbo and 2.0 litre fuel injection models) and/or out to the heater matrix, oil cooler and other associated systems. When the engine is cold, the thermostat remains closed, and the coolant only circulates as described. When the coolant reaches a predetermined temperature, however, the thermostat opens, and the coolant passes through the top hose to the radiator. As the coolant circulates across the radiator, it is cooled by the inrush of air when the car is in forward motion. Airflow is supplemented by the action of the electric cooling fan(s) when necessary. Upon reaching the other side of the radiator, the coolant is now cooled and the cycle is repeated.

When the engine is at normal operating temperature, the coolant expands, and some of it is displaced into the expansion tank, This coolant collects in the tank, and is returned to the radiator when the system cools.

On T12 and early T72 models a vertical-flow radiator is used, with top and bottom tanks, while on later T72 models (from July 1987 on) a crossflow radiator is used, which has right and left-hand side tanks.

The impeller type water pump is mounted on the right-hand end of the engine, and is driven from the crankshaft pulley via a drivebelt.

On most models, a single, seven-bladed cooling fan is mounted on the radiator and driven by an electric motor. It is controlled by a relay and thermostatic switch. Where a two-speed fan motor is fitted, an additional relay and switch are provided. On some models, a supplementary four-bladed fan is fitted as well, controlled by its own relay and the main fan's thermostatic switch.

Note that there are some differences between the cooling systems fitted to different models. Where automatic transmission is fitted, a cooler for the transmission fluid is built into the bottom (or left-hand side, as appropriate) tank, connected to the transmission by flexible hoses and fluid pipes. This fluid cooler is an integral part of the radiator and cannot be repaired or renewed separately. Turbo and automatic transmission models have an engine oil cooler, which is located on the rear of the cylinder block, and connected to the main cooling system. On 2.0 litre fuel injection and Turbo models, there is a coolant connection to the throttle chamber.

Note: When servicing the cooling system note that antifreeze is poisonous and should be kept out of reach of children; it will also attack paintwork, and must not be allowed to contact the timing belt or other drivebelts.

If the engine is hot, the electric fan(s) may start rotating even if the engine is not running, so be careful to keep hands, hair and loose clothing well clear when working in the engine compartment.

To avoid the risk of personal injury through burns and scalding, never disturb any part of the cooling system while it is still hot.

2 Routine maintenance

1 Every week, check the coolant level, when the engine and radiator are **cold**.

2 Check the level at the expansion tank; if the level is below the 'Min' line, top up to the 'Max' line using only the specified antifreeze/water mixture (Fig. 2.1). If the expansion tank is empty, check the level in the radiator and top it up to the filler opening (Fig. 2.2), then refit the radiator cap and refill the expansion tank to the 'Max' line (photos). Direct the tank filler cap breather into the wing aperture.

3 With a sealed type cooling system, topping-up should only be necessary at very infrequent intervals. If this is not the case, and

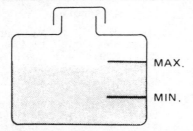

Fig. 2.1 Checking coolant level at expansion tank (Sec 2)

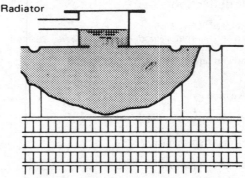

Fig. 2.2 Correct coolant level at radiator (Sec 2)

frequent topping-up is required it is likely that there is a leak in the system, or that the engine is overheating. Check all hoses and joint faces for any staining or actual wetness, and rectify as necessary. If no leaks can be found, it is advisable to have the system pressure-tested, as the leak could possibly be internal. It is a good idea to keep a careful check on the engine oil level in these circumstances, as a serious internal coolant leak can often cause the level in the sump to rise, thus confirming suspicions.

4   At the service intervals given in *'Routine maintenance'* at the beginning of this Manual, carefully inspect all the hoses, hose clips and visible joint gaskets for cracks, corrosion, deterioration or leakage. Renew any hoses and clips that are suspect, and also renew any gaskets or reseal any joint faces, if necessary. See Section 8 of this Chapter.

5   Check all drivebelts for looseness (see Section 7 of this Chapter) and check for signs of unusual wear or damage such as cuts or fraying. Renew any worn or damaged drivebelt.

6   At the less-frequent service intervals indicated, drain, flush and refill the cooling system using fresh antifreeze, as described in Sections 3, 4, and 5 respectively.

Note: *If the radiator cap* **must** *be removed before the engine and radiator have cooled down (though this is inadvisable), the pressure in the cooling system must first be released. Cover the cap with a thick layer of cloth, to avoid scalding, and slowly turn the cap anti-clockwise as far as the first stop. When the hissing has stopped, indicating that pressure is released, slowly depress the cap and turn it further until it can be removed. At all times, keep well away from the radiator filler neck.*

3   Cooling system – draining

1   The cooling system must not be drained until the engine and radiator have completely cooled down. See Section 1.

2   Move the heater temperature control knob to the maximum 'Hot' position.

3   If the additional working space is required, remove the engine

compartment left-hand front undershield, which is secured by five bolts.

4   Remove the radiator cap and place a suitable container underneath the radiator left-hand end.

5   On vertical-flow radiators, open the drain tap (Fig. 2.3). On crossflow radiators, slacken the clip and carefully ease the bottom hose off the radiator outlet (Fig. 2.4). Allow the coolant to drain into the container. If the coolant is old or fouled, unbolt the expansion tank and empty it.

6   The above procedure will suffice for most normal draining operations, but note that the coolant remaining in the engine can be drained, if required, by unscrewing the cylinder block drain fittings. On carburettor models drain plugs are screwed into the front (photo) and rear (some later models only) of the block, next to cylinder No. 4. On some models a

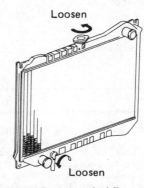

Fig. 2.3 Draining coolant – vertical-flow radiator (Sec 3)

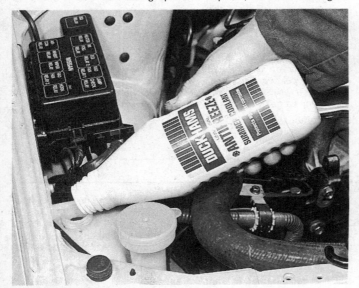

2.2A Coolant level should be checked normally, and topped up if necessary at expansion tank

2.2B Top up at radiator if expansion tank is found to be empty

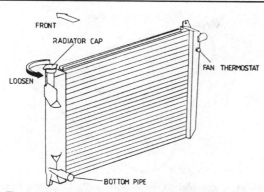

Fig. 2.4 Draining coolant – crossflow radiator (Sec 3)

3.6 Cylinder block drain plug (typical) – carburettor model

second, smaller, plug is screwed into the front of cylinder Nos 1 and 2. On refitting, apply a suitable sealant to the plug threads and tighten securely. On 2.0 litre fuel injection models, remove the two screws securing the heater feed metal pipe to the fitting screwed into the front of the block and carefully pull the pipe away from the fitting (noting the presence of the gasket) to allow coolant to escape. Renew the gasket if necessary and tighten the screws evenly and securely on refitting. On Turbo models, the procedure is essentially the same, but access behind the turbocharger is extremely limited. Ensure that the turbocharger and

exhaust system have fully cooled before attempting to disconnect the pipe.

7   Once the coolant has fully drained, flush the system as described in the next Section of this Chapter, then refill the system as described in Section 5.

4   Cooling system – flushing

1   With time, the cooling system may gradually lose its efficiency, as the radiator core becomes choked with rust, scale deposits from the water, and other sediment. To minimise this, Nissan recommend that as well as using good quality antifreeze and soft water, the system is flushed whenever the coolant is renewed. Proceed as follows.

2   With the coolant drained, refit the bottom hose or close the drain tap and refill the system with fresh water. Refit the radiator cap, start the engine and warm it up to normal operating temperature, then stop it and (after allowing it to cool down completely) drain the system again. Repeat as necessary until only clean water can be seen to emerge. Finally, refill with the specified coolant mixture.

3   If the specified coolant mixture has been used and has been renewed at the specified intervals, the above procedure will be sufficient to keep the system clean for a considerable time. If the system has been neglected, however, a more thorough operation is required, as follows.

4   To flush the system, first drain the coolant as described in the previous Section.

5   Disconnect the top hose at the thermostat housing and disconnect the bottom hose (if not already disconnected) at the radiator outlet.

6   Insert a garden hose into the top hose, and allow water to circulate through the radiator until it runs clean from the bottom outlet.

7   To flush the engine, remove the thermostat as described in Section 11, and insert the garden hose into the thermostat housing. Allow water to flow through the engine until it runs clear from the bottom hose. Refit the thermostat on completion.

8   In severe cases of contamination, reverse-flushing of the radiator may be necessary. To do this, remove the radiator as described in Section 9, invert it and insert the garden hose into the bottom outlet. Continue flushing until clear water runs from the top hose outlet.

9   The use of chemical cleaners should be necessary only as a last resort. The regular renewal of antifreeze should prevent excessive contamination of the system.

5   Cooling system – refilling

1   With the cooling system drained and flushed out, close the drain tap or refit the bottom hose. Do not forget to refit the cylinder block drain plug or heater feed pipe, if disturbed.

2   Prepare a sufficient quantity of the specified coolant mixture (see

5.3A Refilling radiator with coolant

5.3B Refill expansion tank to 'Max' line

Section 6 of this Chapter). Allow for a surplus so as to have a reserve supply for topping-up.

3   Fill the system slowly through the radiator filler opening, then fill the expansion tank up to the 'Max' line and refit the radiator and expansion tank caps (photos).

4   Start the engine and run it at no more than idle speed until it has warmed up to normal operating temperature. Watch the temperature gauge to check for signs of overheating.

5   Stop the engine and allow it to cool down **completely,** then remove the radiator cap and top the level up to the filler opening. Refit the radiator cap, top the expansion tank up to the 'Max' line and refit its filler cap, directing its breather into the wing aperture. Wash off with fresh water any spilt coolant.

6   After refilling the system, always check carefully all components of the system (but especially any unions disturbed during draining and flushing) for signs of coolant leaks. Fresh antifreeze has a searching action which will rapidly expose any weak points in the system.

Note: *If, after draining and refilling the system, symptoms of overheating are found which did not occur previously, then the fault is almost certainly due to trapped air at some point in the system causing an airlock and restricting the flow of coolant; usually the air is trapped because the system was refilled too quickly. In some cases airlocks can be released by tapping or squeezing the various hoses. If the problem persists, stop the engine and allow it to cool down completely, then remove the coolant temperature gauge sensor (carburettor models) or water temperature sensor (Turbo and 2.0 litre fuel injection models) from the thermostat housing. Since this is the highest (accessible) point in the system it should be possible to bleed out any trapped air from the sensor aperture.*

6   Coolant mixture

1   The antifreeze in the coolant should be renewed at regular intervals (see *Routine maintenance*). This is necessary not only to maintain the antifreeze properties, but also to prevent corrosion which would otherwise occur as the corrosion inhibitors become progressively less effective.

2   Always use a good quality ethylene glycol-based antifreeze with non-phosphate corrosion inhibitors, containing **no** methanol, and which is suitable for use in mixed metal cooling systems. This should be mixed in the correct ratio with clean soft water; if you live in a hard water area use filtered rainwater that has been collected in a non-metallic container.

3   Before adding fresh antifreeze, the cooling system should be completely drained and flushed, and all hoses checked for condition and security.

4   The ratio of antifreeze to water should be maintained at at least 30/70% all year round. The recommended ratios and levels of protection are given in the Specifications.

5   After filling with antifreeze, a label should be attached to the radiator, stating the type and concentration of antifreeze used, and the date installed. Any subsequent topping-up should be made with the same type and concentration of antifreeze.

6   Do not use engine antifreeze in the screen washer system, as it will cause damage to the vehicle paintwork. Screen washer antifreeze is available from most motor accessory shops.

7   Drivebelt – adjusting, removal and refitting

Note: *The arrangement of drivebelts for the water pump, alternator, power-assisted steering pump and air-conditioning compressor vary according to model – see Figs. 2.5, 2.6 and 2.7. The water pump will share its drivebelt with the alternator or power-assisted steering pump, according to model*

Adjustment

1   First check all along the length of the belt concerned, cleaning any dirt out of its grooves and looking for signs of wear, of damage such as cracks or fraying, or for signs of contamination by oil or coolant. Renew any belt which shows signs of any of these conditions.

2   To check a belt's tension, apply a force of 98N (22 lbf) to the point

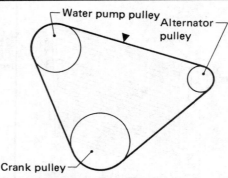

Fig. 2.5 Checking drivebelt deflection – 1.6L, 1.6LS without power-assisted steering (Sec 7)

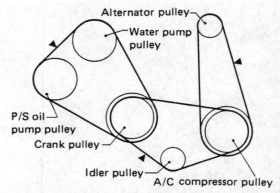

Fig. 2.6 Checking drivebelt deflection – Executive models with air conditioning (Sec 7)

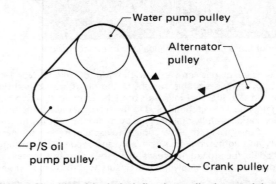

Fig. 2.7 Checking drivebelt deflection – all other models with power-assisted steering (Sec 7)

indicated in Fig. 2.5, 2.6 or 2.7 (whichever is relevant) and measure carefully the belt's deflection at that point.

3   If the deflection measured is more than the specified limit, tighten the belt as detailed below until its deflection is reduced to the specified adjustment range. If a new belt is being fitted, note that in some cases a tighter setting is specified for the initial adjustment.

Alternator drivebelt

4   To adjust the alternator drivebelt, slacken both pivot bolts under the alternator, slacken the adjuster lockbolt and tighten (or slacken, if necessary) the adjuster nut or bolt. When the setting is correct tighten the bolts securely.

Power-assisted steering pump drivebelt

5   To adjust the power-assisted steering pump drivebelt, slacken the pivot bolt under the pump, slacken the adjuster lockbolt and tighten (or slacken, if necessary) the adjuster nut (photos). When the setting is correct, tighten the bolts securely.

Air conditioning compressor drivebelt

6   To adjust the air conditioning compressor drivebelt, slacken the idler pulley locknut, then tighten (or slacken, if necessary) the adjuster bolt that projects beneath the idler assembly. When the setting is correct tighten the locknut to the specified torque wrench setting.

7.5A Power-assisted steering pump pivot bolt (arrowed) – seen from underneath

7.5B Power-assisted steering pump adjuster lockbolt A and adjuster nut B

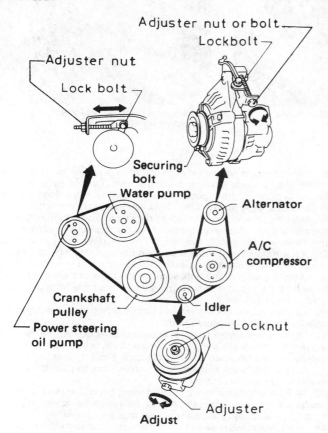

Fig. 2.8 Drivebelt adjusting details – typical (Sec 7)

Removal and refitting
Note: *In some cases it is necessary to first remove another drivebelt before the belt concerned can be withdrawn. For example, to remove the power-assisted steering pump drivebelt the alternator (or air conditioning compressor) drivebelt must be removed first.*

7   To remove the alternator or power-assisted steering pump drivebelt, slacken the alternator or pump pivot bolt(s), slacken the adjuster lockbolt and unscrew the adjuster nut or bolt. Swivel the alternator or pump towards the engine until the belt can be removed from the pulleys.
8   To remove the air conditioning compressor drivebelt, slacken the

locknut and the adjuster drawbolt and the belt can be removed from the pulleys.
9   Refitting is the reverse of the removal procedure. Adjust the belt(s) as described above, noting the tighter setting specified in some cases if a new belt is being fitted.

8   Cooling system hoses and connections – removal, refitting and inspection

Note: *In some cases the coolant flow is indicated by an arrow painted on the hose end. These should be noted so that the hose can be correctly connected on reassembly (photo).*

1   The hoses should be inspected periodically and renewed if any sign of cracking or perishing is discovered. The most likely area for this is around the clips which secure each hose to its unions. Particular attention should be given if regular topping-up has become necessary. The cooling system can be considered to be a semi-sealed arrangement, the only normal coolant loss being minute amounts through evaporation in the expansion tank. If significant quantities have vanished the system must be leaking at some point and the source of the leak should be investigated promptly.
2   To disconnect the hoses, use a screwdriver or pliers, as applicable, to slacken the clips then slide them along the hose clear of the union spigot. Carefully work the hose off its spigots (photos). The hoses can be worked off with relative ease when new or when hot; **do not**, however, attempt to disconnect the system when it is hot (see Section 1.)
3   **Warning:** *the radiator hose unions are fragile;* **do not use excessive force** *when attempting to remove the hoses.* If a hose proves stubborn, try to release it by rotating it on its unions before attempting to work it off. If all else fails, cut the hose with a sharp knife then slit it at each union so that it can be peeled off in two pieces. While expensive, this is preferable to buying a new radiator.
4   Serious leakage will be self-evident, though slight leakage can be more difficult to stop. It is likely that the leak will only be apparent when the engine is running and the system is under pressure, and even then the rate of escape may be such that the hot coolant evaporates as soon as it reaches the atmosphere, although traces of antifreeze should reveal the source of the leak in most cases. If not, it will be necessary to pressurise the cooling system when cold, thereby enabling the source of the leak to be pinpointed. The car should be taken to a Nissan dealer or similar who has the necessary pressure-testing equipment.
5   In some cases the leak may be due to a broken head gasket. If this proves to be the case it will be necessary to remove the cylinder head for investigation (see Chapter 1).
6   Other possible sources of leakage are the water pump and its gasket, the thermostat housing gasket or the cylinder block fittings and

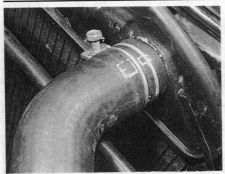

8.0 Radiator top hose connection (vertical-flow radiator)

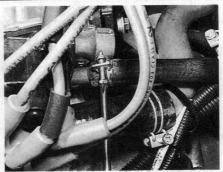

8.2A Disconnecting heater feed hose from metal tube – 2.0 litre fuel injection models

8.2B Heater feed hose connected to cylinder block elbow fitting – early carburettor models

8.2C Heater return hose connected to coolant return tube – typical

8.8A Refitting top hose to thermostat housing

8.8B Position hose clip behind spigot flared end before tightening

core plugs. These should be renewed, if necessary, as described in this Chapter or Chapter 1.

7   When refitting a hose, first slide the clips on to the hose then work the hose onto its unions. If it is stiff, use soap as a lubricant or soften it by soaking it in boiling water, but take care to prevent scalding.

8   Work each hose end fully on to its spigot, check that the hose is settled correctly and is properly routed, then slide each clip along the hose until it is behind the spigot flared end before tightening it securely (photos).

9   Check carefully for leaks as soon as possible after disturbing any part of the cooling system.

9   Radiator and expansion tank – removal, inspection and refitting

Radiator

1   On turbo engine models, slacken the clamps securing the air intake ducting and resonator assembly to the airflow meter and turbocharger, unbolt the assembly's mounting brackets from the body front panel and disconnect the breather hose from the rocker cover. Withdraw the complete assembly and use clean, lint-free rag to pack the airflow meter and turbocharger openings so that dirt and debris cannot enter either.

2   On all cars, remove the engine compartment left-hand front under-shield, which is secured by five bolts.

3   Drain the cooling system by disconnecting the radiator bottom hose. See Section 3 of this Chapter.

4   Disconnect the radiator top hose and expansion tank hose. With-draw the expansion tank hose clear of the radiator (photos).

5   On cars with automatic transmission, slacken the clips and discon-nect from the radiator fluid pipes the two flexible hoses; note or label each hose to ensure that it is refitted correctly. Plug or cap the pipes and hoses to minimise the loss of fluid. If the radiator is to be repaired or renewed, drain the transmission fluid from its heat exchanger section.

6   On all cars, disconnect the battery negative lead.

7   Disconnect from the rear of the radiator the wiring for the ther-mostatic switch(es) and the electric cooling fan motor(s) (photo).

8   The radiator is secured at each corner by a rubber mounting (each attached by a single hexagon-headed screw). The top mountings are bolted to the body front panel, while the bottom mountings are each secured by a single nut (photos). Check carefully that the electric cooling fan shroud or bracket is not attached directly to the body front panel at any point. If so, remove the screw or nut (as applicable) to ensure that the radiator and cooling fan can be removed as a single unit. On Executive models, note that the air conditioning system condenser will remain on its own mountings, in the body front panel.

9   Undo the screws and nuts securing the radiator mountings to the body front panel and withdraw the radiator assembly from the engine compartment (photo).

10   If required, the cooling fan and shroud or bracket assembly can be unbolted from the radiator (photo).

11   If the radiator was removed because of clogging causing overheat-ing then try reverse flushing or, in severe cases, use a radiator cleanser strictly in accordance with the manufacturer's instructions.

12   Use a soft brush and air line or garden hose to clear the radiator matrix of leaves, insects etc.

13   A leaking radiator may be sealed using one of the many products available from motor accessory stores. To make a permanent repair by soldering is a job best left to a specialist radiator repairer.

14   If the radiator is renewed, ensure that the replacement is of exactly the correct type; check the fin pitch as well as the more obvious points when comparing the two. Several different types have been fitted to the cars covered in this manual.

15   Check the mountings for condition and renew them if necessary (photo).

16   Refitting is a reversal of removal, but check carefully that the radiator is settled easily and without strain on its mountings before tightening the retaining nuts and screws securely (photo).

17   Refill the cooling system as described in Section 5 of this Chapter. On cars with automatic transmission, top up the fluid level as described in Chapter 7.

Radiator cap

18   The cap should be cleaned and checked whenever it is removed.

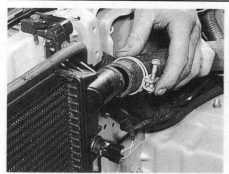

9.4A Disconnecting top hose from crossflow radiator

9.4B Disconnecting expansion tank hose

9.4C Expansion tank hose connections to vertical-flow radiator

9.7A Disconnecting thermostatic switch wires – crossflow radiator shown

9.7B Disconnecting electric cooling fan wires

9.8A Unbolting radiator top mounting ...

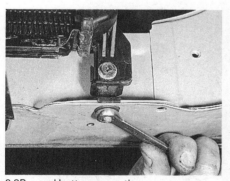

9.8B ... and bottom mounting

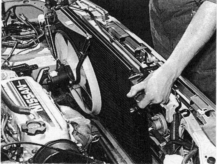

9.9 Withdrawing (crossflow type) radiator and cooling fan assembly

9.10 Remove mounting bolts (arrowed) to separate radiator from cooling fan

Check that its sealing surfaces are clean and undamaged. and that they mate correctly with those of the radiator. Check the negative-pressure valve by pulling it gently open (Fig. 2.9); the valve should spring closed immediately it is released.

19   The cap's performance can be checked using a cap pressure-tester (cooling system tester). On applying pressure, the cap's pressure relief valve should hold until the specified pressure is reached, at which point it should open.

20   If there is any doubt about the cap's performance, it must be renewed.

21   If the cap is to be renewed, ensure that the replacement is of exactly the correct type and rating; this will be marked on the cap's warning label (silver on models up to July 1988, yellow on later models).

Expansion tank

22   As soon as the engine and radiator have cooled down completely (see Section 1), remove the radiator cap and disconnect the expansion tank hose from the radiator filler neck (photo).

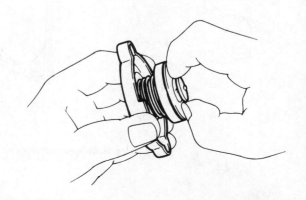

Fig. 2.9 Checking radiator cap negative-pressure valve (Sec 9)

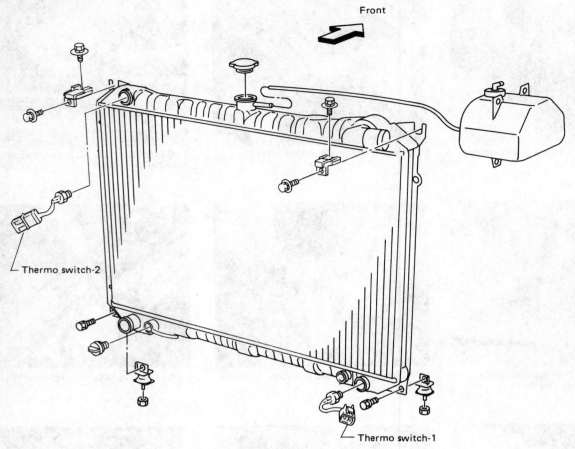

Front

Thermo switch-2

Thermo switch-1

Twin cooling fan equipped model

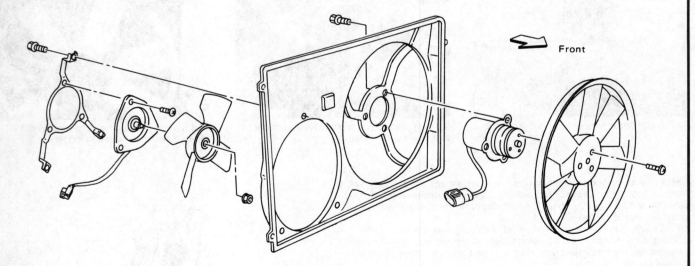

Front

Fig. 2.10 Vertical-flow radiator and electric cooling fan – typical (Secs 9 and 10)

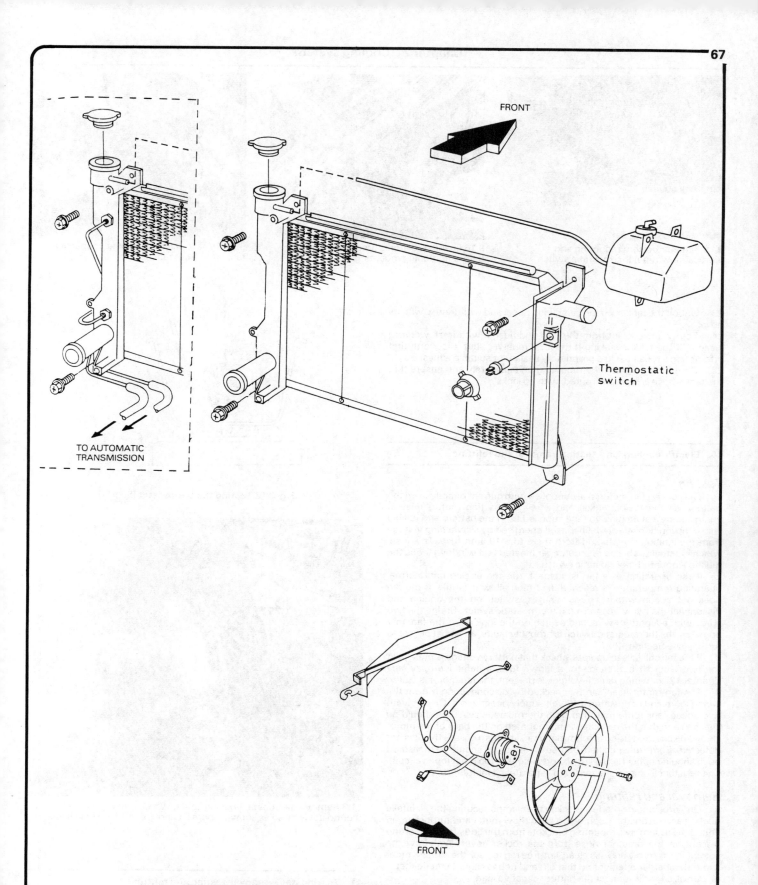

FRONT

TO AUTOMATIC
TRANSMISSION

Thermostatic
switch

FRONT

Fig. 2.11 Crossflow radiator and electric cooling fan – typical (Secs 9 and 10)

9.15 Radiator bottom mounting and (vertical-flow type) thermostatic switch

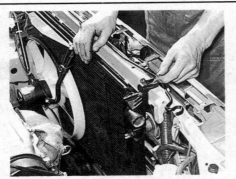

9.16 Ensure radiator is properly settled before tightening mountings

9.22 Release clip to disconnect expansion tank hose from radiator

23   Unbolt the tank from the inner wing panel and withdraw it, with its hose.
24   Empty any coolant from the tank and flush it with fresh water to clean it. If the tank is leaking it must be renewed, but it is worth first attempting a repair using a proprietary sealant or suitable adhesive.
25   On refitting, tighten the mounting bolts securely and ensure that the tank's hose is correctly routed, with no kinks.

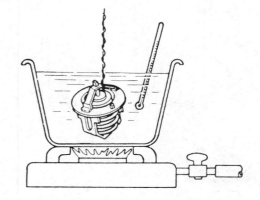

Fig. 2.12 Testing the thermostat (Sec 11)

---

10   Electric cooling fan – testing, removal and refitting

Testing

1   The cooling fan motor(s) are supplied with current directly from the battery via the fusible link(s) and a relay. This (fan motor) relay is energised by a switching voltage supplied from the battery and fusible link to the ignition relay (which is itself energised by a switching voltage from the ignition switch) and from there to a 10 amp fuse. This fuse, which is actually labelled rear defogger (heated rear window) feeds the radiator-mounted thermostatic switch.
2   If the operation of a fan is suspect, run the engine until normal operating temperature is reached, and then allow it to idle. If the fan does not cut in within a few minutes, switch off the engine and disconnect the two wires from the thermostatic switch. Bridge the two wires with a length of wire, and switch on the ignition. If the fan now operates, the thermostatic switch is probably faulty, and must be tested further (see Section 12).
3   If the fan still fails to operate, check that battery voltage is present at the two wires. If not, check for a blown fuse, a defective relay (see Chapter 12), or wiring fault. If voltage is present, the fan motor is faulty.
4   The fan motor itself can be checked by disconnecting it from the wiring loom and connecting a 12 volt supply directly to it. On cars with two-speed fans remember that both thermostatic switches should be checked and that the resistance unit mounted on the back of the motor should be checked using an ohmmeter or similar, to ensure that it is not defective. Some (unspecified) degree of resistance should be measured but it should neither be too little (short circuit) or too great (open circuit). The resistance unit can be renewed separately if faulty.

Removal and refitting

5   On Turbo engine models, slacken the clamps securing the air intake ducting and resonator assembly to the airflow meter and turbocharger, unbolt the assembly's mounting brackets from the body front panel and disconnect the breather hose from the rocker cover. Withdraw the complete assembly and use clean, lint-free rag to pack the airflow meter and turbocharger openings so that dirt and debris cannot enter either.
6   On all cars, disconnect the battery negative lead.
7   Disconnect the wiring from the cooling fan motor(s).
8   Unbolt the cooling fan and shroud or bracket assembly and withdraw it from the rear of the radiator.
9   The fan can be removed from the motor shaft by unscrewing the screws or nut.
10   Refitting is the reverse of the removal procedure.

11.3 Remove thermostat housing cover. When refitting, ensure thermostat is fitted as shown – note location of air bleed hole/jiggle valve

---

11   Thermostat – removal, testing and refitting

1   Cover the drivebelts as much as possible with a thick layer of cloth; coolant should not be allowed to contact any of the drivebelts and should be kept off the paintwork as much as possible (see Section 1 of this Chapter).

2   Drain off about 2 litres (3.5 Imp pints) of coolant. See Section 3 of this Chapter.
3   Disconnect the top hose from the thermostat housing cover, then unbolt and remove the cover (photo).
4   Discard the gasket and withdraw the thermostat. If it is stuck tight do not lever it by its bridge piece, but cut around its edge using a sharp pointed knife.
5   The thermostat can be tested easily for correct functioning if this should be in doubt but note that if it remains in the open position at room temperature it is faulty, and must be renewed as a matter of course.
6   Boil a pan of water and suspend the thermostat on a piece of cord, Fig. 2.12. Lower the thermostat into the hot water, but do not let it touch the pan, and it should be seen to open on immersion. Remove the thermostat from the water and it should be seen to close. This is a rudimentary test but it will identify a failed thermostat. With a thermometer you can check the correct opening temperature and maximum valve lift (see Specifications). Note that the opening temperature is stamped on the unit's mounting flange, on the outer (radiator-side) face. The thermostat should close at 5°C (9°F) below its rated opening temperature.
7   If the unit does not start to open, or is not fully open at the specified temperatures (see Specifications) or if it does not close when removed from the water, then it must be discarded, and a new unit fitted.
8   When renewing the thermostat, make sure that the replacement item is the correct one for your car as thermostats are made for a wide range of different models and conditions. You can drive without a thermostat in an emergency; no harm will result but the engine will not warm up properly.
9   Clean the mating faces of the thermostat housing and its cover and fit a new gasket.
10   Locate the thermostat so that the air bleed hole/jiggle valve is uppermost.
11   Tighten the bolts to the specified torque setting, then refit the top hose and top up the coolant in the radiator and expansion tank (see Section 5). Check carefully for any signs of coolant leakage after running the engine, and wash off any spilt coolant.

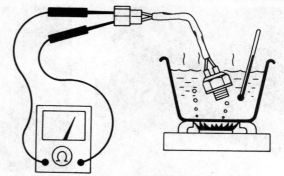

Fig. 2.13 Testing the electric cooling fan thermostatic switch (Sec 12)

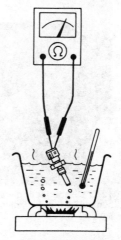

Fig. 2.14 Testing the water temperature sensor – fuel injection models (Sec 12)

---

12   Cooling system electrical switches – testing, removal and refitting

Electric cooling fan thermostatic switch(es)

1   Refer to Section 10 of this Chapter for details of a quick test which should eliminate most faulty switches.
2   To conduct a thorough test the switch must first be removed from the radiator, as follows. First disconnect the switch wires and check that the engine and radiator are completely cool.
3   To prevent spillage once the switch has been removed, either drain off a small amount of coolant, or remove the radiator cap to release any residual pressure.
4   On vertical-flow radiators, unscrew the switch from the radiator, and swiftly plug the aperture with a cork or similar; take care not to damage the radiator, and do not use anything which might leave foreign matter inside the cooling system. On refitting, apply a suitable sealant to the switch threads and tighten it securely. Check the coolant level, and top up if necessary, as described in Section 2.
5   On crossflow radiators, rotate the switch retainer one-quarter turn anti-clockwise and pull it out of the radiator housing (photo), then withdraw the switch itself and discard the rubber seal. Plug the hole. Refitting is the reverse of the removal procedure, noting that a new seal must be fitted whenever the switch is disturbed.
6   To test the switch, connect an ohmmeter or similar, or a battery and bulb test circuit to it (using two spare wires, on crossflow-radiator switches) and suspend the switch in a pan of water which is being heated (Fig. 2.13). Measure the temperature of the water with a thermometer. Do not let the switch or the thermometer touch the pan itself.
7   The switch contacts should close to the 'On' position (ie continuity should exist) when the water reaches the temperature specified. Stop heating the water and allow it to cool down. The switch contacts should open to the 'Off' position when the water cools to the temperature specified.
8   Note that switch number 1 is fitted to the radiator right-hand side (top or bottom) and controls the fan motor(s) through one or more fan

motor relays. Switch number 2 is fitted only to models with a two-speed main fan motor; it is screwed into the radiator upper left-hand side.
9   If the switch does not move at the specified temperatures it must be renewed.
10   Note that, on carburettor-engined and Turbo models there is a connection from the switch to the idle-up system (Chapter 3).

Coolant temperature gauge sensor (thermal transmitter)

11   The coolant temperature gauge mounted in the instrument panel is controlled by a sensor (referred to as a thermal transmitter in the wiring diagrams) that is screwed into the rear of the intake (inlet) manifold at the thermostat housing (photos).
12   The sensor contains a thermistor, which is an element whose electrical resistance decreases at a predetermined rate as its temperature rises.
13   To check the circuit quickly, switch on the ignition, disconnect the sensor's wire and earth it to the engine; the temperature gauge needle should switch across to the full 'Hot' position and return to 'Cold' position when the wire is disconnected. If the gauge behaves as described then the sensor is probably faulty and should be checked further; if not, the fault is in the gauge itself or the wiring.
14   To test the sensor fully it must first be removed as follows. With the engine and radiator completely cool, remove the radiator cap to release any residual pressure, disconnect the sensor's wire and unscrew the sensor. Plug the aperture to minimise the loss of coolant.
15   The test is similar to that described in paragraph 6 above. Connect an ohmmeter between the sensor's terminal and its hexagon-shaped body, heat the water and measure the resistance as the temperature rises. Compare the results obtained with those listed in the Specifications.
16   If the sensor's performance varies significantly from that specified the sensor must be renewed.
17   On refitting, apply sealant to the sensor's threads and tighten it carefully, to the specified torque setting. Check the coolant level and top up if necessary; see Section 2 of this Chapter.

12.5 On crossflow radiators remove retainer to release thermostatic switch

12.11A Coolant temperature gauge sensor – carburettor models

12.11B Coolant temperature gauge sender – 2.0 litre fuel injection models (Turbo similar)

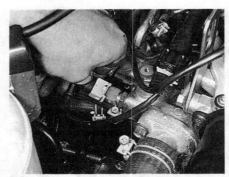

12.22 Disconnecting water temperature sensor 2.0 litre fuel injection models (Turbo similar)

12.24 Removing water temperature sensor – 2.0 litre fuel injection models (Turbo similar)

Water temperature switch – automatic transmission

18   All carburettor-engined cars with automatic transmission are fitted with a separate thermostatic switch which is screwed into the rear of the intake (inlet) manifold at the thermostat housing.

19   Removal and refitting are similar to the procedures described in paragraphs 14 and 17 above.

20   To test the switch, proceed as described in paragraph 6 above. Specific details are not provided by which the switch can be tested, but its contacts should close to the 'On' position at approximately normal coolant operating temperature.

21   If the switch is faulty it must be renewed.

Water temperature sensor – Turbo and 2.0i GSX models

22   To monitor the engine's temperature, the control unit receives a signal from a temperature sensor which is screwed into the thermostat housing (photo). The control unit is therefore controlled by the temperature of the coolant.

23   The sensor contains a thermistor, which is an element whose electrical resistance decreases at a predetermined rate as its temperature rises.

24   Remove and refit the sensor as described in paragraphs 14 and 17 above (photo).

25   To test the sensor quickly, disconnect its wires and measure the resistance across its terminals with the engine completely cold. Connect the sensor again, start the engine and warm it up to normal operating temperature. Then stop the engine, disconnect the sensor wires and measure the resistance again; there should be a considerable reduction in resistance, approximately corresponding to the values specified (see Specifications).

26   To test the sensor fully, remove it and connect a multimeter across its terminals, then suspend it in a pan of water which is being heated from a low temperature (Fig. 2.14). Use a thermometer to measure the temperature, but do not allow the sensor or the thermometer to touch the pan itself. As the water is heated through the specified temperature range note the corresponding resistance readings and compare them with those specified.

27   If the sensor is faulty it must be renewed.

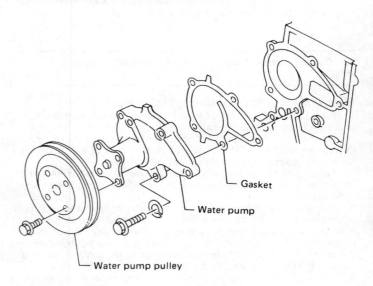

Gasket

Water pump

Water pump pulley

Fig. 2.15 Water pump components (Sec 13)

13   Water pump – removal and refitting

Note: *Water pump failure is indicated by coolant leaking from the gland at the right-hand end of the pump, or by rough and noisy operation, usually accompanied by excessive play of the pump spindle. Repair or overhaul of a faulty pump is not possible, as internal parts are not available separately. In the event of failure, a replacement pump must be obtained.*

1   Drain the cooling system as described in Section 3 of this Chapter, then disconnect the radiator top hose from the thermostat housing cover.

2   Remove the timing belt and tensioner assembly as described in Chapter 1, Section 5.

3   Unbolt the pump, noting the location of the lockwashers under four of the five bolts and of the power-assisted steering pump adjuster bracket. Discard the pump gasket and clean carefully the cylinder block mating surface.

4   As noted above, the pump must be renewed if it is faulty in any way.

5   On refitting, carefully clean the mating surfaces of the pump and the cylinder block, then use a thin smear of grease to stick a new gasket in place and refit the pump. Tighten its mounting bolts evenly to the specified torque setting; do not omit the bracket or lockwashers.

6   Refit the timing belt as described in Chapter 1.

7   Connect the top hose to the thermostat housing, then refill the cooling system as described in Section 5 of this Chapter.

8   Wash off any spilt coolant and check carefully for any signs of coolant leaks (especially around the disturbed joints) after running the engine.

14   Fault diagnosis – cooling system

Symptom	Reason(s)
Overheating	Low coolant level (this may be the result of overheating or other reasons, such as neglect or leakage)
	Faulty temperature gauge (gauge or sensor) showing incorrect reading
	Radiator blockage (internal or external) or grille restricted
	Coolant flow restriction due to kinked or collapsed hose or clogged engine waterway
	Broken or slipping water pump drivebelt
	Faulty thermostat
	Faulty electric cooling fan thermostatic switch
	Faulty electric cooling fan motor
	Faulty radiator cap
	Engine oil level low or oil of incorrect grade
	New engine not yet run-in
	Cylinder head gasket blown
	Cylinder head or block distorted or cracked
	Fuel system fault (weak mixture) – see Chapter 3
	Ignition system fault (ignition timing incorrect or faulty distributor) – see Chapter 4
	Exhaust system partially blocked
	Brakes binding – see Chapter 9
Overcooling	Faulty temperature gauge (gauge or sensor) showing incorrect reading
	Thermostat missing, faulty or of incorrect rating
Coolant loss – external*	Loose hose clips
	Perished or cracked hoses
	Radiator core leaking
	Heater matrix leaking
	Radiator cap faulty
	Expansion tank leaking
	Water pump or thermostat housing leaking
	Core plug leaking
	Other joint face leak
	Boiling due to overheating
Coolant loss – internal*	Cylinder head gasket blown
	Cylinder head, block or inlet manifold cracked or warped
	Leak into transmission fluid at radiator (automatic transmission only)
Excessive corrosion	Infrequent draining and flushing of system
	Use of incorrect coolant mixture ingredients, especially antifreeze
	Combustion gases contaminating coolant

*If source of coolant loss is not evident, have system pressure tested

Note: This Section is not intended to be an exhaustive guide to fault diagnosis, but summarises the more common faults which may be encountered during a car's life. Consult a dealer for more specific advice.

Chapter 3 Fuel, exhaust and emission control systems

Contents

Specifications

Part A: Carburettor engines

General

System type..	Rear mounted fuel tank, mechanical fuel pump, dual barrel carburettor
Fuel tank capacity (approx)	60 litres (13.2 Imp gals)
Fuel octane rating (see Section 15):	
1.6 litre models up to engine no. 190258 (July 1987)	88 RON (Premium unleaded)
All other models..	97 RON (4-star leaded or super/super plus unleaded*)

These models can use Premium grade unleaded if the ignition timing is first retarded (Chapter 4)

Carburettor type:	
1.6 and 1.8 litre models..	Nikki 21E304
2.0 litre models	Hitachi DCR-342

Carburettor calibration

1.6 litre models:

Carburettor model number:

Early models..	21E304-A11
Late models	21E304-G3

	Primary	Secondary
Main jet:		
T12 models..	100	180
T72 models..	103	180
Slow jet:		
T12 models..	44	80
T72 models..	44	90
Power jet:		
T12 models..	50	
T72 models..	60	
Throttle chamber bore...................................	30.0 mm (1.18 in)	34.0 mm (1.34 in)
Venturi diameter...	23.7 mm (0.93 in)	30.0 mm (1.18 in)
Main air bleed...	55	60
Slow air bleed	190	60

1.8 litre models:

Carburettor model number:

Manual transmission	21E304-A4
Automatic transmission	21E304-D8

	Primary	Secondary
Main jet:		
T12 models..	100	170
T72 models..	103	170
Slow jet:		
Manual transmission	44	90
Automatic transmission	44	80
Throttle chamber bore...................................	Not available	Not available
Venturi diameter...	Not available	Not available
Main air bleed...	55	60
Slow air bleed	190	60
Power jet	50	

2.0 litre models:

Carburettor model number:

Manual transmission	DCR342-101
Automatic transmission	DCR342-102

	Primary	Secondary
Main jet:		
T12 models..	106	160
T72 models (manual transmission)................	106	165
Main air bleed:		
T12 models..	60	60
T72 models..	75	60
Slow jet:		
T12 models..	47	115
T72 models..	47	100
Slow air bleed	170	60

Carburettor adjustments

Idle speed:	
1.6 litre models up to engine no. 190258 (July 1987)	650 ± 50 rpm – increase to 850 rpm if ignition timing advanced (Chapter 4)
1.6 litre models from engine no. 190259...........................	700 rpm
1.8 and 2.0 litre models:	
Manual transmission	650 ± 100 rpm
Automatic transmission	750 ± 100 rpm ('N' position)

Note: *Idle-up system (Section 19) increases idle speed by 50 to 200 rpm*

Carburettor adjustments (continued)

CO level at idle speed	$1.0 \pm 0.5\%$
Fuel level – valve closed ('h1', Fig. 3.18):	
1.6 litre models	2.1 to 3.1 mm (0.083 to 0.122 in)
1.8 litre models	Not available
2.0 litre models	8.6 to 9.6 mm (0.339 to 0.378 in)
Fuel level – valve fully open ('h2', Fig. 3.21):	
1.6 litre models	0.5 to 1.5 mm (0.020 to 0.059 in)
1.8 litre models	Not available
2.0 litre models	4.5 to 5.5 mm (0.178 to 0.217 in)
Fast idle speed:	
1.6 litre models	2100 to 2400 rpm
1.8 litre models	Not available
2.0 litre models:	
en Manual transmission	2500 to 2800 rpm
Automatic transmission	2900 to 3200 rpm
Fast idle clearance ('A', Fig. 3.23):	
1.6 litre models	0.60 ± 0.07 mm (0.024 ± 0.003 in)
1.8 litre models	Not available
2.0 litre models:	
Manual transmission	0.73 ± 0.07 mm (0.029 ± 0.003 in)
Automatic transmission	0.88 ± 0.07 mm (0.035 ± 0.003 in)
Dashpot touch speed	2000 to 2400 rpm
Dashpot clearance:	
1.6 litre models	0.51 ± 0.10 mm (0.020 ± 0.004 in)
1.8 litre models	Not available
2.0 litre models	0.55 ± 0.10 mm (0.022 ± 0.004 in)
Vacuum break test – applied vacuum	-53.3 kPa (-15.74 in Hg)
Vacuum break clearance 'R1', Fig. 3.30:	
1.6 litre models	1.40 ± 0.15 mm (0.055 ± 0.006 in)
1.8 litre models	Not available
2.0 litre models	1.95 ± 0.15 mm (0.077 ± -0.006 in)
Vacuum break clearance 'R2', Fig. 3.31:	
1.6 litre models	2.48 ± 0.30 mm (0.098 ± 0.012 in)
1.8 litre models	Not available
2.0 litre models	3.62 ± 0.30 mm (0.143 ± 0.012 in)
Air filter	Champion W206
Fuel filter	Champion L102
Fuel pump pressure	19.6 to 26.5 kPa (2.8 to 3.8 psi)

Accelerator cable adjustment

Stopper bolt length ('L', Fig. 3.7)	6.5 to 7.5 mm (0.26 to 0.30 in)
Free play at pedal pad centre	1.0 to 3.0 mm (0.04 to 0.12 in)

Torque wrench settings

See Part D below

Part B: Turbo engines

General

System type	Rear mounted fuel tank, electric fuel pump, computer controlled fuel injection system, turbocharged
Fuel tank capacity (approx)	60 litres (13.2 Imp gals)
Fuel octane rating (see Sections 15 and 40)	97 RON (4-star leaded only)

Fuel injection system adjustments

Idle speed	650 ± 100 rpm
FICD speed (Turbo Executive)	800 to 900 rpm
CO level at idle speed:	
Standard	2.0% maximum
Under warm-up enrichment	8.0% maximum
Dashpot touch speed	2200 ± 200 rpm

Fuel filter

Champion L102

Fuel pressure

Maximum variation	206 to 255 kPa (30 to 37 psi)
Regulated fuel pressure	250.1 kPa (36 psi)

Turbocharger

Standard boost pressure	43.3 to 48.7 kPa (6.3 to 7.1 psi)
Emergency relief valve operates at	52.0 kPa (7.5 psi)
Shaft axial play	0.013 to 0.091 mm (0.0005 to 0.0036 in)

Accelerator cable adjustment
Stopper bolt length ('L', Fig. 3.7) .... 1.0 to 2.0 mm (0.04 to 0.08 in)
Free play at pedal pad centre .... 1.0 to 3.0 mm (0.04 to 0.12 in)

Torque wrench settings .... See Part D below

Part C: 2.0 litre fuel injection engines
General
System type... Rear mounted fuel tank, electric fuel pump, computer-controlled
fuel injection system
Fuel tank capacity (approx) .... 60 litres (13.2 Imp gals)
Fuel octane rating.. 97 RON (4-star leaded) or super/super plus unleaded*)
*This model can use Premium grade unleaded if the ignition timing is first retarded (see Chapter 4)

Fuel injection system adjustments
Idle speed .... 800 ± 50 rpm
FICD speed (Executive)... 950 to 1050 rpm
CO level at idle speed .... 1.5 ± 0.5%
Dashpot touch speed:
    Manual... 2200 to 2600 rpm
    Automatic .... 3300 to 3700 rpm

Fuel filter .... Champion L102

Fuel pressure
Maximum variation... 255 to 304 kPa (37 to 44 psi)
Regulated fuel pressure .... 299.1 kPa (43 psi)

Accelerator cable adjustment
Stopper bolt length ('L', Fig. 3.7) .... 5.0 to 6.0 mm (0.20 to 0.24 in)
Free play at pedal pad centre .... 1.0 to 3.0 mm (0.04 to 0.12 in)

Torque wrench settings .... See Part D below

Part D: All models

Torque wrench settings

	Nm	lbf ft
Fuel tank mounting bolts	31 to 42	23 to 31
Fuel hose clamp screws	1 to 1.5	0.5 to 1
Electric fuel pump/fuel gauge sender unit mounting bolts	2.3 to 3	2 to 2.5
Mechanical fuel pump mounting nuts	11 to 13	8 to 9.5
Accelerator pedal bracket mounting bolts	3 to 4	2.5 to 3
Accelerator pedal stopper bolt locknut	8 to 12	6 to 9
Carburettor mounting nuts	12 to 18	9 to 13
Throttle valve switch bolts (Turbo)	2 to 2.4	1.5 to 2
Throttle chamber Allen bolts	18 to 22	13 to 16
IAA unit mounting fasteners	6.4 to 8.3	4.5 to 6
Air regulator mounting bolts	5 to 6	4 to 4.5
Fuel injector mounting bolts:		
Turbo	2.5 to 3.2	2 to 2.5
2.0 litre fuel injection models	6.4 to 8.3	4.5 to 6
Intake manifold front stay bolts:		
Turbo	16 to 22	12 to 16
2.0 litre fuel injection models	20 to 25	15 to 18.5
Intake manifold rear stay (2.0 litre fuel injection models):		
10 mm	38 to 46	28 to 34
8 mm	18 to 22	13 to 16
Intake collector to manifold (2.0 litre fuel injection models)	18 to 22	13 to 16
Intake manifold nuts and bolts (cold)	20 to 25	15 to 18.5
PCV valve	29 to 39	21.5 to 29
PCV valve mounting bracket bolts (Turbo)	6.4 to 8.3	4.5 to 6
Exhaust manifold nuts and bolts (cold)	20 to 29	15 to 21.5
Exhaust manifold heat shield bolts	4 to 5	3 to 4
Turbocharger mounting nuts	Not available	Not available
Turbocharger-to-exhaust outlet nuts	22 to 29	16 to 21.5
Turbocharger heat shield bolts	4 to 5	3 to 4
Turbocharger oil feed pipe union nuts	16 to 24	12 to 17.5
Turbocharger coolant pipe union banjo bolts	11 to 15	8 to 11
Turbocharger oil outlet pipe union nut	39 to 59	29 to 43.5
Exhaust downpipe-to-manifold nuts (cold):		
2.0 litre fuel injection	41 to 48	30 to 35.5
All other models	26 to 36	19 to 26.5
Exhaust system flange joint nuts or bolts	31 to 42	23 to 31
Exhaust system mounting bolts	8 to 12	6 to 9

PART A: CARBURETTOR ENGINES

1 General description

The fuel system consists of a rear-mounted fuel tank, a fuel pump mechanically operated from the camshaft and a dual barrel carburettor incorporating an automatic choke.

The light alloy intake (inlet) manifold is coolant heated to improve the atomisation of the fuel/air mixture.

The exhaust manifold is of cast iron construction and incorporates a heated air box as part of the air intake system.

The exhaust system fitted as original equipment is of three-section type incorporating a flexible section, a silencer and expansion box, and is suspended on rubber mountings under the car.

The air cleaner incorporates an automatically controlled air temperature flap.

The emission control systems fitted are the throttle dashpot, the Boost Controlled Deceleration Device (BCDD), the Positive Crankcase Ventilation (PCV) system and the evaporative emission control system. Refer to the relevant Sections of this Chapter for details.

2 Precautions to be observed when servicing the fuel system

Warning: *Petrol is extremely flammable, particularly when in the form of vapour. Precautions must be taken, as described below, to prevent the risk of fire or explosion when working on any part of the fuel system. Note that petrol vapour is heavier than air and will collect in inspection pits or poorly ventilated corners of buildings. Avoid getting petrol in the eyes or mouth and try to avoid skin contact. In case of accidents flush the affected area immediately with copious quantities of water and seek prompt medical advice.*

1　Always perform service procedures in a well-ventilated area to prevent the build-up of fumes.

2　Never work in a building containing a gas appliance with a pilot light, or any other form of naked flame. Ensure that there are no naked light bulbs or any sources of flame or sparks nearby.

3　Do not smoke (or allow anyone else to smoke) while in the vicinity of petrol or of components containing petrol. Remember the possible presence of petrol vapour from these sources and move well clear before smoking.

4　Check all electrical equipment belonging to the house, garage or workshop where work is being carried on (see the *Safety first!* section of this manual). Remember that certain electrical appliances such as drills, cutters etc create sparks in the normal course of operation and must not be used near petrol or any component containing petrol. Again, remember the possible presence of petrol fumes before using electrical equipment.

5　Always mop up any spilt fuel and safely dispose of the paper towel or rag used.

6　Any stored petrol, or petrol that is drained off during servicing work, must be kept in sealed containers that are suitable for holding petrol and clearly marked as such; the containers themselves should be kept in a safe place. Note that this last point applies equally to the fuel tank, if it is removed from the car; also remember to keep its filler cap closed at all times.

7　Before working on any part of the fuel system always switch off the ignition at the very least; preferably disconnect the battery (negative terminal first) to prevent the risk of sparks due to short circuits or to improperly-connected components. If test procedures require the use of electricity be careful to check all connections before starting work.

8　Read carefully the *Safety first!* section of this manual before starting work.

3 Routine maintenance

Carry out the following procedures at the intervals given in *'Routine maintenance'* at the beginning of the Manual.

Check idling speed and mixture

1　Refer to Section 17.

Check the exhaust system

2　With the car over an inspection pit or supported on axle stands, check the exhaust system and mountings for security and condition. Any signs of a leak can be confirmed by running the engine at idling speed and temporarily placing a wad of rag over the end of the exhaust tailpipe. Any leak will then be shown up by exhaust gases blowing through the hole.

Check the air cleaner automatic temperature control

3　Check the vacuum hose to the sensor and motor for condition and security.

4　With the engine cold and stopped, disconnect the intake (inlet) duct and check that the internal flap is fully down and closing the warm air inlet.

5　Start the engine and check that the flap rises to open the warm air inlet.

6　Increase the engine speed momentarily and check that the flap rises slightly as the vacuum is increased.

7　As the engine warms up, check that the flap gradually lowers to close the warm air inlet.

Check the crankcase ventilation system

8　The positive crankcase ventilation (PCV) valve is screwed into the manifold on the carburettor mounting flange.

9　The valve can be checked by disconnecting the supply hose from the oil separator assembly. With the engine idling, strong suction should be felt when a finger is placed over the valve end, with a pronounced hissing noise (Fig. 3.1). If no suction is felt, or hissing heard, renew the valve.

10　Check that pressure can be felt at the supply hose end from escaping crankcase vapours. If none can be felt (and if the idle speed increases or stabilises when the oil filler cap is removed and the ventilation system components are in their normal positions) check that the oil separator is not blocked with burnt oil etc, or oil leaks will rapidly result due to the increased crankcase pressure.

11　Remove the air cleaner cover (Section 4) and withdraw the small PCV filter. Clean it in a suitable solvent and check it for splits or other damage; renew the filter if it is badly clogged or damaged. Refit the filter and air cleaner cover.

12　Disconnect the system's hoses and check that both are free from blockages, splits or cracks; clean or renew the hose(s) if necessary.

Check the engine breather and vacuum hoses

13　High temperatures in the engine compartment can cause the deterioration of the rubber and plastic hoses used for engine, accessory and emission systems operations. Periodic inspection should be made for cracks, loose clamps, material hardening and leaks.

14　Some, but not all, hoses are secured to the fittings with clamps. Where clamps are used, check to be sure they haven't lost their tension, allowing the hose to leak. If clamps aren't used, make sure the hose has

Fig. 3.1 Checking the PCV valve operation (Sec 3)

4.1A Release spring clips and unscrew wing nut ...

4.1B ... to release air cleaner cover ...

4.2 Removing filter element – PCV filter arrowed

not expanded and/or hardened where it slips over the fitting, allowing it to leak.

Renew the fuel filter
15   Refer to Section 7.

Check the fuel system
16   Check the fuel pump for security, condition and leaks.
17   Check all the fuel lines for security and damage with the car over an inspection pit or supported on axle stands.
18   Inspect the fuel tank for damage and for secure mountings.

Renew the air cleaner filter element
19   Refer to Section 4.

Renew the PCV filter
20   Refer to paragraph 11 above, renewing the filter irrespective of its apparent condition.

4.6 Tightening wing nut as described in text

4   Air cleaner filter element – renewal

1   Release the spring clips, unscrew the central wing nut and lift the cover from the air cleaner (photos).
2   Lift out the element (photo).
3   Wipe clean the inside of the air cleaner body and cover.
4   The genuine Nissan element does not require cleaning between the specified renewal intervals. If non-genuine elements are used they can be cleaned as follows.
5   Tap the element to remove the loose dust, then use an air line from inside the element to remove the remaining dust.
6   Refit the element and air cleaner cover. To secure the cover correctly locate it on the body and element seal, screw down the wing nut until it touches the metal washer, then tighten the nut through four full turns. Do not overtighten the nut (photo). Finally, refit the spring clips.

5   Air cleaner – removal and refitting

1   Remove the air cleaner filter element (Section 4).
2   Slacken the clips securing the air intake (inlet) flexible duct and warm air intake (inlet) hose to the air cleaner body, then disconnect the flexible duct (photos).
3   Disconnect the crankcase ventilation hose (photo).
4   Unbolt the mounting bracket from the rocker cover (photo).
5   Lift the air cleaner body, disconnecting the vacuum hoses from the distributor, carburettor and intake (inlet) manifold and disconnecting the warm air intake (inlet) hose (photos).
6   If required, the flexible duct can be unbolted from the left-hand side of the engine compartment (photo).
7   Refitting is a reversal of removal.

5.2A Slackening air intake flexible duct clip ...

5.2B ... to release duct from air cleaner

5.3 Disconnecting crankcase ventilation hose

5.4 Unbolting air cleaner mounting bracket

5.5A Disconnect vacuum hoses from distributor ...

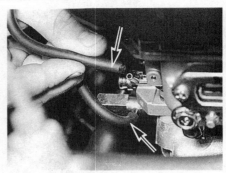

5.5B ... from carburettor and intake (inlet) manifold

5.5C Disconnecting warm air intake (inlet) hose

5.6 Flexible duct mounting screws

6   Air cleaner Automatic Temperature Control – general

1   The temperature of incoming air is regulated by the Automatic Temperature Control (ATC) system to permit the carburettor settings to be as weak as possible to improve the engine's warm-up time and to prevent carburettor icing.

2   This is accomplished by drawing in cold air from an intake at the front of the car, and hot air from a collector box on the exhaust manifold and blending them. The proportion of hot and cold air is varied by the position of a flap valve in the intake spout which itself is controlled by a vacuum motor. The vacuum pressure is regulated by a temperature sensor located within the air cleaner body to ensure that the appropriate degree of intake (inlet) manifold vacuum is applied to the flap valve, thus maintaining the air temperature within the preset limits.

3   Check the system as described in Section 3.

4   To check the operation of the components, a vacuum pump is required. If one is available proceed as follows, if not, have the tests carried out by a dealer.

5   Detach the vacuum hose at the motor and connect a vacuum pump to the motor. Apply a vacuum up to 22 kPa (6.5 in Hg) and retain this whilst checking the flap valve.

6   If the flap valve is now open, then the temperature sensor is faulty and must be renewed. If the valve remains shut, the motor is faulty and must be renewed (photos).

6.6A Air cleaner ATC temperature sensor ...

6.6B ... and vacuum motor

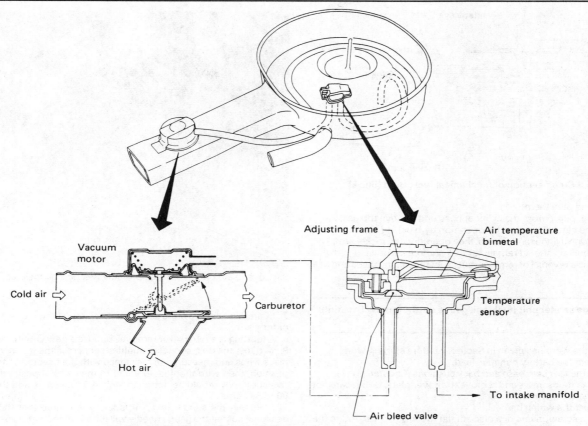

Fig. 3.2 Air cleaner Automatic Temperature Control components (Sec 6)

7.2 Fuel filter is clipped to bulkhead

8.4 Fuel pump mounting nuts 'A', inlet hose 'B', outlet hose 'C', return hose 'D'

7   Fuel filter – renewal

1   Refer to the warnings given in Section 2 before starting work.
2   The fuel filter is clipped to the left-hand side of the bulkhead. Note which way round it is fitted (photo).
3   Release the filter from the clip, then loosen the two hose clips, release the hoses and withdraw the filter.
4   Fit the new filter using a reversal of the removal procedure.

8   Fuel pump – testing, removal and refitting

1   Refer to the warnings given in Section 2 before starting work.
2   The fuel pump is of sealed type, no provision being made for cleaning (Fig. 3.3).
3   To remove the pump, first remove the air cleaner assembly complete (Section 5).
4   Note the location of the inlet, outlet and return hoses (photo), then

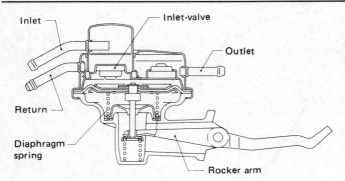

Fig. 3.3 Cross-section of mechanical fuel pump (Sec 8)

Labels: Inlet, Inlet-valve, Outlet, Return, Diaphragm spring, Rocker arm

disconnect and plug them.

5   Unbolt the pump from the cylinder head and remove the gasket.

6   The pump can be checked for operation by blocking the outlet and return ports with a finger and thumb, then operating the rocker arm. The air pressure built up should remain for two or three seconds.

7   Refitting is a reversal of removal, but clean the mating faces and fit a new gasket.

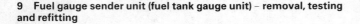

9   Fuel gauge sender unit (fuel tank gauge unit) – removal, testing and refitting

1   Refer to the warnings given in Section 2 before starting work.

2   Disconnect the battery negative lead.

3   Remove the rear seat base and back cushions (Chapter 11).

4   Extract the four screws and remove the cover plate, taking care not to damage the wiring (photo).

5   Disconnect the wiring harness.

6   Using two screwdrivers or a piece of flat metal as a lever, rotate the unit's lock plate until it releases.

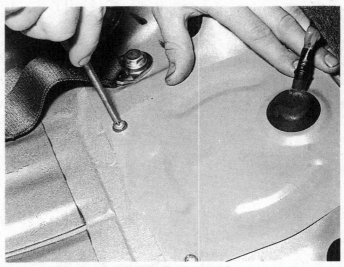

9.4 Cover plate under rear seat protects fuel tank gauge unit

7   Carefully withdraw the sender unit; taking care not to bend the float or float arm.

8   Refitting is a reversal of removal, but use a new O-ring.

9   To test the unit, connect a multimeter across the green/yellow and black wires and measure the resistance with the float raised to the 'Full' position, then with the float lowered to the 'Empty' position. The first measurement should be approximately 4.5 to 6 ohms and the second, 80 to 83 ohms.

10   Renew the sender unit if it is faulty, but note that the circuit is designed so that the gauge needle will remain in the same position even when the ignition is switched off.

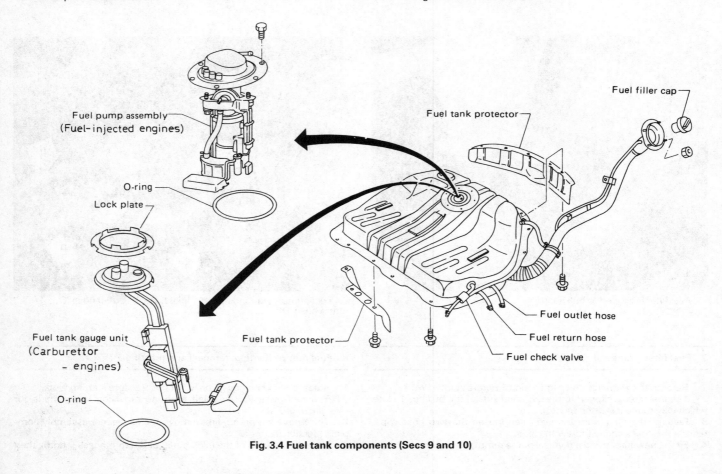

Labels: Fuel pump assembly (Fuel-injected engines), O-ring, Lock plate, Fuel tank gauge unit (Carburettor – engines), O-ring, Fuel tank protector, Fuel tank protector, Fuel filler cap, Fuel outlet hose, Fuel return hose, Fuel check valve

Fig. 3.4 Fuel tank components (Secs 9 and 10)

10.4 Early models are fitted with a fuel tank drain plug

10.6 Fuel tank supply and return hoses

10.7 Slacken clip to release filler tube from filler neck

10.10A Fuel tank front left-hand mounting bolts

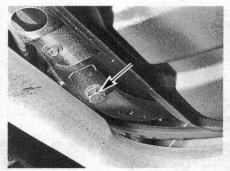

10.10B Fuel tank front right-hand mounting bolt

10.10C Fuel tank rear mounting bolt

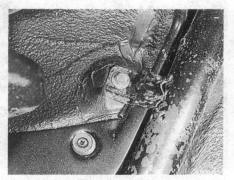

10.12A Filler neck mounting bolt

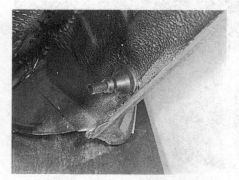

10.12B Breather tube outlet in rear wing

10 Fuel tank – removal, repair and refitting

1 Refer to the warnings given in Section 2 before starting work.

2 Disconnect the battery negative lead.

3 Chock the front wheels, then jack up the rear of the car and support on axle stands.

4 Remove the fuel tank filler cap, then unscrew the drain plug (where fitted – photo) and drain the fuel into a sealed container. Refit the drain plug.

5 If a drain plug is not fitted, either the petrol must be syphoned out or the tank must be removed with petrol still inside. This will obviously require care when disconnecting hoses and plugging the tank openings.

6 Loosen the clips, then disconnect and plug the supply and return hoses (photo).

7 Loosen the clip and disconnect the convoluted filler tube (photo).

8 Remove the fuel gauge sender unit (Section 9).

9 Support the weight of the fuel tank with a jack and interposed block of wood.

10 Unscrew the mounting bolts (photos) and lower the fuel tank until the breather tubes can be disconnected. Lower the tank to the floor.

11 Note the location of the protector plates, then extract the screws and remove them from the tank.

12 If necessary, the filler neck and tubes (photos) can be removed from the body.

13 If the tank contains sediment, swill it out with fuel or have it steam cleaned. Any repairs should be left to a specialist. Do not under any circumstances attempt to solder or weld a fuel tank.

14 Refitting is a reversal of removal, but make sure that the hoses are connected correctly.

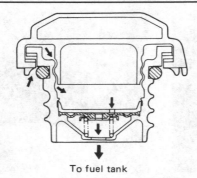

Fig. 3.5 Cross-section of fuel filler cap (Sec 11)

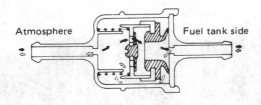

⇐ Evaporative fuel flow
← Fresh air flow

Fig. 3.6 Cross-section of check valve (Sec 11)

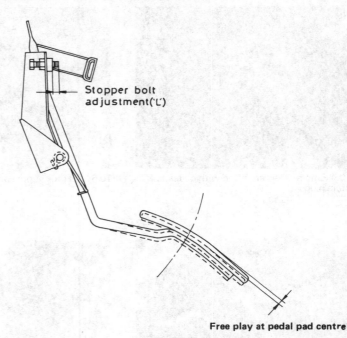

Free play at pedal pad centre

Fig. 3.7 Accelerator pedal and cable settings (Sec 12)

11.5 Location of evaporative emission control check valve

12.2 Accelerator cable adjusting nuts at carburettor

11   Evaporative emission control system – general

1   To minimise the escape into the atmosphere of unburned petrol vapour, particularly while the car is parked, all models are fitted with an evaporative emission control system.

2   This consists of a filler cap which is sealed against escaping vapour pressure but incorporates a vacuum relief valve which allows the entry of air to replace petrol consumed while the car is in motion. A check valve fitted to the tank breather is spring-loaded to allow vapours to escape only after significant pressure has accumulated; it also allows air to enter the tank when required.

3   To check the filler cap valve, wipe it clean and suck through it. Slight resistance should be encountered initially until the valve is heard to click open, when the resistance should disappear. It should not be possible to blow backwards through the filler cap. Renew the filler cap if the valve is clogged or faulty.

4   To test the check valve, blow through it from the fuel tank side.

Considerable resistance should be felt, with only a small amount of air passing through. On sucking (or blowing from the 'open' end), the valve should allow air to pass freely. Renew the valve if it is clogged or faulty.

5   The check valve is situated in the breather tube above the tank's front left-hand corner (photo). It may be necessary to remove the mounting bolts and to lower the tank to gain access to the valve.

12   Accelerator cable – adjustment

1   First check that the pedal height is correct by checking that the stopper bolt threaded end is protruding by the amount given in the Specifications (Fig. 3.7).

2   Adjust the outer cable position on the carburettor bracket so that with the accelerator pedal fully released, the free play at the pedal pad is between 1.0 and 3.0 mm (0.04 and 0.12 in). Tighten both adjusting nuts on completion (photo).

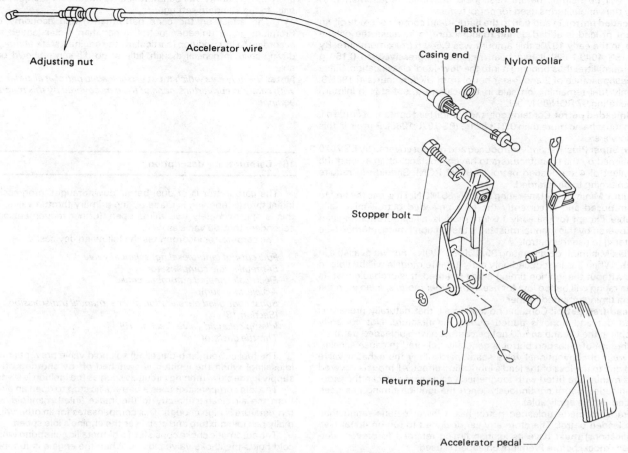

Fig. 3.8 Accelerator pedal and cable (Secs 13 and 14)

13 Accelerator cable – removal and refitting

1   Remove the air cleaner (Section 3).
2   Release the wiring from the clip at the carburettor end of the cable.
3   Unscrew the adjusting nuts and remove the outer cable from the bracket.
4   Release the inner cable from the throttle pulley.
5   Working inside the car, unhook the inner cable from the top of the pedal.
6   Remove the split plastic washer and withdraw the cable from the bulkhead into the engine compartment.
7   Refitting is the reverse of removal. Check the pedal height and adjust the cable (Section 12).

14 Accelerator pedal – removal and refitting

1   Disconnect the cable from the pedal (Section 13).
2   Unbolt the pedal bracket from the bulkhead (photo).
3   If necessary, extract the 'E' ring and separate the pedal from the bracket. Recover the spring.
4   Refitting is a reversal of removal, but apply a little grease to the cable end fittings and pedal shaft.

15 Unleaded petrol – general

Note: *The information given below and in the Specifications of this Chapter and of Chapter 4 is correct at the time of writing and applies only to petrols sold in the UK. If updated information is required, check with a Nissan dealer. If travelling abroad consult one of the motoring organisa-*

14.2 Accelerator pedal mounting bracket

tions (or a similar authority) for advice on the petrols available and their compatibility with your car.

1   Nissan's recommended fuel for the cars covered in this manual is given in the Specifications of this Chapter, followed by the equivalent petrol currently on sale in the UK.
2   RON and MON are different testing standards; RON stands for Research Octane number (also written as RM), while MON means Motor Octane Number (also written as MM).

3   It will be helpful, before describing individual requirements, to clarify the various terms used for petrol types:

4   **Leaded petrol:** In addition to the natural lead content of crude oil, an amount of lead is added during manufacture to increase the octane rating. In the early 1970s this amount was 0.640 g (maximum)/litre. By 1985 (BS 4040:1985) it had been reduced progressively to 0.150 g (maximum)/litre, thus bringing it into the **'low-lead'** classification. Since the disappearance of 2 and 3-star petrol from UK forecourts in 1988/9, the only fuel remaining on sale in this category is 4-star, minimum octane rating 97 RON/86 MON.

5   **Unleaded petrol:** Contains only the natural lead content of crude oil, which must be no more than 0.013 g/litre (BS 7070:1985). Petrols in this category are:

Super/Super Plus: Recently introduced and not yet covered by BS 7070 but claimed by the manufacturers to have an octane rating at least the equivalent of 4-star leaded petrol (ie 97/98 RON). Should not require ignition timing to be retarded.

Premium: Minimum octane rating 95 RON/85 MON. This was the first to be introduced and is currently the only unleaded petrol universally available. Except for the early 1.6 litre models, all carburettor-engined cars covered by this manual must have the ignition timing retarded (see Chapter 4) to use this petrol.

Regular: Minimum octane rating 90 RON/80 MON – not yet available in the UK. When it is introduced only early 1.6 litre models will be able to use it without the ignition timing being retarded. It is probable that its octane rating will be too low for use in the other models, even with the ignition timing retarded further.

6   **Lead-free petrol:** Contains no lead at all; that naturally present is refined out and none is added during manufacture. Not currently available in the UK and should not be confused with unleaded petrol.

7   The use of unleaded petrol is generally believed to cause accelerated wear of conventional valve seats (particularly the exhaust valve seats) due to the loss of the lead's lubricating effect. All models covered in this manual are fitted with toughened valve seats and can therefore use unleaded petrol continuously (once the ignition timing has been retarded, where applicable).

8   Premium grade unleaded petrol has a lower octane rating than 4-star leaded petrol. Therefore any car designed to run on 4-star (see Specifications) **must** have its ignition timing retarded to prevent detonation (knock) before Premium unleaded is used.

9   If the manufacturer's claims are to be believed, Super grade unleaded petrol is at least the equivalent of 4-star's octane rating. Therefore no adjustment (or 'conversion') is necessary before using Super unleaded in any car covered in this manual.

10   Once a car's ignition timing is retarded (if necessary) to use Premium grade unleaded petrol, if can use this or either of the two higher grades (4- star or Super unleaded) as required. However, if the car is to be run **only** on the higher grades for a significant period, performance and economy will be improved by advancing the ignition timing back to the standard setting.

11   The effect on the car's performance and economy of using Premium grade unleaded petrol rather than 4-star leaded will vary according to its condition (particularly the engine's state of tune) and the driving style. In general though, little or no difference should be noticeable.

Note: *The only cars which* **must** *use unleaded petrol at all times are those with catalytic convertors; none of the cars covered by this manual are so equipped.*

16   Carburettor – description

The carburettor is of dual barrel, downdraught, progressive type. Initial throttle opening is made by the primary throttle valve, but after this is approximately two thirds open, further movement opens the secondary throttle valve as well.

The carburettor incorporates the following devices:

Fuel cut-out (anti-dieseling) solenoid valve
Bi-metallic idle compensator
Electrically heated automatic choke
Accelerator pump
Boost controlled deceleration device (manual transmission)
(Section 18)
Idle-up solenoid valve (Section 19)
Throttle dashpot

The fuel cut-out (anti-dieseling) solenoid valve prevents running-on (dieseling) when the ignition is switched off by shutting off the fuel supply in the slow-running circuit as soon as the ignition is switched off.

The idle compensator uses a bi-metallic strip to open an air passage from the air cleaner directly to the intake (inlet) manifold when the temperature is high enough. This compensates for an otherwise abnormally rich idle mixture and stabilises the engine's idle speed.

The automatic choke consists of a bi-metallic coil spring which when cold holds the choke valve closed. When the engine is turning over, a current from the alternator triggers the auto choke/lamp check relay so that power is fed from the battery to the choke assembly. This heats the spring, causing it to open the choke valve. A vacuum unit opens the choke valve, if necessary, under conditions of high manifold vacuum (cruising).

The throttle dashpot delays throttle closure on lifting the accelerator pedal, thus ensuring that all fuel remaining in the manifold is burned, rather than passed straight into the exhaust.

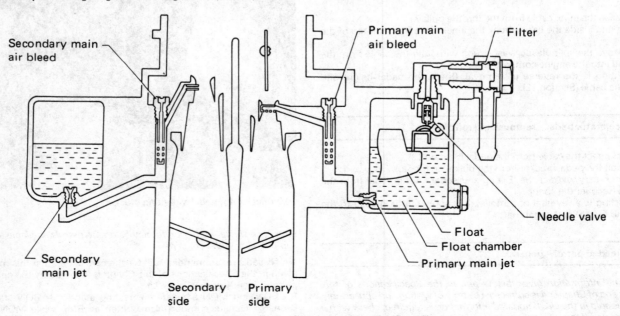

Fig. 3.9 Carburettor main system – typical (Sec 16)

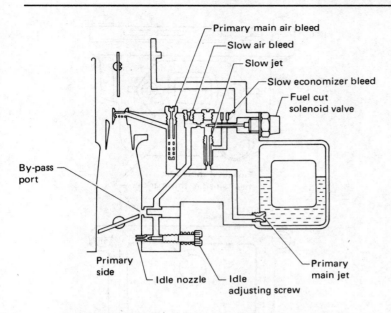

Fig. 3.10 Carburettor slow-running system – typical (Sec 16)

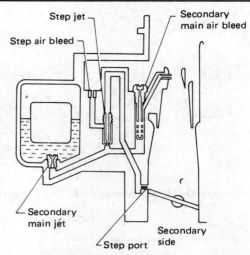

Fig. 3.11 Carburettor step system – typical (Sec 16)

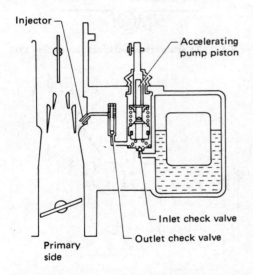

Fig. 3.12 Carburettor accelerator pump system – typical (Sec 16)

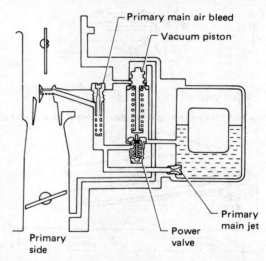

Fig. 3.13 Carburettor power valve system – typical (Sec 16)

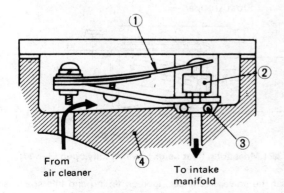

Fig. 3.14 Components of idle compensator (Sec 16)

1 Bi-metallic strip   3 O-ring
2 Rubber valve   4 Carburettor

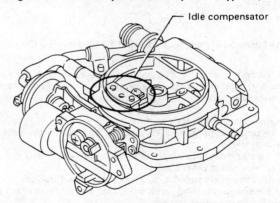

Fig. 3.15 Location of idle compensator – 1.6 and 1.8 litre models (Sec 16)

17 Carburettor – adjustments and checks

1 Refer to the warnings given in Section 2 before starting work.

Idle speed adjustment

2 Park the car on a flat surface, apply the handbrake firmly and chock the roadwheels, then select neutral (manual transmission) or the 'N' position (automatic).

CA20 engine

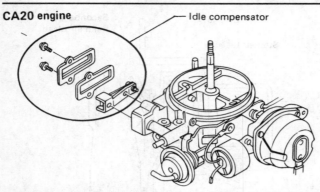

Fig. 3.16 Location of idle compensator – 2.0 litre models (Sec 16)

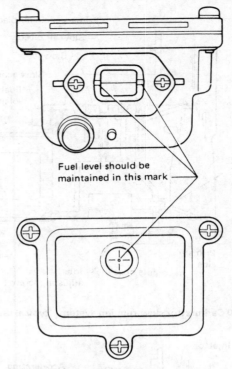

Fig. 3.17 Carburettor fuel level marks (Sec 17)

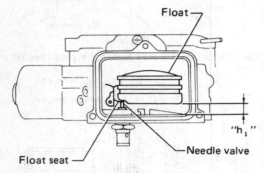

Fig. 3.18 Measuring float height – valve closed (Sec 17)

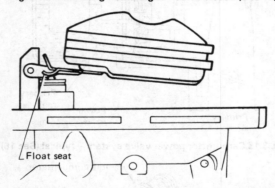

Fig. 3.19 Location of float seat – 1.6 and 1.8 litre models (Sec 17)

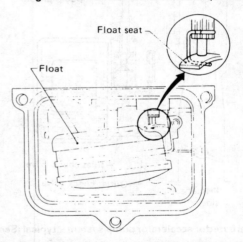

Fig. 3.20 Location of float seat – 2.0 litre models (Sec 17)

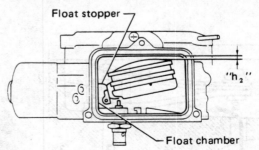

Fig. 3.21 Measuring float height – valve fully open (Sec 17)

3   Have the engine at normal operating temperature with the valve clearances and ignition timing correctly set. On models without a tachometer, connect one to the engine in accordance with the maker's instructions.

4   Allow the engine to idle for two minutes.

5   Race the engine at between 2000 and 3000 rpm two or three times, then allow it to idle.

6   Check that all electrical components are switched off and disconnect the electric cooling fan motor(s).

7   Check that the idling speed is as given in the Specifications. If not, adjust the idle speed adjusting screw to correct (photo). Reconnect the electric cooling fan motor(s).

Idle mixture adjustment

8   The idle mixture adjusting screw is of tamperproof type and a special screwdriver (Nissan part number KV10108300) is required to turn it. Proprietary versions of this screwdriver are available (photo). Also, a CO meter (exhaust gas analyser) would be useful, and a tachometer, where necessary.

9   The idle mixture is preset at the factory and should require no further adjustment. If, due to a change in engine characteristics (carbon build-up, bore wear etc), or after a major carburettor overhaul the mixture becomes incorrect, it can be set as follows.

10   First warm the engine up to normal operating temperature and

ensure that the valve clearances, ignition timing and idle speed are correct. Disconnect the electric cooling fan motor(s).

11   If a CO meter is available, follow its manufacturer's instructions to check the CO level. If adjustment is required, turn the idle mixture adjusting screw in very small increments until the setting is correct.

12   If a CO meter is not available, the procedure outlined below can, in

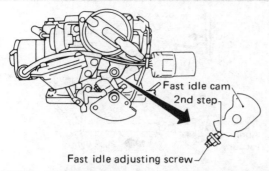

Fast idle cam
2nd step

Fast idle adjusting screw

Fig. 3.22 Setting fast idle linkage to measure fast idle speed (Sec 17)

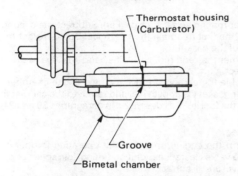

Dash pot

Adjusting screw

Fig. 3.24 Dashpot and throttle lever adjusting screw – 2.0 litre shown (Sec 17)

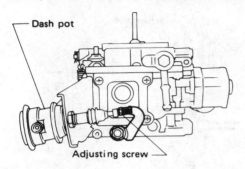

Thermostat housing (Carburetor)

Groove

Bimetal chamber

Fig. 3.26 Automatic choke bimetal cover-to-carburettor alignment marks (Sec 17)

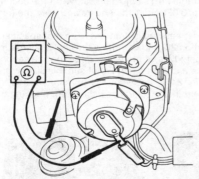

Fig. 3.28 Checking condition of automatic choke heater (Sec 17)

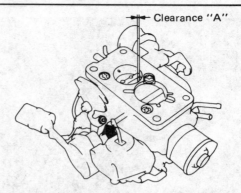

Clearance "A"

Fig. 3.23 Primary throttle valve-to-carburettor venturi wall clearance (Sec 17)

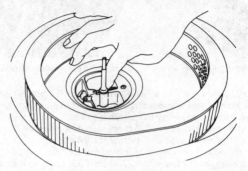

Fig. 3.25 Checking automatic choke valve (Sec 17)

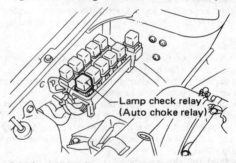

Lamp check relay (Auto choke relay)

Fig. 3.27 Location of lamp check/auto choke relay (Sec 17)

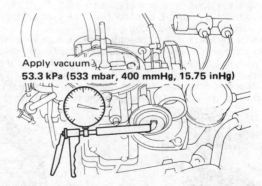

Apply vacuum
53.3 kPa (533 mbar, 400 mmHg, 15.75 inHg)

Fig. 3.29 Applying vacuum to vacuum break diaphragm (Sec 17)

skilled hands, produce an equally accurate result. For most owners, however, it would be best to regard it as a basic setting procedure only, which should then be checked by a competent mechanic using proper test equipment. An accurate tachometer is required.

13   With the engine prepared as described in paragraph 10 above, stop it and screw in the idle mixture adjusting screw until it bottoms lightly (**do not** overtighten it or the tip will be damaged), then unscrew it through exactly two full turns. **Note:** If the presence of the limiter cap makes this impossible, the car must be taken to a Nissan dealer for the work to be done. Restart the engine and allow it to idle.

14   Clear any excess fuel from the intake (inlet) manifold by racing the engine at between 2000 and 3000 rpm two or three times, then allow it to idle.

15   Adjust the idle speed to 730 rpm (manual transmission) or 830 rpm (automatic) using the idle speed adjusting screw.

16   Slowly turn the idle mixture adjusting screw in small amounts first

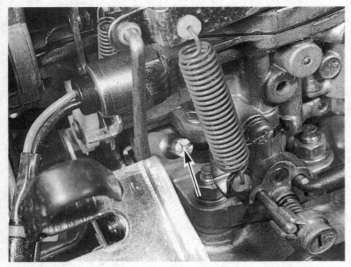

17.7 Idle speed adjusting screw – 1.6 and 1.8 litre models shown

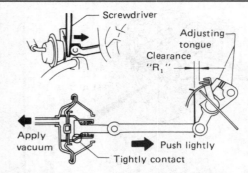

Fig. 3.30 Checking vacuum break clearance R1 (Sec 17)

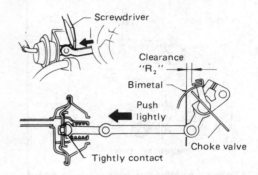

Fig. 3.31 Checking vacuum break clearance R2 (Sec 17)

in one direction, then in the other, until the position is found at which the engine runs fastest and smoothest. If the speed rises significantly, use the idle speed adjusting screw to restore it to 730 (or 830) rpm.

17   If adjustments take more than three minutes, clear any excess fuel from the manifold as described in paragraph 14 above.

18   When the idle mixture adjusting screw setting is such that the engine is running, at its fastest, at 730 (or 830) rpm, reduce the idle speed to the standard specified setting by screwing the idle mixture adjusting screw slowly inwards.

19   When the idle speed is correct, stop the engine, disconnect any test equipment and reconnect the electric cooling fan motor(s).

Fuel level check
20   The fuel level can be checked easily by parking the car on a flat, level surface and running the engine at idle speed.

21   The level of petrol in the float chamber should be at the mark(s) on the sight glass or its rim (see Fig. 3.17, and photo).

22   If adjustment is required, remove the carburettor (Section 20).

23   On 1.6 and 1.8 litre models, remove the choke chamber (Section 21). On 2.0 litre models, remove the float chamber cover and sight glass.

24   Invert the choke chamber or (as applicable) carburettor and ensure it is absolutely horizontal.

25   Raise the float, then lower it slowly until the seat just touches the tip of the float needle valve and measure the clearance between the top of the float and the top of the chamber (clearance 'h1', Fig. 3.18).

26   If adjustment is required, carefully bend the float seat until the setting is correct (Figs. 3.19 and 3.20).

27   Next raise the float (carburettor still inverted) until the float stopper touches the pivot post or chamber wall (as applicable) and measure the clearance between the bottom of the float and the base of the float chamber (clearance 'h2', Fig. 3.21). On 1.6 and 1.8 litre models it will be necessary to measure the depth of the chamber from the centre body mating surface (or gasket) and the height of the float bottom above the

choke chamber mating surface (or gasket). Subtract the second measurement from the first to obtain the clearance. Do not forget to include the thickness of the gasket.

28   If adjustment is required, carefully bend the float seat until the setting is correct.

29   Reassemble the carburettor using a new choke chamber or float chamber cover gasket (as applicable) and refit it to the car (Section 20).

30   Recheck the fuel level as described in paragraphs 20 and 21 above.

Fast idle check
31   First warm the engine up to normal operating temperature and ensure that the valve clearances, ignition timing, idle speed and mixture and the fuel level are all correct.

32   Connect a tachometer (if required) following its manufacturer's instructions.

33   Set the fast idle arm's adjusting screw on the second step of the fast idle cam (Fig. 3.22). Start the engine and note the (fast idle) speed obtained.

34   If the speed measured is different from that specified, remove the carburettor (Section 20) and withdraw the choke chamber (Section 21).

35   With the fast idle arm adjusting screw on the second step of the fast idle cam, use a drill bit or similar of suitable size to ensure that the clearance 'A' (Fig. 3.23), between the primary throttle valve and the venturi wall is within the tolerances specified. If adjustment is neces-

17.8 Special screwdriver is required to turn idle mixture adjusting screw

17.21 Note marks for checking fuel level – also idle-up and BCDD control solenoids (arrowed)

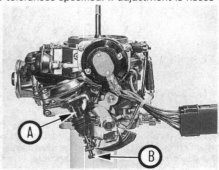

17.41 Dashpot 'A', throttle lever adjusting screw 'B' – 1.6 and 1.8 litre models

17.46 Vacuum break diaphragm 'A', automatic choke heater 'B', choke valve 'C'

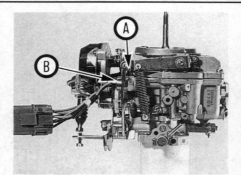

17.56 Accelerator pump linkage 'A', fuel cut solenoid 'B'

17.57 Carburettor wiring harness connector plug

sary, slacken its locknut and screw the fast idle adjusting screw in or out. Tighten the locknut securely when the setting is correct.

36   Reassemble the carburettor and refit to the car (Sections 20 and 21) then repeat the test (paragraphs 31 to 33 above).

Dashpot adjustment

37   First warm up the engine to normal operating temperature and ensure that the valve clearances, ignition timing, accelerator cable adjustment, idle speed and mixture and the fuel level are all correct.
38   Connect a tachometer (if required), following its manufacturer's instructions.
39   With the engine idling, open the throttle pulley/lever slowly by hand until the lever is just touching the dashpot plunger. Note the engine speed at this position.
40   If adjustment is required (see Specifications) remove the carburettor (Section 20) and withdraw the choke chamber (Section 21).
41   Use a drill bit or similar of suitable size to ensure that the clearance 'A', (Fig. 3.23) between the primary throttle valve and the venturi wall is within the tolerances specified, then screw the throttle lever adjusting screw in or out (photo) until it just touches the tip of the dashpot plunger (Fig. 3.24).
42   Reassemble the carburettor and refit it to the car (Sections 20 and 21) then repeat the test (paragraphs 37 to 39 above).

Automatic choke operation

43   With the engine cold, remove the air cleaner cover.
44   Check that the choke valve is fully closed and ensure that it moves smoothly and easily through its full travel (Fig. 3.25).
45   Remove the air cleaner body (Section 5), then check that the groove in the bi-metal cover is aligned with that on the carburettor body (Fig. 3.26). Always align these marks if the assembly is ever dismantled.
46   Check the automatic choke heater wiring and connections (as far as possible), then start the engine and allow it to idle until it has reached normal operating temperature. The choke valve should move smoothly to the fully open position (photo).
47   If the choke valve does not operate correctly, check that full battery voltage is available at the heater terminal when the engine is running. If not, check the lamp check/auto choke relay (Chapter 12 and Fig. 3.27) and wiring until the fault is found.
48   If battery voltage is available, use a multimeter or a dry battery and bulb test circuit to check for continuity between the heater terminal and the carburettor body (Fig. 3.28). If no continuity is found, the heater's bi-metallic spring element is broken and the complete assembly must be renewed.

Vacuum break adjustment

Note: *This test requires a vacuum pump. If one is not available, have the check carried out by a dealer*

49   Check the choke valve is closed, as described in paragraphs 43 and 44 above then remove the air cleaner body (Section 5).
50   Disconnect the rubber tube and apply the specified vacuum to the vacuum break diaphragm (Fig. 3.29).
51   With reference to Fig. 3.30, use a screwdriver to push the linking rod in the direction shown (closing the choke valve) and measure the clearance 'R1'. If this is not within the specified tolerances, bend as necessary the adjusting tongue.

52   With reference to Fig. 3.31, use a screwdriver to push the linking rod back towards the diaphragm until it seats lightly, then measure the clearance 'R2'. If this is incorrect repeat the check and adjust clearance 'R1' more accurately.
53   Release the vacuum and reconnect the rubber tube, then refit the air cleaner (Section 5).

Accelerator pump operation

54   With the engine stopped, remove the air cleaner cover.
55   Fully open the throttle lever and check that the pump injector injects fuel into the primary bore smoothly.
56   If not, check the accelerator pump linkage and piston (Section 21) – photo.

Fuel cut-out (anti-dieseling) solenoid valve operation

57   With the engine idling, disconnect the carburettor wiring (photo); the engine should stop immediately. The internal valve should be heard to close audibly if a battery is connected and disconnected across its wires. Renew the solenoid if it is faulty.

Throttle valve microswitch (automatic transmission) operation

58   To check the switch, disconnect the carburettor wiring and use a multimeter or dry battery and bulb test circuit to check for continuity with the throttle closed or open, testing between the green/black wire terminal and the carburettor body. The switch's contacts are normally open.
59   Renew the switch if it is faulty.

---

18   Boost Controlled Deceleration Device (BCDD) – general

1   This device is fitted to engines with manual transmission (photo). It

18.1 Location of BCDD – 1.6 and 1.8 litre models shown

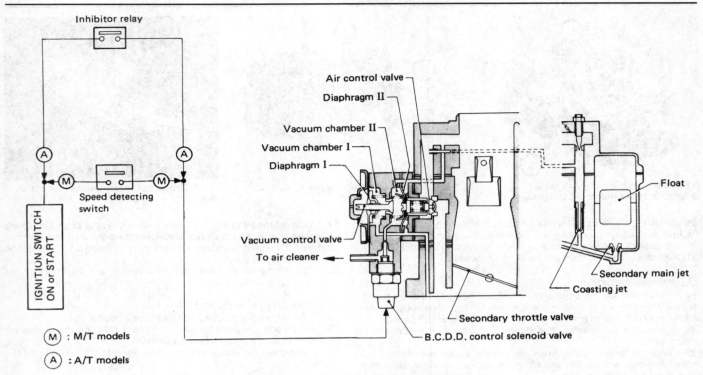

Fig. 3.32 Boost Controlled Deceleration Device (Sec 18)

is designed to reduce the emission of HC (hydrocarbon) and engine oil vapour during deceleration on the overrun with the throttle valve closed. During the period of high intake manifold vacuum, the system operates to admit additional mixture to ensure complete combustion.

2   On engines with automatic transmission, the BCDD is replaced by a solenoid valve, activated by the starter inhibitor/reversing lamp switch (Chapter 7) when the 'N' or 'P' positions are selected.

3   If the device develops a fault, it should be checked by a Nissan dealer.

19   Carburettor idle-up system – general

1   This system increases engine idle speed by 50 to 200 rpm whenever any heavy load is placed on the engine by the power-assisted steering pump or the alternator, to maintain a stable idling speed and

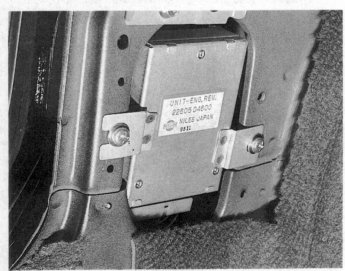

19.3 Location of engine revolution control unit

ensure sufficient battery charging.

2   The system is activated by the power-assisted steering pressure switch (Chapter 10), the heater fan switch (Chapters 11 and 12), the electric cooling fan number 1 thermostatic switch (Chapter 2) and by the lighting switch (Chapter 12).

3   The system is controlled by the engine revolution control unit (Chapter 12) which is located behind the footwell left-hand side trim panel (photo).

4   When activated by one of the switches, the control unit retracts a solenoid-operated valve to open a mixture bypass passage.

5   If the idle speed does not increase whenever any of the switches are activated, test the switch as described in the relevant Chapter of this manual.

6   To test the idle-up solenoid valve, disconnect the carburettor wiring and connect a 12 volt battery across the valve's wires. The valve should be heard to click on or off as the battery is connected and disconnected. Renew the valve if faulty.

7   If the control unit is thought to be faulty it can be tested only by the substitution of a known serviceable unit (Chapter 12).

20   Carburettor – removal and refitting

1   Refer to the warnings given in Section 2 before starting work.
2   Remove the air cleaner (Section 5).
3   Disconnect the fuel hose and plug it (photo).
4   Disconnect the accelerator cable (Section 13).
5   Disconnect the carburettor wiring.
6   Disconnect the distributor vacuum hose.
7   Unscrew the four mounting nuts and remove the carburettor from the intake (inlet) manifold. Plug the intake with a wad of clean cloth.
8   Refitting is a reversal of removal, but use a new mounting flange gasket.

21   Carburettor – overhaul

1   Refer to the warnings given in Section 2 before starting work.
2   It is rare for the carburettor to require complete dismantling; indeed,

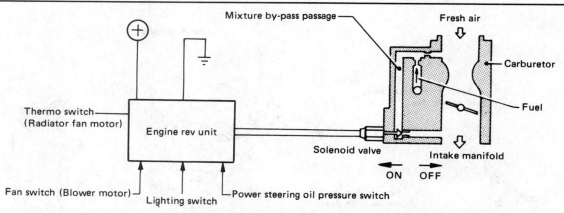

Fig. 3.33 Idle-up system (Sec 19)

where this is required, then it would probably be more economical to renew the complete unit. Normally it will be sufficient to remove the choke chamber and clean the float chamber and jets.

3 Before removing the carburettor, check the fuel level (Section 17).

4 With the carburettor removed, clean away external dirt.

5 Disconnect the accelerator pump and choke fast idle linkages and disconnect the return springs.

6 Extract the screws and lift the choke chamber from the carburettor body. Remove the gasket.

7 On the DCR carburettor, extract the screws and remove the sight glass, surround, and float.

8 Unscrew and remove the jets with reference to Figs. 3.34, 3.35 and 3.38, noting the location of each jet. **Do not** disturb the position of the throttle and idle mixture adjusting screws.

9 Clean the jets with air from a tyre pump – on no account probe them with wire, or their calibration will be ruined. Check the float and the inlet needle valve for damage and wear. If necessary, extract the screws and detach the throttle chamber from the main body.

10 With the carburettor dismantled and worn parts renewed, obtain a repair kit which will contain all the necessary new gaskets and other renewable items.

11 Reassembly is a reversal of dismantling, but if the fuel level needs adjustment, this can be checked during the course of reassembly as can the fast idle linkage setting, the dashpot setting and vacuum break (Section 17).

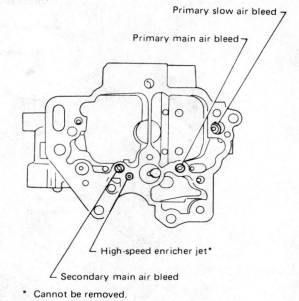

* Cannot be removed.

Fig. 3.34 Location of jets (choke chamber) – 2.0 litre models (Sec 21)

20.3 Disconnect and plug the fuel hose (arrowed)

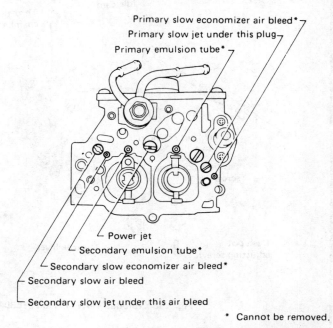

* Cannot be removed.

Fig. 3.35 Location of jets (centre body) – 2.0 litre models (Sec 21)

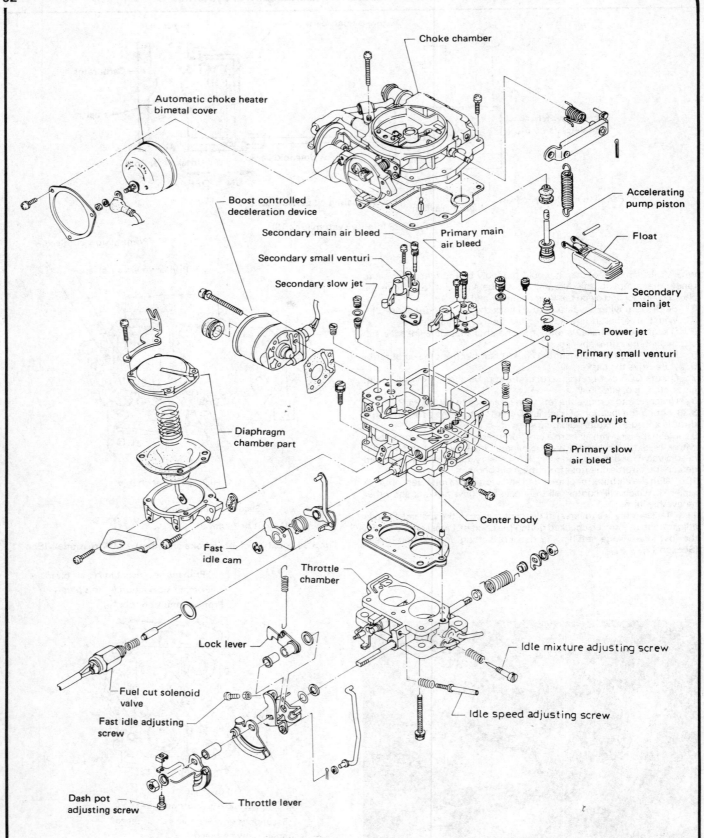

Automatic choke heater bimetal cover

Choke chamber

Boost controlled deceleration device

Secondary main air bleed

Secondary small venturi

Secondary slow jet

Primary main air bleed

Accelerating pump piston

Float

Secondary main jet

Power jet

Primary small venturi

Diaphragm chamber part

Primary slow jet

Primary slow air bleed

Center body

Fast idle cam

Throttle chamber

Lock lever

Idle mixture adjusting screw

Fuel cut solenoid valve

Fast idle adjusting screw

Idle speed adjusting screw

Dash pot adjusting screw

Throttle lever

Fig. 3.36 Exploded view of Nikki 21E304 carburettor – 1.6 and 1.8 litre models (Sec 21)

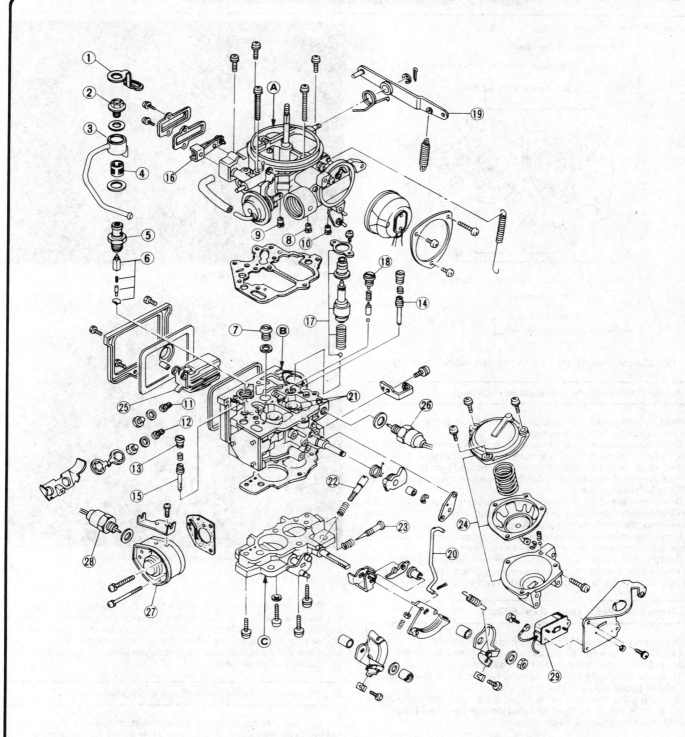

Fig. 3.37 Exploded view of Hitachi DCR342 carburettor – 2.0 litre models (Sec 21)

A	Choke chamber	8	Primary main air bleed	18	Plug	25	Float
B	Centre body	9	Secondary main air bleed	19	Accelerator pump lever	26	Fuel cut-out (anti-dieseling) solenoid valve
C	Throttle chamber	10	Primary slow air bleed	20	Accelerator pump link rod	27	BCDD – manual transmission
1	Locking tab	11	Primary main jet	21	Primary and secondary small venturis	28	BCDD control solenoid valve
2	Banjo bolt	12	Secondary main jet	22	Idle speed adjusting screw	29	Throttle valve microswitch (automatic transmission)
3	Banjo union	13	Secondary slow air bleed	23	Idle mixture adjusting screw		
4	Fuel filter	14	Primary slow jet	24	Diaphragm assembly		
5	Float needle valve body	15	Secondary slow jet				
6	Float needle assembly	16	Idle compensator				
7	Power valve	17	Accelerator pump assembly				

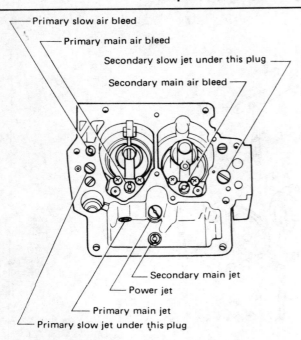

— Primary slow air bleed
— Primary main air bleed
Secondary slow jet under this plug —
Secondary main air bleed —

Secondary main jet
Power jet
Primary main jet
Primary slow jet under this plug

Fig. 3.38 Location of jets – 1.6 and 1.8 litre models (Sec 21)

23.2 Exhaust manifold and heat shield

23.4 Always renew exhaust system flange gaskets

22 Intake (inlet) manifold – removal and refitting

1　Refer to the warnings given in Section 2 before starting work.
2　Disconnect the battery negative lead.
3　Drain the cooling system, then disconnect the cooling system (and heater, where applicable) hoses from the manifold (Chapter 2). Note that the thermostat and its housing cover will be removed with the manifold.
4　Remove the carburettor (Section 20). Disconnect the oil separator-to-PCV valve breather hose.
5　Disconnect the spark plug leads and the coolant temperature gauge sensor wire, also the vacuum servo unit vacuum hose (Chapter 9) and, where fitted, the econometer vacuum hose.
6　Undo the manifold retaining nuts and bolts and withdraw the manifold from the cylinder head studs. Recover the gasket.
7　Refitting is the reverse sequence to removal but use a new gasket and ensure that the mating faces are clean. Tighten the manifold nuts and bolts to the specified torque. Refill the cooling system (Chapter 2).

23 Exhaust manifold – removal and refitting

1　Disconnect the exhaust downpipe from the manifold.
2　Disconnect the warm air intake (inlet) hose from the manifold heat shield, and unbolt the heat shield if required (photo).
3　Undo the manifold retaining nuts and withdraw the manifold from the cylinder head studs. Recover the gasket.
4　Refitting is the reverse of removal, but use a new gasket (photo) and ensure that the mating surfaces and stud threads are clean. Tighten the manifold nuts to the specified torque.

24 Exhaust system – removal and refitting

1　The exhaust system is in three sections with a braided flexible joint beneath the rear of the engine. The sections are connected by flange joints with gaskets (Fig. 3.39).
2　To remove the exhaust system, position the car over an inspection pit or jack it up and support on axle stands. Unscrew the nuts and separate the downpipe from the exhaust manifold. Unbolt the sections, then release the mounting rubbers and remove the system (photos).
3　If removal of the intermediate or tail sections is complicated by the anti-roll bar, unbolt the anti-roll bar mounting clamps, slacken the bar-to-connecting link (front) or strut (rear) nuts or bolts and swing the bar down (Chapter 10).

4　When fitting the exhaust, renew the flange gaskets as a matter of course, and the mounting rubbers as necessary. Make sure that no component of the system is likely to touch adjacent parts of the bodyframe or suspension when deflected within the full extent of movement of its flexible mounting. Note the location of the earth strap on the central flange bolt (photo).

25 Positive Crankcase Ventilation (PCV) system – general

1　The positive crankcase ventilation system reduces emissions of unburned hydrocarbons (HC) into the atmosphere by using fresh air to return blow-by gases and oil vapour from the crankcase into the intake (inlet) tract to be burned.
2　The system requires that the crankcase be sealed, and employs a sealed oil filler cap and dipstick.
3　The system consists of a connecting hose from the air intake (inlet) to the rocker cover, an oil separator containing a steel mesh which collects oil droplets and allows them to drain back to the sump, and the one-way PCV valve which is screwed into the intake (inlet) manifold downstream of the throttle valve. The valve will admit gases only into the manifold; it will not permit flow in the reverse direction.
4　Under conditions of high manifold depression (idling, deceleration) the gases will be positively sucked out of the crankcase and into the intake (inlet) manifold, to be replaced by fresh air from the air intake (inlet).

24.2A Exhaust system
downpipe-to-manifold retaining nuts

24.2B Downpipe-to-intermediate section
flange joint and mounting

24.2C Rear silencer rubber mounting

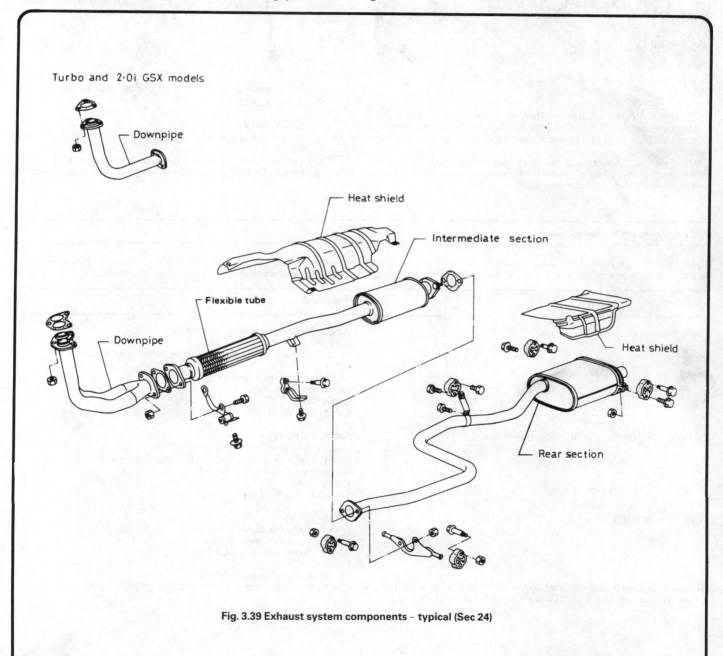

Fig. 3.39 Exhaust system components – typical (Sec 24)

24.4 Earth strap at intermediate to rear section flange joint

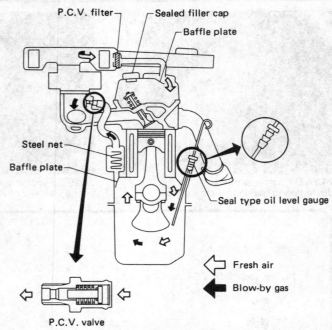

Fig. 3.40 PCV system (Sec 25)

5   Under conditions of low manifold depression (acceleration, full throttle) the gases will be forced, by the higher crankcase pressure, through the PCV valve and back through the air intake (inlet) hose into the air filter.

6   If the engine is worn and has raised crankcase pressure due to excessive blow-by, some of the flow will return through the air intake (inlet) connection under all conditions.

7   The PCV filter is fitted to stop dirt etc getting into the crankcase and to prevent the air cleaner element from being fouled excessively with oil.

---

26   Fault diagnosis – fuel system

Note: High fuel consumption and poor performance are not necessarily due to fuel system faults. Make sure that the ignition system is properly adjusted, that the brakes are not binding and that the engine is in good mechanical condition before tampering with the fuel system.

Symptom	Reason(s)
Fuel consumption excessive	Air cleaner choked, giving rich mixture Leak from tank, pump or fuel lines Float chamber flooding due to incorrect level or worn needle valve Carburettor incorrectly adjusted Idle speed too high Choke faulty Excessively worn carburettor
Lack of power, stalling or difficult starting	Faulty fuel pump Leak on suction side of pump or in fuel line Intake (inlet) manifold or carburettor flange gaskets leaking Carburettor incorrectly adjusted Faulty choke Emission control system defect
Poor or erratic idling	Weak mixture Leak in intake manifold Leak in distributor vacuum pipe Leak in crankcase ventilation hose Leak in brake servo hose Emission control system defect

Note: This Section is not intended to be an exhaustive guide to fault diagnosis but summarises a few of the more common faults which may be encountered during a car's life. Consult a dealer for more specific advice.

PART B: TURBO ENGINES

27 General description

Note: *Some basic checks of the system components are included in this Chapter. However, the complexity of the system prevents many problems from being accurately diagnosed by the home mechanic. If a problem develops in the system which cannot be pinpointed by the checks listed here, it is best to take the vehicle to a Nissan dealer to locate the fault.*

The components of the fuel injection system are shown in Fig. 3.41, with Fig. 3.42 showing how they are interconnected.

The complete system covers both fuel and ignition systems. Components of the ignition system are covered in detail in Chapter 4, but are also mentioned here at several points because of the multiple roles performed by some of them. The fuel system is best understood if it is considered as three sub-systems; the fuel delivery system, the air metering or induction system and the electrical signalling system.

Fuel from the tank is delivered under pressure by an electric fuel pump. The amount of fuel to be injected is determined by the injection pulse duration as well as by the difference between fuel pressure and intake (inlet) manifold depression. The Electronic Concentrated Control System (ECCS) control unit controls only the injection pulse duration. For this reason, the difference between the fuel pressure and intake (inlet) manifold depression must be maintained at a constant level. Since the intake (inlet) manifold depression varies with engine operating conditions, a pressure regulator is placed in the fuel line to regulate the fuel pressure in response to changes in the intake (inlet) manifold pressure. Where manifold conditions are such that the fuel pressure could be beyond that specified, the pressure regulator returns surplus fuel to the tank.

An injection of fuel occurs twice each engine cycle. Because the injection signal comes from the control unit, all four injectors operate simultaneously and independent of the engine stroke. Each injection supplies half the amount of fuel required by the cylinder, and the length of the injection period is determined by information fed to the control unit by various sensors included in the system.

Elements affecting the injection duration include engine speed and piston position (distributor/crank angle sensor, Chapter 4), amount of incoming air (airflow meter), engine temperature (water temperature sensor, Chapter 2) and throttle valve position (throttle valve switch). Mixture enrichment for starting and warm-up and for acceleration or heavy engine loads is provided by varying the injector pulse width according to information pre-programmed into the ECCS control unit.

The system's components function as follows:

ECCS control unit

The Electronic Concentrated Control System (ECCS) control unit, also known as the Engine Control Unit (ECU), is a microcomputer with electrical connectors for receiving input/output signals and for power supply, inspection lamps and a diagnostic mode selector. The control unit regulates the amount of fuel that is injected, as well as the ignition timing, idle speed, fuel pump operation and the feedback of the mixture ratio.

Turbocharger

The turbocharger, installed on the exhaust manifold, is designed to compress the intake air flowing from the air cleaner. The turbocharger uses two turbines. One turbine, situated in the exhaust gas flow, is turned by the gases leaving the exhaust manifold. It then turns the other turbine, which compresses the intake air and sends it into the intake (inlet) manifold.

To prevent the boost pressure from becoming excessive, the system is equipped with a bypass valve (wastegate) which opens at a predetermined pressure to allow exhaust gases to bypass the turbocharger and go straight into the exhaust pipe.

Emergency relief valve

To prevent an abnormal rise in boost pressure, and possible engine damage, in case the bypass valve should fail to open properly, an emergency ('pop- off') valve is installed as a safety device in the intake (inlet) manifold. The valve opens when the pressure in the intake manifold is above that specified.

Distributor/crank angle sensor

See Chapter 4.

Airflow meter

The airflow meter measures the mass flow rate of intake air and incorporates the idle mixture adjusting screw. The control circuit emits an electrical output signal which varies in relation to the amount of heat dissipated from a hot wire placed in the stream of intake air.

Water temperature sensor

See Chapter 2.

Throttle valve switch

The throttle valve switch is bolted to the left-hand side of the throttle chamber and actuates in response to accelerator pedal movement. The switch is equipped with a contact for the idle position. The contact closes when the throttle valve is positioned at idle and opens when it is at any other position.

Dashpot

The throttle dashpot is an emission control device which delays throttle closure on lifting the accelerator pedal, thus ensuring that all fuel remaining in the intake (inlet) manifold is burned, rather than passed straight into the exhaust.

Detonation (knock) sensor

See Chapter 4.

Fuel injector

The fuel injector, which supplies each cylinder with fuel, is a small, precision solenoid valve. As the ECCS control unit sends the signal to each fuel injector, the coil built into the injector pulls the needle valve back and fuel is sprayed through the nozzle into the intake (inlet) manifold. The amount of fuel injected is controlled by the ECCS control unit by injection pulse duration.

Power transistor

See Chapter 4.

Ignition HT coil

See Chapter 4.

Fuel pump

The fuel pump, which is located in the fuel tank, is a wet type pump where the vane rollers are directly coupled to a motor which is filled with fuel.

Air regulator

The air regulator gives an air bypass when the engine is cold to allow fast idle during warm-up. A bi-metal heater and rotary shutter are built into the air regulator. When the bi-metal temperature is low, the air bypass port is open. As the engine starts and electric current flows through a heater, the bi-metal begins to rotate the shutter to close off the bypass port. The air passage remains closed until the engine is stopped and the bi-metal temperature drops.

IAA unit

The Idle Air Adjusting (IAA) unit is mounted on the right-hand end of the inlet manifold and controls idle speed by regulating the amount of air that bypasses the throttle valve. Activated by the ECCS control unit only when the throttle valve switch contact is closed, the IAA unit regulates the air according to signals from the control unit, which determines the best idle speed for the current engine temperature, engine speed and gear position from information pre-programmed into it. The IAA unit incorporates the idle speed adjusting screw, the vacuum control valve, the idle-up control solenoid valve and, on Turbo Executive models, the FICD solenoid valve.

Idle-up solenoid valve

The idle-up solenoid valve is screwed into the IAA unit. The solenoid is actuated to stabilize idle speed when the engine load is heavy from

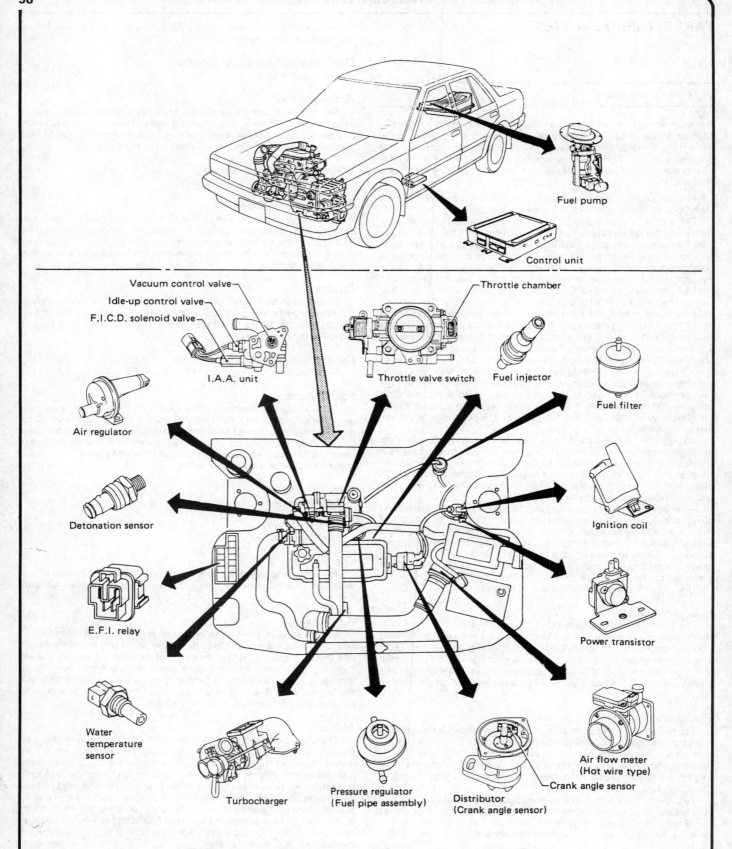

Fuel pump

Control unit

Vacuum control valve

Idle-up control valve

F.I.C.D. solenoid valve

Throttle chamber

I.A.A. unit

Throttle valve switch

Fuel injector

Fuel filter

Air regulator

Detonation sensor

E.F.I. relay

Ignition coil

Power transistor

Water temperature sensor

Turbocharger

Pressure regulator (Fuel pipe assembly)

Distributor (Crank angle sensor)

Air flow meter (Hot wire type)

Crank angle sensor

Fig. 3.41 Location of Turbo engine management system components (Sec 27)

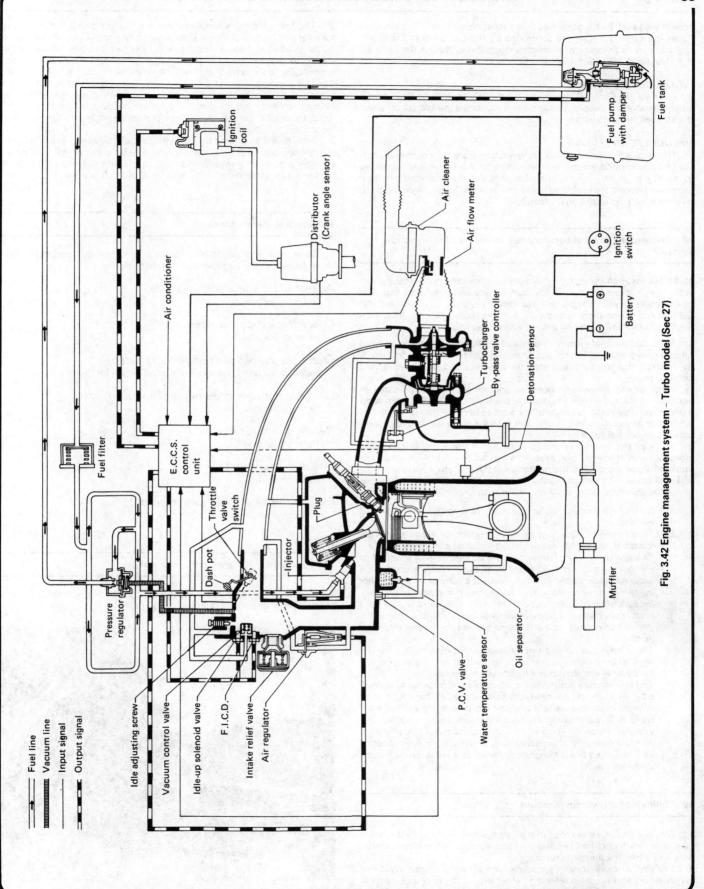

Fig. 3.42 Engine management system – Turbo model (Sec 27)

accessories such as the power-assisted steering pump or the alternator. Apart from the fact that it is controlled by the ECCS control unit and regulates an air bypass rather than mixture, the system is the same as that described in Section 19 of this Chapter.

FICD solenoid valve

The Fast Idle Control Device (FICD) is exactly the same as the idle-up solenoid valve but supplementary to it. It increases the idle speed when the air conditioning system is in use.

Vacuum control valve

The vacuum control valve is provided to reduce the engine lubricating oil consumption when the intake (inlet) manifold vacuum increases to a very high level during deceleration. As the manifold vacuum increases beyond the specified value, the valve will open, allowing air to be drawn into the intake (inlet) manifold.

28   Precautions to be observed when servicing a fuel injection system

Note: *The instructions and warnings below are* **additional** *to those given in Section 2 of this Chapter. Before starting any servicing work read first that Section for information on basic safety precautions, then read this Section for information relevant to fuel injection systems. Note also Section 53 of this Chapter on turbocharger precautions.*

1   Note that the fuel system consists of the fuel tank, with its cap and related hoses, the fuel pump and filter, the fuel feed and return hoses, the fuel rail, the pressure regulator, the injectors and any other related components.
2   Most of the above components contain fuel under pressure in normal use; always relieve any residual pressure (Section 29), then wrap a paper towel or clean rag around the joint to prevent fuel spraying out whenever any component is disturbed, and wear suitable eye protection to prevent personal injury.
3   Because the system operates at high fuel pressure, any leak can affect system efficiency and present a serious fire risk. Also, since the intake air flow is critical to the operation of the system, even a slight air leak will cause an incorrect air/fuel mixture. **Note:** *Certain precautions should be observed when working on the system:*

(a) *Do not disconnect either battery cable while the engine is running.*
(b) *Prior to removing any system component, be sure the ignition switch is Off and the negative battery cable is disconnected.*
(c) *The system's wiring harness should be kept at least four inches (10 mm) away from adjacent harnesses. This includes a CB antenna feeder cable. This is to prevent electrical pulses in other systems from interfering with the injection system's operation.*
(d) *Be sure all wiring connections are tight, clean and secure, as a poor connection can cause extremely high voltage surges in the ignition coil which could damage the ignition system components.*
(e) *The accelerator should* **not** *be depressed prior to starting the engine. Immediately after starting,* **do not** *rev the engine unnecessarily and* **do not** *rev it just before switching off.*
(f) *The idle mixture adjustment screw is sealed by a 'tamperproof' plug. In some EC countries (though not yet in the UK) it is an offence to drive a vehicle with broken or missing tamperproof seals. Before disturbing a tamperproof seal, satisfy yourself that you will not be breaking any local or national laws by doing so, and fit a new seal after adjustment is complete where required by law. Do not break tamperproof seals on a vehicle which is still under warranty.*

29   Relieving fuel system pressure

1   Owners should remember that all components of the fuel system from the tank to the fuel rail and injectors contain fuel which is under pressure when the engine is running.
2   The pressure will remain for some time after the engine has been switched off and must be relieved before any of these components is disturbed for servicing work.

3   The first method is simply to remove the fuel pump fuse from the fuse panel (Chapter 12), then start the engine and allow it to idle until it stops. When the engines dies, turn it over two or three times on the starter to ensure that fuel pressure is released, then switch off the ignition. Do not forget to refit the fuse when work is complete.
4   The second method can be used if the engine has just been switched off. Disconnect the pressure regulator vacuum hose from the intake manifold vacuum stub and suck as hard as possible to open the regulator diaphragm. The pressure will then disperse into the fuel tank. Reconnect the vacuum hose.
5   Note that with both of these methods fuel may still be present in the system components; it will merely no longer be under pressure. Take all suitable precautions (see Section 28) to prevent the risk of fire or of personal injury when working on any part of the fuel system.

30   Routine maintenance

Carry out the following procedures at the intervals given in *'Routine maintenance'* at the beginning of this manual.

Adjust idling speed and mixture
Refer to Section 41.

Check the exhaust system
Refer to Section 3.

Check the crankcase ventilation system
Refer to Section 3, with reference to Section 59.

Check the engine breather and vacuum hoses
Refer to Section 3.

Renew the fuel filter
Refer to Section 33.

Check the fuel system
Refer to Section 3.

Renew the air cleaner filter element
Refer to Section 31.

31   Air cleaner filter element – renewal

1   To remove the element, unscrew the six retaining screws at the top of the cleaner housing and lift the cover (photo).

31.1 Remove retaining screws to release air cleaner cover

31.2 Lift cover and withdraw element – note 'UP' marking

32.3 Air cleaner cover is joined to intake (inlet) duct in front wing

2   Carefully lift the element out of the housing (photo).
3   The genuine Nissan element does not require cleaning between the specified renewal intervals; if non-genuine elements are used they can be cleaned as described in Section 3.
4   Fit the new (or cleaned) element in the housing ('UP' mark upwards), lower the cover and tighten the screws securely.

32 Air cleaner – removal and refitting

1   Remove the air cleaner filter element (Section 31).
2   Withdraw the cover from the wing-mounted intake (inlet) duct (photo).
3   Slacken the clamp and release the air intake (inlet) duct from the airflow meter.
4   Release the wire clip and unplug the wiring connector from the airflow meter.
5   Unbolt the air cleaner housing from the inner wing panel and withdraw it, complete with the airflow meter. The meter can be unbolted if required.
6   Refitting is the reverse of removal.

33 Fuel filter – renewal

1   Refer to the warnings given in Sections 2 and 28 before starting work.
2   Relieve fuel system pressure (Section 29).
3   Renew the filter as described in Section 7.

34 Fuel pump/fuel gauge sender unit – removal, testing and refitting

1   Refer to the warnings given in Sections 2 and 28 before starting work.
2   Relieve fuel system pressure (Section 29).
3   Disconnect the battery negative lead.
4   Remove the rear seat base and back cushions (Chapter 11).
5   Extract the four screws and remove the cover plate, taking care not to damage the wiring (photo).
6   Disconnect the wiring harness (photo).
7   Disconnect the fuel feed hose from the top of the pump and plug it.
8   Remove the retaining screws and carefully withdraw the unit, taking care not to damage it.

9   Refitting is the reverse of removal, but fit a new O-ring.
10   The fuel gauge sender unit can be tested as described in Section 9.
11   The fuel pump should be tested only with the pump installed in the tank and its connecting hose securely fastened. Connect a 12 volt battery to the pump wires (Fig. 3.43); if the pump does not work it is faulty and must be renewed.

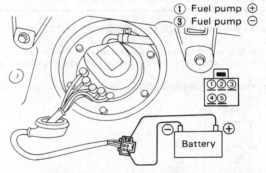
① Fuel pump ⊕
③ Fuel pump ⊖

Fig. 3.43 Checking the electric fuel pump (Sec 34)

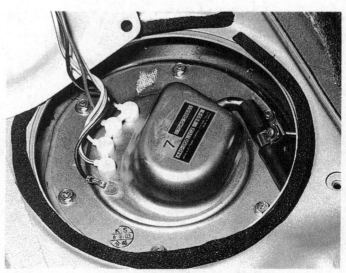
34.5 Remove cover plate to reach fuel pump/fuel gauge sender unit

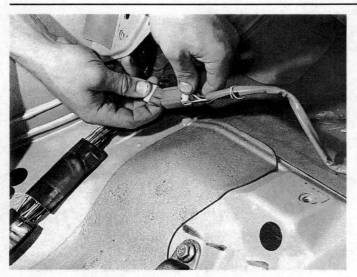

34.6 Disconnecting fuel pump/fuel gauge sender unit wiring

12   Note that on some models the fuel pump circuit is fitted with a relay, located in the engine compartment relay holder (Chapter 12), that is designed so that should the engine stop (causing the alternator to turn off and the oil pressure to drop), the fuel pump will cease to operate.

35   Fuel tank – removal, repair and refitting

1   Refer to the warnings given in Sections 2 and 28 before starting work.
2   Relieve fuel system pressure as described in Section 29.
3   Remove or disconnect the fuel pump/fuel gauge sender unit (Section 34).
4   The remainder of the procedure is as described in Section 10.

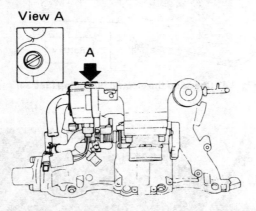

Fig. 3.44 Location of idle speed adjusting screw (Sec 41)

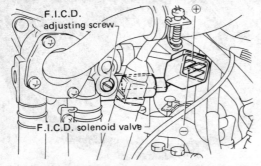

Fig. 3.45 Location of FICD components – Executive (Sec 41)

36   Evaporative emission control system – general

Refer to Section 11.

37   Accelerator cable – adjustment

Refer to Section 12.

38   Accelerator cable – removal and refitting

Noting that there is no need to remove the air cleaner, proceed as described in Section 13.

39   Accelerator pedal – removal and refitting

Refer to Section 14.

40   Unleaded petrol – general

1   Refer first to Section 15.
2   **Do not** use Premium grade unleaded petrol (or retard the ignition timing) in Turbo or Turbo Executive models; the engine's minimum octane requirement is 97 RON.
3   At the time of writing, the only petrol of this octane, and approved to BS, on sale in the UK is 4-star leaded.
4   Owners should note, however, that (if the manufacturer's claims are to be believed) the Super/Super Plus grades of unleaded petrol do have suitable octane ratings. Check with the oil company concerned or with Nissan themselves as to whether this petrol can be used in Turbo models.
5   Note that the Turbo engine is fitted with toughened valve seats and can therefore accept the continuous use of unleaded, as long as a petrol of high enough octane rating is available.

41   Fuel injection system adjustments

1   Refer to the warnings given in Sections 2 and 28 before starting work.
2   Park the car on a flat surface, apply the handbrake firmly and chock the roadwheels, then select neutral.

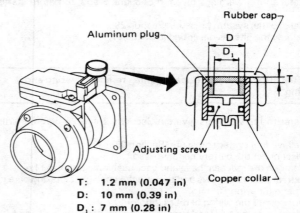

T: 1.2 mm (0.047 in)
D: 10 mm (0.39 in)
D_1:   7 mm (0.28 in)

Fig. 3.46 Idle mixture adjusting screw tamperproof plug details (Sec 41)

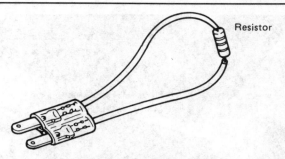

Fig. 3.47 2.5 k ohm resistor and adaptor harness required when adjusting idle mixture (Sec 41)

3   Ensure that the valve clearances and ignition timing are correctly set, then disconnect the electric cooling fan motor(s).

4   The idle mixture is set during production and therefore it is normally only the idle speed which may require adjustment. The mixture adjusting screw is fitted with a tamperproof plug which must be removed to make an adjustment.

Idle speed adjustment

5   Warm the engine up to normal operating temperature.

6   Check that the electric cooling fan motor(s) is disconnected and switch off all lights and other electrical accessories, including the air conditioning system, where fitted.

7   Make up a wiring adaptor as shown in Chapter 4, Fig. 4.16, or obtain one from a Nissan dealer, then connect it as shown. Connect a tachometer.

8   Race the engine at between 2000 and 3000 rpm two or three times, then allow it to idle for one minute.

9   Check that the idle speed is within the specified range. If adjustment is required turn the idle speed adjusting screw in the rear of the IAA unit (Fig. 3.44).

FICD speed adjustment

10   Prepare the car and check the idle speed as described above; adjust it if necessary.

11   When the basic idle speed is correct, switch on the air conditioning system and check that the idle speed increases to that specified. If adjustment is required, turn the FICD adjusting screw in the right-hand side of the IAA unit (Fig. 3.45).

12   If the idle speed does not increase, stop the engine and disconnect the FICD solenoid valve wiring at its connector plug. Then connect a battery across the wire terminals; the solenoid valve should be heard to click open and closed as the battery is connected and disconnected. If the solenoid valve is faulty it must be renewed.

Idle mixture adjustment

13   If the mixture must be adjusted due to a change in engine characteristics (carbon build up, bore wear etc), adjust the idle speed first, then stop the engine.

14   Note that the idle mixture should be checked using a CO meter (exhaust gas analyser). If this is not available the car should be taken to a

41.17 Idle mixture adjusting screw in beneath tamperproof plug in airflow meter

Nissan dealer for the work to be done. For emergency use a basic setting procedure is given which will enable the car to start and run until it can be checked by a competent mechanic using proper test equipment. An accurate tachometer and a 2.5 k ohm resistor are required.

15   To check the idle mixture, first warm the engine up to normal operating temperature and ensure that the valve clearances, ignition timing and idle speed are correct, as described above.

16   Connect the CO meter following its manufacturer's instructions and check the CO level at idle speed. If adjustment is required proceed as follows:

17   Remove the rubber cap from the mixture adjusting screw (photo), then carefully drill a small hole in the aluminium plug and prise it out (Fig. 3.46).

18   Disconnect the water temperature sensor wiring (photos) and connect a 2500 ohm resistor across the connector terminals (Fig. 3.47).

19   With the engine at its normal operating temperature, first clear any excess fuel from the inlet manifold as described in paragraph 8 above. Repeat this at intervals if any adjustments take more than three minutes to complete. Recheck the CO level.

20   The CO level should have increased significantly, since the fitting of the resistor has fooled the ECCS control unit into thinking that the engine is cold, when it is actually fully warmed up, and the injection system is therefore delivering enriched mixture for starting and warm-up.

21   Turn the idle mixture adjusting screw (which is actually a variable resistor) **gently** and in small increments until the CO level is reduced to less than 8%. Switch off the engine, remove the resistor and reconnect the water temperature sensor.

22   Restart the engine, clear any excess fuel from the intake (inlet) manifold as described in paragraph 8 above, then recheck the CO level

41.18A Disconnect wiring from water temperature sensor ...

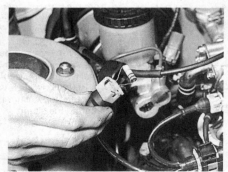

41.18B ... and fit resistor when adjusting idle mixture

41.29 Throttle pulley/lever and dashpot

and idle speed; both should be correct. Stop the engine, disconnect any test equipment and fit a new tamperproof plug to the airflow meter, then refit the rubber cap. Reconnect the electric cooling fan motor(s).

23   To set the idle mixture without a CO meter first connect an accurate tachometer (paragraph 7) and prepare the car as described in paragraph 15 above.

24   Stop the engine and remove the tamperproof plug from the airflow meter then insert a 2.5 k ohm resistor as described in paragraphs 17 and 18 above. Start the engine and clear any excess fuel from the intake (inlet) manifold as described in paragraph 8 above.

25   Gently turn the idle mixture adjusting screw each way until the fastest idle speed is obtained, then stop the engine, remove the resistor and reconnect the water temperature sensor.

26   Restart the engine and clear any excess fuel from the intake (inlet) manifold (paragraph 8) then check the idle speed and reduce it, if necessary, to that specified using the idle speed adjusting screw (paragraph 9).

27   Stop the engine and reconnect the electric cooling fan motor(s). Do not fit a new tamperproof plug until the mixture has been checked using a CO meter.

Dashpot adjustment

28   First warm up the engine to normal operating temperature and ensure that the valve clearances, ignition timing, idle speed and mixture and accelerator cable adjustments are all correct.

29   With the engine idling, open the throttle pulley slowly by hand until the lever is just touching the dashpot plunger. Note the (dashpot touch) engine speed at this point (photo).

30   If adjustment is required, screw the throttle lever adjusting screw in or out until the setting is correct.

Throttle valve switch adjustment

31   The switch must be set so that its contacts open at 900 ± 250 rpm.

32   Connect an accurate tachometer to the engine following its manufacturer's instructions and using, if required, the adaptor shown in Chapter 4, Fig. 4.16.

33   Release the wire clip securing the throttle valve switch connector plug, then start the engine and allow it to idle.

34   Slacken the switch mounting bolts and keep the engine running at a fast idle while the connector is unplugged and a multimeter set to the resistance function (or a battery and bulb test circuit) is connected across the switch's terminals.

35   There should be continuity across the switch terminals (29 and 30) when the throttle valve is closed to the idle position. When the valve is opened slightly, the contacts should open so that there is no continuity. Renew the switch if it is faulty.

36   Hold the engine at a speed of 950 ± 250 rpm, then slowly rotate the switch from the idle position until its contacts open. Hold it steady at that point and tighten the bolts.

37   Recheck the setting before stopping the engine, disconnecting the test equipment and reconnecting the switch wiring.

---

42   ECCS control unit – general

The control unit is located under the passenger seat. Refer to Chapter 12.

---

43   Airflow meter – removal and refitting

1   Slacken the clamps and withdraw the air intake (inlet) duct from the front of the airflow meter.

2   Release the wire clip and unplug the wiring connector from the airflow meter (photo).

3   Unbolt the airflow meter from the front of the air cleaner housing.

4   Note that the airflow meter's hot wire (photo) is fragile; ensure it is clean and undamaged.

5   Refitting is the reverse of removal, using a new gasket. If a new unit has been fitted, check the idle speed and mixture as soon as possible (Section 41).

43.2 Airflow meter is mounted on front of air cleaner housing

43.4 Do not disturb airflow meter hot wire

---

44   Air intake (inlet) ducting and resonator assembly – removal and refitting

1   A series of moulded plastic or rubber ducts is used to conduct intake (inlet) air from the air cleaner and airflow meter to the turbocharger and from the turbocharger to the intake (inlet) manifold or IAA unit.

2   Note that whenever any part of the air intake (inlet) ducting is disturbed, always pack the openings with clean rag to prevent the entry of dirt or debris. Do not forget to remove the rag on reassembly.

3   To remove any part of the ducting, release or slacken the clamps securing each end, unbolt the mounting brackets from the body front panel (where applicable) and withdraw it.

4   Refitting is the reverse of removal. Where a rubber seal or gasket is used (photo), ensure it is correctly located on the mating stub before securing the clamp.

---

45   Throttle chamber – removal and refitting

1   Slacken the clamps and withdraw the turbocharger-to-throttle chamber air intake (inlet) tube and IAA unit bypass tube (Section 44).

2   Disconnect the accelerator cable from the throttle pulley (Refer to Section 38).

3   Release the wire clip and unplug the wiring connector from the throttle valve switch.

4   Check that the engine and radiator have completely cooled down, then remove the radiator cap to release any residual cooling system pressure. Slacken the clamps and disconnect the small diameter coolant hoses from beneath the throttle chamber. Place a layer of rag to catch as much as possible of the small amount of coolant that will escape. Plug the hose ends to prevent dirt entering the cooling system.

5   Unbolt the throttle chamber from the intake (inlet) manifold and withdraw it.

6   Refitting is a reverse of removal, noting the following points:

   (a) *Always fit a new throttle chamber gasket and tighten to the specified torque setting the four Allen bolts*

   (b) *Reconnect the coolant hoses and top up the cooling system to replace any spilt coolant (Chapter 2)*

   (c) *If a new unit has been fitted, check the throttle valve switch setting (Section 41)*

46   Throttle valve switch – removal and refitting

1   Mark the relationship of the switch to the throttle chamber, if it is to be refitted.

2   Release the wire clip and unplug the wiring connector from the switch.

3   Remove the two bolts (photo) and lift the throttle valve switch from the throttle chamber. **Note:** *Any time the throttle valve switch bolts are loosened it will be necessary to readjust the switch.*

4   Reverse the removal procedures for installation but do not tighten the switch bolts yet.

5   Set the switch position as described in Section 41.

47   IAA unit – removal and refitting

1   Disconnect the battery negative lead.

2   Disconnect the air intake (inlet) bypass tube from the IAA unit (Section 45) and slacken the clamps securing the air regulator bypass hoses.

3   Disconnect the IAA unit wiring connector plug(s) (photo).

4   Unbolt the IAA unit from the intake (inlet) manifold and withdraw it, separating it from the air regulator hoses.

5   Do not attempt to dismantle the IAA unit. The vacuum control valve should be available separately (check with your dealer), but not the idle-up control or FICD solenoid valves. If any of these components is thought to be faulty, seek the advice of a Nissan dealer.

6   Refitting is the reverse of removal, using a new gasket and tightening the bolts to the specified torque setting. If a new unit has been fitted, the idle speed and mixture will require checking (Section 41).

48   Air regulator – removal, testing and refitting

1   Disconnect the battery negative lead.

2   Release the wire clip and unplug the wiring connector from the air regulator.

3   Slacken the clamps securing the air regulator bypass hoses (photo).

4   Unbolt the air regulator from the PCV valve bracket and withdraw it, separating it from the air hoses.

5   The regulator bi-metal heater can be tested for continuity by connecting a multimeter (set to the resistance function), or a battery and bulb test circuit, across its terminals. If continuity does not exist the heater is faulty and the air regulator must be renewed.

6   The air regulator's performance can be checked by squeezing shut the U-shaped air hose between the air regulator and the intake (inlet) manifold when the engine is idling. If the engine is cold the idle speed should drop; if the engine is fully warmed up to normal operating temperature the idle speed should not be affected.

44.4 Rubber seal is fitted at turbocharger end of intake (inlet) tube

46.3 Throttle valve switch – one mounting bolt shown

47.3 Air intake (inlet) bypass tube 'A', IAA unit connector 'B', IAA unit mounting bolts 'C'

48.3 PCV valve 'A', air regulator wiring connector 'B', air hose clamps 'C'

49.7 Pressure regulator vacuum hose 'A', boost sensor vacuum hose 'B', vacuum servo unit vacuum hose 'C', fuel feed hose 'D', fuel return hose 'E'

7   With the air regulator removed, it is possible to check that the shutter is open when hot and closed when cold. If the regulator is faulty it must be renewed.

8   Refitting is the reverse of removal.

49 Intake (inlet) manifold – removal and refitting

1   Refer to the warnings given in Sections 2 and 28 before starting work.

2   Disconnect the battery negative lead.

3   Drain the cooling system, then disconnect the cooling system hoses from the throttle chamber and intake (inlet) manifold (Chapter 2). Note that the thermostat and its housing cover will be removed with the manifold.

4   Remove the turbocharger-to-throttle chamber air intake (inlet) tube and IAA unit bypass tube (Section 44).

5   Disconnect the accelerator cable (Section 38).

6   Releasing the connector wire clips where fitted, disconnect the wiring from the throttle valve switch, all injectors, the coolant temperature gauge and water temperature sensors, the air regulator and the IAA unit.

7   Disconnect the fuel pressure regulator, vacuum servo unit and boost sensor vacuum hoses from the intake (inlet) manifold (photo).

8   Relieve fuel system pressure (Section 29) and disconnect the fuel hoses from the fuel rail. Ensure the hoses are labelled so that they can be refitted correctly and place a rag around the connection to catch any spilt fuel.

9   Note that the pressure regulator/fuel rail assembly, throttle chamber and IAA unit can be removed with the intake (inlet) manifold, if required.

10   Disconnect the spark plug leads and the oil separator-to-PCV valve breather hose.

11   Check that all wiring and hoses have been disconnected from above and below the manifold, then undo the retaining nuts and bolts and withdraw the manifold from the cylinder head studs. Recover the gasket.

12   Refitting is the reverse of removal, but use a new gasket and ensure that the mating faces are clean. Tighten the manifold nuts and bolts to the specified torque setting. Refill the cooling system (Chapter 2).

50 Emergency relief valve – removal and refitting

1   With the engine stopped and fully cooled down, unscrew the valve from the intake (inlet) manifold (photo).

2   Refitting is the reverse of removal. Apply a smear of suitable sealant to the valve threads and tighten the valve securely.

51 Pressure regulator/fuel rail assembly – removal and refitting

1   Refer to the warnings given in Sections 2 and 28 before starting work.

2   Relieve fuel system pressure (Section 29).

3   Disconnect the battery negative lead.

4   Disconnect the fuel feed and return hoses from the unions. Ensure the hoses are labelled so that they can be refitted correctly and place a rag around the connection to catch any spilt fuel.

5   Remove the turbocharger-to-throttle chamber air intake (inlet) tube (Section 44).

6   Disconnect the accelerator cable (Section 38).

7   Disconnect the spark plug leads.

8   Disconnect the pressure regulator vacuum hose.

9   Releasing the wire clips, unplug the wiring connector from each of the injectors.

10   Undo the bolts securing the pressure regulator/fuel rail assembly and each of the injectors (photo). Withdraw the complete assembly (fuel

50.1 Emergency relief (pop-off) valve

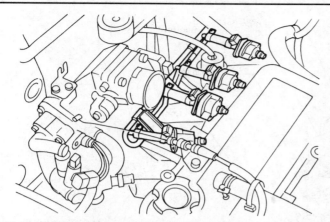

Fig. 3.48 Removing pressure regulator/fuel rail assembly and fuel injectors (Sec 51)

rail and all injectors) taking care not to bend the fuel rail or to damage any of the injectors (Fig. 3.48).

11   Do not remove the injectors unless absolutely necessary (Section 52).

12   Refitting is the reverse of removal, using new injector seals. Check carefully for any signs of fuel leakage, especially at all disturbed unions, when the engine is restarted.

13   Note that testing the fuel system pressure requires the use of a vacuum pump, to apply measured vacuum to the pressure regulator, and a suitable pressure gauge. This work is, therefore, best left to a suitably equipped Nissan dealer.

52   Fuel injectors – testing, removal and refitting

1   Remove the pressure regulator/fuel rail assembly (Section 51).

2   Slacken the clamp and pull each injector and hose from the fuel rail stub.

3   The hoses are a tight fit on the injectors and to remove them it will be necessary to use a 150 watt soldering iron to cut into the braided reinforcement (Fig. 3.49).

4   Refitting is a reversal of removal, but new hoses must be fitted using the following procedure. Clean the injector extension and refit the hose socket, then dip the end of the hose in fuel and push the hose fully onto the injector.

5   The injectors themselves can be checked by using a multimeter (set to the resistance function), or a battery and bulb test circuit, to check that there is continuity across each injector's terminals. If no continuity exists the injector is faulty and must be renewed.

6   If the injectors are thought to be dirty, it is worth trying one of the proprietary injector cleaning treatments (eg Holt Lloyd's Redex Injector Treatment) before resorting to drastic measures such as renewing a fouled injector.

53   Turbocharger – precautions

1   The turbocharger is driven by exhaust gases and routinely operates at extremely high temperatures. The turbocharger castings retain heat for a very long time and must not be touched for a period of at least three hours after the engine was last run. Even at this time, it is advisable to wear heavy gloves to prevent burns.

2   High rotation speed in the turbocharger means that bearing life and operation is dependent upon a constant flow of engine oil to the shaft's plain bearings; note that the shaft actually floats on a thick film of oil. Careful attention should be paid to the condition of the oil lines and the tightness of their fittings. Never overtighten the banjo bolts, as this will deform the unions and cause leakage.

3   Because the turbocharger is dependent upon clean oil, drain the engine oil and change the oil filter any time the turbocharger is removed. If a bearing fails in the turbocharger or in the engine, flush all engine and turbocharger oil passages completely before reassembly.

51.10 Each fuel injector is bolted to intake (inlet) manifold

4   A turbocharger is a ducted fan, and, like any turbine, its greatest enemy is dirt and foreign objects. A stray nut, metal chip or rock passing through a turbine rotating at 120 000 rpm can cause extreme damage. The best defence against foreign object damage is to work on your engine and turbocharger unit only after the engine has been cleaned. Cover all inlets and pipes. Account for every nut, bolt, screw and washer before starting the engine after assembly is complete.

5   The turbocharger is a close tolerance, expensive component and servicing or repairs should be left to a dealer service department or specialist with turbocharger repair experience. Apart from the information in the following Sections, any other work on the turbocharger or its related components is beyond the scope of the average reader.

6   **Do not** *run the engine with the air intake (inlet) hose disconnected.* The turbocharger rotates fast enough to cause grave personal injury, and there is a chance of foreign bodies being sucked in and damaging the unit (see paragraph 4).

7   **Do not** *rev the engine immediately after start-up.* Wait a few seconds for oil pressure to become established at the shaft bearings. This is especially important after an oil filter change, when the pressure may take a significant time to build up.

8   **Do not** *switch the engine off without allowing it to idle for at least 10 seconds.* Switching off immediately after a run can leave the turbocharger rotating at high speed with no oil pressure available at the bearings.

9   **Always** *change the engine oil and filter at the specified intervals and* **do not** *use cheap oil.* Turbocharged engines demand far more of their oil than do normally-aspirated units, so use only the specified grades of oil or higher. However expensive this may appear, it will be cheaper than a new turbocharger.

10   **Do not** *poke fingers or anything else into the turbocharger while its turbines are still spinning.* Always wait for the blades to stop completely and for the turbocharger to cool down before starting work.

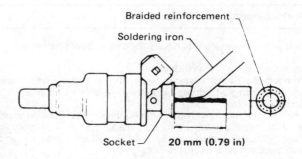

Fig. 3.49 Method of removing hose from injector (Sec 52)

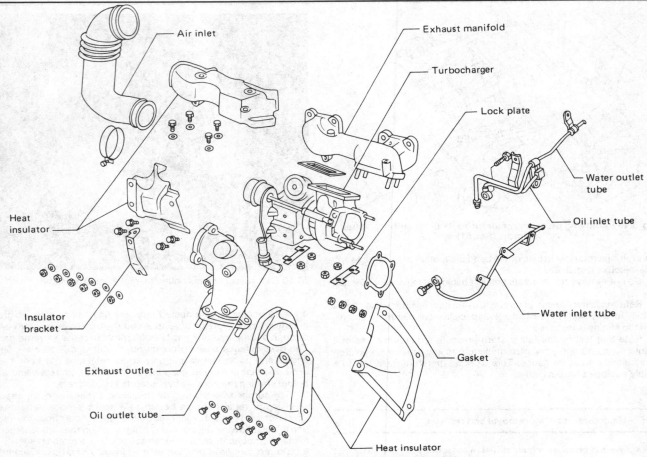

Fig. 3.50 Turbocharger and related components (Sec 54)

54.3 Plug turbocharger openings whenever intake ducts are removed

54.4 Exhaust system downpipe-to-outlet retaining nuts

54.5 Exhaust manifold and turbocharger with heat shields removed

54 Turbocharger – removal and refitting

1   Wait until all components have **fully** cooled down before starting work.

2   Drain the cooling system (Chapter 2).

3   Remove the airflow meter-to-turbocharger intake (inlet) ducting and the turbocharger-to-throttle chamber/IAA unit intake (inlet) tube (Section 44) – photo.

4   Undo the three retaining nuts securing the exhaust front downpipe to the turbocharger (photo), unbolt the exhaust system front mounting from the bellhousing and pull the downpipe downwards as far as possible. Secure it clear of the turbocharger.

5   Unbolt and remove the turbocharger heat shields (photo).

6   Slacken the clamp and disconnect the oil return hose from the turbocharger union. Plug the hose to prevent the entry of dirt and mop up any oil spilt. Unscrew the oil feed pipe union at the cylinder block or turbocharger end, whichever is most easily reached. Temporarily seal the pipe end to prevent the loss of oil (photo).

7   Unscrew the banjo union bolts securing the turbocharger coolant pipes at the front and rear of the unit; collect the sealing washers.

8   Flatten back the lock plate raised tabs and undo the turbocharger-to- exhaust manifold mounting nuts. Withdraw the turbocharger, complete with the exhaust outlet.

9   Clean carefully all mating surfaces and threads.

10   Refitting is the reverse of the removal procedure, using new gaskets and sealing washers. The lock plates should be renewed when all their tabs have been used once (photos).

11   Refill the cooling system and check for leaks (Chapter 2).

12   Note that it is recommended that the engine oil and filter should be changed whenever the turbocharger is disturbed.

54.6 Oil return hose clamp 'A', coolant feed pipe banjo union 'B'

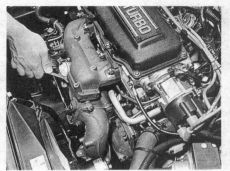

54.10A Tightening one of turbocharger mounting nuts

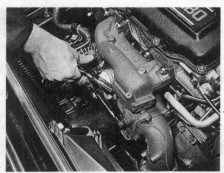

54.10B Bending lock plate tab against nut to secure it

55 Turbocharger – inspection

Note: *If any of the internal components, such as the waste gate, bearing(s) or oil seals are defective it will be necessary to renew the turbocharger as an assembly unless a specialist can be found who will recondition the unit.*

1   If the engine is lacking power, check for air leaks around the compressor, inlet/outlet tubes or the inlet manifold and correct any faulty connection.
2   If the engine shows excessively high engine power check for a disconnected or cracked rubber hose on the bypass valve. Replace the hose if a defect is found.
3   If the engine exhibits excessively high oil consumption or the exhaust shows pale blue smoke, check for oil leaks at the lubricating oil passage connection.
4   Further checks will require removal of the turbocharger (Section 54).
5   With the turbocharger on the work bench, inspect the turbine wheels by visually checking for cracks, clogging, deformity or other damage.
6   Spin the wheels and check for free movement and abnormal noise or friction.

Checking axial play

7   Check axial play using a dial indicator through the inlet opening on the compressor shaft (Fig. 3.51).
8   Using hand pressure only, move the turbine as far away from the dial indicator as possible and zero the indicator. Push the turbine toward the dial indicator and compare the reading obtained with that specified. If axial play is excessive, the turbocharger must be renewed.

56 Exhaust manifold – removal and refitting

1   Remove the turbocharger (Section 54).
2   Proceed as described in Section 23, noting that there is no warm air intake (inlet) hose.
3   Refitting is the reverse of removal.

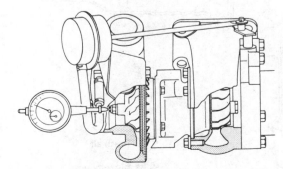

Fig. 3.51 Measuring turbocharger shaft axial play (endfloat) (Sec 55)

57 Exhaust system – removal and refitting

Refer to Section 24.

58 Fuel injection system – self diagnosis

1   The ECCS control unit incorporates a self-diagnosis facility which determines whether some of the components which supply it with information are faulty or not. The fault may be in the component itself or in the wiring, including any related diodes and/or relays. See the relevant wiring diagram for details.
2   The ECCS control unit indicates faults (or otherwise) by means of a numerical code shown by two LEDs, one red and one green. The red LED flashes first and represents the 'ten' digit while the green represents the 'unit' digit, so that if the red LED flashes three times, followed by the green LED flashing twice this indicates code number 32.
3   If a fault is suspected proceed as follows.
4   First locate the ECCS control unit under the passenger seat.
5   Remove the retaining bolts and pull the control unit out so you can handle it. **Caution:** *The self-diagnosis results are retained in the memory by a small current flow from the battery. Disconnecting the battery cable or the ECCS's 15-pin connector erases the memory stored. Always perform the self-diagnosis regarding intermittent checks before disconnecting.*
6   Verify the diagnosis mode selector (photo) is turned fully counterclockwise using a small screwdriver.
7   Turn the ignition switch On. If the engine will not start, turn it over on the starter motor for at least two seconds before starting self-diagnosis.

58.6 Self-diagnosis mode selector 'A' and LEDs 'B'

8   Check that both LED's light up. If not, check the battery terminals and EFI/fuel pump relay to ensure that the control unit is receiving battery voltage.
9   When both LED's light up, use a small screwdriver to **gently** turn the diagnosis mode selector fully clockwise.
10   Depress the accelerator pedal once, then release it.
11   Start the engine and allow it to idle.
12   On Executive models, switch off the air conditioning system, switch it on again, then switch it off.
13   Watch the LEDs and write down the code displayed; compare it with the table below.

Displayed code	Probable fault
11 (1 red flash, 1 green flash)	Faulty distributor/crank angle sensor or circuit
12 (1 red flash, 2 green flashes)	Faulty airflow meter or circuit
13 (1 red flash, 3 green flashes)	Faulty water temperature sensor or circuit
21 (2 red flashes, 1 green flash)	Fault in ignition system. See Chapter 4
22 (2 red flashes, 2 green flashes)	Faulty fuel pump or circuit
23 (2 red flashes, 3 green flashes)	Faulty throttle valve switch or circuit
31 (3 red flashes, 1 green flash)	On standard Turbo models, no fault found – on Executive models, no signal to control unit from air conditioning system
32 (3 red flashes, 2 green flashes)	Faulty ignition switch or circuit. See Chapter 12
34 (3 red flashes, 4 green flashes)	Faulty detonation (knock) sensor. See Chapter 4
44 (4 red flashes, 4 green flashes)	No fault found (Executive models only)

Note: *On occasion, two fault codes may be displayed. If one of these is code 11 always check the distributor/crank angle sensor first.*

14   Turn the diagnosis mode selector fully counterclockwise then switch off the ignition and repair the fault.
15   When the fault is repaired, always erase the memory as follows.
16   Switch on the ignition, turn the diagnosis mode selector fully clockwise and keep it there for at least two seconds.
17   Turn the diagnosis mode selector fully counterclockwise and keep it there for at least two seconds, then switch off the ignition.
18   Refit the control unit and passenger seat.
19   Where the self-diagnosis procedure indicates a fault in any particular circuit, always check first the physical condition of the wiring and connections; usually, faults are due to loose connections or broken wires.
20   If the wires are in good condition, check the component (as described in this manual, if a test procedure is given). If the component

is in good condition the fault should, by a process of elimination, lie in the ECCS control unit.
21   **Always** have your suspicions confirmed by a Nissan dealer before going to the expense of renewing any component.

59   Positive Crankcase Ventilation (PCV) system – general

The system functions as described in Section 25 of this Chapter, except that a PCV filter is not necessary and a flame trap is fitted in the rocker cover breather hose. Refer to Fig. 3.52 for details.

60   Fault diagnosis – fuel injection system

The Sections of this Chapter include a general description of how each component works, with component removal and refitting instructions and test procedures that are within the scope of the home mechanic. Before assuming a fault in either the fuel or ignition systems always check the obvious first; fuel filter, air filter, spark plugs, amount of petrol in tank etc. The ignition system and the fuel system are closely interrelated but can be checked separately. The diagnosis of some of the components requires specialized tools, equipment and training. If checking and servicing become too difficult or if a procedure is beyond your ability, consult a dealer service department. Remember, the most frequent cause of fuel and ignition problems is simply a loose or broken vacuum hose or wire, so always check the hose and wiring connections first.

When carrying out checks, in addition to the warnings given in Sections 2 and 28 of this Chapter, note the following:

(a)   When installing a battery, be particularly careful to avoid reversing the positive and negative cables.
(b)   Do not subject components, particularly the ECCS control unit to severe impact during removal or refitting.
(c)   Do not be careless during troubleshooting. Even slight terminal contact can invalidate a testing procedure and even damage one of the numerous transistor circuits.
(d)   Never attempt to work on the ECCS control unit or open its cover.
(e)   If you are inspecting electronic control system components during rainy weather, make sure water does not enter any part. When washing the engine compartment, do not spray these parts or their connectors with water.

PART C: 2.0 LITRE FUEL INJECTION ENGINES

61   General description

The fuel injection system is easiest to understand if each of its sub-systems are considered separately. These can be divided into

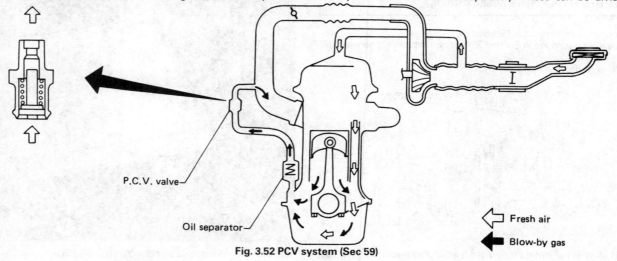

P.C.V. valve

Oil separator

Fresh air

Blow-by gas

Fig. 3.52 PCV system (Sec 59)

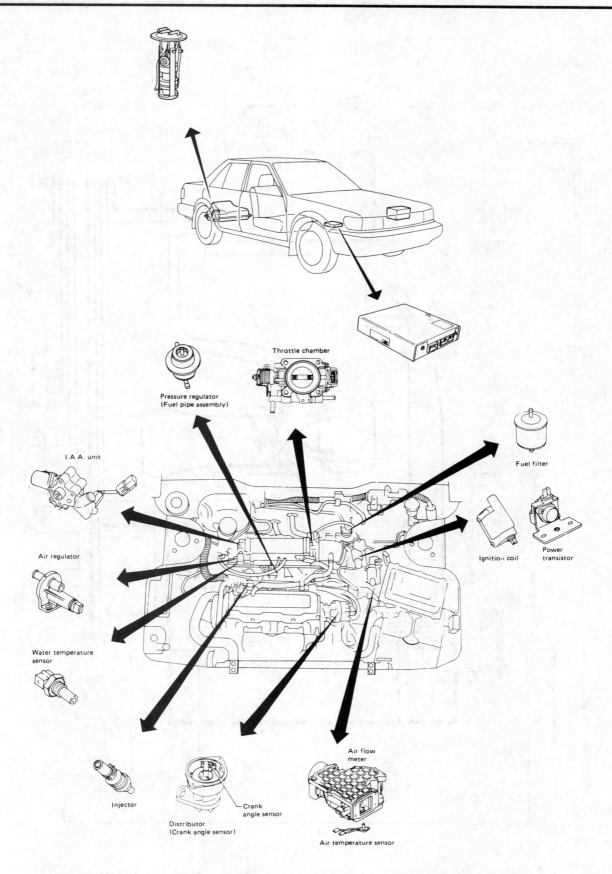

Throttle chamber

Pressure regulator
(Fuel pipe assembly)

Fuel filter

I.A A. unit

Air regulator

Ignition coil

Power
transistor

Water temperature
sensor

Air flow
meter

Injector

Crank
angle sensor

Distributor
(Crank angle sensor)

Air temperature sensor

Fig. 3.53 Location of 2.0 litre fuel injection engine management system components (Sec 61)

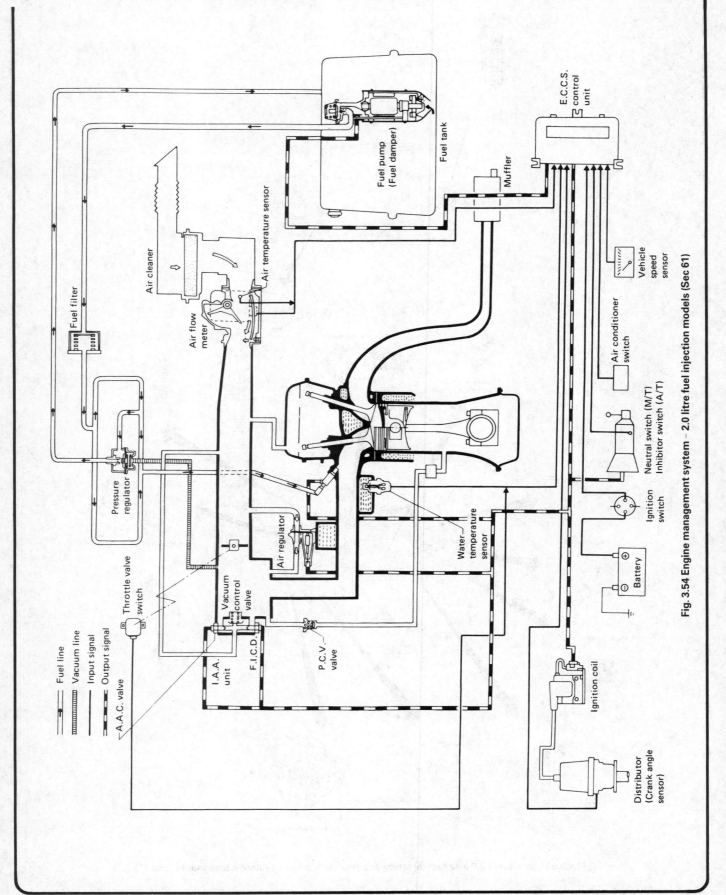

Fig. 3.54 Engine management system – 2.0 litre fuel injection models (Sec 61)

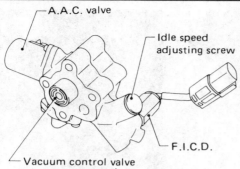

Fig. 3.55 IAA unit components (Sec 61)

three; the fuel delivery system, the air metering or induction system and the electrical components. Refer to the accompanying illustration for details.

The fuel system starts with the fuel tank in which is housed the electric roller-cell fuel pump. This is protected by a gauze filter on its pick-up side and a full-flow filter on its delivery side. When the ignition is switched on and the starter motor operated, the pump supplies fuel to the fuel rail only while the engine is running. The pressure of fuel is controlled by the vacuum-operated pressure regulator which returns fuel continuously to the tank. Although the regulator relies on intake (inlet) manifold depression for normal operation, it also incorporates a spring-loaded safety valve. The injectors are solenoid-operated and are opened and closed by electrical impulses from the ECCS control unit; the correct moment is signalled by the control unit based on the information it is receiving from the distributor/crank angle sensor. Actuating an injector solenoid pulls back a needle valve against spring pressure and allows a controlled amount of fuel to pass from the fuel rail via a small filter, through each injector, and to spray out into the intake (inlet) port; all four injectors operate simultaneously, twice each engine cycle.

The induction system takes cool air from next to the radiator and passes it through the pleated-paper air filter element and into the airflow meter. This measures the temperature of the incoming air, via a sensor in its intake, and also its volume. The force of the incoming air deflects a sensor flap which converts this movement into voltage by a potentiometer; the information from these two sensors is fed to the ECCS control unit. The sensor flap is spring-loaded to provide controlled operation and is L-shaped so that pressure variations can be damped out by the movement of the other flap arm in a secondary damping chamber. To permit adjustment of the air/fuel mixture at idle, a bypass duct is fitted into the airflow meter and controlled by a metering screw. By controlling the amount of un-metered air which is allowed to bypass the sensor flap, the screw effectively provides a form of mixture control. From the airflow meter the air passes via the throttle chamber into the plenum chamber intake (inlet) collector and from there to the intake (inlet) manifold. A throttle valve switch is fitted to the outside of the throttle chamber and provides the ECCS control unit with information about throttle valve position. It has two sets of contacts, one for idle and one for full throttle. The dashpot is as described in Section 27. The Idle Air Adjusting (IAA) unit is mounted on the intake (inlet) collector's right-hand end, and controls idle speed in response to signals from the ECCS control unit by regulating the amount of air that bypasses the throttle valve. Activated by the ECCS control unit only when the throttle valve switch idle contact is closed and vehicle speed is less than 5 mph, the IAA units' Auxiliary Air Control (AAC) valve regulates the air according to the control unit's signals, which are determined from information pre-programmed into its memory. This gives the best idle speed for the current engine speed, temperature and gear position, and also takes into account battery voltage and air conditioning system operation (where fitted). The IAA unit (Fig. 3.55) incorporates the idle speed adjusting screw, the vacuum control valve, the AAC valve and (only connected on Executive models) the FICD solenoid valve. The vacuum control and FICD solenoid valves are as described in Section 27. The only remaining component of the induction system is the air regulator which is also as described in Section 27.

The heart of the electronic system is the ECCS control unit which uses microprocessors to collate information about the volume and temperature of the incoming air (airflow meter), the engine speed (ignition system), the throttle valve position (throttle valve switch), and the engine temperature (water temperature sensor); it also notes the

car's speed (vehicle speed sensor), the gear position (reversing lamp/gear position switch or starter inhibitor/reversing lamp switch, as appropriate), and whether the air conditioning system (where fitted) is in operation. The control unit then sends signals to the air regulator, AAC valve and fuel pump, to the power transistor and (in pulses of varying duration) to the fuel injectors. A failsafe system is included which sets the injection pulse duration at a fixed preset value in the event of airflow meter failure and assumes fixed water temperature values in the event of water temperature sensor failure.

Some basic checks of the system components are included in this Chapter. However, the complexity of the system prevents many problems from being accurately diagnosed by the home mechanic. If a problem develops in the system which cannot be pinpointed by the checks listed here, it is best to take the vehicle to a Nissan dealer to locate the fault.

62 Precautions to be observed when servicing a fuel injection system

Refer to Section 28.

63 Relieving fuel system pressure

Refer to Section 29.

64 Routine maintenance

Carry out the following procedures at the intervals given in 'Routine maintenance' at the beginning of this manual:

Adjust idling speed and mixture
Refer to Section 75.

Check the exhaust system
Refer to Section 3.

Check the crankcase ventilation system
Refer to Section 3, with reference to Section 90.

Check the engine breather and vacuum hoses
Refer to Section 3.

Renew the fuel filter
Refer to Section 33.

Check the fuel system
Refer to Section 3.

Renew the air cleaner filter element
Refer to Section 31.

65 Air cleaner filter element – renewal

Refer to Section 31.

66 Air cleaner – removal and refitting

1 Remove the air cleaner filter element (Section 31). Disconnect the battery negative lead.
2 Withdraw the cover from the wing-mounted intake (inlet) duct.
3 Slacken its clamp and release the air intake (inlet) duct from the airflow meter.

66.5A Air cleaner housing top mounting screw

66.5B Air cleaner housing lower mounting screw

66.5C Airflow meter connector is underneath unit

4   Disconnect the ignition HT coil wiring, the distributor (HT) lead, the power transistor wiring and release the clip securing the wiring harness to the airflow meter bracket.

5   Unbolt the air cleaner housing and airflow meter bracket from the inner wing panel (five screws or bolts) and withdraw the complete assembly until the airflow meter wiring connector plug can be reached. Release the wire clip and unplug the connector (photos). Withdraw the air cleaner housing and airflow meter.

6   The airflow meter can be unbolted if required.

7   Refitting is the reverse of removal.

67   Fuel filter – renewal

Refer to Section 33.

68   Fuel pump/fuel gauge sender unit – removal, testing and refitting

Refer to Section 34.

69   Fuel tank – removal, repair and refitting

Refer to Section 35.

70   Evaporative emission control system – general

Refer to Section 11.

71   Accelerator cable – adjustment

Refer to Section 12.

72   Accelerator cable – removal and refitting

Refer to Section 38 (photos).

73   Accelerator pedal – removal and refitting

Refer to Section 14.

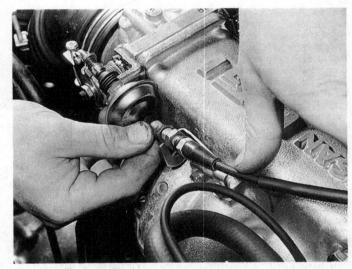

72.1A Slacken adjusting nuts to release accelerator cable from bracket ...

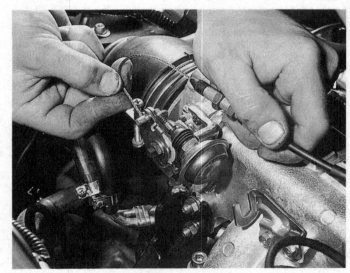

72.1B ... release inner cable from throttle pulley

74   Unleaded petrol – general

1   Refer to Section 15.

2   The engine is designed to use 4-star (or Super/Super Plus grade

75.8A To adjust idle speed, disconnect AAC valve ...

75.8B ... and throttle valve switch wiring ...

75.9A ... remove rubber plug from IAA unit ...

75.9B ... and turn idle speed adjusting screw

75.19A To remove airflow meter tamperproof plug ...

75.19B ... drill small hole in centre of plug ...

75.19C ... screw in self-tapping screw and withdraw with pliers

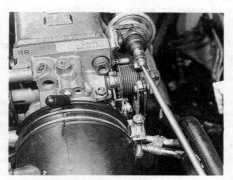

75.29 Adjusting dashpot touch speed

75.31 Using multimeter to check when throttle valve switch contacts open

unleaded) but can use Premium grade unleaded continuously if the ignition timing is first retarded (Chapter 4).

75 Fuel injection system adjustments

1   Refer to the warnings given in Sections 2 and 28 before starting work.
2   Park the car on a flat surface, apply the handbrake firmly and chock the roadwheels, then select neutral (manual transmission) or the 'N' position (automatic).
3   Ensure that the valve clearances and ignition timing are correctly set, then disconnect the electric cooling fan motor(s) and switch off all electrical loads, such as the lights, and the air conditioning system (where fitted).
4   The idle mixture is set during production and therefore it is usually only the idle speed which may require adjustment. The idle mixture

adjusting screw is fitted with a tamperproof plug which must be removed to make an adjustment.

Idle speed
5   Warm the engine up to normal operating temperature.
6   Clear any excess fuel from the intake (inlet) manifold by racing the engine two or three times to between 2000 and 3000 rpm, then allow it to idle for one minute. Repeat this at regular intervals if any adjustment takes more than three minutes to complete.
7   Check that the idle speed is within the specified range (see Specifications). If an accurate tachometer is to be used, obtain or make up the adaptor harness shown in Chapter 4, Fig. 4.16.
8   If adjustment is required, stop the engine and disconnect the AAC valve and throttle valve switch wiring (photos), releasing the wire clips before unplugging the connectors.
9   Restart the engine and adjust engine speed to 725 rpm by turning the idle speed adjusting screw in the IAA unit (photos); turn clockwise to reduce idle speed.
10 Stop the engine, reconnect the throttle valve switch and AAC

valve, restart the engine and clear any excess fuel from the intake (inlet) manifold (paragraph 6 above) then check the idle speed – it should be correct.

11   Note that in practice, it may be found that the engine will not run slowly enough with the AAC valve and throttle valve switch disconnected (actually 500 rpm on the project car) to obtain the specified idle speed when they are reconnected. In such a case it will be necessary to adopt a trial- and-error approach, by turning the screw in increments of half-a-turn at a time until the correct speed is obtained.

FICD speed – Executive

12   Prepare the car and check the idle speed as described above; adjust the idle speed if necessary.
13   When the basic speed is correct, switch on the air conditioning system and check that the idle speed increases to that specified.
14   There is no adjustment as such. If the FICD solenoid valve is not functioning correctly, test it as described in Section 41 and renew it if necessary.

Idle mixture

15   If the mixture must be adjusted due to a change in engine characteristics (carbon build-up, bore wear etc), adjust the idle speed first, then stop the engine.
16   Note that the idle mixture should be checked using a CO meter (exhaust gas analyser). If this is not available the car should be taken to a Nissan dealer for the work to be done. For emergency use a basic setting procedure is given which will enable the car to start and run until it can be checked by a competent mechanic using proper test equipment. An accurate tachometer will be required.
17   To check the idle mixture, first warm up the engine to normal operating temperature and ensure that the valve clearances, ignition timing and idle speed are correct, as described above.
18   Connect the CO meter following its manufacturer's instructions and check the CO level at idle speed. If adjustment is required, proceed as follows.
19   Locate the tamperproof plug at the 'corner' of the airflow meter nearest the throttle chamber (note that there are two plugs, one on top and one beneath). Carefully drill a small hole in the plug, remembering that it is not very thick, then screw in a self-tapping screw and extract the plug and screw with pliers (photos).
20   Clear any excess fuel from the intake (inlet) manifold (see paragraph 6 above) then turn the idle mixture adjusting screw in small increments until the CO level is correct; turn clockwise to richen the mixture. Recheck the idle speed and adjust it if necessary.
21   When the setting is correct, stop the engine and tap a new tamperproof plug into place. Disconnect any test equipment.
22   To set the idle mixture without a CO meter first connect an accurate tachometer and prepare the car as described in paragraph 17 above.
23   Stop the engine and remove the tamperproof plug from the airflow meter, as described in paragraph 19 above. Disconnect the AAC valve and throttle valve switch wiring.
24   Start the engine and clear any excess fuel from the intake (inlet) manifold (see paragraph 6 above), then allow it to idle.
25   Turn the idle mixture adjusting screw gently each way until the fastest idle speed is obtained, then turn the screw one full turn counter-clockwise.
26   The idle speed should now be 750 ± 50 rpm. If adjustment is required, turn the idle speed adjusting screw (see paragraph 9 above).
27   When the specified speed is obtained, stop the engine and reconnect the throttle valve switch and AAC valve, then restart the engine and check that the idle speed is restored to the normal specified value.
28   Do not fit a new tamperproof plug until the mixture has been checked using a CO meter.

Dashpot

29   Refer to the relevant part of Section 41 (photo).

Throttle valve switch

30   The switch must be set so that its idle contacts open at 1050 ± 200 rpm.
31   Adjust the switch setting as described in the relevant part of Section 41 (photo).
32   When testing the switch (ignition switched off) note that it has a second set of contacts (terminals 24 and 30) which should open at full throttle only. Renew the switch if either is faulty.

76.0 ECCS control unit is located under passenger seat

76   ECCS control unit – general

Refer to Section 42 (photo).

77   Airflow meter – removal and refitting

1   Withdraw the airflow meter complete with the air cleaner housing (Section 66).
2   The airflow meter can then be unbolted from the air cleaner.
3   If required the meter mounting brackets can be unbolted (photo).
4   Note that the temperature sensor is located in the meter intake, behind the air cleaner housing-to-meter adaptor (photos). The sensor should not, however, be disturbed as it is not available separately. If either the meter potentiometer or the temperature sensor are faulty the complete assembly must be renewed.
5   Check that the meter flap moves smoothly and easily through its full travel. If the movement is jerky or restricted the meter must be renewed, unless a specialist can be found to repair it.
6   Refitting is the reverse of removal. If a new unit has been fitted, check the idle speed and mixture as soon as possible (Section 75).

78   Air intake (inlet) duct – removal and refitting

Refer to Section 44.

79   Throttle chamber – removal and refitting

1   Slacken the clamps and withdraw the airflow meter-to-throttle chamber intake (inlet) duct (Section 44).
2   Remove and refit the throttle chamber as described in Section 45, paragraphs 2 to 6, referring to Section 75 for details of throttle valve switch resetting, if required (photo). **Note: Do not,** under any circumstances, disturb the relationship of the primary and secondary throttle valves. These are set on manufacture and will be almost impossible to synchronise correctly if disturbed (photo).

77.3 Unbolting airflow meter brackets

77.4A Remove air cleaner housing-to-airflow meter adaptor ...

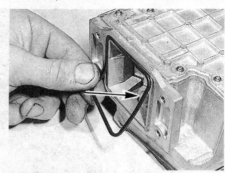

77.4B ... to check temperature sensor (arrow) and meter flap action

79.2A Throttle chamber coolant hoses and two mounting bolts

79.2B Do not alter setting of throttle valves

80 Throttle valve switch – removal and refitting

Noting that the switch resetting procedure is given in Section 75, refer to Section 46 (photo).

81 IAA unit – removal and refitting

1   Disconnect the battery negative lead.
2   Release the wire clip and unplug the AAC valve wiring connector. On Executive models, disconnect the FICD solenoid valve wiring.
3   Slacken the clamps and disconnect the air hoses from the IAA unit cover and inner (next to the intake (inlet) collector) unions.
4   Undo the two screws and two nuts (and their lock washers) which secure the IAA unit cover.
5   Withdraw the cover and remove the gasket.
6   Withdraw the AAC valve section, with the valve and remove the gasket.
7   Withdraw the FICD solenoid valve section, with the FICD solenoid valve and vacuum control valve; remove the gasket.
8   Note that while the FICD solenoid and AAC valves can be removed separately (photos), they are available only as part of the relevant section of the IAA unit. The vacuum control valve can be renewed only as part of the FICD solenoid valve section.
9   Refitting is the reverse of removal, using new gaskets and tighten-

80.0 Throttle valve switch mounting bolts (arrowed)

ing the screws and nuts to the specified torque setting. If the FICD solenoid valve section has been renewed, the idle speed and mixture will require checking (Section 75).

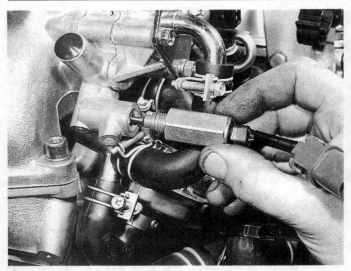

81.8A Removing FICD solenoid valve from IAA unit

81.8B Removing AAC valve from IAA unit

82   Air regulator – removal, testing and refitting

Refer to Section 48 (photo).

83   Inlet collector and manifold – removal and refitting

1   Refer to the warnings given in Sections 2 and 28 before starting work.
2   Disconnect the battery negative lead.
3   Remove the airflow meter-to-throttle chamber intake (inlet) duct and rocker cover breather hose (Section 44).
4   Releasing the connector wire clips, where fitted, disconnect the wiring from the throttle valve switch, all four injectors, the coolant temperature gauge and water temperature sensors, the air regulator, the AAC valve and the FICD solenoid valve (where appropriate) – photo. Unclip the wiring harness and secure it clear of the inlet manifold.
5   Disconnect the spark plug (HT) leads.
6   Drain the cooling system, then disconnect the cooling system hoses from the throttle chamber intake (inlet) manifold. Note that the thermostat and its housing cover will be withdrawn with the manifold.
7   Disconnect the accelerator cable (Section 38).
8   Disconnect the fuel pressure regulator, vacuum servo unit and econometer vacuum hoses from the intake (inlet) collector (photos).
9   Disconnect the oil separator-to-PCV valve breather hose.
10   Relieve fuel system pressure (Section 29) and disconnect the fuel hoses from the fuel rail. Ensure the hoses are labelled so that they can be refitted correctly and place a rag around the connection to catch any spilt fuel.

82.0 Withdrawing air regulator

11   Note that the throttle chamber, air bypass tube and hoses, fuel pressure regulator/fuel rail assembly, air regulator/PCV valve bracket and IAA unit need not be removed from the inlet collector and manifold unless required. The whole assembly can be withdrawn as a single unit and dismantled on the workbench.
12   Check that all wiring and hoses have been removed from above and below the intake (inlet) manifold/collector. Unbolt the front and rear

83.4 Disconnecting injection system components

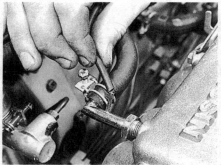

83.8A Disconnecting econometer vacuum hose ...

83.8B ... and vacuum servo unit vacuum hose from intake (inlet) collector stub

84.0A Relieve system pressure before disconnecting fuel hoses

84.0B Disconnecting fuel injector wiring

84.0C Fuel injector mounting on intake (inlet) manifold

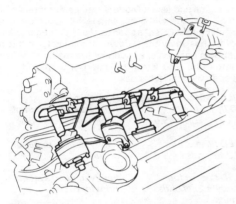

Fig. 3.56 Removing pressure regulator/fuel rail assembly and fuel injectors (Sec 84)

stays from the manifold/collector.

13   Undo the retaining nuts and bolts and withdraw the intake (inlet) manifold and collector from the cylinder head studs. Recover and discard the gasket.

14   Refitting is the reverse of removal, but use new gaskets and ensure that the mating faces are clean. Tighten the manifold nuts and bolts to the specified torque setting. Refill the cooling system (Chapter 12).

84   Pressure regulator/fuel rail assembly – removal and refitting

Proceed as described in Section 51, paragraphs 1 to 4 (photo) and 7 to 13 (photos).

85   Fuel injectors – testing, removal and refitting

Refer to Section 52.

86   Exhaust manifold – removal and refitting

Refer to Section 23, noting that there is no warm air intake (inlet) hose.

87   Exhaust system – removal and refitting

Refer to Section 24.

88   Vehicle speed sensor – testing, removal and refitting

1   The vehicle speed sensor is a reed switch which rotates with the speedometer to provide a pulse signal to the ECCS control unit corresponding to the car's speed. It is mounted in the instrument panel.

2   To test the sensor, first locate the ECCS control unit under the passenger seat, remove its mounting bolts and pull it out. Disconnect the 16-pin connector.

3   Connect a multimeter set to the resistance function (or a battery and bulb test circuit) between the blue/green wire (terminal 29) on the harness side of the connector and earth.

4   Raise the front of the car and spin one of the roadwheels. Continuity between the wire terminal and earth should come and go, the speed varying with that of the roadwheel.

5   If the speed sensor is not working, remove the instrument panel (Chapter 12) and check for continuity between the sensor and the ECCS control unit connectors. Trace and repair the fault if no continuity is found.

6   If the wiring is in good condition the sensor is probably faulty and should be renewed.

89   Fuel injection system – self-diagnosis

1   The ECCS control unit incorporates a self-diagnosis facility which determines whether some of the components which supply it with information are faulty or not. The fault may be in the component itself, or in the wiring, including any related diodes and/or relays. See the relevant wiring diagram for details.

2   The ECCS control unit indicates faults (or otherwise) by means of a numerical code shown by two LEDs, one red and one green. In Mode III the red LED flashes first and represents the 'ten' digit while the green represents the 'unit' digit, so that if the red LED flashes three times, followed by the green LED flashing twice, this indicates code number 32.

3   This facility is useful to diagnose malfunctions in major sensors and actuators of the ECCS system. There are five modes in the self-diagnosis system.

Mode I – Not fitted to UK models.
Mode II – Not fitted to UK models.
Mode III – Self diagnosis – This mode stores all malfunctioning diagnostic items in its memory. It will be stored in the ECU memory until the starter is operated fifty times, or until the power supply to the ECU is interrupted.
Mode IV – Switches ON/OFF diagnosis – During this mode, the inspection lamp monitors the idle contacts of the throttle valve switch, the starter switch, vehicle speed sensors and other switches with an ON/OFF condition.
Mode V – Real time diagnosis – The moment the malfunction is detected, the display will be presented. This is the mode in which the malfunction can be observed during a road test, as it occurs.

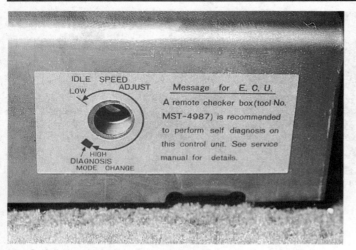

89.4 Self diagnosis mode selector – ignore idle speed reference

Selecting self-diagnosis modes

4   Locate the ECCS control unit under the passenger seat, remove its mounting bolts and pull it out. Identify the diagnosis mode selector (photo) and the two LEDs just in front of the selector. Ignore the reference to idle speed adjustment; this does not apply to UK models.
5   Switch on the ignition and use a small screwdriver to gently turn the diagnostic mode selector fully clockwise.
6   When the LEDs start to flash, count the number of times. They will flash once, then twice, then three times, then four times, then five times, then back to once and repeat the cycle. Each self-diagnostic mode is represented by the corresponding number of flashes, eg Mode III is three flashes.
7   When the appropriate number of flashes appears, immediately turn the diagnosis mode selector fully counterclockwise.
8   When the ignition switch is turned off during diagnosis, in any mode, and then turned on again after the power to the ECCS control unit has dropped off completely, the diagnosis will automatically return to Mode I.

Self diagnosis – Mode III

9   If a fault is suspected, start the engine and warm it fully up to normal operating temperature (if possible). If it will not start, turn it over on the starter motor for at least two seconds before starting self-diagnosis.
10   Select Mode III (see paragraphs 4 to 7 above).
11   Watch the LEDs and write down the code displayed (paragraph 2 above); compare it with the table below.

Displayed code	Probable fault
11 (1 red flash, 1 green flash)	*Faulty distributor/crank angle sensor or circuit*
12 (1 red flash, 2 green flashes)	*Faulty airflow meter or circuit*
13 (1 red flash, 3 green flashes)	*Faulty water temperature sensor or circuit*
14 (1 red flash, 4 green flashes)	*Faulty vehicle speed sensor or circuit*
21 (2 red flashes, 1 green flash)	*Fault in ignition system. See Chapter 4*
22 (2 red flashes, 2 green flashes)	*Faulty fuel pump or circuit*
23 (2 red flashes, 3 green flashes)	*Faulty throttle valve switch (idle contact)*
24 (2 red flashes, 4 green flashes)	*Faulty throttle valve switch (full throttle contact)*
31 (3 red flashes, 1 green flash)	*Faulty ECCS control unit*
41 (4 red flashes, 1 green flash)	*Faulty air temperature sensor or circuit*
55 (5 red flashes, 5 green flashes)	*No fault found*

12   Erase the memory by turning the diagnostic mode selector fully clockwise. After the inspection lamps have flashed 4 times, turn the mode selector fully counterclockwise. This will erase any signals the

ECCS control unit has stored concerning a particular component.
13   Switch off the ignition and repair the fault.

Self diagnosis – Mode IV

14   Switch on the ignition and select Mode IV (see paragraphs 4 to 7 above).
15   Check that the red LED goes out.
16   Start the engine, and check that the red LED lights when the ignition switch is in the 'Start' position. If not, check the ignition switch and power supply from the battery (Chapter 12).
17   With the engine idling, check that the red LED goes out when the accelerator pedal is depressed. If not, check the throttle valve switch idle contacts and wiring.
18   Drive the car and have a passenger check that the green LED lights when road speed exceeds 12 mph. If not, check the vehicle speed sensor and wiring.
19   Switch off the ignition to cancel the self-diagnosis.

Self diagnosis – Mode V

20   Start the engine and select Mode V (see paragraphs 4 to 7 above).
21   Either park the car with the engine idling or drive it with a passenger watching the LEDs. As soon as the LEDs begin to flash, count the number of flashes and write it down immediately. In this mode the fault code is shown once only, as soon as the malfunction is noted by the ECCS control unit, and is not repeated or stored in its memory. Compare the code with the table below.

Displayed code	Probable fault
Red LED flashes once every 3.2 seconds for 9.6 seconds	*Faulty distributor/crank angle sensor or circuit*
Green LED flashes twice every 3.2 seconds for 9.6 seconds	*Faulty airflow meter or circuit*
Green LED flashes four times every 3.2 seconds for 9.6 seconds	*Faulty ignition system primary circuit*
Red LED flashes three times every 3.2 seconds for 9.6 seconds	*Faulty fuel pump or circuit*

22   If the LEDs have not flashed after five minutes of self-diagnosis it can be assumed that no fault has been detected in this mode.
23   Switch off the ignition to cancel the self-diagnosis.
24   Note that this mode is sensitive enough to detect small defects in wiring and connections, particularly dirt or corrosion on terminals. Check all these points in a circuit carefully before suspecting the component itself.

General

25   Where a self-diagnosis procedure indicates a fault in any particular circuit, always check the physical condition of the wiring and connections first. Usually, faults are due to loose connections or broken wires.
26   If the wires are in good condition, check the component (as described in this manual, if a test procedure is given). If the component is in good condition the fault should, by a process of elimination, lie in the ECCS control unit.
27   **Always** have your suspicions confirmed by a Nissan dealer before going to the expense of renewing any component.

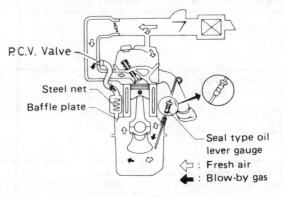

Fig. 3.57 PCV system (Sec 90)

90   Positive Crankcase Ventilation (PCV) system – general

This system functions as described in Section 25 of this Chapter, except that a PCV filter is not necessary. Refer to Fig. 3.57 for details.

91   Fault diagnosis – fuel injection system

Refer to Sections 26 and 60.

Chapter 4 Ignition system

Contents

Specifications

System type
Carburettor models .... Electronic, with centrifugal and vacuum-controlled advance
Fuel injection models .... Electronic, with computer-controlled advance

Engine
Firing order .... 1 – 3 – 4 – 2 (No 1 at timing belt end of engine)
Direction of crankshaft rotation .... Clockwise (viewed from right-hand side of car)

Distributor
Type
    Early 1.6 litre models .... Hitachi D4R83-22
    Late 1.6 litre models .... Hitachi D4R87-01
    1.8 litre carburettor models .... Hitachi D4R83-25
    2.0 litre carburettor models .... Hitachi D4R85-09
    Fuel injection models .... Hitachi D4P83-07
Direction of rotor arm rotation .... Anti-clockwise (viewed from left-hand side of car)
Reluctor/stator air gap – carburettor models .... 0.3 to 0.5 mm (0.012 to 0.020 in)
Distributor cap minimum resistance .... 50 M ohm
Rotor arm minimum resistance .... 50 M ohm
Carbon point (brush) minimum length .... 10 mm (0.39 in)
Centrifugal advance range (carburettor models):*
    D4R83-22 .... 0° at 1200 rpm to 19° at 5200 rpm
    D4R87-01, D4R83-25 .... 0° at 1400 rpm to 20° at 4400 rpm
    D4R85-09 .... 0° at 1200 rpm to 21° at 4800 rpm
*Crankshaft degrees and rpm
Vacuum advance range (carburettor models):†
    D4R83-22 .... 0° at –9.3 kPa (–2.75 in Hg) to 20° at –46.7 kPa (–13.79 in Hg)
    D4R87-01 .... 0° at –9.3 kPa (–2.75 in Hg) to 15° at –46.7 kPa (–13.79 in Hg)
    D4R83-25, D4R85-09 .... 0° at –13.3 kPa (–3.93 in Hg) to 20° at –46.7 kPa (–13.79 in Hg)
†Crankshaft degrees

Ignition HT coil
Type:
    Carburettor models .... Hitachi HP5-13E or Hanshin STC 106
    Turbo model .... Hanshin, or Hitachi MCC 106
    Fuel injection (non-Turbo) models .... Hanshin SMC 100
Primary winding resistance – at 20°C (68°F):
    Carburettor models .... 1.3 to 1.7 ohm
    Fuel injection models .... 0.8 to 1.0 ohm
Secondary winding resistance – at 20°C (68°F):
    Carburettor models .... 7.4 to 11.2 k ohm
    Fuel injection models .... 7.6 to 11.4 k ohm

Spark plugs
Type:
1.6 and 2.0 litre models..Champion RC7YC or RC7YCC
1.8 litre carburettor models ....Champion RC9YC or RC9 YCC
Turbo model...Champion RC7YC, RC7YCC or RC7YC4
Electrode gap:
Carburettor models ....0.8 to 0.9 mm (0.032 to 0.035 in)
Fuel injection models ....1.0 to 1.1 mm (0.039 to 0.043 in)

Spark plug (HT) leads
Maximum resistance ....30 k ohm per lead (see Fig. 4.2)
Champion part number...CLS 4 (boxed set)

Ignition timing
Standard:
1.6 litre models up to engine number 190258 (July 1987)* ....5 ± 1° BTDC at idle, vacuum hose disconnected and plugged
1.6 litre models from engine number 190259 (July 1987)....................8° BTDC at idle, vacuum hose disconnected and plugged
1.8 litre carburettor models ....5 ± 1° BTDC at idle, vacuum hose disconnected and plugged
2.0 litre carburettor models ....3 ± 1° BTDC at idle, vacuum hose disconnected and plugged
Turbo model...15 ± 1° BTDC at idle
Fuel injection (non-Turbo) models ....15 ± 2° BTDC at idle, throttle switch and AAC valve disconnected
*To increase performance, timing may be advanced to 9° (Premium grade unleaded petrol) or 12° (4-star leaded petrol)
For Premium grade (95 RON) unleaded petrol:
1.6 litre models up to engine number 190258 (July 1987) ....Standard setting (no adjustment required)
1.6 litre models from engine number 190259 (July 1987)....................4° BTDC at idle, vacuum hose disconnected and plugged
1.8 litre carburettor models ....TDC ± 1° at idle, vacuum hose disconnected and plugged
2.0 litre carburettor models ....2 ± 1° ATDC at idle, vacuum hose disconnected and plugged
Turbo model...**Do not** use Premium grade unleaded petrol
2.0 litre fuel injection models ....10 ± 2° BTDC at idle, throttle switch and AAC valve disconnected

Torque wrench settings

	Nm	lbf ft
Spark plug	20 to 29	15 to 21.5
Distributor mounting bolts	16 to 20	12 to 15
Detonation (knock) sensor	25 to 34	18.5 to 25

PART A: CARBURETTOR MODELS

1   General description

The ignition system is divided into two circuits, low tension (primary) and high tension (secondary). The low tension circuit consists of the battery, ignition switch, primary coil windings and the transistorised IC (integrated circuit) ignition unit and signal generating system inside the distributor. The signal generating system comprises the reluctor, stator and magnet. The high tension (HT) circuit consists of the secondary coil windings, the heavy ignition lead from the centre of the distributor cap to the coil, the rotor arm and the spark plug leads and spark plugs.

The distributor is mounted on the left-hand end of the cylinder head and is driven by the camshaft.

The ignition advance is a function of the distributor and is controlled both mechanically and by a vacuum operated system. The mechanical governor mechanism consists of two weights which move out from the distributor shaft due to centrifugal force, as the engine speed rises. As they move outwards, they rotate the reluctor relative to the distributor shaft and so advance the spark. The weights are held in position by two light springs and it is the tension of the springs which is largely responsible for correct spark advancement.

The vacuum controller consists of a diaphragm, one side of which is connected via a small bore hose to the carburettor and the other side to the distributor. Depression in the inlet manifold, which varies with engine speed and throttle position, causes the diaphragm to move, so moving the baseplate and advancing or retarding the spark.

Warning: *The voltages produced by electronic ignition systems are considerably higher than those produced by a conventional system. Extreme care must be taken when working on the system with the ignition switched on, particularly by persons fitted with a cardiac pacemaker.*

2   Routine maintenance

1   At the intervals given in 'Routine maintenance' at the beginning of this manual, carry out the following service operations.

Check the ignition timing
2   Refer to Section 5 of this Chapter.

Check the spark plugs
3   Remove the air cleaner or intake (inlet) ducting from the carburettor (Chapter 3).
4   Identify the spark plug (HT) leads for position, then disconnect them from the spark plugs by pulling on the suppressor caps, not the leads.
5   Brush or blow away any accumulated dirt from the recesses in the cylinder head.
6   Unscrew and remove the spark plugs using a deep socket or box spanner. Do not allow the tool to tilt, otherwise the ceramic insulator may be cracked or broken.
7   The spark plug gap is of considerable importance, and if it is too large or too small, the size of the spark and its efficiency will be seriously impaired. For the best results the spark plug gap should be set in accordance with the Specifications at the beginning of this Chapter.
8   To set it, measure the gap with a feeler gauge, and then bend open, or close the outer plug electrode until the correct gap is achieved. The centre electrode should never be bent as this may crack the insulation and cause plug failure if nothing worse.
9   Special spark plug electrode gap adjusting tools are available from most motor accessory stores.
10   Before fitting the spark plugs, wash each one thoroughly again in a suitable solvent in order to remove all trace of abrasive powder and then apply a trace of grease to the plug threads.
11   Screw each plug in by hand until it seats lightly but firmly on its gasket. This will make sure that there is no chance of cross-threading.
12   Tighten to the specified torque setting. If a torque wrench is not available tighten Champion plugs through (no more than) ¼ of a turn. **Do not** overtighten the spark plugs.

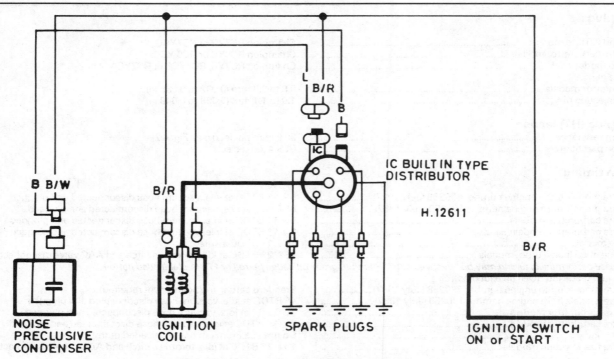

B/R
B
L
IC
B B/W
B/R
L

IC BUILT IN TYPE DISTRIBUTOR

H.12611

B/R

NOISE PRECLUSIVE CONDENSER

IGNITION COIL

SPARK PLUGS

IGNITION SWITCH ON or START

Fig. 4.1 Ignition circuit – carburettor models (Sec 1)

Note: *Black/red wire is black/white on later models*

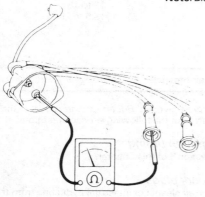

Fig. 4.2 Measuring resistance of HT leads (Sec 2)

13   When reconnecting the spark plug (HT) leads, make sure that they are refitted in their correct order, 1-3-4-2. No 1 cylinder being at the timing belt end of the engine, and the distributor rotor turning anti-clockwise when viewed from the left-hand side of the engine compartment. The original equipment leads are numbered to aid identification.

Renew the spark plugs
14   At the specified intervals the spark plugs must be renewed, regardless of their apparent condition, to preserve the engine's performance and economy and to help minimise pollution.
15   Remove the old plugs as described above, noting their condition and taking corrective action where necessary (see spark plug colour page), then disconnect them.
16   Ensuring that the new plugs are of exactly the correct grade, as specified in this manual or by Nissan, set the electrode gap (paragraphs 8 to 10 above) and install them.

2.17 Remove retaining screws to release distributor cap

2.20 Remove rubber cap (where fitted) to check HT coil connectors

3.2 Disconnecting distributor vacuum hose

3.3 Distributor earth wire connector

3.4A Remove retaining screws ...

3.4B ... to release distributor cap

3.7 Unscrewing distributor mounting bolt

Check the distributor cap and spark plug (HT) leads

17   Remove the screws (photo) and lift the distributor cap from the distributor. Disconnect the main lead from the ignition coil.

18   Wipe clean the leads and the distributor cap.

19   Using an ohmmeter, check for continuity between the segments inside the distributor cap and the spark plug or coil end of each lead. If a reading in excess of 30 k ohm is obtained, clean the distributor cap outer terminals and check again. If there is no improvement renew the leads (as a set, never singly) and/or the distributor cap. If an intermediate fault is suspected, shake or twist gently each lead while testing its resistance.

20   Finally, withdraw the HT coil rubber cap (where fitted), wipe clean the coil terminals and check that the coil and its connections are securely fastened (photo).

21   Refit the disturbed components, noting paragraph 15 above when reconnecting the leads.

3 Distributor – removal and refitting

1   Remove the oil filler cap and turn the crankshaft clockwise (using a spanner on the crankshaft pulley bolt) until No 1 cylinder intake (inlet) valve has opened and closed again, then slowly turn it a little further until the pulley's (black or orange) TDC mark aligns with the timing belt cover pointer. No 1 cylinder is now at TDC on the compression stroke. Disconnect the battery negative lead.

2   Disconnect the hose from the vacuum controller and plug it (photo).

3   Disconnect the distributor earth wire from its terminal (photo).

4   Mark the relationship of the cap to the distributor body, undo the two retaining screws and withdraw the distributor cap (photos).

5   The rotor arm brass segment should be pointing to the location of the No 1 cylinder spark plug (HT) lead segment on the distributor cap. If

3.9A Distributor coupling drive dogs are offset ...

3.9B ... to engage with slots (arrowed) in camshaft locating plate

3.15 Showing reluctor peaks aligned with stator posts at firing point (arrowed)

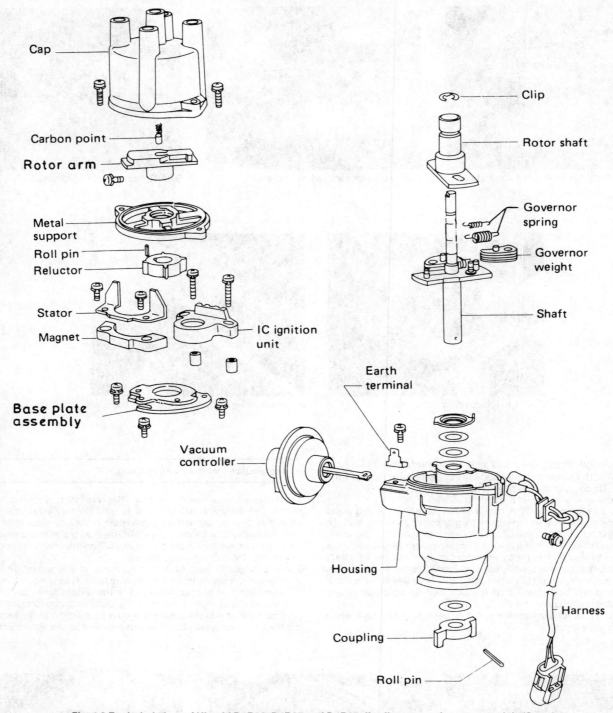

Cap

Carbon point

Rotor arm

Metal
support

Roll pin

Reluctor

Stator

Magnet

IC ignition
unit

**Base plate
assembly**

Vacuum
controller

Clip

Rotor shaft

Governor
spring

Governor
weight

Shaft

Earth
terminal

Housing

Coupling

Roll pin

Harness

Fig. 4.3 Exploded view of Hitachi D4R83, D4R85 and D4R87 distributor – carburettor models (Sec 4)

necessary, mark the relationship of the rotor arm to the distributor body.

6   Using a scriber or centre punch, mark the relationship of the distributor body to the cylinder head. Disconnect the distributor wires at the connector plug.

7   Unbolt the distributor (photo) and withdraw it. Do not disturb the crankshaft setting while the distributor is removed, or rotate the distributor shaft (unless the unit is to be overhauled).

8   On refitting, check first that No 1 cylinder is at TDC on the compression stroke; see paragraph 1 above.

9   With the rotor arm pointing to No 1 cylinder (distributor cap) segment and the distributor body/cylinder head marks (that were made

on removal) aligned, refit the distributor to the cylinder head. Rotate the rotor arm very slightly to assist the distributor coupling drive dogs to enter the slots in the camshaft locating plate (photos). Refit the distributor mounting bolts.

10   Note that the distributor coupling drive dogs are offset so that they will fit only one way into the camshaft locating plate slots.

11   Refit the distributor cap, ensuring it is correctly located, then reconnect the earth wire and distributor wiring.

12   Check, and adjust if necessary, the ignition timing (Section 5). Unplug and reconnect the vacuum hose.

13   Note that if a new distributor is to be fitted (or no marks were made

on removal) the following procedure should produce a basic setting which will enable the engine to start and run while the ignition timing is accurately set.

14   Position No 1 cylinder at TDC on the compression stroke (see paragraph 1 above), then turn the engine slightly anti-clockwise until the timing belt cover pointer aligns with the appropriate crankshaft pulley mark (see Specifications) ie so that the engine is in the firing position.

15   Turn the distributor rotor arm to the location of the No 1 cylinder distributor cap segment and position it precisely by aligning the two nearest reluctor peaks with the stator blades (photo).

16   Maintain, as closely as possible, the relationship of the rotor arm to the distributor body while the distributor is installed (paragraphs 9 to 12 above).

4   Distributor – overhaul

1   Remove the distributor from the car (Section 3).
2   Remove the retaining screw (photo) and withdraw the rotor arm.
3   Remove the support plate (photo).
4   Note the fitted position of the reluctor, then extract the roll pin and withdraw the reluctor from the shaft.

5   Remove the two screws and withdraw the stator and magnet.
6   Remove the wiring harness support screw from the distributor body (photo). Identify the wires for position, disconnect them from the IC ignition unit, then release the rubber grommet and withdraw the harness.
7   Remove the two screws and lift out the IC ignition unit. Recover the spacers.
8   Where fitted, undo the screw securing the vacuum controller arm to the base plate.
9   Remove the three screws and lift out the base plate assembly while disconnecting the vacuum control arm.
10   Mark the coupling in relation to the shaft.
11   Drive out the roll pin and remove the coupling and thrustwasher.
12   Slide the shaft from the body, noting the position of the thrust washers.
13   Remove the screw and withdraw the vacuum controller, noting the location of the earth terminal.
14   Mark the rotor shaft in relation to the mainshaft, then extract the upper E-clip and withdraw the rotor shaft, governor weights and springs.
15   Clean and examine all components and renew any that are worn or damaged.
16   Carefully wipe clean the distributor cap and check it for cracks or signs of fine black lines from any of the spark plug (HT) lead terminals which might indicate 'tracking'. Renew the cap if either condition is found.

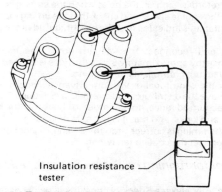

Fig. 4.4 Testing insulation of distributor cap (Sec 4)

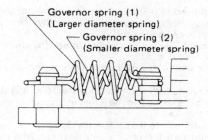

Fig. 4.5 Installation of governor weight springs (Sec 4)

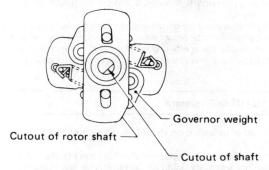

Fig. 4.6 Correct location of rotor shaft on distributor main shaft (Sec 4)

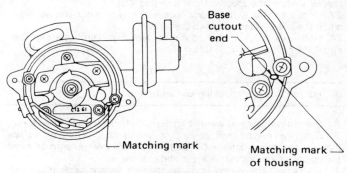

Fig. 4.7 Distributor base plate matching marks (Sec 4)

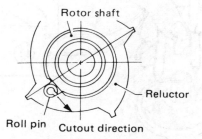

Fig. 4.8 Correct location of roll pin in reluctor (Sec 4)

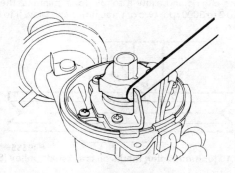

Fig. 4.9 Checking reluctor/stator air gap (Sec 4)

4.2 Rotor arm is retained by a single screw

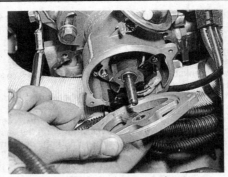

4.3 Withdrawing metal support plate

4.6 Distributor wiring harness and support screw

17   If a suitable insulation tester is available, check that the resistance between any two terminal segments is a minimum of 50 M ohm (Fig. 4.4). Similarly, check that there is no continuity between the rotor arm brass segment and the arm body. Renew the cap or rotor arm if there is any sign of the insulation breaking down. Check that the cap carbon point (brush) is not worn to the minimum length specified or less; renew it if necessary.

18   Reassembly is a reversal of dismantling, but observe the following points.

19   Apply high melting point grease to the governor weight pivots, governor springs, rotor shaft, base plate assembly, vacuum controller arm, and support plate bearing surface.

20   When fitting the governor weights, attach the small springs first then the large springs (Fig. 4.5).

21   Fit the rotor shaft to the main shaft with the cut-outs as shown in Fig. 4.6.

22   Fit the base plate with the matching marks (Fig. 4.7) aligned.

23   When fitting the reluctor to the rotor shaft, position the roll pin cut-out as shown in Fig. 4.8).

24   Refit the distributor to the car (Section 3).

25   If necessary, turn the engine until two opposite peaks on the reluctor are aligned with the two stator blades.

26   Using a feeler blade, check that the air gap between the peaks and blades is within the specified tolerance (Fig. 4.9).

27   If adjustment is necessary, loosen the two stator screws, reposition the stator, then re-tighten the screws.

28   Refit the support plate, the rotor arm and distributor cap then check the ignition timing (Section 5).

5   Ignition timing – checking and adjusting

1   Start the engine and warm it up to normal operating temperature.

2   Stop the engine and connect a timing light according to the manufacturer's instructions. Check that the crankshaft pulley marks and timing belt cover pointer are clean and easily seen.

3   Disconnect the wiring from the radiator electric cooling fan motor(s). Ensure that all electrical accessories are switched off.

4   Disconnect the vacuum hose from the distributor and plug it.

5   Start the engine and allow it to idle for 2 minutes, then race the engine up to 2 to 3000 rpm two or three times and allow it to settle back to idle speed.

6   Check that the idle speed is correct (Chapter 3).

7   Aim the timing light at the crankshaft pulley and check that the pointer aligns with (or between) the appropriate pulley marks (see Specifications and Fig. 4.10).

8   If adjustment is required, loosen the distributor mounting bolts and turn the distributor body clockwise to advance the ignition, or anti-clockwise to retard it. Tighten the bolts when the setting is correct.

9   Increase the engine speed and check that the timing mark advances from the pointer; this indicates that the centrifugal advance mechanism is operating.

10   Unplug and reconnect the vacuum hose. The ignition timing should advance (by approximately 8°) as the hose is connected, indicating that the vacuum controller is functioning.

11   If either the centrifugal or vacuum advance system do not work properly, remove the distributor and overhaul it (Sections 3 and 4). In the case of the vacuum advance, do not forget to check that the hose is clear of blockages and kinks, and that it is not split or leaking.

12   When the timing is correct, stop the engine, disconnect the timing light and reconnect the cooling fan wiring.

Adjustment for running on Premium grade unleaded petrol

13   On most models (see Specifications) it will be necessary to retard the ignition timing, by up to 5°, to prevent detonation (knocking) and/or pre-ignition ('pinking') if the car is run on Premium grade (95 RON) unleaded petrol.

Note: *This detonation or pre-ignition cannot always be detected (by ear) and it should not be assumed that because the engine appears to be running normally the ignition does not need to be retarded. Failure to retard the ignition can result in serious damage to the engine.*

6   Ignition HT coil – general

1   The coil is mounted on the left-hand side of the engine compartment.

2   Testing of the coil consists of checking the primary and secondary windings for continuity using an ohmmeter or low wattage test lamp,

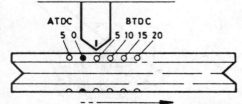

Fig. 4.10 Ignition timing marks on crankshaft pulley (Sec 5)

Note: *TDC mark painted black or orange, others white*

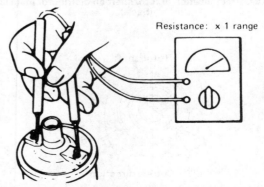

Fig. 4.11 Testing ignition HT coil primary windings (Sec 6)

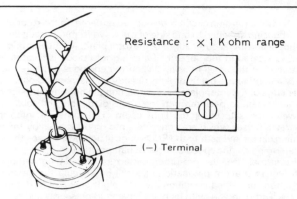

Fig. 4.12 Testing ignition HT coil secondary windings (Sec 6)

(Figs. 4.11 and 4.12). Using the ohmmeter the resistance of each circuit can be checked and compared with the specified tolerances. Note that the readings obtained will vary slightly with temperature, therefore the coil should be tested (where possible) after the engine has been running for at least 15 minutes so that it is at normal operating temperature.

7 Fault diagnosis – ignition system

1 Electronic ignition systems are normally very reliable. Faults are most likely to be due to loose or dirty connections, or 'tracking' of HT voltage due to dirt, dampness or damaged insulation.
2 The old practice of checking for a spark by holding the live end of an HT lead a short distance away from the block is not recommended by the makers, since there is a risk of damaging the coil insulation. For the same reason, diagnosing misfires by pulling off one plug cap at a time is also forbidden. In either case there is the risk of a powerful electric shock.

Engine will not start
3 If the engine will not turn over on the starter motor, or turns very slowly, check first the battery and starter motor. Connect a voltmeter across the battery terminals (meter positive probe to battery positive terminal), disconnect the ignition HT coil lead from the distributor cap and earth it, then note the voltage reading obtained while turning over the engine on the starter motor for (no more than) ten seconds. If the reading obtained is less than 9.6 volts the battery, starter motor or charging system is faulty; refer to Chapter 12. If the reading is above 9.6 volts, note and record the battery's open-circuit voltage with no load applied (Chapter 12, Section 5).
4 If the ignition system seems completely dead, use a multimeter to check for full battery voltage at the ignition HT coil and distributor IC ignition unit black/white (or black/red) wire terminals. If battery voltage is not present, check the supply from the battery via the ignition switch to the distributor and ignition HT coil and repair any faults found.
5 With the ignition switched on, check for full battery voltage at the distributor IC ignition unit blue wire. If battery voltage is not present, check the ignition HT coil primary windings (Section 6). Renew the coil if faulty.
6 To check the distributor IC ignition unit earth circuit, disconnect the distributor earth wire and connect a voltmeter between the distributor earth terminal and the battery negative terminal (meter positive probe to distributor), disconnect the ignition coil HT lead from the distributor cap and earth it, then note the voltage reading obtained while turning over the engine on the starter motor for (no more than) ten seconds.
7 If the reading obtained is 0.5 volts or less, renew the distributor IC ignition unit (Section 4). If it is more than 0.5 volts, check the distributor and engine earths, also the battery connections and chassis earth points.
8 The operation of the IC ignition unit itself can be tested only by the substitution of a new component.
9 The above tests will eliminate any faults in the low tension (LT) circuit. Check the high tension (HT) circuit as described below.

Engine misfires
10 An irregular misfire suggests a loose connection or an intermittent

fault on the LT side of the system, or an HT fault on the coil side of the rotor arm.
11 Inspect the coil and the distributor for loose connections.
12 Make sure that the coil tower, the distributor cap and the HT leads are clean and dry. Measure the resistance of the HT lead from the coil to the distributor cap (Section 2).
13 Inspect the inside of the distributor cap and the rotor arm for visible damage, 'tracking' (thin black lines) and burning. Check that the carbon point (brush) in the cap is intact and free to move. Test the rotor arm as described in Section 4, or by substitution.
14 Regular misfiring is almost certainly due to a fault in the distributor cap, HT leads or spark plugs. Since disconnecting plug leads with the engine running is forbidden, the author suggests the use of a timing light (strobe) on each plug lead in turn to verify the presence of HT voltage.
15 If HT is not appearing on one particular lead, the fault is in the lead or the distributor cap. If HT is present on all leads, the fault is in a spark plug. Remove the plugs and renew them, or clean and re-gap them (Section 2).
16 If no HT is present, check the coil secondary windings (Section 6). Renew the coil if faulty.

PART B: FUEL INJECTION MODELS

8 General description

The ignition systems fitted to the fuel injection models (both Turbo and non-Turbo) are an integral part of the fuel injection systems described in Chapter 3, thus forming a complete engine management system. The two systems are basically similar in operation as far as the ignition element is concerned.

The main components are the ECCS control unit, the distributor (incorporating the crank angle sensor), the power transistor and ignition coil, the detonation (knock) sensor (Turbo only) as well as the battery and ignition switch.

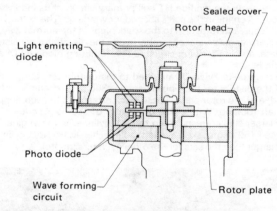

Fig. 4.13 Cross-section through distributor/crank angle sensor (Sec 8)

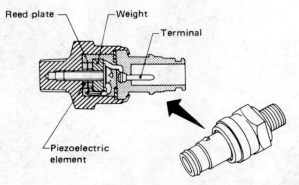

Fig. 4.14 Cross-section through detonation (knock) sensor – Turbo models (Sec 8)

8.0 No 1 cylinder 180° signal slit 'A', 180° signal slits 'B', 1° signal slits 'C'

The ECCS control unit (Chapter 3) takes information from the distributor/crank angle sensor to determine engine speed and crankshaft (piston) position; from the airflow meter to determine the amount of incoming air; from the water temperature sensor (Chapter 2) to determine engine temperature; from the throttle valve switch to determine throttle position; and (on Turbo models only) from the detonation (knock) sensor (see below). All information is collated by the control unit and used to determine the optimum ignition timing setting for any particular set of engine operating conditions, derived from information pre-programmed into the unit.

The control unit sends a signal to the power transistor at the chosen ignition timing setting. The transistor amplifies this signal and connects and disconnects the ignition HT coil primary circuit, thus inducing the required HT voltage in the coil's secondary windings. This is fed via the distributor cap and rotor arm to the spark plugs in the normal way.

The crank angle sensor assembly inside the distributor consists of a rotor plate, a wave forming circuit, a light emitting diode (LED) and a photo diode.

The rotor plate, which is attached to the distributor shaft, is in the base of the distributor housing. There are 360 slits machined into the outer edge of the rotor plate. These slits correspond to each degree of crankshaft rotation. Within this outer row of slits is a series of four slightly larger slits corresponding to each cylinder in the engine. They are spaced 180 degrees (crankshaft) apart. The slit for No 1 cylinder is slightly larger than the slits for the other cylinders (photo).

The wave forming circuit is positioned underneath the rotor plate. A small housing attached to one side of the wave forming circuit encloses the upper and lower outer edges of the rotor plate. A light emitting diode (LED) is located in the upper half and a photo diode is located in the lower half of the small housing. When the engine is running, the LED emits a continuous beam of light directly at the photo diode. As the outer edge of the rotor plate passes through the housing, the slits allow the light beam to pass through the photo diode, but the solid spaces between the slits block the light beam. This constant interruption generates pulses which are converted into on-off signals by the wave forming circuit and sent to the ECCS control unit, which uses the signal to determine engine speed and crankshaft position.

In normal use, the pre-programmed ignition timing settings are sufficient to prevent detonation ('knock') by keeping the engine well away from operating conditions which might give rise to detonation. But the Turbo engine, with its higher manifold pressures and temperatures as well as its increased spark advance, requires extra protection in the form of a detonation sensor.

This sensor detects detonation as pressure applied to its piezoelectric element. This is converted into a voltage signal which is sent to the ECCS control unit. Whenever the control unit detects this signal it retards the ignition timing until the detonation disappears, when the ignition timing is returned to normal. Note that the detonation sensor system only functions when required; it should not operate under normal driving conditions (unless, for example, the wrong grade of fuel is used.)

Warning: *Because of the higher voltage generated by the electronic ignition system, extreme caution should be taken whenever an operation is performed involving ignition components. This not only includes the distributor, coil and ignition system wiring, but related items which are connected to the system as well, such as the plug connections, tachometer and any testing equipment. Consequently, before any work is performed, such as replacing ignition components or even connecting test equipment, the ignition should be turned off and the battery negative lead disconnected. Never disconnect any of the ignition HT leads when the engine is running or the power transistor for ignition HT coil will be permanently damaged.*

9 Routine maintenance

Refer to Section 2 of this Chapter, noting the comments on checking the ignition timing made in Section 12.

10 Distributor/crank angle sensor – removal and refitting

1   Proceed as described in Section 3 of this Chapter, noting that there is no vacuum hose on these models (photos).

10.1A Disconnecting earth wire – note distributor/cylinder head timing marks

10.1B Distributor sealing O-ring can be renewed, if required

Are your plugs trying to tell you something?

Normal.
Grey-brown deposits, lightly coated core nose. Plugs ideally suited to engine, and engine in good condition.

Heavy Deposits.
A build up of crusty deposits, light-grey sandy colour in appearance.
Fault: Often caused by worn valve guides, excessive use of upper cylinder lubricant, or idling for long periods.

Lead Glazing.
Plug insulator firing tip appears yellow or green/yellow and shiny in appearance.
Fault: Often caused by incorrect carburation, excessive idling followed by sharp acceleration. Also check ignition timing.

Carbon fouling.
Dry, black, sooty deposits.
Fault: over-rich fuel mixture.
Check: carburettor mixture settings, float level, choke operation, air filter.

Oil fouling.
Wet, oily deposits. Fault: worn bores/piston rings or valve guides; sometimes occurs (temporarily) during running-in period.

Overheating.
Electrodes have glazed appearance, core nose very white – few deposits. Fault: plug overheating. Check: plug value, ignition timing, fuel octane rating (too low) and fuel mixture (too weak).

Electrode damage.
Electrodes burned away; core nose has burned, glazed appearance. Fault: pre-ignition. Check: for correct heat range and as for 'overheating'.

Split core nose.
(May appear initially as a crack). Fault: detonation or wrong gap-setting technique. Check: ignition timing, cooling system, fuel mixture (too weak).

WHY DOUBLE COPPER IS BETTER FOR YOUR ENGINE.

Unique Trapezoidal Copper Cored Earth Electrode — 50% Larger Spark Area — Copper Cored Centre Electrode

Champion Double Copper plugs are the first in the world to have copper core in both centre <u>and</u> earth electrode. This innovative design means that they run cooler by up to 100°C – giving greater efficiency and longer life. These double copper cores transfer heat away from the tip of the plug faster and more efficiently. Therefore, Double Copper runs at cooler temperatures than conventional plugs giving improved acceleration response and high speed performance with no fear of pre-ignition.

TRAPEZOIDAL COPPER CORED EARTH ELECTRODE
NEW TRAPEZOIDAL COPPER CORED EARTH ELECTRODE — CONVENTIONAL SOLID NICKEL ALLOY EARTH ELECTRODE
50% INCREASE IN SPARK AREA

EARTH ELECTRODE TEMPERATURE VS ENGINE SPEED
SOLID NICKEL EARTH ELECTRODE
COPPER CORED EARTH ELECTRODE
TEMPERATURE — ENGINE SPEED

Champion Double Copper plugs also feature a unique trapezoidal earth electrode giving a 50% increase in spark area. This, together with the double copper cores, offers greatly reduced electrode wear, so the spark stays stronger for longer.

 FASTER COLD STARTING

 FOR UNLEADED OR LEADED FUEL

 ELECTRODES UP TO 100°C COOLER

 BETTER ACCELERATION RESPONSE

 LOWER EMISSIONS

 50% BIGGER SPARK AREA

 THE LONGER LIFE PLUG

Plug Tips/Hot and Cold.
Spark plugs must operate within well-defined temperature limits to avoid cold fouling at one extreme and overheating at the other.
Champion and the car manufacturers work out the best plugs for an engine to give optimum performance under all conditions, from freezing cold starts to sustained high speed motorway cruising.
Plugs are often referred to as hot or cold. With Champion, the higher the number on its body, the hotter the plug, and the lower the number the cooler the plug. For the correct plug for your car refer to the specifications at the beginning of this chapter.

Plug Cleaning
Modern plug design and materials mean that Champion no longer recommends periodic plug cleaning. Certainly don't clean your plugs with a wire brush as this can cause metal conductive paths across the nose of the insulator so impairing its performance and resulting in loss of acceleration and reduced m.p.g.
However, if plugs are removed, always carefully clean the area where the plug seats in the cylinder head as grit and dirt can sometimes cause gas leakage.
Also wipe any traces of oil or grease from plug leads as this may lead to arcing.

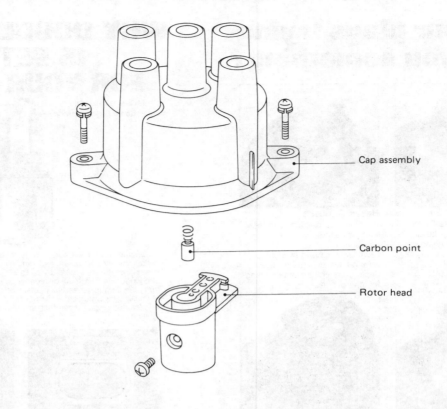

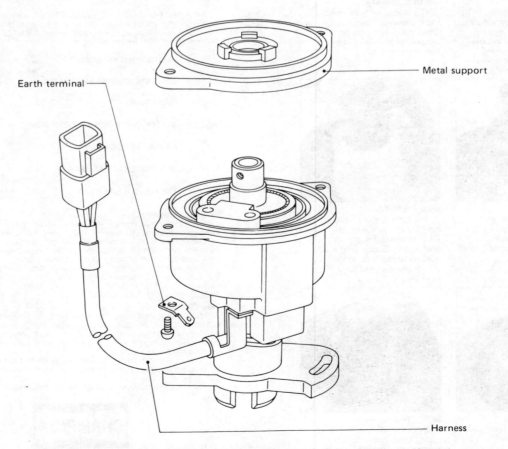

Cap assembly

Carbon point

Rotor head

Metal support

Earth terminal

Harness

Fig. 4.15 Exploded view of Hitachi D4P83 distributor/crank angle sensor (Sec 11)

11.3A Unscrew retaining screw ...

11.3B ... to release rotor arm ...

11.3C ... peel off cap gasket ...

2   If fitting a new distributor (or one with no timing marks made on removal) remove the rotor arm, gasket and metal support/sealed cover plate, then rotate the distributor shaft until the larger No 1 cylinder signal slit (see photo 8.0) is centred underneath the wave forming circuit housing. This will give a setting equivalent to that described in paragraph 15 of Section 3.

11 Distributor/crank angle sensor – overhaul

1   The only components available separately for the distributor are the cap and carbon point (brush), the rotor arm, the wiring lead and the cap gasket and sealing O-ring. The crank angle sensor components are not available separately.
2   The distributor cap, rotor arm and carbon point can be checked as described in Section 4 of this Chapter.
3   The crank angle sensor rotor plate can be checked for dirt or damage by removing the distributor cap, removing the rotor arm retaining screw and withdrawing the rotor arm, followed by the cap gasket and the metal support/sealed cover (photos). Use a gentle jet of compressed air or a soft brush to clean the rotor plate. If any damage is found the complete distributor assembly must be renewed.
4   If the crank angle sensor electrical components are thought to be faulty they can be tested only by substitution of the complete assembly.

12 Ignition timing – checking and adjusting

1   The procedure is as described in Section 5 of this Chapter, noting the following points:

(a) *Do not disconnect the radiator electric cooling fan motor(s) on non-Turbo models, but note that the AAC valve and throttle valve switch must be disconnected while any adjustments necessary are made*
(b) *There is no vacuum hose to disconnect*

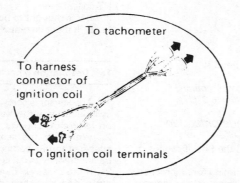

11.3D ... and withdraw sealed cover to check rotor plate

(c) *If an accurate tachometer is required, an adaptor harness, Nissan part number EG11150000 (Turbo) or EG11160000 (non-Turbo) will be required to connect between the ignition HT coil primary windings and their wiring loom connector. The tachometer can then be connected to the adaptor's terminal*
(d) *Note that while engine speed can be increased above idle to check that the ignition timing is advancing, this is an academic exercise since the advance is entirely computer-controlled and there is no information available with which the results obtained can be compared. If this aspect of the ECCS control unit's performance is thought to be at fault, it can be tested only by the substitution of a known good unit. For normal checking purposes, it is sufficient to ensure that the appropriate pulley mark aligns with the timing belt cover pointer at idle speed.*

To tachometer

To harness
connector of
ignition coil

To ignition coil terminals

Fig. 4.16 Adaptor for connecting separate tachometer (Sec 12)

13.1A Ignition HT coil 'A', power transistor 'B' (Turbo models)

13.1B Ignition HT coil, (non-Turbo models) – disconnecting earth wire ...

13.1C ... primary circuit (low tension) wires ...

13.1D ... and distributor cap HT lead

14.1 Location of power transistor (non-Turbo models)

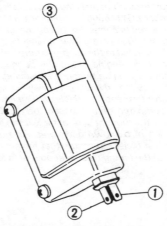

Fig. 4.17 Testing ignition HT coil (Sec 13)

Primary windings – Terminals 1 (positive) to 2 (negative)
Secondary windings – Terminals 2 (negative) to 3 (HT)

Adjustment for running on Premium grade unleaded petrol

2   On non-Turbo models, refer to Section 5 and the Specifications of this Chapter.

3   On Turbo models, **do not** retard the ignition timing for any reason, or use Premium grade unleaded petrol; the minimum octane requirement of this engine is 97 RON (unleaded or leaded). Refer to Chapter 3.

---

13   Ignition HT coil – general

---

1   Apart from the fact that the coil is of a moulded type (photos), refer to Section 6 of this Chapter for details.

2   Test connections are shown in Fig. 4.17.

---

14   Power transistor – general

---

1   The power transistor is secured by two screws next to the ignition HT coil (photo).

2   If it is thought to be faulty it can be tested as shown in Fig. 4.18. If faulty, it must be renewed.

---

15   Detonation (knock) sensor – general (Turbo models only)

---

1   The sensor is screwed into the cylinder block between Nos 2 and 3 cylinders. It is at the rear on most models but may be found at the front on some early engines.

2   Whenever the sensor is disturbed it must be tightened to the specified torque setting. Do not overtighten it or its performance may be affected, even if it is not physically damaged.

3   If the sensor is thought to be faulty, first check its connector plug and wiring, then check it by substituting a known good unit. If faulty, the sensor must be renewed.

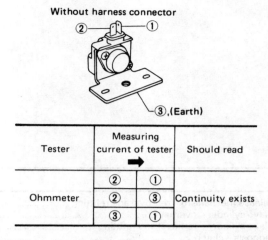

Without harness connector

③,(Earth)

Tester	Measuring current of tester →		Should read
Ohmmeter	②	①	
	②	③	Continuity exists
	③	①	

Fig. 4.18 Testing the power transistor (Sec 14)

16   ECCS control unit – general

Refer to Chapter 3.

17   Fault diagnosis – ignition system

1   Refer first to the general comments at the beginning of Section 7 of this Chapter, and note the warning given in Section 8.

Engine will not start
2   First check the battery and starter motor (Section 7, paragraph 1).
3   Attach an inductive timing light to each spark plug (HT) lead, one at a time, and crank the engine.

    (a)   If the light flashes, voltage is reaching the plug; check the spark plugs.
    (b)   If the light does not flash, proceed to the next step.

4   Inspect the spark plug (HT) leads, distributor cap and rotor arm (Sections 2 and 4).
5   If the engine still won't start, check the ignition HT coil (see Section 13).
6   If the HT (secondary circuit) is in good order and the ignition system is still dead, the fault must be in the primary circuit.
7   Use a multimeter to check for continuity between the No 3 terminals of the (disconnected) ECCS control unit connector plug and the power transistor connector plug, then between the No 5 terminals of each plug. Check the transistor itself (Section 14).
8   If the fault is still not isolated the car should be taken to a Nissan dealer for attention. Do not attempt to 'test' the ECCS control unit.

Engine misfires
9   Refer to Section 7, but note that any testing of individual components should be left to a Nissan dealer. The self-diagnosis facility (Chapter 3) may be useful in locating a fault, but apart from this, the options that are open to the home mechanic are limited. As a general rule, always check first (by substitution if necessary) the spark plugs, spark plug (HT) leads, distributor cap and rotor arm.

Chapter 5 Clutch

Contents

Specifications

General

Type	Single dry plate, with diaphragm spring
Release mechanism type:	
1.6 litre models	Mechanical (cable-operated)
All other models	Hydraulic

Adjustment

Pedal height (measured from pedal pad to bulkhead – Fig. 5.3, dimension 'H')	190 to 200 mm (7.480 to 7.874 in)
Pedal free play (Fig. 5.3, dimension 'A'):	
1.6 litre models	12.5 to 17.5 mm (0.492 to 0.689 in)
All other models	1.0 to 3.0 mm (0.039 to 0.118 in)
Release lever free play – 1.6 litre models (Fig. 5.4, dimension 'B')	2.5 to 3.5 mm (0.098 to 0.138 in)

Master cylinder

Make	Tokico
Bore internal diameter	15.875 mm (0.625 in)

Slave cylinder

Make	Nabco
Bore internal diameter	19.050 mm (0.750 in)

Friction plate

	Outer diameter x inner diameter x thickness
Dimensions of friction material facings:	
1.6, 1.8 non-Turbo and 2.0 litre models, up to late 1988	215 x 140 x 3.5 mm (8.465 x 5.512 x 0.138 in)
1.6 litre and 1.8 non-Turbo models, late 1988 on	215 x 145 x 3.6 mm (8.465 x 5.709 x 0.142 in)
Turbo models, up to late 1988	225 x 150 x 3.5 mm (8.858 x 5.906 x 0.138 in)
Turbo and 2.0 litre models, late 1988 on	228 x 150 x 3.6 mm (8.976 x 5.906 x 0.142 in)
Overall thickness (loaded):	
1.6, 1.8 non-Turbo and 2.0 litre models, up to late 1988	7.8 to 8.2 mm (0.307 to 0.323 in) at 3923 N (882 lbf) load
1.6 litre and 1.8 non-Turbo models, late 1988 on	7.7 to 8.3 mm (0.303 to 0.327 in) at 4000 N (899 lbf) load
Turbo models, up to late 1988	8.0 to 8.4 mm (0.315 to 0.331 in) at 3923 N (882 lbf) load
Turbo and 2.0 litre models, late 1988 on	7.9 to 8.5 mm (0.311 to 0.335 in) at 4500 N (1012 lbf) load
Friction material wear limit (minimum distance from friction material surface to rivet heads)	0.3 mm (0.012 in)
Maximum runout of friction material	1.0 mm (0.039 in)
Maximum spline backlash (measured at friction plate outer edge)	0.9 mm (0.035 in)

Lubricants and fluids

Hydraulic fluid type/specification	Hydraulic fluid to FMVSS 116, DOT 3 or 4 (Duckhams Universal Brake and Clutch Fluid)
Grease (see text for application)	Lithium-based grease including molybdenum disulphide (Duckhams LBM 10)

Torque wrench settings

	Nm	lbf ft
Pedal mounting bracket bolts	8 to 11	6 to 8
Pedal pivot bolt retaining nut	16 to 22	12 to 16
Pedal stop bolt locknut	16 to 22	12 to 16
Cable bracket mounting bolts	8 to 12	6 to 9
Cable adjuster locknut	3 to 4	2.5 to 3
Master cylinder pushrod locknut	8 to 11	6 to 8
Master cylinder mounting nuts	8 to 11	6 to 8
Master cylinder piston stop screw	1.5 to 2.9	1 to 2.5
Master cylinder reservoir band clamp screw	3 to 4	2.5 to 3
Hydraulic pipe union nuts	15 to 18	11 to 13
Flexible hose unions	17 to 20	12.5 to 15
Slave cylinder union banjo bolt (later models only)	Not available	Not available
Hydraulic pipe or flexible bracket mounting bolts	8 to 14	6 to 10
Slave cylinder mounting bolts	30 to 40	22 to 29.5
Slave cylinder bleed nipple	6 to 10	4.5 to 7.5
Cover assembly mounting bolts	22 to 29	16 to 21.5

1 General description

All manual transmission models are fitted with a dry single plate diaphragm spring clutch to provide the driver with a means of smoothly taking up the drive on starting off and of interrupting the drive when changing gear and stopping.

The clutch consists of a friction plate, a cover assembly, a release bearing and the release mechanism. All of these components are contained in the large cast aluminium bellhousing sandwiched between the engine and the transmission. On 1.6 litre models the release mechanism is mechanical, being operated by a cable, while on 1.8 and 2.0 litre models the mechanism is hydraulic, comprising a master cylinder, a slave cylinder and the connecting hydraulic pipes and flexible hose.

The friction plate is fitted between the engine flywheel and the clutch pressure plate and is allowed to slide on the transmission input shaft splines. It consists of two circular facings of friction material riveted in position to provide the clutch bearing surface and a spring-cushioned hub to damp out transmission shocks.

The cover assembly is bolted to the engine flywheel and is located by three dowel pins; it comprises the clutch cover, the diaphragm spring and the pressure plate. When the assembly is bolted securely to the flywheel, drive is transmitted from the crankshaft via the flywheel and clutch cover to the friction plate (these last three components being clamped securely together by the pressure plate and diaphragm spring) and from the friction plate to the transmission input shaft. To interrupt the drive, the spring pressure must be relaxed. This is achieved by a sealed, ball-race release bearing which is fitted concentrically around the transmission input shaft; when the driver depresses the pendant clutch pedal the release bearing is pressed against the fingers at the centre of the diaphragm spring. Since the spring is held by rivets between two annular fulcrum rings, the pressure at its centre causes it to deform so that it flattens and thus releases the clamping force it exerts, at its periphery, on the pressure plate.

On 1.6 litre models, depressing the clutch pedal pulls the control cable inner wire and rotates the release shaft by acting on the lever at the shaft's upper end, above the bellhousing. Mounted on the shaft's lower end, inside the bellhousing, is the release fork; this is located to the left of the release bearing so that the bearing is forced against the diaphragm spring when the release mechanism is operated.

On 1.8 and 2.0 litre models, depressing the clutch pedal acts on a short pushrod to move forwards the piston in the master cylinder which is mounted on the engine compartment side of the bulkhead on the right-hand side. Hydraulic pressure is transmitted to the slave cylinder, (which is mounted on the outside of the bellhousing at the front), and causes its piston to move outwards. A short pushrod acts on the upper end of the release fork which is pivoted on a ball-headed stop screwed into the bellhousing. Since the fork's lower end is located to the left of the release bearing, the slave cylinder piston's movement is reversed to force the release bearing against the diaphragm spring.

As the friction plate facings wear, the pressure plate moves towards the flywheel, thus causing the diaphragm spring fingers to move towards the release bearing and reducing the clearance which must be present between the spring and bearing. To prevent clutch slip on 1.6 litre models the clutch cable must be periodically adjusted to restore this clearance. On 1.8 and 2.0 litre models adjustment is made automatically at the hydraulic system master cylinder.

2 Routine maintenance

Carry out the following procedures at the intervals given in 'Routine maintenance' at the beginning of this Manual.

Check the hydraulic fluid level – 1.8 and 2.0 litre models

1 Check that the hydraulic fluid level in the clutch master cylinder translucent reservoir is between the 'Max' and 'Min' lines marked on the reservoir. If the level is below the 'Min' line, top up to between the level lines using only good quality fluid of the specified type from a freshly-opened container (photo).

2 If frequent topping-up is necessary, check carefully for signs of fluid leaks from the various components of the system. Any leaks found should be cured immediately by the renewal of the seal or component concerned.

3 While a specific service interval is not given by the manufacturer, owners should note that the clutch hydraulic fluid should be renewed at regular intervals; this task can be carried out whenever the brake fluid is renewed. See 'Routine maintenance' at the beginning of this Manual.

Note: *Hydraulic fluid is an effective paint stripper and will also attack plastics. If any is spilt, it should be washed off immediately using copious quantities of fresh water. Always use good quality fluid of the specified type and ensure that it comes from a freshly-opened sealed container; brake fluid is hygroscopic (it absorbs moisture from the air), so old fluid may be contaminated and unfit for further use.*

General inspection

4 Check carefully all visible components of the system and ensure that all are securely fastened and free from damage or deterioration of any sort. Check that the hydraulic pipes and hose (or control cable, as applicable) are not chafing against any other component. On 1.8 and 2.0 litre models check carefully for signs of fluid leaks.

2.1 Use only fluid of specified type when topping-up clutch master cylinder

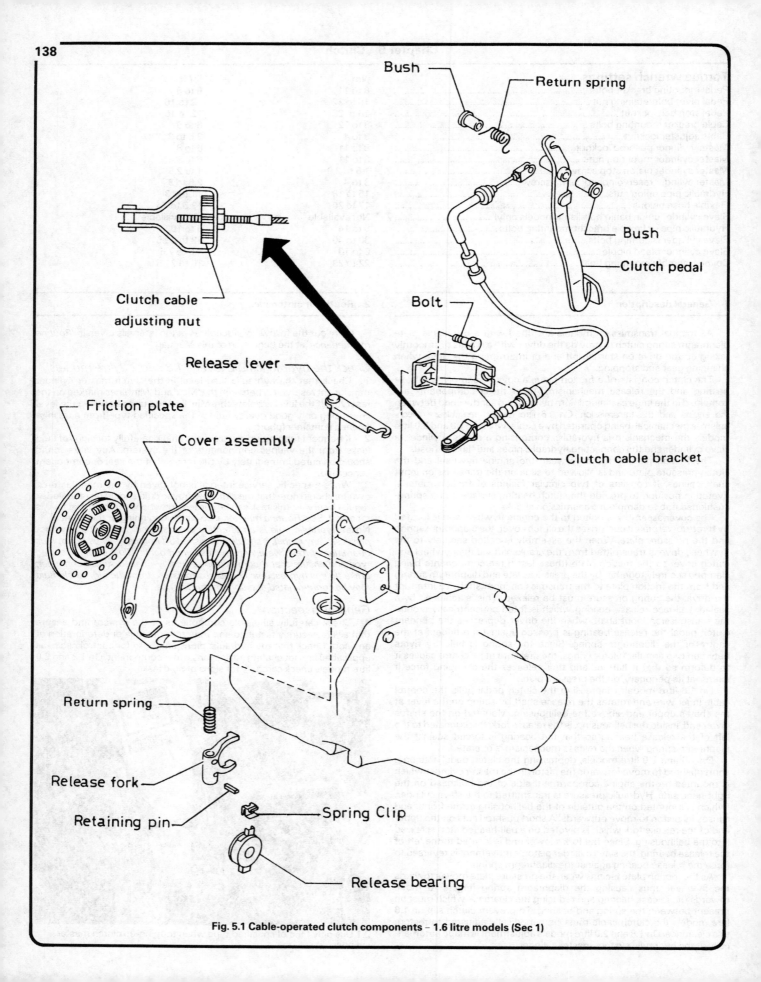

Bush

Return spring

Bush

Clutch pedal

Clutch cable
adjusting nut

Bolt

Release lever

Clutch cable bracket

Friction plate

Cover assembly

Return spring

Release fork

Retaining pin

Spring Clip

Release bearing

Fig. 5.1 Cable-operated clutch components – 1.6 litre models (Sec 1)

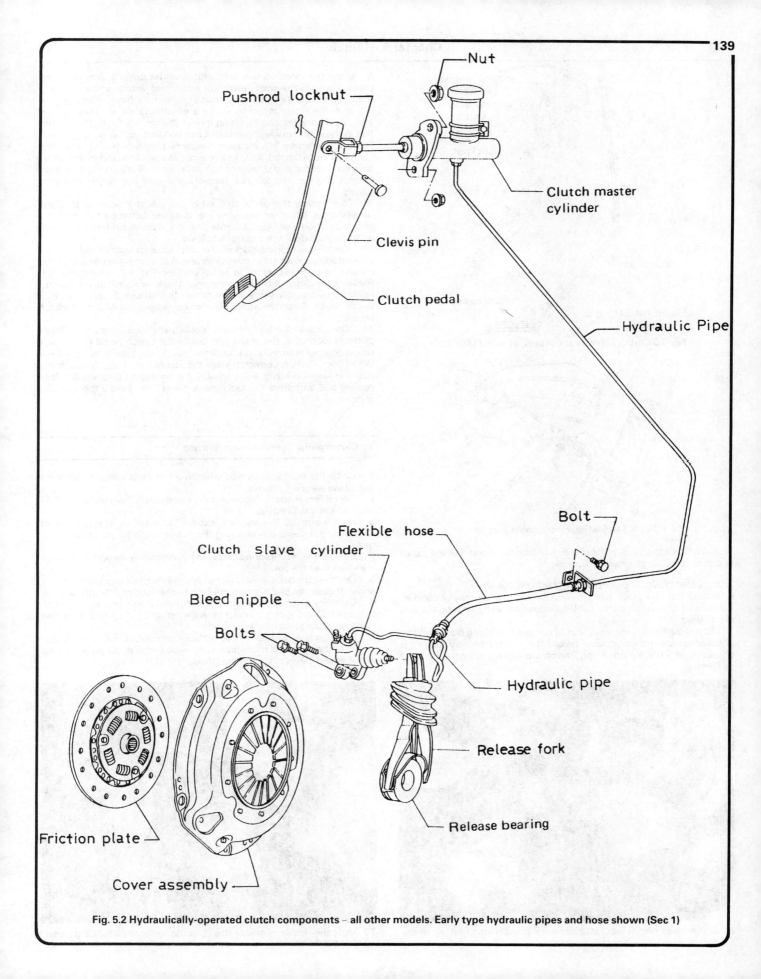

Fig. 5.2 Hydraulically-operated clutch components – all other models. Early type hydraulic pipes and hose shown (Sec 1)

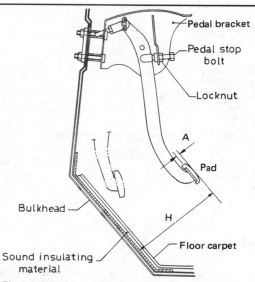

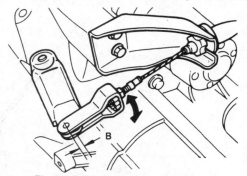

Fig. 5.3 Clutch adjustment details, at pedal (Sec 2)

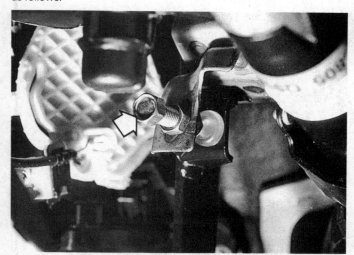

Fig. 5.4 Adjusting clutch cable (Sec 2)

5   Check that the pedal pivot is properly lubricated and that the clutch operates correctly as described below.

Check the clutch operation and adjustment

6   Check that the clutch pedal moves smoothly and easily through its full travel and that the clutch itself functions correctly with no trace of slip or drag.

7   The pedal height, once set, should not need resetting but should be checked as a matter of course before the pedal free play setting is altered or, on 1.6 litre models only, the control cable is adjusted. Proceed as follows.

8   Undo the three screws and withdraw the driver's door sill tread panel. Remove the single retaining screw and withdraw the footwell right-hand side trim panel, releasing it from its front retaining clip. Remove the single retaining screw and withdraw the throttle pedal stop. Peel back the carpet, lifting it over the driver's footrest, until the flap in the sound insulating material can be lifted up. With reference to Fig. 5.3 (dimension 'H'), measure the pedal height from the pedal pad centre to the bulkhead. If the height is not as specified slacken the pedal stop bolt locknut and screw the bolt in or out until the setting is correct (photo). Tighten the locknut securely and refit the carpet and trim panels.

9   To measure the pedal free play, depress the pedal until slight resistance is felt, then measure the distance between this and the at-rest position (see Fig. 5.3, dimension 'A'). If the pedal free play is not as specified, adjust the setting as follows.

10   On 1.6 litre models, slacken the cable adjuster locknut and turn the knurled adjuster nut at the release lever end of the control cable until the release lever free play is as specified (see Fig. 5.4, dimension 'B'). Recheck the clutch pedal free play; since these two settings are directly related it follows that if one is correct the other should also be correct, or within limits. When the setting is correct, tighten the adjuster locknut securely.

11   On 1.8 and 2.0 litre models, slacken the clutch master cylinder pushrod locknut at the clevis just below the clutch pedal pivot, then screw the pushrod in or out until the pedal free play is as specified. When the setting is correct, tighten the locknut securely. To reach the pushrod and locknut it will probably be necessary to undo the four screws and withdraw the facia lower panel from below the steering column.

3   Clutch pedal – removal and refitting

1   Undo the four screws and withdraw the facia lower panel from below the steering column.

2   On 1.6 litre models, disconnect the clutch cable from the pedal. See Section 4 of this Chapter.

3   On 1.8 and 2.0 litre models, extract the retaining spring clip and withdraw the clevis pin securing the master cylinder pushrod to the pedal.

4   Release the return spring pressure by unhooking the spring end that is looped over the pedal.

5   Unscrew the pedal pivot bolt nut and washer, remove the pivot bolt and withdraw the pedal, complete with bushes and return spring.

6   Carefully clean all components and renew any that are worn or damaged. Check with particular care the return spring and the bearing surfaces of the pivot bushes and bolt.

7   Refitting is a reversal of the removal procedure, but apply a thin smear of the specified multi-purpose grease to the pedal pivot bearing surfaces and clevis pin before installation (photo).

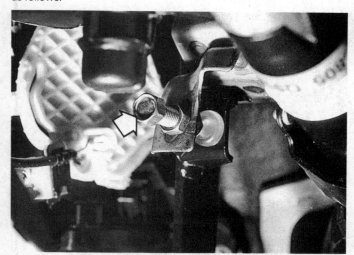

2.8 Clutch pedal height is adjusted by turning pedal stop bolt (arrowed)

3.7 Apply thin smear of grease to all bearing surfaces on refitting pedal – Turbo model shown

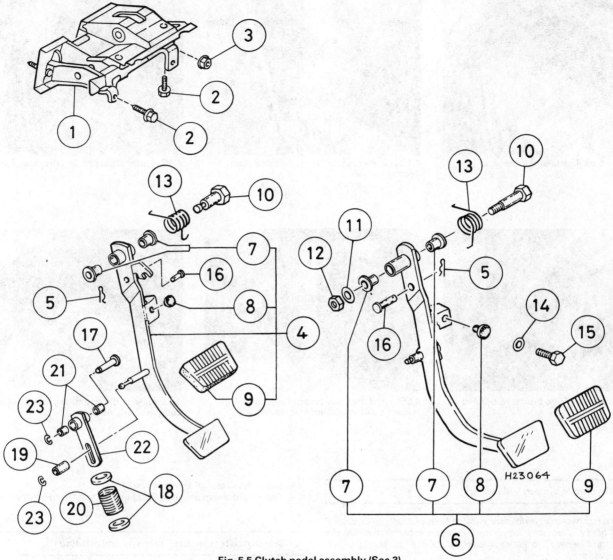

Fig. 5.5 Clutch pedal assembly (Sec 3)

1	Pedal mounting bracket	7	Pedal pivot bushes	13	Return spring	18	Spring seat
2	Bolt	8	Stop pad	14	Washer	19	Collar
3	Nut	9	Pedal rubber pad	15	Pedal stop bolt	20	Pedal assist spring
4	Pedal – Turbo models	10	Pedal pivot bolt	16	Clevis pin (hydraulic clutch	21	Bush
5	Spring clip	11	Washer		only)	22	Pedal assist lever
6	Pedal – non-Turbo models	12	Nut	17	Pin	23	Spring clip
	(hydraulic type shown)						

8   Referring to Section 2 of this Chapter, reset the pedal height and check the pedal free play. Refit the facia panel.

4   Clutch cable – removal and refitting

1   Working in the engine compartment, slacken the adjuster locknut and unscrew the knurled adjuster nut until there is sufficient slack for the cable end clevis pin to be unhooked from the release lever (photos).
2   Disengage the cable from the brackets on the bellhousing and bulkhead, then unscrew the two nuts securing the cable abutment to the bulkhead (photos).
3   Working inside the car, undo the four screws and withdraw the facia lower panel from below the steering column, then reach up and unhook

the cable end clevis pin from the clutch pedal. Return to the engine compartment and withdraw the cable forwards through the bulkhead aperture; note the gasket fitted to the abutment.
4   Examine the cable, looking for worn end fittings or a damaged outer casing and for signs of fraying of the inner wire. Check the operation of the cable; the inner wire should move smoothly and easily through the outer casing, but remember that a cable that appears serviceable when tested off the car may well be much heavier in operation when compressed into its working position. Renew the cable if it shows any sign of wear or damage. **Do not** apply lubricant in an attempt to restore a worn cable.
5   Refitting is a reversal of the removal procedure, but apply a thin smear of the specified multi-purpose grease to the cable end clevis pins before installation (photo).
6   Referring to Section 2 of this Chapter, adjust the cable.

4.1A Slacken cable adjuster locknut ...

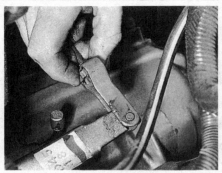

4.1B ... and unscrew knurled adjuster nut, if necessary ...

4.1C ... until cable can be unhooked from release lever

4.2A Release cable from bulkhead bracket (arrowed) ...

4.2B ... and unscrew two nuts (arrowed) to release cable abutment from bulkhead

4.5 Grease cable end fittings on reassembly and check adjustment

5   Clutch hydraulic system – bleeding

Note: *The basic two-man procedure is given here, but refer to Chapter 9 for details of the alternative equipment now available to simplify the operation; the bleeding procedure is identical for both brake and clutch hydraulic systems*

1   Obtain a new, still-sealed, container of the specified type of hydraulic fluid, a clean glass jar, a length of (preferably clear plastic) tubing which will fit tightly over the slave cylinder bleed nipple, a ring spanner to fit the bleed nipple and an assistant.

2   Remove the bleed nipple dust cap and clean the area around the nipple, then fit the spanner and tube to the nipple. Place the other end of the tube in the jar and pour in sufficient fluid to cover the end of the tube. Remove the clutch master cylinder reservoir cap and top it up to the 'Max' level line. Refit the cap loosely, but remember to watch the fluid level and to keep it topped up throughout the bleeding procedure. Do not allow the level to fall below the 'Min' line at any time or there is a risk of further air entering the system.

3   Have an assistant fully depress the clutch pedal several times and maintain pressure on the final stroke.

4   While pedal pressure is maintained, unscrew the bleed nipple (approximately one turn) and allow the compressed fluid and air to flow into the jar. The assistant should maintain pedal pressure, following it down to the floor if necessary, and should not release it until ordered to do so. When the flow stops, tighten the bleed nipple again, release the pedal slowly and check the reservoir fluid level.

5   Repeat the steps given in paragraphs 3 and 4 until the fluid emerging from the bleed nipple is free from air bubbles. Remember to watch the reservoir fluid level.

6   When no more air bubbles appear, tighten the bleed nipple securely, remove the tubing and spanner and refit the dust cap. Check the reservoir fluid level and top up if necessary, then tighten the reservoir

cap securely. Wash off any spilt fluid.

7   Dispose of the expelled fluid safely – it is not fit to be re-used.

6   Clutch master cylinder – removal and refitting

1   Referring to Section 5 of this Chapter, connect a length of tubing to the slave cylinder bleed nipple, unscrew (one turn) the bleed nipple and repeatedly depress the clutch pedal until the system has been emptied and all the fluid has drained into the glass jar.

2   Working inside the car, undo the four screws and withdraw the facia lower panel from below the steering column.

3   Reach up and extract the retaining spring clip, then withdraw the clevis pin securing the master cylinder pushrod to the clutch pedal.

4   Returning to the engine compartment, unscrew the union nut and disconnect the hydraulic pipe; use a piece of rag to mop up any spilt fluid.

5   Unscrew the two mounting nuts and withdraw the master cylinder from the bulkhead.

6   Refitting is a reversal of the removal procedure, but apply a thin smear of the specified multi-purpose grease to the pushrod clevis pin before it is refitted to the clutch pedal. Check the pedal height (see Section 2) as soon as the master cylinder is securely fastened to the bulkhead and the pushrod is connected to the pedal.

7   Connect the hydraulic pipe to the master cylinder and carefully tighten the union nut. Refill the reservoir with fresh hydraulic fluid of the specified type, unscrew (one turn) the bleed nipple and depress repeatedly the clutch pedal until fluid can be seen emerging from the bleed nipple into the tubing. Bleed the system, as described in Section 5 of this Chapter, to remove all traces of air. Wash off any spilt fluid.

8   Referring to Section 2 of this Chapter, check the clutch pedal free play and adjust it if necessary.

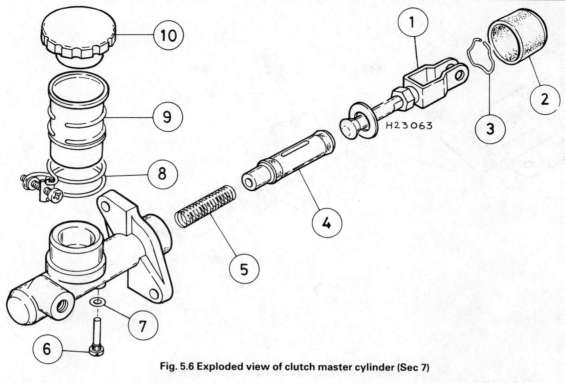

Fig. 5.6 Exploded view of clutch master cylinder (Sec 7)

1 Pushrod	4 Piston assembly	7 Sealing washer	9 Reservoir
2 Dust cover	5 Return spring	8 Reservoir band	10 Reservoir cap
3 Stopper ring	6 Piston stop screw		

Groove

Fig. 5.7 Master cylinder piston assembly fitting details (Sec 7)

7 Clutch master cylinder – overhaul

1 Remove the master cylinder as described in Section 6 of this Chapter, then clean it thoroughly.

2 Peel back the rubber dust cover, then extract the stopper ring from the master cylinder bore and withdraw the pushrod assembly. Slacken the locknut and unscrew the clevis to permit the removal of the dust cover.

3 Using a screwdriver to press the piston in against spring pressure, unscrew the piston stop screw. With the stop screw and sealing washer fully removed, extract the piston assembly and spring from the master cylinder; if necessary tap the assembly on a block of wood to jar them free. Note the fitted position of the piston seals.

4 The reservoir body can be released, if required, by slackening the reservoir band clamping screw.

5 Thoroughly clean all components using only methylated spirit or clean hydraulic fluid. Never use mineral-based solvents such as petrol or paraffin which will attack the hydraulic system's rubber components.

6 Carefully examine all parts of the master cylinder, looking carefully for signs of wear or damage. In particular the cylinder bore and piston must be perfect; free from any signs of scratches, corrosion, or wear. If there is any doubt about the condition of any part of the master cylinder, it must be renewed. Note that while it is good practice to renew the piston seals whenever they are disturbed, they are only available from Nissan dealers as part of the piston repair kit.

7 On reassembly, soak the new piston assembly, stop screw sealing washer and return spring in clean hydraulic fluid, and also smear clean fluid inside the master cylinder bore before installation. It should be stressed that all components must be absolutely clean on reassembly and that only clean hydraulic fluid of the specified type should be used as a lubricant, except for the pushrod inner end and the dust cover sealing lips, which must be lubricated with a smear of rubber grease.

8 Fit the return spring to the piston assembly and insert the two into the master cylinder bore. Take great care not to damage the piston seal edges as they enter the bore, and rotate the piston so that its slot aligns with the stop screw threaded hole, as shown in Fig. 5.7. Press the piston fully in against spring pressure and refit the stop screw and sealing washer. Check that the piston moves smoothly in the bore.

9 Fit the stopper ring and dust cover to the pushrod, then screw the locknut and clevis on to the pushrod end. Insert the assembly into the master cylinder, press the stopper ring into its groove and refit the dust cover.

10 Refit the reservoir, if removed, and carefully tighten the band clamping screw.

11 Refit the master cylinder to the car as described in Section 6 of this Chapter.

8 Clutch slave cylinder – removal and refitting

1 To minimise the loss of fluid, either remove the master cylinder reservoir cap and then tighten it down on to a piece of polythene, or clamp the system's flexible hose using a brake hose clamp, a G-clamp or a similar tool. Alternatively use the procedure outlined in Section 6, paragraph 1 of this Chapter to drain the system completely.

2 Unscrew the union nut (early models) or banjo bolt (later models) and disconnect the hydraulic pipe or hose; note the sealing washer on each side of the hose union on later models.

3 Unscrew the two mounting bolts and withdraw the slave cylinder complete with, on Turbo and turbo Executive models, the heat shield. Take care not to spill any fluid on the car's paintwork.

4 Refitting is a reversal of the removal procedure, but apply a smear of

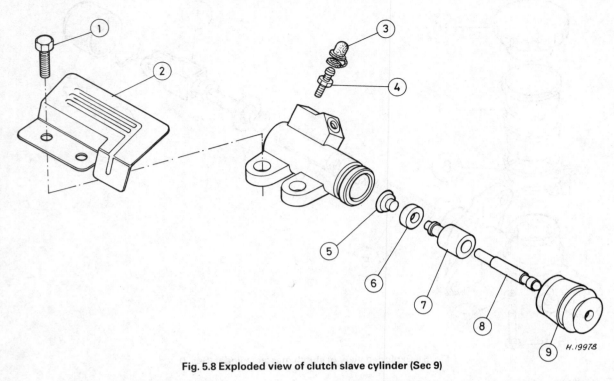

Fig. 5.8 Exploded view of clutch slave cylinder (Sec 9)

1	Bolt	4	Bleed nipple
2	Heat shield – Turbo models	5	Piston spring
3	Dust cap		

6	Piston seal	8	Pushrod
7	Piston	9	Dust cover

molybdenum disulphide grease to the pushrod end before installation.

5   Connect the hydraulic pipe or hose to the slave cylinder; on later models always fit new sealing washers each side of the banjo union. Tighten the union nut or bolt securely.

6   Remove the master cylinder reservoir cap and discard the piece of polythene or unclamp the flexible hose, as appropriate. Connect the bleeding tube and glass jar (see Section 5 of this Chapter) to the slave cylinder bleed nipple, unscrew (one turn) the bleed nipple and depress the clutch pedal repeatedly until fluid can be seen emerging from the bleed nipple into the tubing. Bleed the system, as described in Section 5 of this Chapter, to remove all traces of air and wash off any spilt fluid.

7   Referring to Section 2 of this Chapter, check the clutch pedal free play and adjust it if necessary.

9   Clutch slave cylinder – overhaul

1   Remove the slave cylinder as described in Section 8 of this Chapter, then clean it thoroughly.

2   Peel off the rubber dust cover, then withdraw the pushrod. Tap the cylinder on to a wooden block to release the piston and its spring. Remove the seal from the piston, noting carefully which way round it is fitted.

3   Thoroughly clean all components using only methylated spirit or clean hydraulic fluid. Never use mineral-based solvents such as petrol or paraffin which will attack the hydraulic system's rubber components.

4   Discard the rubber seals, which should be renewed as a matter of course whenever the cylinder is dismantled and are available as a repair kit. Carefully examine all other components, renewing any that show signs of wear, damage or corrosion. In particular check the cylinder bore and piston, which must be perfect and free from scratches or scoring. If any such imperfections are found, the complete cylinder assembly must be renewed.

5   On reassembly soak the piston, spring and the new piston seal in clean hydraulic fluid and also smear clean hydraulic fluid in the cylinder

bore before installation. It should be stressed that all components must be absolutely clean on reassembly and that the piston assembly should be refitted wet, using only clean hydraulic fluid as a lubricant.

6   Fit the new seal to the piston with its sealing lip towards the spring.

7   Fit the spring to the piston and insert the two into the cylinder bore; take great care not to damage or deform the piston seal's lip as it enters the bore.

8   Press the piston fully into the bore. Smear rubber grease over the pushrod and refit it, followed by the dust cover.

9   Refit the slave cylinder to the car as described in Section 8 of this Chapter.

10   Hydraulic pipes and hose – inspection, removal and refitting

1   On early models the clutch master and slave cylinders are connected by a metal hydraulic pipe which runs along the bulkhead to a bracket bolted to the left-hand inner wing. A flexible hose leads from there to a second metal hydraulic pipe, which leads to the slave cylinder.

2   On later models a metal hydraulic pipe runs along the bulkhead to a bracket bolted to the left-hand inner wing. A flexible hose leads from there to the slave cylinder; it is clipped at its mid-point.

3   When checking the system, first look for signs of leakage at the pipe or hose unions, then examine the flexible hose for signs of cracking, chafing or deterioration of the rubber. Check that the pipes and hose are securely fastened in their clips or brackets.

4   Carefully work along the length of the metal hydraulic pipes looking for dents, damage or corrosion. Corrosion should be polished off and if the depth of pitting is significant the pipe should be renewed.

5   If any pipe or hose is to be renewed, minimise fluid loss by removing the master cylinder reservoir cap and then tightening it down on to a piece of polythene to obtain an airtight seal.

6   Before disconnecting any union, thoroughly clean it and the surrounding area.

7   To unscrew the union nuts it is preferable to obtain a brake pipe

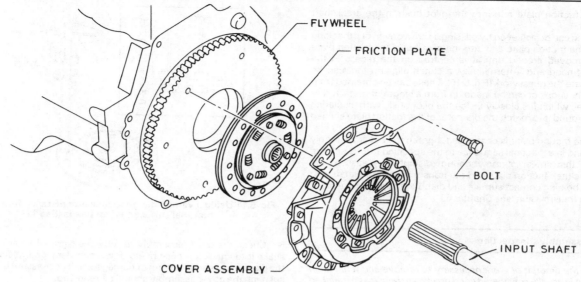

Fig. 5.9 Clutch assembly (Sec 11)

spanner of the correct size; these are available from most large motor accessory shops. Failing this a close-fitting open-ended spanner will be required, but note that if the nuts are tight or corroded their flats may be rounded-off if an open-ended spanner slips. In such a case a self-locking wrench is often the only way to unscrew a stubborn union, but it follows that the hydraulic pipe and damaged nuts must be renewed on re-assembly.

8   If a hydraulic pipe is to be renewed it can be obtained, cut to length and with the end flares and union nuts in place, from Nissan dealers. All that is then necessary is to bend it to shape, following the line of the original pipe, before it is fitted to the car. Alternatively, most motor accessory shops can make up hydraulic pipes from kits, though this requires very careful measurement of the original to ensure that the replacement is of the correct length; the safest answer is usually to take the old pipe to the shop as a pattern.

9   On refitting, do not overtighten the union nuts; the specified torque settings are not high, and it is not necessary to exercise brute force to obtain a sound joint. On later models, always renew the sealing washers on each side of the slave cylinder banjo union whenever they are disturbed.

10   Ensure that the pipes and hose are correctly routed with no kinks and that they are secured in the clips or brackets provided. After refitting, remove the polythene from the reservoir and bleed the hydraulic system as described in Section 5 of this Chapter. Wash off any spilt fluid.

11   Clutch assembly – removal and refitting

1   Unless the complete engine/transmission unit is to be removed from the car and separated for major overhaul (see Chapter 1), the clutch can only be reached after the transmission has been removed. See Chapter 6.

2   Before disturbing the clutch, use chalk or a felt-tip pen to mark the relationship of the cover assembly to the flywheel.

3   Working in a diagonal sequence, slacken the cover assembly bolts by half a turn at a time until spring pressure is released and the bolts can be unscrewed by hand (photo).

4   Prise the cover assembly off its locating dowels and remove the friction plate, noting which way round it is fitted.

5   On reassembly, ensure that the bearing surfaces of the flywheel and pressure plate are completely clean, smooth and free from oil or grease. Use solvent to remove any protective grease from new components.

6   Fit the friction plate so that the longer part of the central splined boss is towards the flywheel and the spring hub assembly faces away from the flywheel.

7   Refit the cover assembly, aligning the marks made on dismantling (if the original cover is re-used) and locating the cover on its three

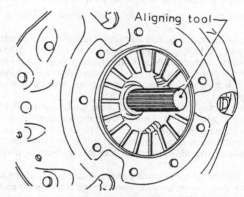

Fig. 5.10 Using a clutch aligning tool to centralise the friction plate (Sec 11)

11.3 Slacken clutch cover bolts as described in text to release safely spring pressure

locating dowels. Fit the mounting bolts but tighten them only finger-tight, so that the friction plate can still be moved.

8   The friction plate must now be centralised so that when the transmission is refitted its input shaft will pass through the splines at the

centre of the friction plate and into the pilot bush in the crankshaft left-hand end.

9   Centralising can be achieved by passing a screwdriver, or other long bar, through the friction plate and into the pilot bush; the friction plate can then be moved around until it is centred on the recess in the crankshaft left-hand end. Alternatively, a clutch aligning tool can be used to eliminate the guesswork (Fig. 5.10). These can be obtained from most accessory shops or can be made up from a length of metal rod or wooden dowel, which fits closely inside the pilot bush, with insulating tape wound around it to match the diameter of the friction plate splined hole.

10   When the friction plate is centralised, tighten the cover assembly bolts evenly and in a diagonal sequence to the specified torque setting.

11   Apply a thin smear of molybdenum disulphide grease to the splines of the clutch friction plate and the transmission input shaft, and to the release bearing contact surface and diaphragm spring fingers.

12   Refit the transmission (see Chapter 6.)

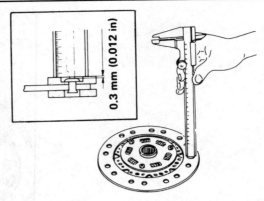

Fig. 5.11 Using a vernier gauge to measure distance from friction material surface to rivet heads (Sec 12)

12   Clutch assembly – inspection

Note: *Due to the amount of work necessary to remove and refit clutch components, it is usually considered good practice to renew as a matched set the clutch friction plate, cover assembly and release bearing, even if only one of these is actually worn enough to require renewal.*

1   Remove the clutch assembly, as described in Section 11 of this Chapter.

2   When cleaning the clutch components, remove dust using a clean dry cloth and working in a well-ventilated atmosphere, then dispose of the cloth safely; asbestos dust is harmful and must not be inhaled (see *'Safety first!'*). Although some friction materials may no longer contain asbestos it is safest to assume that they do, and to take precautions accordingly.

3   Check the friction plate facings for signs of wear (Fig. 5.11), damage or oil contamination. If the distance from the friction material surface to any of the rivets is less than 0.3 mm (0.012 in), if the friction material is cracked, burnt, scored or damaged, or if it is contaminated with oil or grease, (shown by shiny black patches), the friction plate must be renewed.

4   If the friction material is still serviceable, check that the centre boss splines are unworn, that the torsion springs are in good condition and securely fastened and that all the rivets are tightly fastened. If any wear or damage is found, the friction plate must be renewed.

5   If the friction material is fouled with oil, this must be due to an oil leak either from the crankshaft left-hand oil seal or sump/cylinder block joint or from the transmission input shaft. Renew the seal or repair the joint as described in Chapter 1 or 6, as appropriate.

6   Check the cover assembly for obvious signs of wear or damage; shake it to check for loose rivets or worn or damaged fulcrum rings. If the diaphragm spring is worn or damaged, or if its pressure is in any way suspect, the cover assembly should be renewed.

7   Examine closely the machined bearing surfaces of the pressure plate and of the flywheel; these should be clean, completely flat and free from scratches or scoring. If either is discoloured from excessive heat or shows signs of cracks it should be renewed, although minor damage of this nature can sometimes be polished away using emery paper.

8   Check the release bearing as described in Section 14 of this Chapter.

13   Clutch release mechanism – removal and refitting

Removal and refitting – all models

1   Unless the complete engine/transmission unit is to be removed from the car and separated for major overhaul (see Chapter 1), the clutch release mechanism can only be reached after the transmission has been removed. See Chapter 6.

2   Refitting is as described in Chapter 6.

Dismantling and reassembly – 1.6 litre models

3   Prising the two spring clips clear of the release fork arms, pull the release bearing off its guide sleeve. Pull the spring clips off the bearing tongues, noting how they are fitted.

4   Rotate the release shaft until the fork retaining pins can be driven out, using a hammer and a parallel-sided pin punch, into the cavities in the bellhousing wall (see Fig. 5.13).

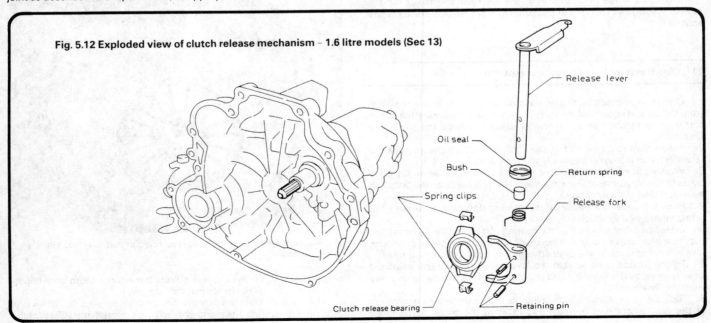

Fig. 5.12 Exploded view of clutch release mechanism – 1.6 litre models (Sec 13)

Release lever

Oil seal

Bush

Return spring

Spring clips

Release fork

Clutch release bearing

Retaining pin

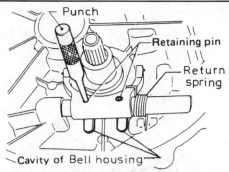

Fig. 5.13 Driving out release fork retaining pins – 1.6 litre models (Sec 13)

5   Withdraw the release lever and shaft, collecting the fork and return spring as they drop clear.

6   An oil seal and pivot bush are fitted to the bellhousing at the release shaft's upper bearing. If worn or damaged the seal can be levered out, taking care not to damage its housing, and a new seal can be tapped into place. The bush can be extracted either by using an internally-expanding bearing puller or by using a tap to cut a thread in the bush, so that a bolt, nut and washer can be screwed into the bush. Hold the bolt steady and tighten the nut against the bellhousing (with the washer preventing damage to the housing) to draw the bush out of its bore. Tap the new bush into the housing using a suitable drift; a stepped, parallel-sided drift would be ideal but is not necessary if care is taken.

7   On refitting, apply a thin smear of molybdenum disulphide grease to the release shaft and insert it into the housing (photo). Fit the return spring to the shaft with its straight end against the bellhousing wall, then fit the release fork.

8   Press the shaft fully into its lower bearing, ensuring that it is properly greased, then rotate the shaft to its correct position, align the release fork holes with those in the shaft and tap the fork retaining pins fully into place. Fit the return spring as shown in Fig. 5.13.

9   Press the spring clips into place on the release bearing tongues (photo).

10   Apply a smear of molybdenum disulphide grease to the release bearing guide sleeve, to the release fork ends, to the release bearing spring clips, to the groove in the release bearing's centre bore and to the bearing's contact surface with the diaphragm spring fingers. Use only the thinnest possible smear of grease, as any surplus may melt and find its way on to the friction plate facings.

11   Fit the release bearing over the guide sleeve and press it into place until the spring clips lock into the fork ends.

Dismantling and reassembly – all other models

12   Peel off the rubber dust cover from the bellhousing opening and pull it off the release fork. Use a screwdriver or similar to prise the retainer spring from the ball-headed stop.

13   Pull the release fork upwards and out of the bellhousing aperture until the release bearing spring clips are released from the fork ends. Withdraw the release bearing and release fork. Note exactly how the spring clips are fitted before removing them from the release bearing tongues.

14   The ball-headed stop can be unscrewed from the bellhousing wall if required. Ensure it is securely tightened on refitting.

15   On reassembly, apply a thin smear of molybdenum disulphide grease to the ball-headed stop and release fork socket, to the release fork ends and release bearing spring clips, to the guide sleeve and release bearing centre bore and to the bearing's contact surface with the diaphragm spring fingers. Use only the thinnest possible smear of grease, as any surplus may melt and find its way on to the friction plate facings.

16   Ensuring that they are correctly located, press the spring clips into place on the release bearing tongues.

17   Ensure that the retaining spring is in place on the release fork, insert the fork into the bellhousing aperture from the inside and fit the release bearing to the fork. Install the bearing on its guide sleeve, ensuring that the fork ends fit correctly into the spring clips and the fork socket fits over the ball-headed stop.

18   Use a screwdriver to clip the retainer spring behind each side of the stop. Refit the rubber dust cover.

14   Clutch release mechanism – inspection

1   Check the release mechanism, renewing any component which is worn or damaged. Carefully check all bearing surfaces and points of contact.

2   When checking the release bearing itself, note that it is often considered worthwhile to renew it as a matter of course (see Section 12). Check that the contact surface rotates smoothly and easily, with no sign of noise or roughness and that the surface itself is smooth and unworn, with no signs of cracks, pitting or scoring. If there is any doubt about its condition the bearing must be renewed.

13.7 Grease clutch release shaft bearing surfaces before refitting – 1.6 litre models

13.9 Fit spring clips as shown to release bearing tongues – 1.6 litre models

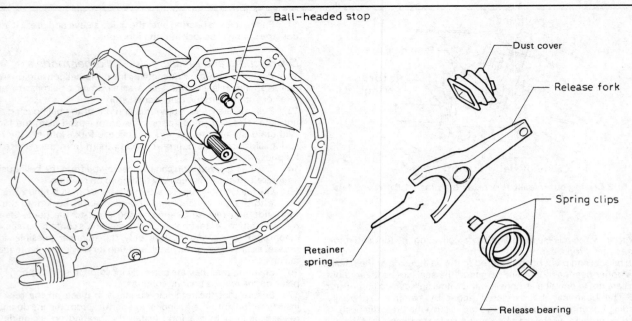

Fig. 5.14 Exploded view of clutch release mechanism – 1.8 and 2.0 litre models (Sec 13)

15   Fault diagnosis – clutch

Symptom	Reason(s)
Judder when taking up drive	Loose engine transmission mountings Badly worn or oil contaminated friction material Worn or corroded splines on transmission input shaft or friction plate centre boss Worn or damaged cable Faulty master or slave cylinder Faulty cover assembly
Clutch drag (failure to disengage, gears cannot be meshed)	Incorrect pedal adjustment Incorrect cable adjustment Damaged cable Loss of hydraulic fluid or air in system Faulty master or slave cylinder Friction plate sticking on transmission input shaft splines Faulty cover assembly
Clutch slip (increase in engine speed does not result in increase in road speed – particularly on gradients)	Incorrect cable adjustment Incorrect pedal adjustment Friction linings worn out or contaminated with oil Release mechanism sticking or partially seized Faulty or worn cover assembly
Noise evident on depressing clutch pedal	Dry, worn or damaged release bearing Faulty release mechanism Faulty cover assembly Worn or corroded splines on transmission input shaft or friction plate centre boss
Noise evident on releasing clutch pedal	Broken friction plate torsion springs Faulty cover assembly Distorted or damaged friction plate Dry or worn pedal pivot bushes Transmission worn or damaged

Note: *This Section is not intended to be an exhaustive guide to fault diagnosis but summarises the more common faults which may be encountered during a car's life. Consult a dealer for more specific advice*

Chapter 6 Manual transmission

Contents

Specifications

General
Type.. Five forward speeds, all with synchromesh, and reverse, integral final drive

Designation:
    1.6 litre models.. RS5F31A
    1.8 (including Turbo) and 2.0 litre models.................... RS5F50A

Gearbox

	1.6 litre models	1.8 and 2.0 litre carburettor models	Fuel injection models
1st	3.333:1 (50/15T)	3.286:1 (46/14T)	3.400:1 (51/15T)
2nd	1.955:1 (43/22T)	1.850:1 (37/20T)	1.955:1 (43/22T)
3rd	1.286:1 (36/28T)	1.207:1 (35/29T)	1.273:1 (42/33T)
4th	0.902:1 (37/41T)	0.911:1 (41/45T)	0.911:1 (41/45T)
5th	0.733:1 (33/45T)	0.740:1 (37/50T)	0.740:1 (37/50T)
Reverse	3.417:1 (41/12,30T)	3.429:1 (48/14,29T)	3.429:1 (48/14,29T)

Final drive
1.6 litre models (up to early 1988)..................................... 4.353:1 (74/17T)
1.6 litre models (1988-on) all 1.8 litre carburettor models........ 4.471:1 (76/17T)
Turbo models... 3.895:1 (74/19T)
2.0 litre models.. 4.167:1 (75/18T)

Lubrication
Oil type/specification... Gear oil to API GL-4, viscosity SAE 80 to 90* (Duckhams Hypoid 80)

See owner's manual for full details
Oil capacity (approximate):
    1.6 litre models, up to February 1987............................ 2.7 litres (4.8 Imp pints)
    1.6 litre models, February 1987-on.............................. 2.8 litres (4.9 Imp pints)
    1.8 (including Turbo) and 2.0 litre models................... 4.7 litres (8.3 Imp pints)

Transmission overhaul data – 1.6 litre models
Gear pinion endfloat:
    Input shaft 5th gear... 0.18 to 0.41 mm (0.0071 to 0.0161 in)
    Output shaft 1st gear... 0.18 to 0.31 mm (0.0071 to 0.0122 in)
    Output shaft 2nd, 3rd and 4th gears............................ 0.20 to 0.40 mm (0.0079 to 0.0158 in)
Snap ring (input shaft) or C-ring (output shaft)-to-groove clearance........ 0 to 0.10 mm (0 to 0.0039 in)

Gear pinion-to-baulk ring clearance:	
Standard..	1.00 to 1.35 mm (0.0394 to 0.0532 in)
Minimum..	0.70 mm (0.0276 in)
Output shaft bearing preload	0.18 to 0.27 mm (0.0071 to 0.0106 in)
Sungear-to-differential case maximum clearance	0.30 mm (0.0118 in)
Differential side bearing preload	0.29 to 0.35 mm (0.0114 to 0.0138 in)
Turning torque:	
Differential only	3.9 to 7.8 Nm (35 to 69 lbf in)
Total transmission	5.9 to 13.7 Nm (52 to 121 lbf in)

Transmission overhaul data – 1.8 and 2.0 litre models

Gear pinion endfloat:	
Input shaft 3rd gear	0.23 to 0.43 mm (0.0091 to 0.0169 in)
Input shaft 4th gear	0.25 to 0.55 mm (0.0098 to 0.0217 in)
Input shaft 5th gear	0.23 to 0.48 mm (0.0091 to 0.0189 in)
Output shaft 1st gear	0.23 to 0.43 mm (0.0091 to 0.0169 in)
Output shaft 2nd gear	0.23 to 0.58 mm (0.0091 to 0.0228 in)
Snap ring or thrustwasher-to-groove clearance:	
Input shaft 3rd/4th synchro-hub	0 to 0.10 mm (0 to 0.0039 in)
Input shaft 4th gear pinion	0 to 0.06 mm (0 to 0.0024 in)
Output shaft 1st/2nd synchro-hub	0 to 0.10 mm (0 to 0.0039 in)
Output shaft 5th gear pinion	0 to 0.15 mm (0 to 0.0059 in)
Gear pinion-to-baulk ring clearance:	
Standard..	1.00 to 1.35 mm (0.0394 to 0.0532 in)
Minimum..	0.70 mm (0.0276 in)
Input shaft endfloat..	0 to 0.06 mm (0 to 0.0024 in)
Output shaft bearing preload	0.25 to 0.31 mm (0.0098 to 0.0122 in)
Sungear-to-differential case clearance	0.10 to 0.20 mm (0.0039 to 0.0079 in)
Differential side bearing preload	0.40 to 0.46 mm (0.0158 to 0.0181 in)
Turning torque:	
Differential only	4.9 to 7.8 Nm (43 to 69 lbf in)
Total transmission	8.8 to 21.6 Nm (78 to 191 lbf in)

Torque wrench settings

	Nm	lbf ft
Filler/level plug:		
Up to February 1987	25 to 34	18.5 to 25
February 1987-on	10 to 20	7.5 to 15
Drain plug:		
1.6 litre models	25 to 34	18.5 to 25
1.8 and 2.0 litre models	15 to 20	11 to 15
Gearchange lever and linkage:		
Control rod-to-striking rod yoke through-bolt retaining nut	17 to 22	12.5 to 16
Control rod-to-gear lever through-bolt retaining nut...........................	16 to 21	12 to 15.5
Support rod bracket-to-bellhousing bolts	27 to 36	20 to 26.5
Support rod-to-bracket nut	31 to 40	23 to 29.5
Support rod-to-gear lever holder bracket nut............................	20 to 25	15 to 18.5
Support rod-to-gear lever socket nuts	8 to 11	6 to 8
Gear lever holder bracket mounting nuts................................	8 to 11	6 to 8
Speedometer pinion assembly retaining screw................................	3.7 to 5.0	2.5 to 4
Reversing lamp switch	20 to 29	15 to 21.5
Gear position switch retaining screw.................................	3.7 to 5.0	2.5 to 4
Starter motor mounting bolts and nut	29 to 39	21.5 to 29
Intake manifold stay-to-bellhousing bolts – 2.0 litre fuel injection models:		
10 mm thread size	38 to 46	28 to 34
8 mm thread size...	18 to 22	13 to 16
Engine/transmission stay-to-cylinder block/crankcase bolts...................	30 to 40	22 to 29.5
Bellhousing-to-cylinder block/crankcase – 1.6 litre models:		
Bolts 25 mm and 35 mm long	16 to 22	12 to 16
All longer bolts and nut	30 to 40	22 to 29.5
Bellhousing-to-cylinder block/crankcase – 1.8 and 2.0 litre models:		
Bolts 25 mm long	30 to 40	22 to 29.5
All longer bolts and nut	43 to 58	32 to 43
Engine/transmission left-hand mounting:		
Through-bolt retaining nut	39 to 49	29 to 36
Mounting-to-inner wing panel bolts	39 to 49	29 to 36
Mounting-to-transmission casing bolts – 1.6 litre models	49 to 59	36 to 43.5
Mounting-to-transmission casing bolts – 1.8 and 2.0 litre models	44 to 54	32.5 to 40
Transmission casing-to-bellhousing bolts................................	16 to 21	12 to 15.5
Crownwheel-to-differential case bolts	74 to 88	54.5 to 65
Transmission components – 1.6 litre models:		
Circular cover-to-transmission casing bolts................................	6.3 to 8.3	4.5 to 6
Input shaft bearing retainer-to-bellhousing bolts	16 to 21	12 to 15.5
Control bracket-to-bellhousing bolts	6.3 to 8.3	4.5 to 6
Reverse detent plug...	19 to 25	14 to 18.5

Torque wrench settings (continued)

	Nm	lbf ft
Reverse detent plunger assembly screws	6.3 to 8.3	4.5 to 6
Switch blanking plugs	15 to 20	11 to 15
Transmission components – 1.8 and 2.0 litre models:		
Reverse lever assembly mounting bolts	16 to 21	12 to 15.5
Reverse detent assembly mounting bolts	16 to 21	12 to 15.5
5th/reverse, 3rd/4th and 1st/2nd detent plugs	16 to 22	12 to 16
Reverse idler shaft bolt	16 to 21	12 to 15.5

PART A : ALL MODELS

1   General description

The transmission is mounted in a cast aluminium alloy casing bolted to the left-hand end of the engine and consists of the gearbox and final drive differential. This type of design is sometimes also called a transaxle. The gearbox is fitted to enable the driver to select the gear ratio which will most closely match the engine's performance with the load imposed on the car. To this end, five forward gear ratios are provided, as well as the reverse gear and neutral position. The differential is fitted to allow the roadwheels to rotate at different speeds (as they must do when the car is cornering) while still maintaining drive to both.

Drive is transmitted from the crankshaft via the clutch to the input shaft, which rotates in ball journal and/or needle roller bearings and has a long extension. The extension carries the clutch friction plate, which is supported in a spigot bush in the crankshaft left-hand end.

From the input shaft, drive is transmitted to the output shaft, which rotates in taper-roller bearings, and from there to the differential crownwheel. This rotates with the differential case and planetary gears, thus driving the sungears and driveshafts. The rotation of the planetary gears on their shaft allows the inner roadwheel to rotate at a slower speed than the outer roadwheel when the car is cornering.

The input and output shafts are arranged side by side, parallel to the crankshaft and driveshaft, so that the gear pinion teeth are in constant mesh. In the neutral position, the gear pinions rotate freely on needle roller bearings or bushes, so drive is not transmitted from the input shaft.

When the driver selects a gear, the selector mechanism causes the appropriate shift fork to move its synchro-sleeve along the shaft to lock the gear pinion to the synchro-hub. Since the synchro-hubs are splined to their shafts, this locks the gear pinion to the shaft so that drive can be transmitted. To ensure that gearchanging can be made quickly and quietly a synchro-mesh system is fitted on all forward gears, consisting of baulk rings, spreader springs and/or shifting inserts, as well as the gear pinions and synchro-hubs. The synchro-mesh cones are formed on the mating faces of the baulk rings and gear pinions. Gear selection is by a floor-mounted lever acting through a remote control linkage on the selector mechanism.

2   Routine maintenance

1   At the intervals given in 'Routine maintenance' at the beginning of this manual, carry out the following service operations on the transmission.

Check for oil leaks
2   Carefully inspect the transmission and bellhousing joint faces and oil seals for signs of damage, deterioration or oil leakage. Check also the reversing lamp or gear position switch (as applicable) and switch blanking plugs.

Check the transmission oil level – 1.6 litre models
3   Park the car on level ground, apply the handbrake firmly and switch off the ignition. Do not start the engine or allow the car to move while checking the oil level.
4   Unscrew the female socket-headed filler/level plug from the front of the transmission (photo) using a suitable drain plug key and spanner. On cars built before February 1987 a 13 mm (½ inch) square key is required; on cars built subsequently a 10 mm square key will be needed.
5   Using a finger, check that the oil level is up to the bottom of the

filler/level plug hole. If topping-up is required, add only good quality oil of the specified type.
6   If the transmission has been overfilled so that oil flows out as soon as the filler/level plug is removed, check that the car is completely level (side-to-side and front-to-rear) then allow the surplus to drain off into a suitable container. Refit the filler/level plug as soon as the flow stops and wash off any spilt oil.
7   When the level is correct, clean the filler/level plug, apply a smear of sealant to its threads and refit it, tightening it to the specified torque setting.

Check the transmission oil level – 1.8 (including Turbo) and 2.0 litre models
8   Park the car on level ground, apply the handbrake firmly and switch off the ignition. Do not start the engine or allow the car to move while

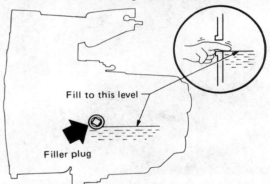

Fig. 6.1 Checking the transmission oil level – 1.6 litre models (Sec 2)

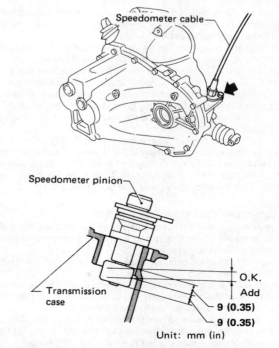

Fig. 6.2 Checking the transmission oil level – 1.8 (including Turbo) and 2.0 litre models (Sec 2)

2.4 Unscrewing filler/level plug – 1.6 litre models

2.11 Topping-up transmission oil – 1.8 (including Turbo) and 2.0 litre models

2.16 Unscrewing drain plug – 1.6 litre models

2.17 Location of drain plug – 1.8 (including Turbo) and 2.0 litre models

checking the oil level.

9   Undo the single retaining screw and withdraw the speedometer pinion assembly from the rear of the transmission; there is no need to disconnect the speedometer cable.

10   Wipe clean the pinion assembly, especially the pinion teeth, and insert the assembly back into the transmission to serve as a dipstick. Ensure that the pinion sleeve sits on the upper surface of the transmission casing as shown in Fig. 6.2. Withdraw the pinion assembly and check that the oil level is within the limits shown, on the pinion teeth.

11   If topping-up is required, add only good quality oil of the specified type (photo). If the level is too high the surplus can be removed using a syringe or similar.

12   When the level is correct, check the sealing O-ring fitted to the speedometer pinion sleeve and renew it if it is worn or damaged, then apply a smear of grease to the O-ring and refit the pinion assembly, ensuring that the gear teeth mesh correctly. Tighten the retaining screw to the specified torque setting and wash off any spilt oil.

Renew the transmission oil – all models

13   This operating is much quicker and more efficient if the car is first taken on a journey of sufficient length to warm the engine/transmission up to normal operating temperature.

14   Park the car on level ground, apply the handbrake firmly and switch off the ignition.

15   Open the bonnet and remove the filler/level plug (1.6 litre models) or the speedometer pinion assembly (all other models) as described above. Place a suitable container under the transmission.

16   On 1.6 litre models use a 13 mm ($\frac{1}{2}$ inch) square drain plug key and suitable spanner to unscrew the female socket-headed drain plug from the transmission casing, below the left-hand driveshaft (photo).

17   On 1.8 (including Turbo) and 2.0 litre models, unscrew the

hexagon-headed drain plug from the bellhousing, below the right-hand driveshaft (photo).

18   Allow the oil to drain completely into the container. If the oil is hot take precautions to prevent the risk of injury.

19   When the oil has fully drained, clean the drain plug, including the magnetic insert (where fitted). On 1.6 litre models apply a smear of sealant to the plug threads and refit it. On all other models, check the condition of the sealing washer and renew it if it is distorted or damaged, then apply a smear of sealant to the plug threads and refit the plug. Tighten the drain plug to the torque setting specified.

20   Refill the transmission with the correct amount of the specified type of oil and check the oil level as described above, then wash off any spilt oil.

3   Gearchange lever and linkage – removal, examination and refitting

Control rod

1   Apply the handbrake firmly, jack up the front of the car and support it securely on axle stands.

2   Working underneath the car at the transmission, unscrew the through-bolt and nut securing the control rod to the selector mechanism striking rod yoke. Take care not to lose the O-rings, bushes and collar from the joint, as they are not available separately (photos).

3   Moving towards the rear of the car, unbolt the heat shield from the underbody and work it clear around the exhaust system to expose the underside of the gear lever – it may be necessary to unbolt the exhaust system mountings in front of and behind the heat shield to provide sufficient movement for this. Note also that one of the four heat shield bolts fastens the exhaust system earth strap.

4   Disconnect the control rod from the gear lever lower end by unhooking the return spring, noting its rubber centre section, and by unscrewing the through-bolt and nut. Again, note the presence of the O-rings, bushes and collar in the gear lever lower end and take care not to lose them (photo).

5   Withdraw the control rod, then check it for damage or distortion and renew it if necessary. Check the joints at both ends to ensure that they move easily and smoothly, without excessive free play. Dismantle, clean and grease the O-rings, bushes and collar in the control rod front joint and gear lever lower end. If any of these are excessively worn they can be renewed only as part of the control rod or gear lever assemblies. Renew the through-bolts if they are worn or damaged.

6   Refitting is the reverse of the removal procedure, noting the following points. Grease the through-bolts before refitting, and tighten their nuts to the specified torque settings. When refitting the heat shield, note that there must be clean metal-to-metal contact from the exhaust system earth strap to the underbody.

Support rod

7   Apply the handbrake firmly, jack up the front of the car and support it securely on axle stands. Remove the heat shield and disconnect the control rod from the gear lever lower end as described in paragraphs 3 and 4 above.

8   Unscrew the single, larger, nut securing the support rod rear end to the holder bracket. Pull the support rod down as far as possible until the

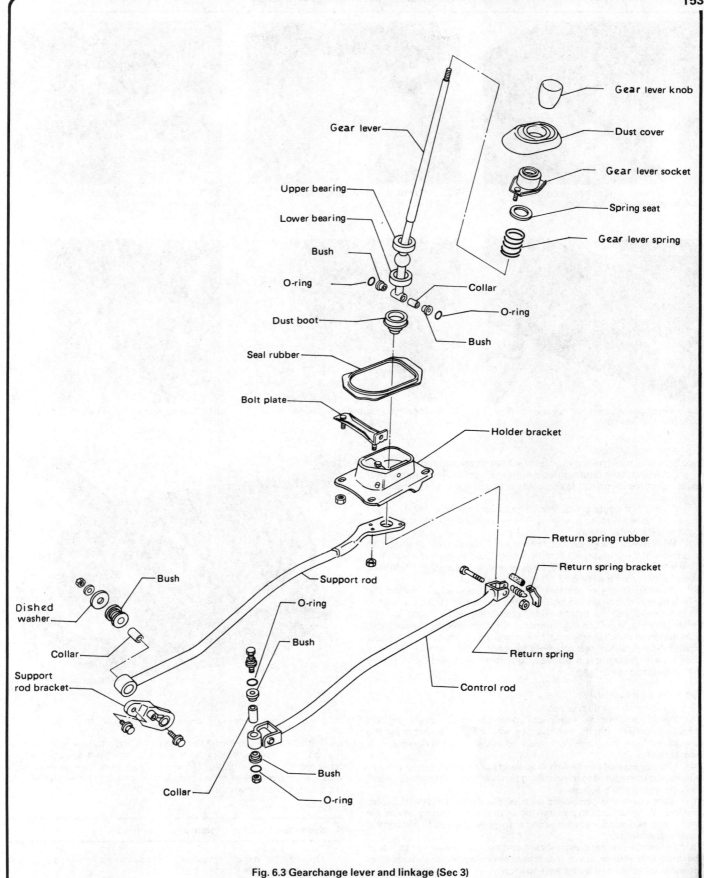

Fig. 6.3 Gearchange lever and linkage (Sec 3)

3.2A Unscrewing gearchange control rod-to-yoke throughbolt nut ...

3.2B ... do not lose joint components – 1.8 and 2.0 litre models

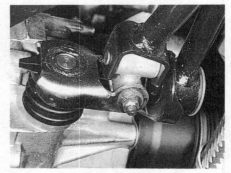

3.2C Gearchange control rod-to-yoke – 1.6 litre models

3.4 View of gearchange control and support rods from underneath

3.9 Disconnecting support rod from transmission – note collar

3.11 Dished washer must be refitted as shown

two nuts which secure the gear lever socket to the support rod can be unscrewed; note the return spring's separate bracket. Separate the gear lever from the support rod, taking care not to damage the centre console or gaiter.

9   Moving to the support rod's front end, unscrew the nut and remove the large dished washer to release it from its bracket; note the rubber bush and the collar (photo).

10   Withdraw the support rod, then check it for damage or distortion and renew it if necessary. Check the rubber bush at the rod's front end for wear. This must be renewed, if necessary, to ensure that there is no free play between the rod and the transmission.

11   Refitting is the reverse of the removal procedure, noting the following points. The dished washer at the support rod front end should be positioned with its convex side against the rubber bush (photo). Grease the gear lever bearing components before refitting the socket to the support rod and take care not to damage the centre console or gaiter while refitting the support rod. Refit the control rod and heat shield as described in paragraph 6 above. Tighten all nuts and bolts to the specified torque settings.

Gear lever assembly

12   Unscrew the gear lever knob.

13   Apply the handbrake firmly, jack up the front of the car and support it securely on axle stands. Remove the heat shield and disconnect the control rod from the gear lever lower end as described in paragraphs 3 and 4 above.

14   Disconnect and pull down the support rod rear end so that the two nuts can be unscrewed to release the gear lever socket from the support rod. See paragraph 8 above.

15   Manoeuvre the gear lever clear of the support rod and holder bracket, taking care not to damage the centre console, the gaiter or the dust cover. Provided that care is taken, there is no need to disturb the latter components.

16   Dismantle the gear lever socket and bearing components, check them for wear and renew any that are excessively worn or damaged. On reassembly, apply a coat of grease to each.

17   Refitting is the reverse of the removal procedure.

18   Note that if the holder bracket is to be removed it can be unbolted

3.18 View of gear lever assembly and holder bracket from above

and withdrawn from beneath the underbody after the gear lever assembly has been removed. Note the rubber seal fitted between the underbody and the bracket (photo). On refitting, however, the centre console must be removed to permit the positioning of the bolt plates from inside the passenger compartment. See Chapter 11.

---

4   Speedometer drive – removal and refitting

---

1   Open the bonnet and disconnect the speedometer drive cable from the transmission. See Chapter 12.

2   Undo the single retaining screw and withdraw the speedometer pinion assembly.

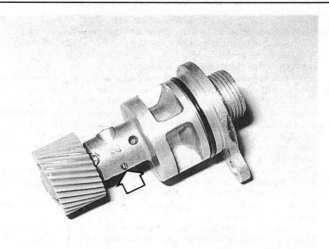

4.3 Drive out roll pin (arrowed) to release speedometer pinion

3   To dismantle the pinion assembly, drive out the retaining roll pin (photo) and withdraw the pinion, noting the number of shims fitted to the pinion.
4   Renew as a matter of course the O-ring and oil seal whenever they are disturbed.
5   Renew the pinion if its teeth are worn or damaged and check the sleeve for cracks or damage.
6   Refitting is a reversal of the removal procedure. Apply a smear of grease or transmission oil to the seal, pinion shaft and O-ring as they are installed and tighten the retaining screw to the specified torque setting.
Note: *The speedometer drive gear can be checked visually by removing the pinion assembly and shining a torch into the aperture. If any of its teeth are damaged, the transmission must be removed from the car and dismantled so that the gear can be renewed; it is pressed onto the differential case.*

5   Transmission oil seals – removal and refitting

Differential side (driveshaft) oil seals

Note: *It is possible to minimise the work necessary to withdraw the driveshafts, without completely removing them from the cover. Use the procedure given in paragraph 3 below, in conjunction with the more detailed information in Chapter 8, Section 3.*

1   Drain the transmission oil (see Section 2 of this Chapter).
2   Remove the underwing shield (see Section 7, paragraph 3).
3   Provided that the car is securely supported and care is taken, it is possible to minimise the work necessary to withdraw the driveshafts as follows. Working as described in Chapter 8, separate the track rod outer balljoint from the hub carrier, slacken the suspension strut top mounting nuts and remove the three mounting plate nuts to separate the hub carrier (and front suspension lower arm balljoint) from the lower arm. Unscrew the three support bearing bolts (right-hand driveshaft, 1.8 and 2.0 litre models only). Prise the driveshaft out of the transmission as described, then pull the whole assembly (roadwheel, hub carrier/suspension strut and driveshaft) outwards and wedge it so that the driveshaft inboard end is clear of the transmission. Take care not to stretch or kink the brake flexible hose.
4   Prise out the seal, taking care not to scratch or damage the seal housing. If difficulty is experienced, an internally-expanding claw-type puller could be adapted to extract the seal, as shown in Fig. 6.4.
5   Dip the new seal in clean oil, fit it to the transmission aperture and drive it squarely into place using as a drift a piece of tubing which bears only on the seal's hard outer edge. If the aperture is parallel-sided, drive the seal home until its outer edge is flush with the surrounding casing; otherwise drive the seal in until it seats on its locating shoulder.
6   Before refitting the driveshaft, check its seal rubbing surface for signs of burrs, scratches or damage which caused the seal to fail in the

first place. It may be possible to polish away faults of this sort using fine abrasive paper.
7   Ensure the driveshaft is clean and greased to protect the seal lips on refitting. See Chapter 8.
8   Refill the transmission with oil as described in Section 2 of this Chapter.

Input shaft (clutch) oil seal
9   Remove the transmission from the car. See Section 7 of this Chapter.
10   On 1.6 litre models, working as described in Section 8 of this Chapter, lift off the transmission casing then remove the output shaft, input shaft and reverse idler assembly. Using a pin punch applied through the hole(s) in the clutch release bearing guide sleeve, drive out the oil seal.
11   On all other models, working as described in Section 12 of this Chapter, lift off the transmission casing and remove the reverse gear components and selector mechanism, then withdraw the input and output shafts. Prise out the seal, taking care not to scratch or damage the seal housing.
12   Dip the new seal in clean oil and drive it squarely into its housing until it seats on its locating shoulder.
13   Before refitting the input shaft, check it for burrs, scratches or damage which caused the seal to fail in the first place. It may be possible to polish away faults of this sort using fine abrasive paper.
14   Ensure the input shaft is clean and greased to protect the seal lips on refitting, then reassemble the transmission as described in the appropriate Section of this Chapter.

Selector mechanism striking rod oil seal
15   Working as described in Section 3 of this Chapter, disconnect the gearchange control rod from the selector mechanism striking rod yoke.
16   Using a suitable pin punch, drive out the roll pin securing the yoke to the end of the striking rod (Fig. 6.5). Remove the yoke and the rubber boot.

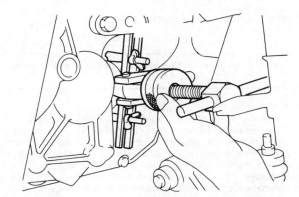

Fig. 6.4 Using a claw-type puller to extract a differential side oil seal (Sec 5)

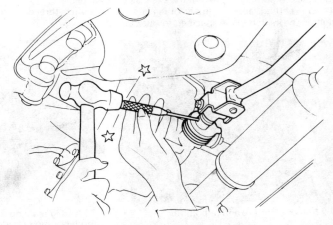

Fig. 6.5 Driving out the selector mechanism striking rod yoke roll pin (Sec 5)

6.1 Reversing lamp switch location – 1.6 litre models

17   Prise or drift the oil seal out of its housing. Take care not to damage either the striking rod or the seal housing.
18   Clean the seal housing area and check carefully for signs of wear or damage which may have caused the seal to fail in the first place.
19   Dip the new seal in clean oil and grease the striking rod, then fit the new seal over the striking rod, taking care not to damage the seal lips. Use a piece of tubing which bears only on the seal's hard outer edge to drive the seal into place.
20   Refit the rubber boot and the yoke, then drive a new roll pin into place to secure the yoke.
21   Refit the control rod as described in Section 3.

6   Reversing lamp/gear position switch – removal, refitting and testing

1.6 litre models
1   The reversing lamp circuit is controlled by a plunger-type switch that is screwed into the left-hand end of the transmission casing (photo).
2   To check the switch, disconnect its wires at the connector joining them to the main wiring loom and use a multimeter (set to the resistance function) or a battery and bulb test circuit, to check that there is continuity between the wires when reverse gear is selected. If this is not the case, and there are no obvious breaks or other damage to the wires, the switch is faulty and must be renewed.
3   To remove the switch, disconnect its wires and unscrew it. Block the hole temporarily to prevent the excessive loss of oil.
4   On refitting, apply a smear of sealant to the switch threads and tighten the switch to the specified torque setting.

1.8 (including Turbo) and 2.0 litre models
5   The gear position switch is bolted to the underside of the transmission casing. It controls the reversing lamp circuit on all these models and also, on those with fuel injection, it sends a signal to the ECCS control unit when the transmission is in neutral.
6   To check the switch, disconnect its wires at the connector block joining them to the main wiring loom and use a multimeter (set to the resistance function), or a battery and bulb test circuit, to check that there is continuity between the green/yellow and green wires when reverse gear is selected, and between the green/red (or green/orange) and black wires when the neutral position is selected. If this is not the case, and there are no obvious breaks or other damage to the wires, the switch is faulty and must be renewed.
7   To remove the switch, disconnect its wires and unscrew the single retaining screw. Carefully prise the switch out of the casing, taking care not to break it. If it proves to be very tight, the transmission must be removed so that the casing can be withdrawn from the switch tapped out from the inside.
8   On refitting, apply a smear of sealant to the switch, check that the O-ring (if fitted) is correctly positioned and tighten the screw to the specified torque setting.

7   Transmission – removal and refitting

Note: *Some means will be required of taking the transmission's weight while it is moved sideways and raised or lowered. A strong trolley jack would be useful, provided that a wooden spacer is available to spread the load and prevent the risk of damage to the transmission casing.*
Also note that it is possible to minimise the work necessary to withdraw the driveshafts, without completely removing them from the car. Use the procedure given in paragraph 10 below, in conjunction with the more detailed information in Chapter 8, Section 3.

1   Park the car on firm level ground and apply the handbrake firmly.
2   Open the bonnet, then disconnect and remove the battery (see Chapter 12) and unbolt the battery tray (photo) to expose the engine/transmission left-hand mounting.
3   Remove the engine compartment left-hand front undershield, which is secured by five bolts, and the left-hand underwing shield, which is secured by four bolts and two plastic clips.
4   Drain the transmission oil. See Section 2 of this Chapter.
5   On 1.6 litre models, disconnect the speedometer drive cable (Chapter 12) and the clutch cable (Chapter 5) from the transmission.
6   On Turbo models, slacken the clamps securing the air inlet ducting and resonator assembly to the airflow meter and turbocharger, unbolt the assembly from the brackets securing it to the body front panel and disconnect the breather hose from the rocker cover. Withdraw the complete assembly and use clean, lint-free rag to pack the airflow meter and turbocharger openings so that dirt and debris cannot enter.
7   On 1.8 (including Turbo) and 2.0 litre models, place a block of wood under the clutch pedal so that it cannot be depressed accidentally, then unbolt the clutch slave cylinder (and heat shield, on Turbo models) from the front of the bellhousing. Remove the spring clip to release the hydraulic pipe and/or flexible hose from the transmission bracket,

7.2 Remove battery and unbolt tray

7.7A 1.8 (including Turbo) and 2.0 litre models – move aside radiator hose and unbolt clutch slave cylinder ...

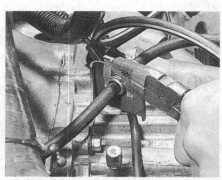

7.7B ... remove spring clip to release flexible hose from transmission ...

7.7C ... and unbolt bracket from inner wing panel

7.8 Disconnecting earth lead – note position switch lead connector (arrowed)

7.15 Engine/transmission left-hand mounting

unbolt the bracket from the inner wing panel, then withdraw the complete slave cylinder assembly (photos). Disconnect the speedometer drive cable and pinion assembly, and secure clear of the transmission.

8 On all models, disconnect the earth lead from the terminal secured by one of the transmission casing bolts and disconnect the reversing lamp/position switch lead at the block connector (photo).

9 Chock the rear wheels, jack up the front of the car and support it securely on axle stands.

10 Provided that the car is securely supported and care is taken, it is possible to minimise the work necessary to remove the driveshafts, as follows. Working as described in Chapter 8, separate the track rod outer balljoints from the hub carriers, slacken the suspension strut top mounting nuts and remove the three mounting plate nuts to separate each hub carrier (and front suspension lower arm balljoint) from its lower arm. Unscrew the three support bearing bolts (right-hand driveshaft, 1.8 and 2.0 litre models only). Prise the driveshaft out of the transmission as described, then pull each whole assembly (roadwheel, hub carrier/suspension strut and driveshaft) outwards and wedge it so that the driveshaft inboard end is clear of the transmission. Take care not to stretch or kink the brake flexible hose.

11 Working as described in Section 3 of this Chapter, disconnect the gearchange control and support rods from the transmission.

12 Support the weight of the transmission using a trolley jack and wooden spacer, an engine hoist, or similar.

13 Noting the position of the engine/transmission front and rear stays and the exhaust system mounting, unscrew all bolts and nuts securing the transmission to the engine. As well as the bellhousing bolts, this includes the starter motor mountings and, on fuel injection (non-Turbo) models, the bolts securing the intake (inlet) manifold stay to the transmission.

14 When the starter motor is released, pull it clear of the bellhousing; there is no need to remove it completely.

15 The engine/transmission left-hand mounting consists basically of two parts; one (two-piece) mounting bolted to the inner wing panel and one mounting, (incorporating a large rubber bush) bolted to the transmission (photo). Unscrew the through-bolt and nut which secure the two-piece mounting, then check that the transmission is supported securely before unbolting the other mounting from the transmission. Note, if fitted, the two large washers on each side of the rubber bush.

16 Withdraw the transmission squarely from the engine, prising it off the locating dowels. Lower the transmission clear of the car and withdraw it.

17 While the transmission is removed, overhaul the clutch assembly and release mechanism as described in Chapter 5.

18 On refitting, check that the mating surfaces of the engine and transmission are completely clean and dry, that all clutch components are in good condition and correctly installed and that the engine/transmission adaptor plate is correctly located on the dowels, which must be clean.

19 Apply a thin smear of molybdenum disulphide grease to the splines of the clutch friction plate, the transmission input shaft splines and tip, and to the release bearing contact surface and diaphragm spring fingers.

20 Offer the transmission up to the engine and engage the input shaft with the clutch friction plate; ensure that the transmission is absolutely square to the engine.

21 Push the transmission into full engagement with the engine, ensuring that it seats correctly on the dowels and that the adaptor plate is not displaced.

22 If the transmission proves reluctant to mate with the engine, try swivelling it slightly, or have an assistant rotate the crankshaft via the pulley bolt, until the input shaft splines engage with those of the friction plate.

23 Once the transmission is fully engaged, refit the bolts and nuts securing it to the engine and tighten them to the torque settings specified. Then refit the engine/transmission left-hand mounting.

24 The remainder of the refitting procedure is the reverse of removal, noting the following points:

(a) Tighten all nuts and bolts to the torque settings specified
(b) Adjust the clutch and check its operation. See Chapter 5
(c) Refill the transmission with the specified type of oil. See Section 2 of this Chapter

PART B : 1.6 LITRE MODELS (RS5F31A)

8 Transmission – dismantling

1 With the transmission removed from the car, clean away external dirt using a water-soluble solvent or paraffin and a stiff brush.

2 Working as described in Chapter 5, remove the components of the clutch release mechanism from the bellhousing. Clean the inside of the bellhousing.

3 With the transmission standing upright on the bellhousing's engine mating surface, unscrew the casing-to-bellhousing bolts and withdraw the casing from the bellhousing (Fig. 6.9). Tilt the casing slightly as it is withdrawn, to prevent the 5th shift fork jamming inside the casing. If the casing is stuck, tap it off carefully, to break the joint, using a plastic hammer.

4 Withdraw the reverse idler spacer, then pull the shift fork shaft out of the forks, noting the coil spring in its bellhousing end (photo).

5 Withdraw the 5th and 3rd/4th shift forks (Fig. 6.10). Do not displace any of the shifter caps fitted over the control bracket lever ends; there are two on models up to February 1988, three on later models.

6 Unbolt the control bracket and withdraw it with the 1st/2nd shift fork, taking care to keep the shifter caps on their respective levers. Withdraw the striking rod detent spring, ball and sleeve from their bore underneath the bracket mounting flange (photo).

7 Lift the output shaft straight out of its bearing outer race; do not lift it at an angle or the resin oil channel will be damaged. Unscrew the retaining screw (photo) and withdraw the speedometer pinion assembly, then lift out the differential assembly.

8 Unscrew the three bolts securing the input shaft bearing triangular retainer, lifting up the reverse idler gear pinion to reach one of the bolts (photo). Place the bellhousing so that the input shaft is horizontal, then drive the shaft out to the left by tapping on its clutch end with a soft-faced mallet. Withdraw the shaft complete with the bearing retainer and

8.4 Withdraw shift fork shaft (arrowed)

8.6 With control bracket removed, detent spring, ball and sleeve (arrowed) can be withdrawn

8.7 Speedometer pinion assembly retaining screw

8.8 Input shaft bearing retainer is secured by three bolts

8.10A Mark position of striking lever on rod before driving out roll pin 'A' – note location of reverse detent plug 'B'

8.10B Selector mechanism striking rod oil seal should be renewed whenever it is disturbed

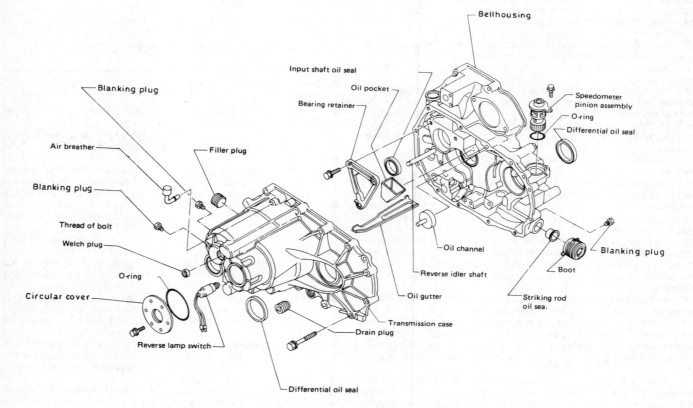

Fig. 6.6 Selector mechanism – 1.6 litre models (Sec 8)

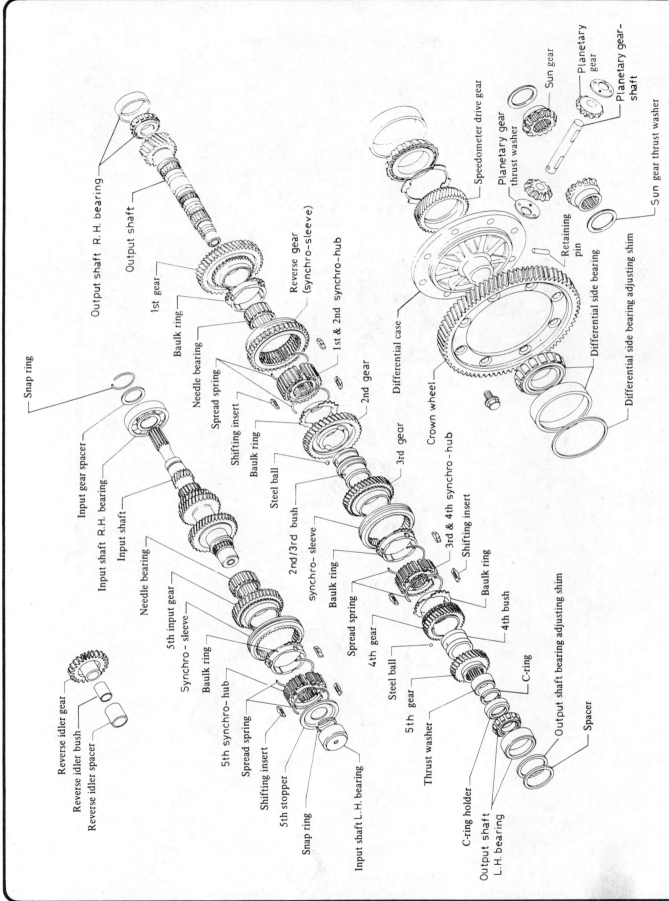

Fig. 6.7 Transmission casing components – 1.6 litre models (Sec 8)

Snap ring

Output shaft R. H. bearing

Output shaft

1st gear

Baulk ring

Needle bearing

Spread spring

Shifting insert

Baulk ring

Steel ball

2nd/3rd bush

Synchro – sleeve

Baulk ring

Spread spring

4th gear

Steel ball

5th gear

Thrust washer

C-ring holder

Output shaft L. H. bearing

Output shaft

C-ring

Output shaft bearing adjusting shim

Spacer

4th bush

Baulk ring

Shifting insert

3rd & 4th synchro-hub

3rd gear

2nd gear

1st & 2nd synchro-hub

Reverse gear (synchro-sleeve)

Input gear spacer

Input shaft R.H. bearing

Input shaft

Needle bearing

5th input gear

Synchro – sleeve

Baulk ring

5th synchro–hub

Spread spring

Shifting insert

5th stopper

Snap ring

Input shaft L. H. bearing

Reverse idler gear

Reverse idler bush

Reverse idler spacer

Speedometer drive gear

Planetary gear thrust washer

Sun gear

Planetary gear

Planetary gear-shaft

Retaining pin

Sun gear thrust washer

Differential side bearing

Differential side bearing adjusting shim

Differential case

Crown wheel

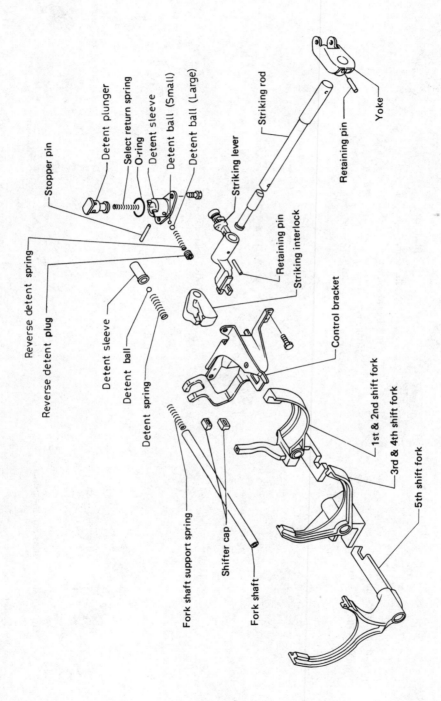

Stopper pin
Detent plunger
Select return spring
O-ring
Detent sleeve
Detent ball (Small)
Detent ball (Large)
Striking lever
Striking rod
Retaining pin
Yoke
Retaining pin
Striking interlock
Control bracket
Reverse detent spring
Reverse detent plug
Detent sleeve
Detent ball
Detent spring
Fork shaft support spring
Shifter cap
Fork shaft
1st & 2nd shift fork
3rd & 4th shift fork
5th shift fork

Fig. 6.8 Geartrain components – 1.6 litre models (Sec 8)

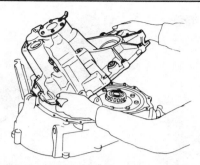

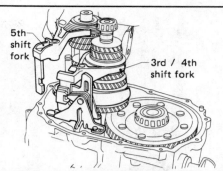

Fig. 6.9 Withdrawing the transmission casing (Sec 8)

Fig. 6.10 Withdrawing the 5th and 3rd/4th shift forks (Sec 8)

reverse idler gear pinion, noting which way round this is fitted. Do **not** attempt to remove the idler gear shaft or it will become a slack fit in the bellhousing.

9   Withdraw the oil pocket from its recess.

10   To dismantle the selector mechanism, use a felt-tip pen or paint to mark the relationship of the striking rod and lever, then use a hammer and a pin punch to drive the roll pin out of the striking lever into the bellhousing recess. Pull the striking rod out of the striking lever and interlock, then out of the bellhousing. Prise the striking rod oil seal out of its housing and discard it with the roll pin. Both these items must be renewed whenever they are disturbed (photos).

11   Using a suitable Torx key, unscrew the reverse detent plug and tip out the detent spring and balls.

12   Using an impact driver if necessary, remove the two retaining screws (photo) and withdraw the reverse detent plunger assembly. Discard the sealing O-ring, which must be renewed whenever it is disturbed.

Bellhousing

13   Renew the input shaft, differential, and striking rod oil seals as described in Section 5 of this Chapter.

14   Do not disturb the switch blanking plug (photo) unless necessary. If it is disturbed, apply a smear of sealant to its threads and tighten it to

the specified torque setting. This also applies to the two blanking plugs in the front of the transmission casing.

15   If either the output shaft or differential side bearing outer races are to be removed, a suitable internally-expanding bearing puller must be obtained, or the bellhousing must be taken to a dealer for the races to be removed (photo). If the output shaft bearing oil channel is broken as a result, a new one must be fitted on reassembly.

16   The shift fork shaft bush can be extracted by heating the bellhousing and using an internally-expanding puller to withdraw it. The same applies to the bush at the opposite end of the shaft, in the transmission casing.

Transmission casing

17   Unscrew and remove the reverse lamp switch.

18   Remove the oil gutter.

19   If the input shaft needle roller bearing is to be renewed, remove the very small welch plug from the transmission casing. Do this by drilling a hole in the plug and then screw in a self-tapping screw. The screw will probably force out the plug or its head can be used to lever it out; a punch can then be used to drive out the bearing. Do **not** disturb the large welch plug (photos).

20   Unbolt the circular cover from the casing and take out the spacer and the output shaft bearing adjusting shim. If the output shaft bearing

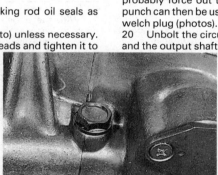

8.12 Removing reverse detent plunger assembly screws

8.14 Neutral switch blanking plug

8.15 Special puller will be needed to extract differential side bearing outer races

8.19A Remove smaller welch plug from transmission casing ...

8.19B ... to drive out input shaft needle roller bearing

8.24 Drawing off input shaft right-hand bearing

8.27 Drawing off output shaft 5th gear pinion

8.36 Drawing off output shaft 1st/2nd synchro-unit and 1st gear pinion

8.37 Output shaft 1st gear pinion needle bearing is split to allow removal

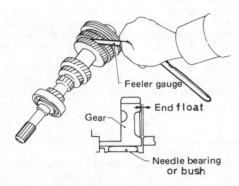

Fig. 6.11 Measuring gear pinion endfloat – input shaft 5th gear shown (Sec 8)

is to be renewed, drive out the old outer race and fit the new one. Discard the cover's sealing O-ring; this must be renewed whenever it is disturbed.
21   If the differential side bearing outer race is to be removed, a special puller will be required. See paragraph 15 above, but note the presence of any preload adjusting shim(s). Renew the oil seal as described in Section 5 of this Chapter.

Input shaft
22   Measure and record the 5th gear pinion endfloat (Fig. 6.11). Extract the snap ring and 5th stopper plate.
23   Remove the 5th gear pinion with synchro-unit and the split needle bearing from inside the gear.
24   The input shaft cannot be dismantled further except to draw off the right-hand bearing after having first extracted the snap ring and taken off the spacer. If a bearing puller is not available, support the bearing and drive the shaft from it (photo). Discard both snap rings.

Output shaft
25   Measure and record the 1st, 2nd, 3rd and 4th gear pinion endfloat.
26   Remove the bearing inner races from each end of the shaft. Use either a bearing puller or press the shaft out of the bearings.
27   Remove the C-ring holder, the C-rings and the thrustwasher. Remove the 5th gear pinion; a puller will be required for this (photo).
28   Remove 4th gear pinion, the gear bush and steel locking ball.
29   Remove the baulk ring.
30   Remove the 3rd/4th synchro-unit; again, a puller may be required.
31   Remove 3rd gear pinion.
32   Remove 2nd/3rd gear bush.
33   Remove the steel locking ball.
34   Remove the 2nd gear pinion.
35   Remove the baulk ring.
36   Remove 1st/2nd synchro-unit with reverse gear (straight cut teeth on synchro-sleeve) together with 1st gear pinion as an assembly. The synchro-hub is tight on the shaft and the best way to remove the assembly if a puller (photo) is not available, is to support under 1st gear pinion and drive the shaft downward using a soft-faced mallet.
37   Remove 1st gear pinion split needle bearing (photo).

Differential
38   Unbolt the crownwheel from the differential case.
39   Using a punch, drive out the planetary gear shaft retaining pin and withdraw the shaft.
40   Withdraw the planetary and sun gears and their thrustwashers. Keep each thrustwasher with its respective gear and label each gear so that it can be returned to its original location.
41   Cut off the speedometer drive gear (photo) and use a bearing puller to draw off the differential side bearings, noting which way round each is fitted and labelling each to ensure that it is refitted in its original location. Withdraw the drive gear stopper.

---

9   Transmission – inspection

1   With the transmission completely dismantled, clean all components and inspect them for wear or damage.
2   Check the gears for chipped teeth and their bushes for wear.
3   Check the shafts for scoring or grooving.
4   Check the bearings for wear by spinning them with the fingers. If they shake or rattle, or show visible signs of wear or damage, then they must be renewed.
5   If any of the gear pinion endfloat measurements recorded before dismantling were outside the specified limits, check the bearing surfaces of the gear, the shaft and the synchro-hub, as well as the fit of the gear on its bearing or bush. Renew any worn components. On reassembly (see Section 10) carefully check that the correct thickness of retaining snap ring or C-ring is used at the shaft end(s).
6   Wear in the synchro-units will normally be revealed by noisy gear changing, but even if this is not the case, it is worthwhile to check the

8.41 Speedometer drivegear (arrowed) must be cut off to permit removal of differential side bearing

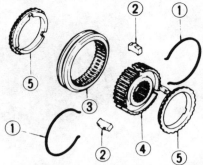

Fig. 6.12 Synchro-unit components (Sec 9)

1   *Spreader spring*   4   *Hub*
2   *Shifting insert*   5   *Baulk ring*
3   *Sleeve*

Fig. 6.14 Fitted direction of synchro-unit spreader springs (Sec 9)

9.6 Check synchro-units (input shaft 5th gear shown) for wear – note engraved 'dashes'

units whenever the transmission is dismantled. Note that some consider it good practice to renew the baulk rings as a matter of course especially if the car has covered a high mileage (photo).

7   To dismantle the synchro-units, first mark the components using paint or a felt-tip pen so that they can be reassembled in the same relative positions. Referring to Fig. 6.12, extract the spreader springs, then push the hubs out of the sleeves and withdraw the shifting inserts from the hubs.

8   Check the synchro components for wear or deformation. Place each baulk ring on its cone and twist it to ensure good contact between the surfaces. Using a feeler blade, check that the gap between gear and baulk ring is not less than the specified minimum (Fig. 6.13). If it is, renew the baulk ring.

9   When reassembling the synchro units, make sure that the spreader springs run in opposite directions when viewed from each side of the unit and that the spring ends do not engage in the same insert (Fig. 6.14).

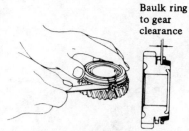

Baulk ring to gear clearance

Fig. 6.13 Checking baulk ring wear (Sec 9)

10   Renew as a matter of course all O-rings, oil seals, roll pins or retaining pins and snap rings which have been disturbed during the overhaul; these should **never** be re-used.

---

10   Transmission – reassembly

Differential

1   Fit a new speedometer drive gear and the stopper to the differential case.
2   Press on the differential bearing inner races.
3   Into the differential case fit the sun gear thrustwashers followed by the sun gears, then the planetary gear thrustwashers followed by the planetary gears. Being careful not to damage the thrustwashers, lubricate and refit the planetary gear shaft.
4   Check that the clearance between each sun gear and the differential case is no more than that specified. If adjustment is necessary, thrustwashers are available in varying thicknesses to take up the difference. When the clearance is correct, drive in a new retaining pin to secure the planetary gear shaft; ensure that the pin is flush with the differential case.
5   Clean the mating surfaces and refit the crownwheel with its chamfered inner edge against the differential case. Clean the threads of the crownwheel bolts and apply thread locking fluid, then screw them in and tighten to the specified torque.

Output shaft

6   Oil all components liberally as they are reassembled.
7   Fit 1st gear pinion split needle bearing.
8   Fit 1st gear pinion.
9   Fit 1st gear pinion baulk ring (photos).
10   Fit 1st/2nd synchro-unit with reverse. Tap the unit down the shaft using a piece of tubing, but hold it together by hand in case the vibration makes it fall apart (photo).
11   Use grease to stick the steel ball in its hole in the shaft (photo). On no account place the ball in the hole in the shaft groove.
12   Fit 2nd gear pinion baulk ring to the pinion cone.
13   Fit 2nd gear pinion to the bush (photo).
14   Fit 2nd/3rd gear bush assembly to the shaft, turning it slowly to engage its cut-out with the ball (photo).
15   Fit 3rd gear pinion to the bush.
16   Fit the baulk ring (photo).

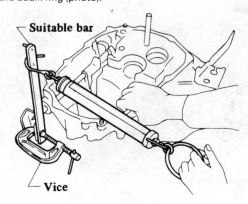

Suitable bar

Vice

Fig. 6.15 Checking reverse detent spring pressure (Sec 10)

10.9A Take the output shaft ...

10.9B ... and fit the 1st gear needle bearing, pinion and baulk ring

10.10 1st/2nd synchro-unit (with reverse) fitted to output shaft

10.11 Position steel ball in shaft hole shown

10.13 2nd gear pinion and baulk ring assembled on 2nd/3rd gear bush – note cut-out

10.14 2nd/3rd gear bush assembly fitted to output shaft

10.16 3rd gear pinion and baulk ring fitted to bush

10.17 3rd/4th synchro-unit

10.18 4th gear bush steel ball fitted to output shaft

10.20 Fitting 4th gear bush

10.21 Fitting 4th gear pinion assembly to bush

10.22 5th gear pinion must be tapped on to shaft splines

10.23 Fitting 5th gear pinion thrustwasher

10.24 Output shaft C-rings are available in different thicknesses

10.25 Fitting the C-ring holder

10.26A Fit the bearing inner race ...

10.26B ... and check again the gear pinion endfloat

10.27A The input shaft

10.27B Fitting 5th gear needle bearing

10.29 Fitting 5th gear pinion and baulk ring

10.31A Fit 5th gear synchro-unit and stopper plate

17   Fit 3rd/4th synchro-unit so that the engraved dashes on the sleeve are visible (photo). Again, it may be necessary to tap the unit down the shaft splines.

18   Using thick grease, stick the 4th gear bush steel ball in its shaft hole (not the hole in the shaft groove) (photo).

19   Fit the baulk ring to the 4th gear pinion.

20   Fit 4th gear bush turning it slowly to engage its cut-out with the ball (photo).

21   Fit 4th gear pinion assembly (photo).

22   Fit 5th gear pinion. Drive it carefully onto the shaft using a piece of tubing (photo).

23   Fit the 5th gear pinion thrustwasher (photo).

24   Fit the C-rings (photo). These are supplied in various thicknesses to correct gear endfloat by reducing to the specified limits the clearance between the C-rings and their groove.

25   Fit the C-ring holder (photo).

26   Press on new bearing inner races to both ends of the mainshaft. Finally, check again the gear pinion endfloat (photos).

Input shaft

27   Fit the split needle roller bearing (photos).

28   Fit 5th gear pinion.

29   Fit the baulk ring (photo).

30   Fit the synchro-unit so that the engraved 'dashes' on the sleeve are visible.

31   Fit the stopper plate and a new snap ring to retain the assembly (photos). Snap rings are available in various thicknesses to correct gear endfloat by reducing to the specified limits the snap ring-to-groove clearance. When the correct thickness snap ring has been selected and fitted, measure the 5th gear pinion endfloat to ensure that it is within the specified limits.

32   Refit the bearing retainer and press on a new right-hand bearing,

10.31B Fit a new circlip to secure assembly

10.32 Refit spacer and a new snap ring

10.33 Differential side bearing (driveshaft) oil seal

10.34 Oil channel recess (arrowed) must be aligned as shown

10.37 Differential side bearing preload shim(s) should be in transmission casing

10.40 Fit oil gutter to transmission casing

10.42 Renew O-ring on refitting reverse detent plunger assembly

10.43 Detent balls and spring

then refit the spacer. Select a new snap ring of the required thickness and fit it to its groove. Check that the snap ring-to-groove clearance is within the specified limits (photo).

Bellhousing
33   Heat the bellhousing to press or drive in the differential side bearing outer race, then fit a new oil seal (photo).
34   When refitting the output shaft bearing outer race, do not forget to install the oil channel first. Align it so that its recessed area faces towards the oil pocket (photo) and ensure that it remains in that position as the outer race is fitted.
35   Use a stepped, parallel-sided drift to refit the shift fork shaft bush.
36   Fit the new oil seals as described in Section 5 of this Chapter.

Transmission casing
37   If the differential side bearings were renewed, fit the new bearing outer race without the adjusting shim(s), then take the transmission casing, bellhousing and differential assembly to a Nissan dealer to have the bearing preload adjusted (photo). See Section 11 of this Chapter. Fit the new oil seal as described in Section 5 of this Chapter.
38   If the output shaft bearing preload is to be adjusted, this is best done as a separate operation before the transmission is reassembled, as described in Section 11. However, it is possible to obtain a similar result by carrying out the procedure during the course of reassembly. If the preload has been adjusted, or does not need adjusting, apply a coat of sealant to the circular cover, fit a new O-ring to its groove and refit the cover, tightening its bolts to the specified torque setting. Working inside the casing, fit the spacer against the cover, followed by the adjusting shim, then use heavy grease to stick the bearing outer race in position. Obviously, none of these should be fitted at this stage if the preload has yet to be adjusted.
39   If the input shaft needle roller bearing was renewed, tap a new small welch plug into the hole in the casing, having coated the outer

10.44 Drive in new roll pin to secure striking lever/interlock on rod

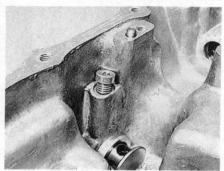

10.45 Reverse detent spring plug is available in different lengths

10.49 Refitting the input shaft, and the reverse idler gear pinion (note spacer)

10.50 Refitting the oil pocket

10.53 Refitting the output shaft

10.54A Fit the detent sleeve to its bore ...

10.54B ... followed by the ball and spring

10.55 Control bracket and shifter caps

10.56A Control bracket located on 1st/2nd shift fork ...

surface with sealant.
40   Fit the oil gutter (photo).
41   Refit the reverse lamp switch.

General reassembly
42   Fit a new O-ring (photo) and smear it with grease, then refit the reverse detent plunger assembly and tighten the retaining screws to the specified torque setting.
43   First refit the small detent ball, then the larger ball, followed by the spring (photo).
44   Grease the striking rod and refit it. If the new oil seal has already been fitted wrap a thin layer of insulating tape over any sharp edges on the rod, to protect the seal lips. Reassemble the striking lever and interlock, fit them to the striking rod and drive a new roll pin into place to secure the assembly (photo). Use the marks made on dismantling to correctly align the striking rod. The notches in its waisted end should align with its detent assembly's bore.

45   The pressure exerted by the reverse detent spring is adjusted by fitting plugs of different lengths; the standard plug is 13.3 mm (0.52 in) long overall (photo). To check the detent pressure proceed as follows.
46   First refit the original plug and tighten it to the specified torque setting. Use a G-clamp to fasten a suitable bar to the striking rod yoke (see Fig. 6.15). Then use a spring balance applied at a known distance from the rod centre to measure the detent force. This should be between 10.3 and 12.7 Nm (91 and 112 lbf in), which can be expressed as 9.1 to 11.2 lbs at 10 in radius from the rod centre, for example.
47   If the force measured is too weak, obtain a longer plug; if it is too strong, obtain a shorter plug. When the setting is correct, apply thread-locking compound to the threads of the selected plug and refit it, tightening it to the specified torque setting.
48   Refit the differential assembly. Refit the speedometer pinion assembly as described in Section 4 of this Chapter.
49   Simultaneously, refit both the input shaft and reverse idler gear pinion (photo), using a soft-faced mallet to tap the shaft fully into the bellhousing.

10.56B ... and reverse idler gear pinion

10.57A Refitting 3rd/4th shift fork ...

10.57B ... and 5th shift fork

10.58 Use grease to stick coil spring in shift fork shaft

50   Refit the oil pocket (photo).
51   Fit the spacer to the reverse idler shaft.
52   Position the triangular-shaped bearing retainer. Apply thread-locking fluid to the screw threads and tighten them to the specified torque setting.
53   Refit the output shaft, carefully meshing the gear teeth with those of the input shaft. As the operation proceeds, push both synchro-sleeves down and hold the reverse idler gear up (photo).
54   Refit the striking rod detent sleeve, ball and spring to their bore (photos).
55   Use grease to stick the shifter caps on their respective control bracket levers (photo).
56   Assemble the control bracket and 1st/2nd shift fork and refit them (photos). Tighten the control bracket bolts to the specified torque setting.
57   Now refit the 3rd/4th shift fork, then the 5th shift fork (photos).
58   Pass the shift fork shaft through the forks making sure that the coil spring is located in the recess at the lower end of the shaft (photo).
59   With the bellhousing standing on the bench with the geartrains vertical, apply sealant to the mating faces of the transmission casing and bellhousing.
60   Lower the casing into position over the geartrains. Tilt the casing as necessary to clear the shift fork.
61   Fit the retaining bolts and tighten to the specified torque setting.
62   If the output shaft bearing preload is still to be adjusted, fit the left-hand bearing outer race and proceed as described in Section 11 of this Chapter. When the correct thickness shim has been selected, use grease to stick it against the bearing outer race, followed by the spacer. Refit the cover as described in paragraph 38 above.
63   The transmission can be checked for correct adjustment, if the

required equipment is available, by measuring the total turning torque. This requires a special tool, Part Number KV38105900 which is forked at one end to fit over the planetary gear shaft. At its other end is an adaptor for a suitable torque wrench (Fig. 6.16). The correct turning torque should be in the specified range if new bearings have been fitted, slightly less if the original bearings are re-used.
64   Refit the components of the clutch release mechanism as described in Chapter 5.
65   Rotating the input shaft to aid selection, check that all gears can be selected with relative ease.

11   Transmission – adjustment

Differential side bearing preload
1   If any of the following components have been renewed during overhaul, then the bearing preload must be adjusted:

   Differential case
   Differential side bearing
   Bellhousing
   Transmission casing

2   Fit the reassembled differential into the bellhousing, check that the side bearing outer race is fitted to the transmission casing without the original adjusting shim(s) and refit the transmission casing. Tighten the retaining bolts to the specified torque setting.
3   The special tools required are a dial gauge and stand (Nissan specify their adaptor/stand Part Number KV38106000, but any suitable clamp or stand may be adapted to fit) and the forked tool KV38105900 (see Section 10, paragraph 63). The latter can be replaced by a length of wooden dowel or similar that is slim enough to fit inside the sun gears and bear against the planetary gear shaft.
4   With the dial gauge pointer bearing against the differential casing, move the differential assembly fully up and down and record the total movement (Fig. 6.17).
5   The thickness of shims required is the amount recorded **plus** a further 0.29 to 0.35 mm (0.0114 to 0.0138 in) and should be made up by

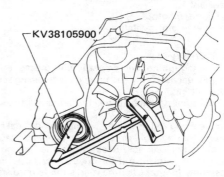

Fig. 6.16 Measuring transmission total/differential turning torque (Secs 10 and 11)

11.11 Refit outer race and tap firmly to seat on bearing

11.13 Output shaft bearing preload adjusting shim A and spacer B

11.14 Refit transmission casing circular cover

one thicker shim (where possible) or two thinner shims. Shims are available through Nissan dealers over a range of thicknesses from 0.44 mm (0.0173 in) to 0.88 mm (0.0346 in).

6   To ensure correct gear tooth meshing, the shim(s) should be fitted only between the differential left-hand side bearing outer race and the transmission casing.

7   The preload setting can be checked by fitting the differential assembly **only** into the bellhousing and refitting the transmission casing. Tighten the retaining bolts to the specified torque setting.

8   Following the procedure outlined in Section 10, paragraph 63, measure the turning torque of the differential only. It should be in the specified range if new bearings have been fitted, slightly less if the originals are re-used, and should not vary by more than 1.0 Nm (9 lbf in) per revolution.

Output shaft bearing preload

9   If any of the following components have been renewed during overhaul, then the bearing preload must be adjusted:

> Output shaft
> Output shaft bearings
> Bellhousing
> Transmission casing

10   Fit the reassembled output shaft into the bellhousing, check that both bearings are fully in place on the shaft and remove the circular cover and O-ring, the spacer, the adjusting shim and the left-hand

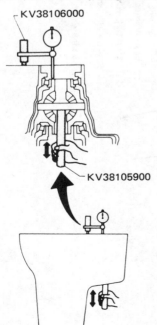

KV38106000

KV38105900

Fig. 6.17 Measuring differential endfloat (Sec 11)

bearing outer race from the transmission casing. Fit the transmission casing to the bellhousing and tighten the retaining bolts to the specified torque setting.

11   Refit the outer race to the shaft end and tap it firmly to ensure it is fully seated (photo).

12   Measure the distance from the transmission casing's machined surface to the outer race, then select a shim (preferably one only) that will reduce the distance to between 2.25 and 2.30 mm (0.0886 and 0.0906 in). Shims are available in increments of 0.05 mm (0.0020 in) over a range of thicknesses from 0.10 mm (0.0039 in) to 1.00 mm (0.0394 in).

13   When the correct thickness shim is selected and placed against the outer race with the spacer (photo), the two together should give the specified bearing preload when compressed by the circular cover.

14   Refit the circular cover as described in Section 10 of this Chapter (photo).

15   If the equipment is available, the transmission's total turning torque can be measured to check the setting. See Section 10, paragraph 63.

PART C : 1.8 (INCLUDING TURBO) AND 2.0 LITRE MODELS (RS5F50A)

12   Transmission – dismantling

1   With the transmission removed from the car, clean away external dirt using a water-soluble solvent or paraffin, and a stiff brush.

2   Working as described in Chapter 5, remove the components of the clutch release mechanism from the bellhousing. Clean the inside of the bellhousing.

3   With the transmission standing upright on the bellhousing's engine mating surface, first remove the gear position switch. See Section 5 of this Chapter.

4   Referring to Fig. 6.21, unscrew the reverse idler shaft bolt, the 3rd/4th detent plug (which carries the gear position switch wire clip) and the 1st/2nd detent plug. Withdraw the detent springs and ball; label them and keeping them separate with their respective plugs. On some cars a double spring may be fitted to the 3rd/4th detent.

5   Unscrew the bolts and lift off the transmission casing. If necessary break the joint by tapping the casing with a mallet. Recover the shims for the input shaft left-hand bearing and the oil channel.

6   If necessary drive out the position switch from the inside of the transmission casing.

7   Select 4th gear, then pull out the reverse idler shaft and remove the reverse idler gear from the reverse lever assembly.

8   Pull out the retaining pin and use a hammer and shim drift to tap out the reverse arm shaft (Fig. 6.22). Discard its O-ring and obtain a new one for reassembly.

9   Unbolt and remove the reverse lever assembly, noting the steel detent ball.

10   Unscrew the 5th/reverse detent plug and extract the spring and ball (Fig. 6.23).

11   Extract the stopper rings from the grooves below the 5th and 3rd/4th shift forks.

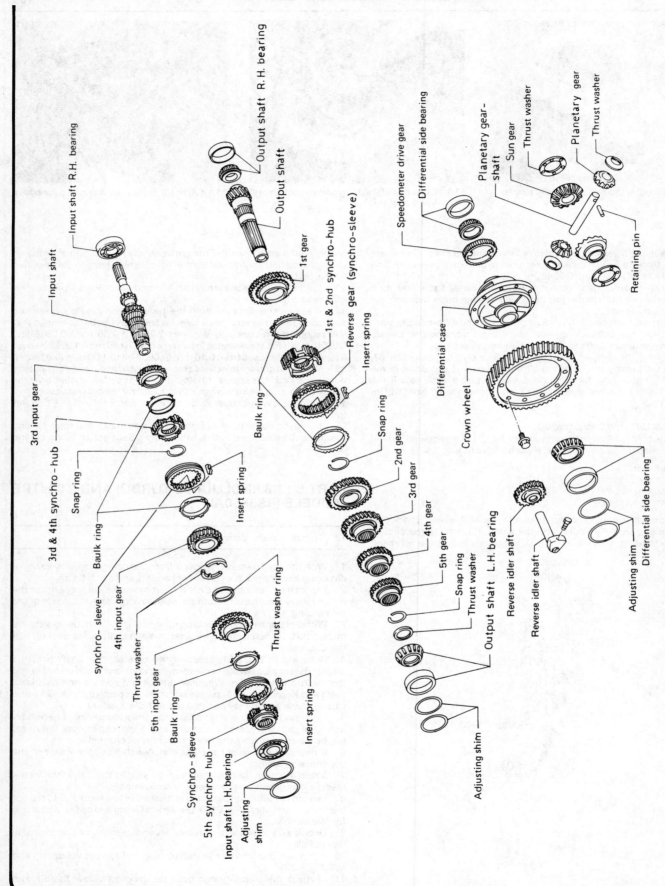

Fig. 6.18 Geartrain components – 1.8 (including Turbo) and 2.0 litre models (Sec 12)

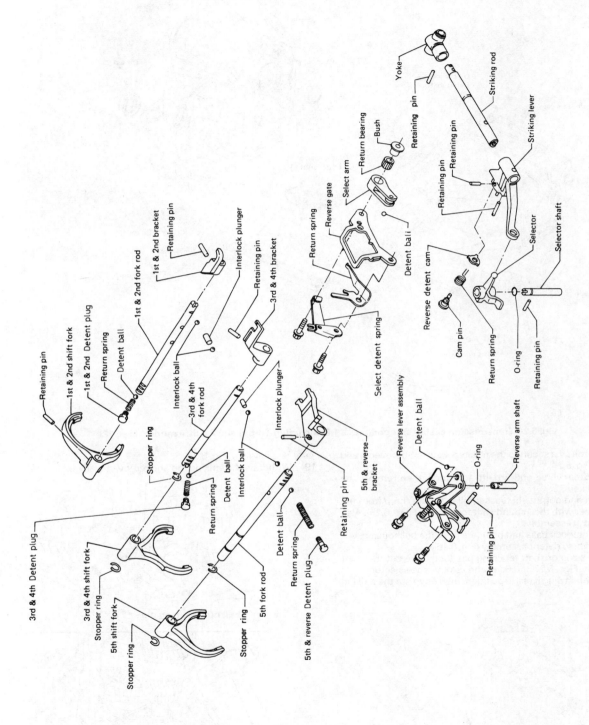

Fig. 6.19 Selector mechanism – 1.8 (including Turbo) and 2.0 litre models (Sec 12)

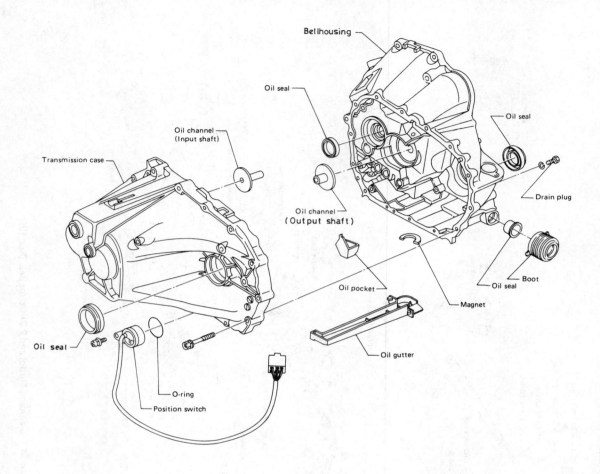

Fig. 6.20 Transmission casing components – 1.8 (including Turbo) and 2.0 litre models (Sec 12)

12   Drive out the roll pins securing the fork brackets to 5th/reverse and 3rd/4th fork rods (Fig. 6.24).
13   Pull out the 5th/reverse and 3rd/4th fork rods, then remove the shift forks and brackets.
14   Grip the input and output shaft assemblies and lift them from the bellhousing, together with the 1st/2nd shift fork and rod (Fig. 6.25). Also lift out the differential assembly.
15   Recover the interlock balls and plungers from the bellhousing.
16   Unbolt the reverse detent assembly (Fig. 6.26).
17   Drive out the selector shaft retaining pin, then drive out the shaft using a narrow drift (Figs. 6.27 and 6.28) and remove the selector.
18   Unscrew the drain plug if still in position, then drive out the striking

lever retaining pin (Fig. 6.29).
19   Withdraw the striking rod and remove the lever.

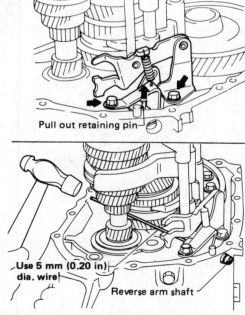

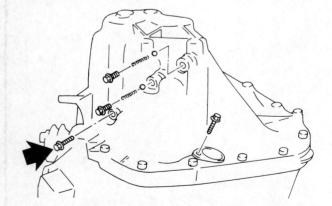

Fig. 6.21 Unscrewing reverse idler shaft bolt (arrowed), detent plugs and position switch bolt (Sec 12)

Fig. 6.22 Removing reverse arm shaft retaining pin (note reverse lever assembly mounting bolts) and driving out shaft (Sec 12)

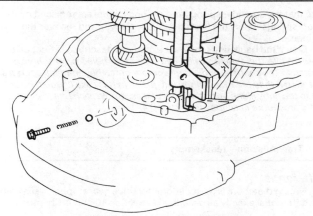

Fig. 6.23 5th/reverse detent plug removal (Sec 12)

Fig. 6.24 5th/reverse and 3rd/4th shift fork rod removal – roll pins arrowed (Sec 12)

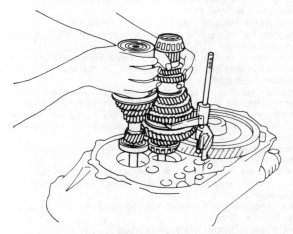

Fig. 6.25 Input and output shaft removal with 1st/2nd shift fork, rod and bracket (Sec 12)

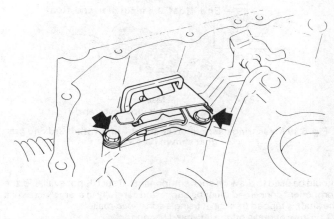

Fig. 6.26 Reverse detent assembly removal (Sec 12)

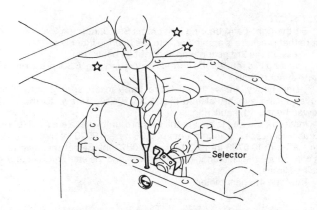

Fig. 6.27 Selector shaft retaining pin removal (Sec 12)

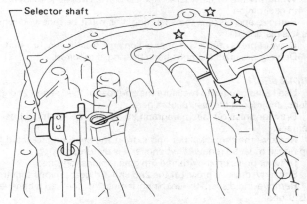

Fig. 6.28 Driving out selector shaft (Sec 12)

Bellhousing

20 Renew the input shaft, differential and striking rod oil seals as described in Section 5 of this Chapter.

21 Refer to Section 8 of this Chapter for details of removing and refitting the output shaft and/or differential side bearing outer races.

22 Remove and clean the oil pocket and magnet.

Transmission casing

23 Remove and install the differential oil seal as described in Section 5 of this Chapter.

24 Refer to Section 8 of this Chapter for details of removing and refitting the output shaft and/or differential side bearing outer races.

Note the presence of any preload adjusting shim(s) between the casing and each outer race.

25 Remove and refit the shift fork shaft bush as described in Sections 8 and 9.

26 Remove and clean the oil gutter.

27 Do not disturb the welch plugs unnecessarily. If necessary, these can be removed as described in Section 8 and new ones can be installed as described in Section 9.

Input shaft

28 Use feeler gauges to measure the endfloat of the 3rd and 4th gear pinions (Fig. 6.30) and a dial gauge to measure that of the 5th gear pinion. Record the measurements obtained.

29 Several components are a tight press-fit on the input (and output) shaft. Preferably a knife-edged bearing puller (see photos 8.27 and 8.36)

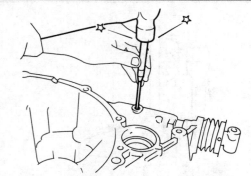

Fig. 6.29 Striking lever retaining pin removal (Sec 12)

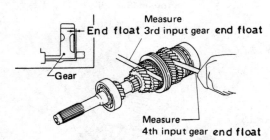

Fig. 6.30 Measuring gear pinion endfloat – input shaft 3rd and 4th gear shown (Sec 12)

should be used to draw off such components. If such is not available, the component concerned must be supported carefully in a large vice while the shaft is tapped through it using a soft-faced mallet.
30   Draw or press off the left-hand bearing.
31   Similarly draw or press off the 5th gear pinion and synchro-unit.
32   Withdraw the thrustwasher ring and thrustwashers, followed by the 4th gear pinion.
33   Remove and discard the snap ring; this must be renewed whenever it is disturbed.
34   Draw or press off the 3rd gear pinion and 3rd/4th synchro-unit.
35   Draw or press off the right-hand bearing, if required.

Output shaft
36   Use feeler gauges to measure the endfloat of the 1st and 2nd gear pinions, and record the results obtained.
37   Draw or press off (see paragraph 29 above) the left-hand bearing inner race.
38   Remove the thrustwasher and extract the snap ring. Discard the snap ring; it must be renewed whenever it is disturbed.
39   Draw or press off the 4th and 5th gear pinions together.
40   Similarly, draw or press off the 2nd and 3rd gear pinions together.
41   Remove and discard the snap ring; it must be renewed whenever it is disturbed.
42   Draw or press off the 1st gear pinion and 1st/2nd synchro-unit (which includes reverse gear) together.
43   Draw or press off the right-hand bearing inner race, if required.

Differential
44   Dismantle the differential as described in the relevant part of Section 8 of this Chapter, noting that there is no speedometer drive gear stopper on these models.

13   Transmission – inspection

1   Working as described in Section 9 of this Chapter, clean and check all transmission components for wear or damage. Renew any that are no longer fit for use, as well as all those items (oil seals, snap rings etc) which must be renewed as a matter of course.
2   When dismantling the synchro-units, mark them as described, but

note that the spreader springs and shifting inserts are replaced by three insert springs. Press the hubs out of the sleeves and recover the insert springs.
3   Check the baulk rings for wear exactly as described in Section 8.
Note: *While the synchro-units can be reassembled on the bench and refitted to the shafts as individual components, they may fall apart from vibration if they are to be drifted into place. In this case it would be better to tap the hubs alone on to the shaft and assemble each unit in place. This is the procedure described in Section 14.*

14   Transmission – reassembly

Differential
1   Noting that there is no speedometer drive gear stopper, reassemble the differential exactly as described in Section 10 of this Chapter.

Output shaft
2   Using a press or a hammer and a length of suitable tubing, install the right-hand bearing inner race.
3   Press on the 1st gear pinion and refit its baulk ring.
4   Ensuring it is refitted the correct way round (Fig. 6.31), press on the 1st/2nd synchro-hub.
5   Using heavy grease to stick the three insert springs into their grooves in the synchro-sleeve (Fig. 6.32), fit the sleeve to the hub, followed by the 2nd baulk ring.
6   Install a snap ring to secure the synchro-unit. These are available in various thicknesses, at increments of 0.05 mm (0.0020 in) over a range from 1.95 mm (0.0768 in) to 2.10 mm (0.0827 in). Select the snap ring that will reduce the clearance between itself and the shaft groove to the specified limits.
7   Press on the 2nd gear pinion, followed by the 3rd gear pinion, the 4th gear pinion and the 5th gear pinion.
8   Install a snap ring to secure the 5th gear pinion. These are available in various thicknesses to reduce the clearance between the snap ring and its groove to the specified limits.
9   When the correct thickness snap ring has been selected and fitted, refit the thrustwasher.
10   Install the left-hand bearing inner race.
11   Measure the 1st and 2nd gear endfloat again to ensure that it is within specified limits.

Input shaft
12   Fit the right-hand bearing inner race. See paragraph 2 above, but ensure that pressure is applied only to the bearing inner race.
13   Press on the 3rd gear pinion and refit its baulk ring.
14   Ensuring it is refitted the correct way round (Fig. 6.33) press on the 3rd/4th synchro-hub.
15   Using heavy grease to stick the three insert springs into their grooves in the synchro-sleeve (Fig. 6.34), fit the sleeve to the hub, followed by the 4th baulk ring.
16   Install a snap ring to secure the synchro-unit. These are available in various thicknesses, at increments of 0.05 mm (0.0020 in) over a range from 1.95 mm (0.0768 in) to 2.10 mm (0.0827 in). Select the snap ring that will reduce the clearance between itself and the shaft groove to the specified limits.
17   Refit the 4th gear pinion.

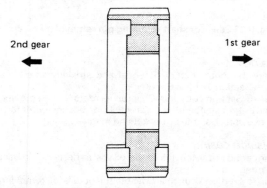

Fig. 6.31 Correct installation of 1st/2nd synchro-hub (Sec 14)

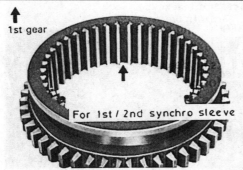

Fig. 6.32 Insert spring location on 1st/2nd synchro-sleeve (Sec 14)

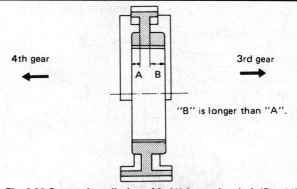

"B" is longer than "A".

Fig. 6.33 Correct installation of 3rd/4th synchro-hub (Sec 14)

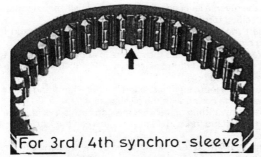

Fig. 6.34 Insert spring location on 3rd/4th synchro-sleeve (Sec 14)

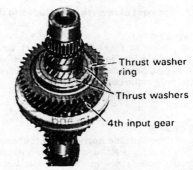

Fig. 6.35 Fitting 4th gear pinion thrustwashers and ring (Sec 14)

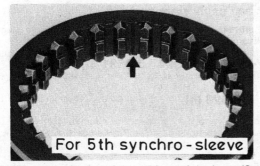

Fig. 6.36 Insert spring location on 5th synchro-sleeve (Sec 14)

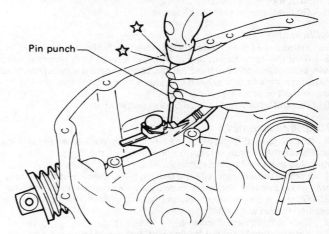

Fig. 6.37 Fitting striking lever retaining pin (Sec 14)

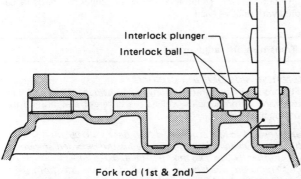

Fig. 6.38 Showing interlock balls and plunger against 1st/2nd shift fork rod (Sec 14)

18   The 4th gear pinion thrustwashers are available in various thicknesses to control gear endfloat, at increments of 0.025 mm (0.0010 in) over a range from 4.500 mm (0.1772 in) to 4.575 mm (0.1801 in). Select a pair that will reduce the clearance between thrustwashers and groove to the specified limits.

19   Use grease to stick the thrustwashers in place and refit the thrustwasher ring over them (Fig. 6.35).

20   Refit the 5th gear pinion and its baulk ring.

21   Ensuring that its shoulder projects towards the shaft left-hand end,

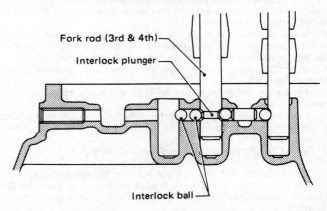

Fig. 6.39 Showing interlock balls engaged with 3rd/4th shift fork rod (Sec 14)

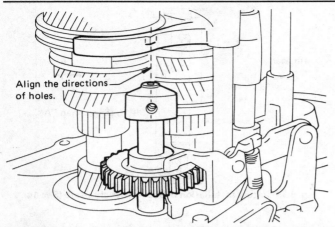

Fig. 6.40 Correct alignment of reverse idler shaft end fitting (Sec 14)

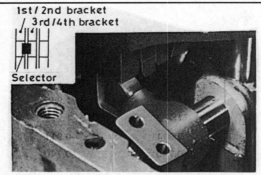

Fig. 6.41 Selector/bracket positioning on refitting transmission casing (Sec 14)

press on the 5th synchro-hub.

22   Using heavy grease to stick the three insert springs into their grooves in the synchro-sleeve (Fig. 6.36), fit the sleeve to the hub.

23   Refit the left-hand bearing. See paragraph 2 above, but ensure that pressure is applied only to the bearing inner race.

24   Measure the 3rd, 4th and 5th gear pinion endfloat again to ensure that it is within limits.

Transmission casing

25   If either the differential side bearing or output shaft bearing has been renewed, the bearing preload will require adjustment; refer to Section 15. Refit the outer races as described in Section 10. If the preload does not require adjustment ensure that the original shims are refitted as they were found.

26   Do not forget to refit the oil gutter.

Bellhousing

27   Install the oil seals as described in Section 5 of this Chapter.

28   Refit the output shaft and differential side bearing outer races as described in Section 10 of this Chapter. There should not be any preload adjusting shims fitted to these bearings, but do not forget to refit the output shaft oil channel.

29   Do not forget to refit the oil pocket and magnet.

General reassembly

30   Locate the striking lever in the bellhousing, then insert the striking rod. Secure the lever by driving in a new retaining pin, Fig. 6.37. Refit the drain plug as described in Section 2.

31   Engage the selector with the striking lever, then insert the selector shaft, using a new O-ring and secure by driving in a new retaining pin.

32   Fit the reverse detent assembly and tighten the bolts to the specified torque setting.

33   Refit the differential assembly.

34   Refit the bracket to the 1st/2nd shift fork rod (if removed) and drive in a new retaining pin to secure them. Refit the 1st/2nd shift fork to the rod and drive in a new retaining pin to secure them. Locate the fork on the 1st/2nd synchro-sleeve.

35   Mesh together the input and output shaft assemblies and refit them to the bellhousing, taking care not to damage the input shaft oil seal. Ensure that the fork rod enters correctly into its bore.

36   Insert the interlock ball, plunger, and further ball to lock the 1st/2nd fork rod (Fig. 6.38).

37   Locate the 3rd/4th shift fork on the input shaft 3rd/4th synchro-sleeve.

38   Locate the bracket and insert the 3rd/4th fork rod. Align the holes and drive in a new retaining pin. Fit a new stopper ring to the groove below the shift fork.

39   Insert the plunger and the two interlock balls to lock the 3rd/4th fork rod.

40   Locate the 5th shift fork on the input shaft 5th synchro-sleeve.

41   Locate the bracket and insert the 5th fork rod. Align the holes and drive in a new retaining pin. Fit a new stopper ring to the groove below the shift fork.

42   Insert the 5th/reverse detent ball and spring, apply sealant to its threads and tighten the detent plug to the specified torque setting.

43   Fit the reverse lever assembly and steel ball, then tighten the bolts to the specified torque setting.

44   Insert the reverse arm shaft, using a new O-ring, and fit a new retaining pin.

45   Select 4th gear. Locate the reverse idler gear, then insert the shaft. Position the shaft end fitting as shown in Fig. 6.40 so that the bolt will enter the threaded hole.

46   Grease the input shaft left-hand bearing shims and locate them in the transmission casing with the oil channel.

47   To aid the refitting of the transmission casing, position the selector either in the 1st/2nd fork rod bracket or between the 1st/2nd and 3rd/4th brackets.

48   Apply sealant to the mating faces of the transmission casing and bellhousing.

49   Lower the transmission casing onto the bellhousing, then fit and tighten the bolts to the specified torque setting.

50   Insert the 1st/2nd and 3rd/4th detent balls and springs. Apply sealing compound to the plug threads, then tighten the plugs to the specified torque setting. Note that a modified, double, spring is available to be fitted to the 3rd/4th detent position, to prevent the transmission jumping out 3rd gear.

51   Refit the reverse idler shaft bolt, applying sealant to its threads and tightening it to the specified torque setting.

52   Refit the gear position switch as described in Section 5 of this Chapter.

53   Check the various adjustments (see Section 15) by measuring the transmission's total turning torque. Proceed as described in Section 10, paragraph 63, but note that the tool now required is available under Part Number KV38106500.

54   Refit the components of the clutch release mechanism as described in Chapter 5.

55   Rotating the input shaft to aid selection, check that all gears can be selected with relative ease.

---

15   Transmission – adjustment

Differential side bearing preload

1   The procedure required is exactly as described in Section 11, noting the following differences, as well as the different preload and turning torque specifications:

   (a)   The forked tool is now Part Number KV38106500
   (b)   The thickness of shims required is the recorded amount plus a further 0.40 to 0.46 mm (0.0158 to 0.0181 in)
   (c)   Shims are available in a range of thicknesses from 0.40 mm (0.0158 in) to 1.20 mm (0.0472 in)

Output shaft bearing preload

2   If any of the following components have been renewed during overhaul, then the shaft bearing preload must be adjusted:

   Output shaft
   Output shaft bearings
   Bellhousing
   Transmission casing

3   Remove the shaft left-hand bearing outer race from the transmission casing and any preload adjusting shim(s). Refit the outer race without shims.

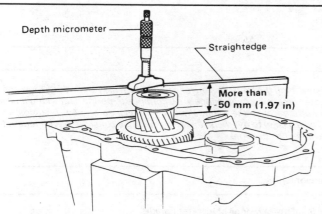

Fig. 6.42 Output shaft bearing preload – measuring dimension 'A'
(Sec 15)

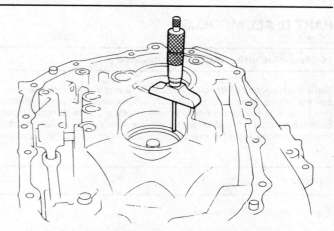

Fig. 6.43 Output shaft bearing preload – measuring dimension 'B'
(Sec 15)

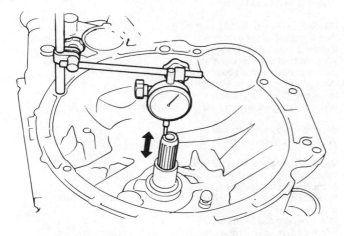

Fig. 6.44 Measuring input shaft endfloat (Sec 15)

8   Subtract 'A' from 'B' to obtain dimension 'C'.
9   The thickness of shims required is 'C' **plus** a further 0.25 to 0.31 mm (0.0098 to 0.0122 in) and should be made up by one thicker shim (where possible) or two thinners shims. Shims are available through Nissan dealers over a range of thicknesses from 0.40 mm (0.0158 in) to 1.20 mm (0.0472 in).
10   The shim(s) should be fitted between the left-hand bearing outer race and the transmission casing.
11   The preload setting can be checked by measuring the transmission's total turning torque. See Section 14 paragraph 53 and Section 10, paragraph 63.

Input shaft endfloat
12   If any of the following components have been renewed during overhaul, then the shaft endfloat must be adjusted:

   Input shaft
   Input shaft bearings
   Bellhousing
   Transmission casing

13   Fit the reassembled input shaft to the bellhousing and use heavy grease to stick the oil channel to its left-hand end.
14   Remove from the transmission casing any input shaft adjusting shims, refit it to the bellhousing and tighten the retaining bolts to the specified torque setting.
15   Attach a dial gauge to the bellhousing so that the input shaft endfloat can be measured.
16   The thickness of shims required is the recorded endfloat **minus** 0 to 0.06 mm (0 to 0.0024 in) and should be made up by one thicker shim (where possible) or two thinner shims. Shims are available through Nissan dealers over a range of thicknesses from 0.40 mm (0.0158 in) to 1.20 mm (0.0472 in).
17   The shim(s) should be fitted between the left-hand bearing outer race and the transmission casing.
18   The endfloat can be checked using the dial gauge once the transmission has been reassembled. Some endfloat should be discernible, up to a maximum of 0.06 mm (0.0024 in), to ensure that there is no preload on the shaft bearings.

4   Clean the mating surfaces of the transmission casing and bellhousing with solvent and remove, if necessary, the shaft right-hand bearing outer race from the bellhousing.
5   Fit the reassembled output shaft to the transmission casing, place the right-hand bearing outer race on the shaft end and press down on it while rotating the shaft to settle the bearings.
6   Obtain a straight edge of at least 50 mm (1.97 in) width and place this across the transmission casing mating surface. Measure from the upper surface of the straight edge to the upper (ie right-hand) end of the bearing outer race. Repeat the measurement at three points around the outer race and calculate the average. Subtract this from the width of the straight edge to obtain the distance by which the outer race protrudes beyond the transmission casing mating surface; let this be dimension 'A' (Fig. 6.42).
7   Measure the distance from the bellhousing mating surface to the shoulder in the output shaft bearing bore against which the bearing outer race will seat. Repeat the measurement at three points around the shoulder and calculate the average; let this be dimension 'B' (Fig. 6.43).

PART D: ALL MODELS

16 Fault diagnosis – manual transmission

Note: *It is sometimes difficult to decide whether it is worthwhile removing and dismantling the transmission for a fault which may be nothing more than a minor irritant. Transmissions which howl, or where the synchromesh can be beaten by a quick gearchange, may continue to perform for a long time in this state. A worn transmission usually needs a complete rebuild to eliminate noise because the various gears, if re-aligned on new bearings, will continue to howl when different wearing surfaces are presented to each other. The decision to overhaul, therefore, must be considered with regard to time and money available, relative to the degree of noise or malfunction that the driver has to suffer.*

Symptom	Reason(s)
Transmission noisy in neutral	Oil level too low or oil of incorrect grade Worn input shaft or bearings Incorrect input shaft endfloat Clutch fault – see Chapter 5
Transmission noisy only when moving (in all gears)	Oil level too low or oil of incorrect grade Worn input shaft or bearings Incorrect input shaft endfloat Worn output shaft or bearings Incorrect output shaft bearing preload Worn differential or side bearings Incorrect differential side bearing preload Worn or chipped output shaft/crownwheel gear teeth
Transmission noisy only when moving (one gear only)	Worn or chipped gear teeth Worn gear pinion bush or bearing
Transmission jumps out of gear	Worn or damaged selector mechanism Weak, worn, or damaged selector mechanism detent components (especially springs) Selector mechanism striking rod or shift fork shaft/rod detent grooves worn Worn or damaged shift forks Worn or damaged synchro-units Incorrect shaft preload/endfloat (as applicable)
Gearchanging noisy	Worn synchro-units (especially baulk rings and cones) Oil of incorrect grade Clutch fault – see Chapter 5
Difficulty engaging gears	Clutch fault – see Chapter 5 Worn or damaged gearchange control rod or broken return spring Worn or damaged selector mechanism Worn or damaged synchro-units

Note: *This Section is not intended to be an exhaustive guide to fault diagnosis, but summarises the more common faults which may be encountered during a car's life. Consult a dealer for more specific advice.*

Chapter 7 Automatic transmission

Contents

Specifications

General

Type .... Torque converter with lock-up system, two epicyclic gearsets giving four forward gear (including overdrive) and reverse, integral final drive

Model RL4F02A

Transmission code number:
1.8 litre models up to early 1988	21X67
All later 1.8 litre models	23X11
2.0 litre models up to early 1988	21X24
2.0 litre carburettor models, 1988-on	23X02
2.0 litre fuel injection models	23X06

Ratios:
1st (1.8 and early 2.0 litre models)	2.785:1
1st (later 2.0 litre models)	2.875:1
2nd	1.545:1
3rd	1.000:1
4th/overdrive	0.694:1
Reverse	2.272:1

Final drive:
1.8 litre models	4.133:1
2.0 litre fuel injection models	Not available
2.0 litre carburettor models	3.876:1

Transmission fluid

Type/specification .... Dexron II type ATF (Duckhams D-Matic)
Capacity (total) .... 6.8 litres (120 Imp pints) approximate

Torque wrench settings

	Nm	lbf ft
Drain plug	15 to 20	11 to 15
Starter inhibitor/reversing lamp switch mounting screws	2.0 to 2.5	1.5 to 2
Speedometer pinion assembly retaining screw	3.7 to 5.0	2.5 to 4
Speedometer case mounting bolts	6.3 to 8.3	4.5 to 6
Transmission fluid pipe banjo bolts	29 to 49	21.5 to 36
Driveplate-to-torque converter mounting bolts	39 to 49	29 to 36
Starter motor mounting bolts and nut	29 to 39	21.5 to 29
Engine/transmission adaptor plate-to-bellhousing bolts	30 to 40	22 to 29.5
Engine/transmission stay-to-cylinder block/crankcase bolts	30 to 40	22 to 29.5
Engine/transmission stay-to-bellhousing bolts	16 to 21	12 to 15.5
Bellhousing-to-cylinder block/crankcase bolts and nut	39 to 49	29 to 36
Dust cover-to-bellhousing bolts	6.3 to 8.3	4.5 to 6
Engine/transmission left-hand mounting:		
Through-bolt retaining nut	64 to 74	47 to 54.5
Mounting-to-transmission casing bolts	44 to 54	32.5 to 40
All other bolts and nuts	39 to 49	29 to 36
Intake (inlet) manifold stay-to-bellhousing bolts – 2.0 litre fuel injection models:		
10 mm thread size	38 to 46	28 to 34
8 mm thread size	18 to 22	13 to 16

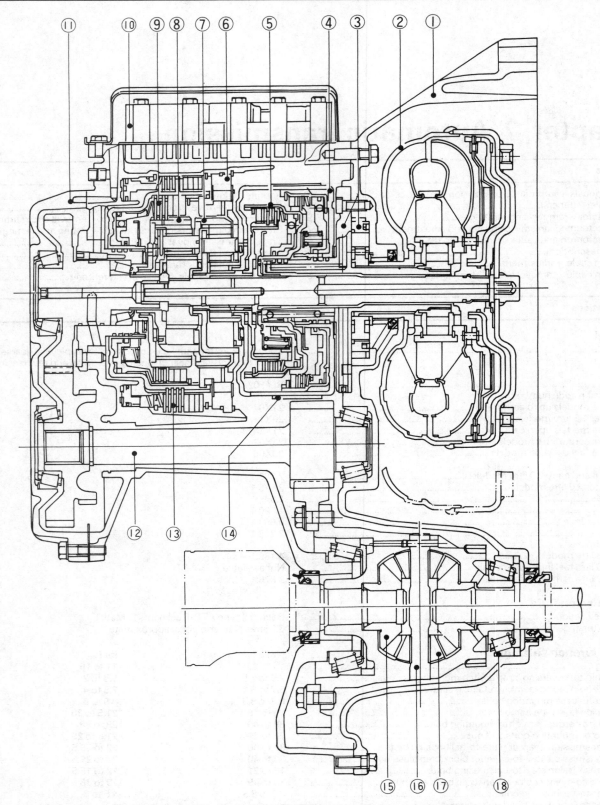

Fig. 7.1 Cross-section through the RL4F02A automatic transmission (Sec 1)

1	Bellhousing	6	One-way clutch	11 Side cover
2	Torque converter	7	Front epicyclic gearset	12 Output shaft
3	Fluid pump	8	Rear epicycle gearset	13 Low and reverse brake
4	Reverse clutch	9	Low clutch	14 Band brake
5	High clutch	10	Control valve assembly	

15	Sun gear
16	Planetary gear shaft
17	Planetary gear
18	Differential side bearing

1 General description

The automatic transmission available as an option on some 1.8 and 2.0 litre models comprises a hydrodynamic torque converter, which replaces the clutch on manual transmission models, and a pair of epicyclic gearsets which are controlled hydraulically by multi-plate clutches and a servo-assisted band brake to produce three forward ratios with an overdrive fourth, and reverse gear. Also included in the assembly is a final drive differential similar to that described in Chapter 6. The complete unit may also be referred to as a 'transaxle'.

The torque converter is a type of fluid coupling which under certain conditions has a torque multiplying effect. As soon as engine speed and load conditions permit, the transmission selects third (or overdrive fourth, if the overdrive button is depressed to the 'On' position) gear and a hydraulically-operated control valve shuts off fluid pressure to the space between the torque converter's outer casing and a sliding lock-up piston. Fluid pressure behind the lock-up piston forces it into contact with the engine end of the outer casing so·that drive is transmitted mechanically, via the lock-up piston and transmission input shaft splines, directly to the transmission. This eliminates any hydraulic slip within the torque converter, thus increasing efficiency and fuel economy during cruising. The lock-up system automatically cuts out whenever the transmission selects first or second gear and an electrically-operated lock-up release circuit (controlled by, on carburettor models, a throttle valve microswitch under the dashpot and a water temperature switch screwed into the thermostat housing) cuts it out whenever the throttle is fully closed or if the engine is still cold.

The gear selector is mounted in the centre console and has six positions: 'P' (Park), 'R' (Reverse), 'N' (Neutral), 'D' (Drive), '2' and '1'. The engine can be started only in positions 'P' or 'N' (preferably 'P'). A lock-out circuit operated through the inhibitor switch and relay ensures that the starter motor cannot be operated in any of the drive positions.

A kickdown mode causes the transmission to select a lower ratio (if engine speed and the car's speed permit) whenever the throttle is opened fully, thus providing extra acceleration for overtaking. Kickdown is controlled by a cable linkage from the acceleration cable pulley.

Note that the transmission fluid is cooled by a heat exchanger built into the radiator. See Chapter 2.

The automatic transmission is a complex unit, but if it is not abused, is reliable and durable. Repair or overhaul procedures are beyond the scope of many dealers, let alone the home mechanic. The contents of this Chapter are therefore confined to those servicing procedures that can be undertaken by the owner. Any fault diagnosis, overhaul or repair work should be entrusted only to a competent Nissan dealer or automatic transmission specialist who has the facilities and skill required to undertake such work.

2 Routine maintenance

1   At the intervals given in 'Routine maintenance' at the beginning of this manual, carefully inspect the transmission joint faces and oil seals for any signs of damage, deterioration or oil leakage and check that the breather tube is clear.
2   Check the transmission fluid as described in the following Section, and at the less frequent intervals specified, renew the fluid as described in Section 4.
3   Carry out a thorough road test, ensuring that all gear changes occur smoothly without snatching and without an increase in engine speed between changes. Check that all gear positions can be engaged with the appropriate movement of the gear selector and, with the vehicle at rest, check the operation of the parking pawl when the 'P' position is selected.

3 Transmission fluid – checking

Note: *Since the fluid level must be checked with the engine running, ensure that the car is parked on level ground with the handbrake firmly applied before opening the bonnet. Be careful also to keep loose clothing and long hair well out of the way of moving components, such as the* radiator fan, and to avoid contact with hot objects such as the exhaust system. See 'Safety first!'.

To ensure that an accurate reading is obtained, the level must be checked with the engine/transmission fully warmed up to normal operating temperature (fluid temperature of approximately 70°C/158°F). If this is not possible, a provisional check can be made with it cold, but the level should be re-checked as soon as possible when the engine/transmission is hot.

Checking the fluid level – engine/transmission warmed up

1   Note that if the car has been driven at high speeds for an extended period, used in heavy traffic in hot weather, or has been used to tow a trailer etc, the fluid temperature will be too high for an accurate reading to be obtained – wait at least 30 minutes for the fluid to cool down before checking the level, as described in paragraph 3 onwards.
2   To make a normal check of the fluid level, take the car on a short journey (of at least 10 minutes duration) until the engine/transmission is fully warmed up to normal operating temperature.
3   Park the car on level ground, apply the handbrake firmly and, with the engine running at no more than idle speed and your foot firmly on the brake pedal, move the gear selector through all positions, ending at the 'P' position.
4   With the engine still idling and the gear selector in the 'P' position, open the bonnet and withdraw the transmission dipstick from the dipstick/filler tube between the battery and the radiator bottom hose (Fig. 7.2).
5   Wipe clean the dipstick using a lint-free rag or paper, insert it fully back into the dipstick/filler tube, then withdraw it again and check the level. Repeat if necessary, to obtain an accurate reading.
6   The level should be between the 'Hot' level marks on the front side of the dipstick (see Fig. 7.3). If topping-up is necessary, add only good quality fluid of the specified type, through the filler tube. A small funnel would be useful to avoid spillage. If the level is too high, the surplus must be drained off.
7   **Never** run the car with the transmission under or over-filled; either condition may cause serious and expensive transmission damage.

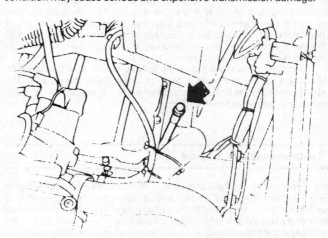

Fig. 7.2 Location of dipstick and dipstick/filler tube (Secs 3 and 4)

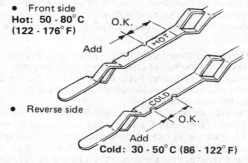

- Front side
  **Hot: 50 - 80°C
  (122 - 176°F)**
- Reverse side
  Cold: 30 - 50°C (86 - 122°F)

Fig. 7.3 Dipstick fluid level markings and corresponding fluid temperature (Secs 3 and 4)

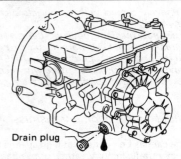

Fig. 7.4 Location of drain plug (Sec 4)

8   When the level is correct, ensure that the dipstick is pressed fully into the tube.

Checking the fluid level – engine/transmission cold

9   Start the engine and run it (as slowly as possible) until it has warmed up to normal operating temperature.
10   Check the fluid level as described in paragraphs 3 to 8 above, but note the level against the 'Cold' level marks on the reverse side of the dipstick (see Fig. 7.3).
11   This is only a provisional check to ensure that the fluid level is approximately correct. As soon as the car can be driven, carry out the full procedure described in paragraphs 2 to 8 above to ensure an accurate check is made.

Checking the fluid condition

12   Whenever the level is checked, examine the condition of the fluid and compare its colour, smell and texture with that of new fluid.
13   If the fluid is dark, almost black, and smells burnt it is possible that the transmission friction material is worn or disintegrating. The car should be taken to an automatic transmission specialist for immediate attention.
14   If the fluid is milky and pink, this is due to the presence of emulsified droplets of water. It may be caused either by condensation after a prolonged period of short journeys or by the entry of water through the dipstick/filler tube or breather. If the fluid does not revert to its normal appearance after a long journey it must be renewed or the car should be taken for expert attention.
15   If the fluid is varnished (ie light to dark brown and tacky) it has oxidised due to overheating or to over- or under-filling. If renewal of the fluid does not cure the problem the car should be taken to an automatic transmission specialist for attention.

4   Transmission fluid – renewal

Note: *The quantity of fluid specified in this Chapter is the total figure which includes that fluid in the torque converter (approximately 2 litres/3.5 pints) as well as that in the radiator heat exchanger section and connecting pipes. Most of this cannot be extracted by removing the drain plug. **Only** if the transmission is being refilled after a complete overhaul, therefore, will the full amount of fluid be required. If the fluid is being renewed as a maintenance operation, only the fluid contained in the transmission itself will be drained, and a smaller amount of fluid will therefore be required to refill it. Note that if contaminated fluid is being replaced, more than one fluid renewal operation may be required to flush out all the old fluid.*

1   Warm the engine/transmission up to normal operating temperature by taking the car on a journey of at least 10 minutes duration.
2   Park the car on level ground, apply the handbrake and select the 'P' position, then switch off the ignition. Open the bonnet and withdraw the dipstick from the dipstick/filler tube.
3   Place a large container of adequate capacity under the transmission, then use a 13 mm (½ in) square drain plug key and suitable spanner to unscrew the female socket-headed drain plug from the lower front edge of the transmission (see Fig. 7.4). Allow the fluid to drain into the container. **Take care** to avoid scalding – the fluid will be very hot.
4   Clean and refit the drain plug, applying a smear of sealant to its threads and tightening it to the specified torque setting.

5   Refill the transmission through the dipstick/filler tube until the fluid is at the top of the 'Cold' level marks on the reverse side of the dipstick.
6   Start the engine and run it until it is warm enough to idle evenly, then slowly move the gear selector through all positions to distribute the fluid throughout the transmission. Return it to the 'P' position.
7   Check the fluid level against the dipstick 'Cold' level marks (see Section 3) and top up if necessary.
8   Take the car on a short journey to fully warm up the engine/transmission, then check the fluid level against the dipstick 'Hot' level marks (see Section 3 of this Chapter.)

5   Kickdown cable – adjustment

1   The adjustment and movement of the kickdown cable linking the throttle to the transmission control valve throttle lever should be checked whenever a fault is suspected in the transmission's gearchange quality or kickdown operation, or whenever the accelerator cable adjustment or engine idle speed is altered.
2   Start by checking the accelerator cable adjustment. See Chapter 3.
3   Slacken fully both of the kickdown cable locknuts ('A' and 'B', Fig. 7.5) at the cable upper end, on each side of the accelerator cable bracket.
4   Open the throttle fully and have an assistant hold the pulley fully-open (position 'P₁', Fig. 7.6) until adjustment is complete.
5   Pull the kickdown cable outer casing 'Q' downwards (direction 'T') until all cable free play is eliminated, then screw locknut 'B' upwards (direction 'U') against the bracket. Back off locknut 'B' by three full turns (actual tolerance specified in 2.75 to 3.25 turns) to set the specified cable free play, then hold it while locknut 'A' is screwed down (direction 'U') and tightened securely. Release the throttle pulley and operate the accelerator pedal to check that both cables function correctly.
6   Note that a similar adjuster, with two locknuts, is fitted to the

Fig. 7.5 Kickdown cable upper adjuster locknuts 'A' and 'B' at accelerator cable bracket (Secs 5 and 6)

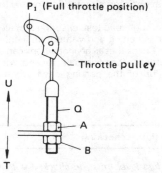

Fig. 7.6 Adjusting kickdown cable (Sec 5)

For significance of annotation, see text

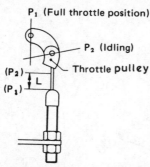

Fig. 7.7 Checking kickdown cable movement (Sec 5)

'L' = 39 to 43 mm (1.54 to 1.69 in)
For P1 and P2 see text

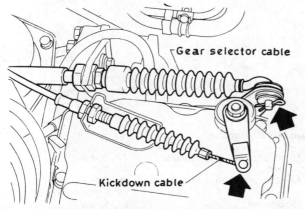

Fig. 7.8 Gear selector and kickdown cable details at transmission (Secs 5, 6, 7 and 8)

kickdown cable lower end (see Fig. 7.8). If there is insufficient adjustment range available at the cable's upper end these two locknuts can be altered to reposition the cable outer as required. Check that they are securely tightened whenever the cable is adjusted.

7   To check the kickdown cable's movement, first check its adjustment, as described above, then check that the cable is routed as smoothly as possible, with no sharp bends or kinks.

8   Check that the accelerator pedal is released and that the throttle pulley is in the fully-closed, idle speed, position (position 'P$_2$', Fig. 7.7). Use white paint or similar to mark the kickdown cable inner wire at the point where it emerges from the cable outer casing.

9   Open the throttle fully and have an assistant hold the pulley fully-opened (position 'P$_1$') while a second mark is made on the cable inner wire at the point where it now emerges from the cable outer casing. Measure the distance 'L' between the two marks (see Fig. 7.7).

10   If the measurement obtained is outside the specified range, check carefully the accelerator cable adjustment, and remove the air filter cover (carburettor models) or intake (inlet) duct (fuel injection models) to check that the throttle valves are fully open when the accelerator pedal is fully depressed – this should, of course, correspond with the throttle pulley 'P$_1$' position. Check also the condition of the kickdown cable itself, renewing it if necessary, and ensure that the transmission control valve throttle lever is fixed securely to its shaft.

6   Kickdown cable – removal and refitting

1   Slacken both of the kickdown cable locknuts fully ('A' and 'B', Fig. 7.5) at the cable upper end, on each side of the accelerator cable bracket. Disengage the cable outer casing from the bracket and its end nipple from the throttle pulley.

2   Similarly, disconnect the cable lower end from the adjuster bracket and throttle lever on the transmission control valve cover (Fig. 7.8). Withdraw the cable.

3   On installation, fit the cable lower end nipple to the transmission control valve throttle lever and position the adjuster in its bracket, then fit the cable upper end nipple to the throttle pulley and position the adjuster in the accelerator cable bracket. Ensure that the cable is routed smoothly, with no sharp bends or kinks. Apply a smear of grease to the cable end nipples.

4   Position the lower adjuster so that it is at the inner limit of its adjustment (see Fig. 7.8) and tighten both locknuts securely. Then adjust the cable and check its movement as described in Section 5 (paragraph 4 onwards) of this Chapter.

7   Gear selector mechanism – checking and adjustment

1   If the regular checks outlined in *'Routine maintenance'* show that the gear selector detents cannot be felt, or that the engagement of gears does not correspond with the indicator at the base of the gear selector, the mechanism must be adjusted as follows.

2   Apply the handbrake firmly and move the gear selector to the 'P' position; check that it locks into place.

3   Open the bonnet and check that there is no lost motion due to slack or missing cable mounting bolts or worn cable end fittings at the transmission selector lever.

4   Jack up the front of the car and support it securely on axle stands.

5   Check that the cable and its end fittings are in good condition, and that the cable brackets are securely fastened to the underbody. If any lost motion is evident between the gear selector and the selector rod, the heat shield covering the selector underside must be removed so that the selector components can be checked for wear. See Section 8 of this Chapter.

6   Slacken both cable adjuster locknuts (Fig. 7.9), then move the transmission selector lever to the 'P' position check that the gear selector is still locked into the 'P' position.

7   Tighten the cable adjuster rear locknut ('X', Fig. 7.10) against the end of the control rod until all slack is just eliminated from the selector mechanism with the rod horizontal and both the gear selector and transmission selector lever still in the 'P' position.

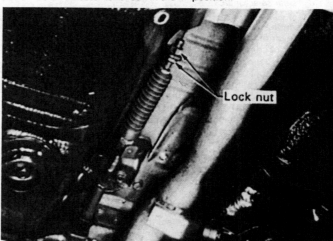

Fig. 7.9 Gear selector mechanism adjuster locknuts (Secs 7 and 8)

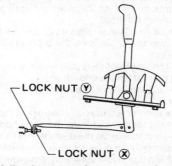

Fig. 7.10 Adjusting gear selector mechanism (Secs 7 and 8)

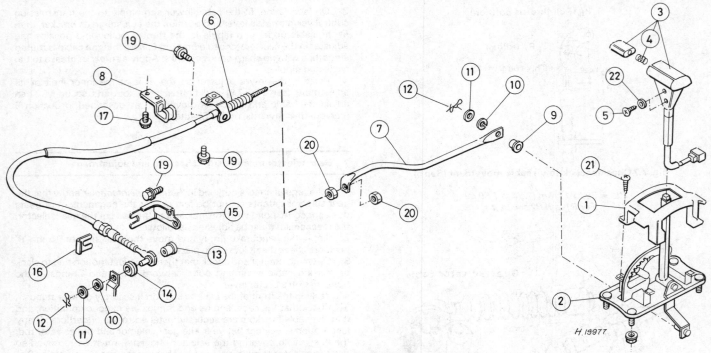

Fig. 7.11 Gear selector mechanism (Secs 7, 8 and 9)

1 Gear position indicator plate	7 Gear selector rod
2 Gear selector assembly	8 Bracket
3 Gear selector knob	9 Grommet
assembly	10 Spring washer
4 Spring	11 Plain washer
5 Screw (2 off)	12 Spring clip
6 Gear selector cable	

13 Pivot bush – later models	17 Screw
only	18 Nut
14 Grommet – early models	19 Bolt
only	20 Adjuster locknut
15 Bracket	21 Screw
16 Spring clip (later models	22 Washer (2 off)
only)	

8   Tighten the cable adjuster front locknut securely ('Y', Fig. 7.10) and apply a smear of grease to the cable end fittings, adjuster threads and other points of contact.
9   Move the gear selector slowly through its full range from 'P' to '1' and back again. The gear selector should move smoothly, without sliding noises and with the detent being felt at each position.
10   If all is well, lower the car to the ground, start the engine and run it at idle speed with the handbrake and brake pedal firmly applied. Move the gear selector slowly through its range and back again, ensuring that a slight shock is felt from the transmission at the correct moment as each gear is selected.

8   Gear selector rod and cable – removal and refitting

1   Apply the handbrake firmly, select the 'P' position, then jack up the front of the car and support it securely on axle stands.
2   Working at the transmission end of the cable, withdraw the spring clip and disconnect the cable from the transmission selector lever, noting carefully the arrangement of the plain and spring washers and the pivot bush or grommet (as fitted).
3   Either slacken the cable adjuster locknuts or remove the spring clip (as applicable) to release the cable from the transmission bracket, or simply unbolt the bracket.
4   Work back along the length of the cable either releasing it from its brackets or unbolting them from the underbody.
5   Unscrew the cable adjuster rear locknut ('X', Fig 7.10) and withdraw the cable from the car.
6   To disconnect the selector rod from the bottom of the gear selector assembly, first unbolt the heat shield from the underbody and work it clear of the exhaust system to expose the underside of the gear selector. It may be necessary to unbolt the exhaust system mountings in front of and behind the heat shield to provide sufficient movement for this. Note also that one of the four heat shield bolts fastens the exhaust system

earth strap.
7   Withdraw the spring clip and disconnect the selector rod from the gear selector lower end, noting carefully the arrangement of the plain and spring washers and the grommet.
8   Carefully clean all components and renew any that are worn or damaged. If the cable is stiff or jerky in operation, especially when compressed in its working position, it must be renewed. Attempts at lubrication are likely to prove only partially successful in curing a stiff cable. Check carefully the pins and selector rod or cable end fittings for signs of wear or damage.
9   On refitting, apply a smear of grease to all cable and rod end fittings and pins, to the adjuster threads and other points of contact.
10   Connect the selector rod to the gear selector, then refit the heat shield. Note that there must be clean metal-to-metal contact at the earth strap connection.
11   Connect the cable to the transmission bracket and selector lever, check that the lever is still in the 'P' position, then route the cable smoothly back along the underbody, securing it in the brackets provided.
12   Screw the cable adjuster front locknut ('Y', Fig. 7.10) as far as possible along the adjuster threads, pass the cable end through the selector rod end and refit the adjuster rear locknut ('X', Fig. 7.10).
13   Adjust the mechanism as described in Section 7 of this Chapter (paragraph 7 onwards).

9   Gear selector – removal and refitting

1   Apply the handbrake firmly and select the 'P' position.
2   Remove the centre console. See Chapter 11.
3   Disconnect the overdrive button and the indicator lamp wiring at their connector plugs. The gear selector knob assembly can now be removed, if required, by extracting the two screws which secure it to the gear selector shaft.

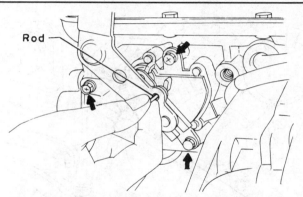

Fig. 7.12 Setting the starter inhibitor/reversing lamp switch
(Secs 10 and 11)

4 Remove the indicator plate, if required, by removing its mounting screws.
5 Jack up the front of the car and support it securely on axle stands, then disconnect the selector rod from the gear selector lower end. See Section 8 of this Chapter (paragraphs 6 and 7).
6 Unscrew the four nuts retaining the gear selector assembly to the underside of the car, then withdraw the assembly from inside the passenger compartment.
7 Note that the overdrive button and its warning lamp are an integral part of the knob and can be renewed only with the knob. To test the switch, check that there is continuity between all three wire terminals only in the 'Off' position.
8 Refitting is the reverse of the removal procedure. Adjust the selector mechanism, if necessary, as described in Section 7 of this Chapter.

10 Starter inhibitor/reversing lamp switch – setting and testing

1 The switch controlling the starter inhibitor and reversing lamp circuits is bolted to the transmission rear face, underneath the gear selector lever. If the starter motor can be operated in any gear position other than 'P' or 'N' (or if it does not work at all, but the remainder of the circuit has been checked), or if the reversing lamps illuminate in any position other than 'R' (or if they do not light at all, but the remainder of the circuit has been checked), the switch setting should be checked and its operation tested. Note that the switch is also incorporated in the BCDD circuit (carburettor models only).
2 **Before** the switch is disturbed in any way, **always** check first that the gear selector mechanism is correctly adjusted.
3 To check the switch setting, apply the handbrake firmly and select the 'N' position. Open the bonnet and check that the transmission selector lever is also in the 'N' position.
4 Obtain a metal rod (such as a drill bit) 4 mm/0.16 in diameter and insert it squarely into the hole in the selector lever (see Fig. 7.12). It should be possible to push the rod into the matching hole in the switch itself.
5 If the switch setting is incorrect, slacken the three switch mounting screws and reposition the switch until the rod will fit squarely through the holes in the lever and switch. Tighten the switch screws securely but do not overtighten them – note the specified torque setting.
6 To test the switch's operation, disconnect its wiring lead at the connector and use a multimeter (set to the resistance function) to check for continuity between the wire terminals indicated at the respective gear positions shown (see Fig. 7.13).
7 If the switch is in good condition and correctly set there should be continuity only when the selector lever is in the appropriate gear position. If continuity is found a significant amount on either side of the position, check the switch setting. If any other fault is found, such as no continuity, the switch must be renewed.

11 Starter inhibitor/reversing lamp switch – removal and refitting

1 Apply the handbrake firmly, check that the ignition is switched off and select the 'N' position.
2 Disconnect the switch wiring at its connector and remove the three

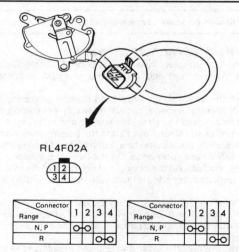

RL4F02A

Connector Range	1	2	3	4
N, P	o─o			
R			o─o	

Connector Range	1	2	3	4
N, P	o─o			
R			o─o	

Fig. 7.13 Testing the starter inhibitor/reversing lamp switch (Sec 10)

switch mounting screws, then withdraw the switch. Pack the aperture with clean rag if there is any fluid loss.
3 On refitting, position the switch on the transmission and lightly refit the mounting screws, then use a metal rod to set the switch accurately as described in Section 10 of this Chapter and connect its wiring lead to the main loom.
4 Mop up any spilt fluid and top up the transmission, if necessary, as described in Section 3 of this Chapter.
5 Check that the switch operates correctly.

12 Speedometer drive – removal and refitting

1 Open the bonnet and disconnect the speedometer drive cable from the transmission. See Chapter 12.
2 If required, the speedometer pinion assembly can be withdrawn separately by unscrewing the single retaining screw and pulling the assembly upwards out of its case.
3 To remove the speedometer case, unbolt it and withdraw it from the transmission, noting the sealing O-ring and the thrustwashers. Withdraw the speedometer gear assembly, noting the two thrustwashers at each end of it. Pack the aperture with clean rag to minimise the loss of fluid.
4 If the speedometer drive or idler gears are damaged they can be renewed separately by driving out the roll pin which secures each to the shaft. Similarly the pinion assembly can be dismantled by driving out the retaining roll pin so that the pinion can be withdrawn from the sleeve. Note the number of shims fitted to the pinion.
5 Renew as a matter of course the O-rings and oil seals whenever they are disturbed.
6 Refitting is a reverse of the dismantling procedure. Apply a smear of clean fluid to the seals and O-rings as they are installed and ensure that the gears mesh correctly. Tighten the bolts and screw to the torque settings specified. Check the fluid level and top up if necessary (see Section 3 of this Chapter.)

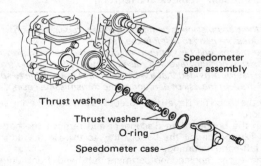

Speedometer gear assembly

Thrust washer

Thrust washer

O-ring

Speedometer case

Fig. 7.14 Speedometer case and drive gear assembly (Sec 12)

13   Transmission oil seals – removal and refitting

Differential side (driveshaft) oil seals

1   Drain the transmission fluid (see Section 4 of this Chapter) and remove the driveshaft(s) and underwing shield(s), as described in Chapter 8.

2   Prise out the seal, taking care not to scratch or damage the seal housing. If difficulty is experienced, an internally-expanding claw-type puller could be adapted to extract the seal, as shown in Fig. 7.15.

3   Dip the new seal in clean fluid, fit it to the transmission aperture and drive it squarely into place using as a drift a piece of tubing which bears only on the seal's hard outer edge. On the left-hand side the seal seats on a shoulder machined in the casing, but on the right-hand side it must be driven in until its outer edge is flush with the surrounding casing (see Fig. 7.1.)

4   Before refitting the driveshaft, check its seal rubbing surface for signs of burrs, scratches or damage which caused the seal to fail in the first place. It may be possible to polish away faults of this sort using fine abrasive paper.

5   Ensure the driveshaft is clean and greased to protect the seal lips on refitting. See Chapter 8.

6   Refill the transmission with fluid as described in Section 4 of this Chapter.

Input shaft (torque converter) oil seal

7   Remove the transmission from the car (see Section 15 of this Chapter) and withdraw the torque converter, taking care not to spill any of its fluid. Check the converter boss for signs of burrs, scratches or damage which caused the seal to fail in the first place. It may be possible to polish away faults of this sort using fine abrasive paper. If the torque converter is worn or damaged sufficiently to require renewal, it is available only as part of the complete transmission assembly.

8   Prise out the seal, taking care not to scratch or damage the input shaft or the seal housing.

9   Dip the new seal in clean fluid, fit it to the transmission aperture and drive it squarely into place using as a drift a piece of tubing which bears only on the seal's hard outer edge. Drive the seal in until its seats on its locating shoulder (see Fig. 7.16).

10   Refit the torque converter and refit the transmission to the car – see Section 15 of this Chapter.

14   Fluid cooler – general

1   The normal operation of the transmission will create a considerable amount of heat which must be minimised to prevent fluid deterioration and transmission damage. This purpose is served by the heat exchanger built into the radiator and connected to the transmission by flexible hoses and fluid pipes.

2   Refer to Chapter 2 for details of servicing procedures.

3   If the fluid pipe banjo unions at the transmission are ever disturbed, always renew the sealing washer on each side of each union and tighten the banjo bolts to the specified torque setting.

15   Transmission – removal and refitting

Note: *If the transmission is being removed for repair, check first that the repairer does not need to test it in the vehicle.*

   Some means will be required of taking the transmission's weight while it is moved sideways and raised or lowered. A strong trolley jack would be useful, provided that a wooden spacer is available to spread the load and prevent the risk of damage to the transmission casing.

1   Park the car on firm level ground, apply the handbrake and select the 'P' position.

2   Open the bonnet, then disconnect and remove the battery (see Chapter 12) and unbolt the battery tray to expose the engine/transmission left-hand mounting.

3   Remove the engine compartment left-hand front undershield, which is secured by five bolts and the left-hand underwing shield, which is secured by four bolts and two plastic clips.

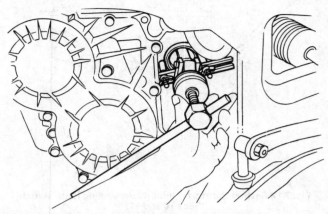

Fig. 7.15 Using a claw-type puller to extract a differential side oil seal (Sec 13)

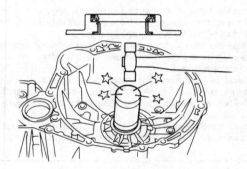

Fig. 7.16 Installing an input shaft oil seal (Sec 13)

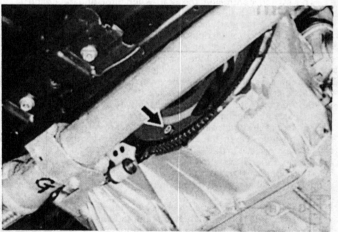

Fig. 7.17 Remove dust cover from bellhousing to expose driveplate to torque converter mounting bolt (arrowed) (Sec 15)

4   Drain the transmission fluid (see Section 4 of this Chapter). Slacken their clips and disconnect from the transmission fluid pipes the two flexible hoses. Note or label each hose to ensure that it is refitted correctly. Either plug or cap the hoses and pipes or allow them to drain into the container, as required.

5   Disconnect the kickdown cable from the transmission. See Section 6 of this Chapter.

6   Disconnect the gear selector cable from the transmission. See Section 8 of this Chapter.

7   Disconnect the wiring lead for the starter inhibitor/reversing lamp switch and the lead for the torque converter lock-up release and overdrive control solenoids.

8   Disconnect the speedometer drive cable (see Chapter 12) and the breather tube.

9   Chock the rear wheels, jack up the front of the car and support it

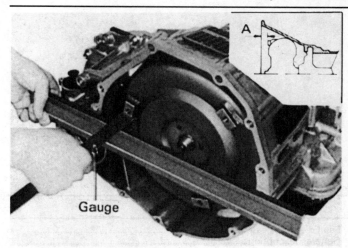

Fig. 7.18 Checking full engagement of torque converter (Sec 15)

A = at least 19 mm (0.75 in)

securely on axle stands, then remove both driveshafts (see Chapter 8.)

10   Working under the car, unbolt the dust cover from the bellhousing, noting the positions of the engine/transmission front and rear stays and the exhaust system mounting.

11   Use chalk or a felt-tip pen to mark the relationship of the torque converter to the driveplate, then unscrew the three driveplate-to-torque converter mounting bolts. Rotate the assembly via the crankshaft pulley bolt to bring each mounting bolt in turn into view in the bellhousing aperture (see Fig. 7.17.) First slacken each bolt in turn, then work round them again, completely unscrewing each one.

12   Support the weight of the transmission using a trolley jack and wooden spacer, an engine hoist, or similar.

13   Unscrew and remove the bolts, and nut, securing the bellhousing to the engine. Unbolt the remaining starter motor mountings (if any) and pull the starter motor clear of the bellhousing – there is no need to remove it completely. On 2.0 litre fuel injection models, unscrew the bolts securing the intake manifold stay to the transmission.

14   The engine/transmission left-hand mounting consists basically of two parts. One (two-piece) mounting is bolted to the inner wing panel and the other, incorporating a large rubber bush, is bolted to the transmission. Unscrew the through-bolt and nut which secure the two

parts of the mounting, then check that the transmission is supported securely before unbolting the mounting from the transmission. Note the two large washers on each side of the rubber bush.

15   Withdraw the transmission from the engine, prising it off the locating dowels, and lower it clear of the car. Be careful to keep the torque converter pressed fully into the bellhousing, or fluid will be spilled from it, and take care not to damage any components.

16   On refitting, ensure that the mating surfaces of the engine and transmission are completely clean and dry and that the engine/transmission adaptor plate is correctly located on the dowels.

17   If the torque converter has been drained or renewed, refill it with approximately 2 litres (3.5 pints) of the specified type of fluid, then fit the torque converter to the transmission, taking care not to damage the oil seal.

18   To ensure the torque converter is fully engaged in the transmission components, use a straight edge and steel rule as shown in Fig. 7.18 to check that the distance 'A' between the bellhousing mating surface and each of the torque converter mounting bosses is at least that specified.

19   Refitting is the reverse of the removal procedure, noting the following points:

(a)   *Use the marks made on dismantling to align the torque converter and driveplate correctly*

(b)   *Tighten all nuts and bolts to the specified torque wrench settings*

(c)   *Adjust the gear selector mechanism (Section 7), the starter inhibitor/reversing lamp switch, if disturbed (Section 10), and the kickdown cable (Section 5)*

(d)   *Refill the transmission with the specified type of fluid*

(e)   *Check carefully the transmission operation as soon as possible*

16   Fault diagnosis – automatic transmission

In the event of a fault occurring on the transmission which cannot be cured by attention to the fluid level or the adjustments described in this Chapter, it is first necessary to determine whether the fault is of a mechanical or hydraulic nature. For this to be done accurately, the transmission must be in the car. Special test equipment is necessary for this purpose, together with a systematic test procedure, and the work should be entrusted to a suitably-equipped Nissan dealer, or automatic transmission specialist.

Do not remove the transmission from the car for repair or overhaul until professional fault diagnosis has been carried out.

Chapter 8 Driveshafts

Contents

Specifications

Type ....
Unequal-length, solid steel, splined to inner and outer constant-velocity joints. Support bearing on right-hand driveshaft on 1.8 and 2.0 litre models

Lubrication (at overhaul only – see text)

Lubricant type ....
Nissan Genuine Grease or that supplied with repair kit

Quantity:

	Inner joint	Outer joint
1.6 litre models	220 to 240 g (7.76 to 8.46 oz)	155 to 175 g (5.47 to 6.17 oz)
All other models	250 to 270 g (8.82 to 9.52 oz)	205 to 225 g (7.23 to 7.94 oz)

Torque wrench settings

	Nm	lbf ft
Driveshaft nut	235 to 314	173 to 232
Support bearing bracket to bearing housing bolts	13 to 19	9.5 to 14
Support bearing bracket to cylinder block bolts – refer to Fig. 8.12:		
Bolt No 1	25 to 35	18.5 to 26
Bolts No 2 and No 4	43 to 58	32 to 43
Bolt No 3	30 to 40	22 to 29.5
Roadwheel nuts	98 to 118	72 to 87
Track rod outer balljoint retaining nut:		
Stage 1	29 to 39	21.5 to 29
Stage 2	Tighten until split pin can be inserted (max torque of 49 Nm/36 lbf ft)	
Front suspension strut top mounting nuts	31 to 42	23 to 31
Front suspension lower arm balljoint mounting plate nuts	76 to 109	56 to 80

1 General description

The drive is transmitted from the differential sun gears to the front wheels by two solid steel unequal-length driveshafts. Both driveshafts are splined near their outer ends to accept the wheel hubs and threaded so that each hub can be fastened by a large nut. Each shaft's inner end is splined to accept the differential sun gear. Two constant velocity joints are fitted to each shaft to ensure the smooth and efficient transmission of drive at all the angles possible as the wheels move up and down with the suspension and as they turn from side to side under steering.

The outer constant velocity joints are of the Rzeppa (or Birfield) ball-and-cage type and are splined to accept the driveshaft itself. Note that while a repair kit is available if the joint bellows only are to be renewed, if the outer joints are to be renewed they can be obtained only as a repair kit which comprises the complete driveshaft and outer joint assembly.

The inner constant velocity joints are of the sliding tripod type, to allow for differences in driveshaft effective length at extremes of suspension travel, and are also splined to accept the driveshaft itself. The left-hand shaft's inner joint, and on 1.6 litre models the right-hand shaft's inner joint, is at the shaft's inner end. On all other models the right-hand shaft's inner joint is approximately half-way between the outer joint and the differential to allow room for the fitting of the support bearing. The joint incorporates an extended shaft section to reach the differential. Note that while a repair kit is available if the joint bellows only are to be renewed, if the joints themselves are to be renewed only the spiders can be obtained separately; the joint bodies can be obtained only as part of an inner joint repair kit.

All 1.8 and 2.0 litre models are fitted with a support bearing, inboard of the right-hand inner constant velocity joint, that is secured by three bolts to a bracket which is itself bolted to the rear of the cylinder block. Note that this bearing is only available as part of the right-hand inner joint repair kit.

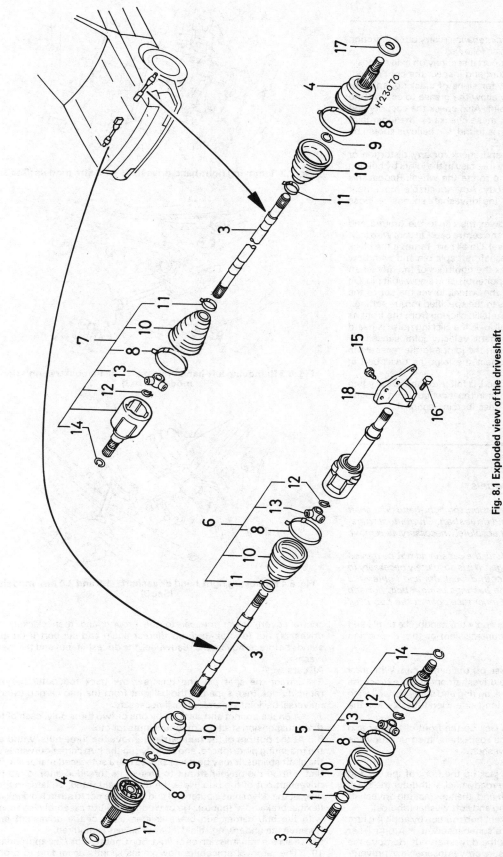

Fig. 8.1 Exploded view of the driveshaft assemblies (Sec 1)

1 Right-hand driveshaft assembly
2 Left-hand driveshaft assembly
3 Driveshaft
4 Outer constant velocity joint
5 Right-hand inner constant velocity joint assembly (1.6 litre models)
6 Right-hand inner constant velocity joint assembly (1.8 and 2.0 litre models)
7 Left-hand inner constant velocity joint assembly
8 Large bellows clip
9 Retaining clip
10 Bellows
11 Small bellows clip
12 Circlip
13 Spider
14 Retaining clip
15 Bolt (4 off)
16 Bolt (3 off)
17 Dust shield (later models only)
18 Support bearing bracket

2 Routine maintenance

1   At regular intervals (see *'Routine maintenance'*) carry out a thorough inspection of the driveshafts and joints as follows.
2   Jack up the front of the car and support it securely on axle stands.
3   Slowly rotate each roadwheel in turn and inspect the condition of the outer joint rubber bellows. Check for signs of cracking, splits or deterioration of the rubber which may allow the grease to escape and lead to water and grit entry into the joint. Also check the security and condition of the bellows clips. Repeat these checks on the inner joint bellows. If any damage or deterioration is found, the bellows should be renewed, as described in Sections 4 or 5.
4   Continue rotating the roadwheel and check for any distortion or damage to the driveshaft. Check for any free play in the joints by holding the driveshaft firmly and attempting to rotate the wheel. Repeat this check whilst holding the inner joint body. Any noticeable movement indicates wear in the joints, wear in the driveshaft splines or loose driveshaft nut.
5   On cars with steel roadwheels, lower the car to the ground and remove the roadwheel trim or prise off the centre cap. On cars with light alloy roadwheels, remove the roadwheel. On all cars, remove the black plastic cap (if fitted‖), extract the driveshaft nut split pin and withdraw the locking ring and soft washer. Check the tightness of the driveshaft nut and reassemble the disturbed components using a new split pin. On cars with light alloy roadwheels, refit the wheel, lower the car to the ground and tighten the roadwheel nuts to the specified torque setting.
6   Road test the car and listen for a metallic clicking from the front as the car is driven slowly in a circle on full lock. If a clicking noise is heard this indicates wear in the outer constant velocity joint caused by excessive clearance between the balls in the joint and the recesses in which they operate. Remove and inspect the joint, as described in Section 4.
7   If vibration, consistent with road speed, is felt through the car when accelerating, there is a possibility of wear in the inner constant velocity joint. Remove and inspect the joint, as described in Section 4.

3 Driveshafts – removal and refitting

Preliminary dismantling – all models

Note: *On models with automatic transmission, the right-hand driveshaft* **must** *be removed before the left-hand driveshaft. On manual transmission models, it is preferable, but not absolutely necessary, to remove the right-hand driveshaft first.*

If both driveshafts have been removed, the car should **not** *be moved or the front hub bearings, may be damaged. If it is absolutely necessary to move the car either temporarily refit both driveshafts and tighten the driveshaft nuts correctly, or preload the bearings using a bolt, nut and washers to clamp the bearing inboard inner race against the hub itself (photo).*

1   With the car standing on its wheels apply the handbrake firmly and select first or reverse gear (manual transmission) or the 'P' position (automatic).

Cars with steel roadwheels
2   Remove the roadwheel trim or prise off the centre cap. Withdraw the black plastic cap (if fitted) from the driveshaft end, then extract the driveshaft nut split pin. Remove the locking ring and soft washer. Using a suitable socket, a strong T-bar and a long extension tube, slacken the driveshaft nut; do not unscrew it yet.
3   Slacken the roadwheel nuts, then jack up the front of the car and support it on axle stands. Remove the roadwheel, then unscrew the driveshaft nut and remove the metal washer.

Cars with light alloy roadwheels
4   Slacken the roadwheel nuts, then jack up the front of the car and support it on axle stands. Remove the roadwheel, withdraw the black plastic cap (if fitted) from the driveshaft end, then extract the driveshaft nut split pin and remove the locking ring and soft washer (photos).
5   Enlist the aid of an assistant to prevent hub rotation by applying firm pressure to the brake pedal, then use a suitable socket, a strong T-bar and a long extension tube to unscrew the driveshaft nut. Remove the metal washer (photo). If the brake pressure proves incapable of preventing hub rotation, temporarily refit the roadwheel (having removed its

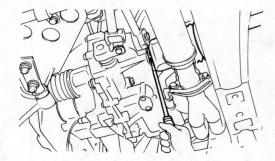

Fig. 8.2 Removing right-hand driveshaft – 1.6 litre models (Sec 3)

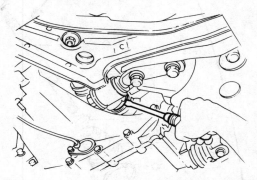

Fig. 8.3 Removing left-hand driveshaft – all manual transmission models (Sec 3)

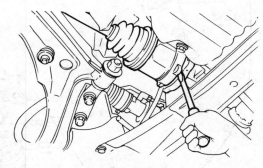

Fig. 8.4 Removing right-hand driveshaft – 1.8 and 2.0 litre models (Sec 3)

centre cover), lower the car to the ground and then slacken the driveshaft nut (photo). Jack up the car again and support it on axle stands before removing the roadwheel, the driveshaft nut and the metal washer.

All cars
6   Extract the split pin and unscrew the track rod outer balljoint retaining nut, then separate the balljoint from the hub carrier, using a universal balljoint separator tool if necessary.
7   Open the bonnet and slacken, by one or two turns only, each of the three suspension strut top mounting nuts (photo).
8   At the bottom of the hub carrier, remove the three nuts, withdraw the mounting plate (photo) and sharply tug the hub carrier outwards off the shaft splines. It may be necessary to use a soft-faced mallet (having first refitted the driveshaft nut to protect its threaded end) to tap the driveshaft out of the hub. Note the dust shield fitted, on later models only, at the driveshaft's outer end and take care not to stretch or kink the flexible brake hose (photo). Tie or wedge the strut assembly, complete with the hub carrier and brake caliper, clear of the driveshaft end. Remove the underwing shield if better access is required.
9   Drain the transmission oil or fluid. See Chapter 6 or 7, as appropriate.
10   The removal procedure now varies slightly according to model and transmission.

3.0 If car is to be moved with driveshaft removed, preload front hub bearings to prevent damage

3.4A On cars with light alloy roadwheels, roadwheel must be removed first to permit removal of split pin and locking ring ...

3.4B ... and soft washer

3.5A Do not forget metal washer behind driveshaft nut

3.5B It may be easier to slacken driveshaft nut with (light alloy) roadwheels in place

3.7 Slacken all suspension strut top mounting nuts (arrowed) to permit strut movement ...

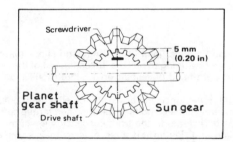

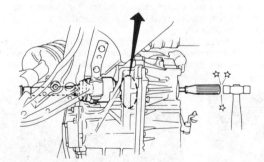

Fig. 8.5 Removing left-hand driveshaft – all automatic transmission models (Sec 3)

1.6 litre models

11   To remove the right-hand driveshaft, use a suitable lever inserted between the body of the inner constant velocity joint and the bellhousing (see Fig. 8.2) to prise out the driveshaft until the retaining clip compresses into its groove and is released from the differential sun gear. Withdraw the driveshaft assembly.
12   To remove the left-hand driveshaft, use a suitable lever inserted

between the body of the inner constant velocity joint and the transmission casing (taking care not to damage the large oil seal on this side) to prise out the driveshaft until the retaining clip compresses into its groove and is released from the differential sun gear. (See Fig. 8.3.) Withdraw the driveshaft assembly.

1.8 and 2.0 litre models with manual transmission

13   To remove the right-hand driveshaft, first unscrew the three bolts securing the support bearing housing to the bracket (photo). Separate the housing from the bracket by rotating it with both hands until a gap has opened into which a suitable lever can be inserted. **Do not** lever against the dust seal on the driveshaft's inner end, or attempt to shift the support bearing from its housing. Prise out the driveshaft (see Fig. 8.4) and withdraw it (photo).
14   If the support bearing bracket is to be removed, this can be done by unscrewing the four bolts which secure the bracket to the rear of the cylinder block. These bolts are, however, extremely awkward of access and it may prove necessary to dismantle part or all of the engine rear mounting to reach them.
15   To remove the left-hand driveshaft, proceed exactly as described in paragraph 12 (and Fig. 8.3) above.

1.8 and 2.0 litre models with automatic transmission

16   To remove the right-hand driveshaft, proceed exactly as described in paragraph 13 (and Fig. 8.4) above.
17   To remove the left-hand driveshaft, the right-hand driveshaft **must** be removed first. Pass a long-bladed screwdriver or similar drift into the differential, via the aperture left by the right-hand driveshaft, over the planetary gear shaft until it rests against the inner end of the left-hand driveshaft (see Fig. 8.5). Tap out the left-hand driveshaft until the retaining clip compresses into its groove and is released from the differential sun gear. Withdraw the driveshaft assembly.

Refitting – all models

18   Refitting both driveshafts is the reverse of the removal procedure, noting the following points.

3.8A ... then remove the balljoint mounting plate to release strut from lower arm

3.8B Pull strut and hub carrier assembly off driveshaft end

3.13A Remove three bolts (two arrowed, one hidden) ...

3.13B ... to release right-hand driveshaft from support bearing bracket

3.22 Refitting the left-hand driveshaft

19   Thoroughly clean the driveshaft itself and the apertures in the transmission and hub carriers to prevent the entry of dirt during refitting. Apply a thin film of grease to the oil seal lips and to the driveshaft splines and shoulders. Check that the bellows clips are securely fastened.

20   Note that the retaining clip at the inner end of the left-hand driveshaft (and of the right-hand driveshaft on 1.6 litre models) **must** be renewed whenever the driveshaft is removed and refitted.

21   When refitting the driveshafts, take great care to prevent damage to the transmission casing oil seals. Nissan specify special tools which guide the shafts through the seal lips on refitting. Provided that the seal lips and shaft ends are lightly greased and that care is taken on refitting, these tools should not be necessary.

22   Insert the left-hand driveshaft into the transmission (photo), engage its splines with those of the differential sun gear, and press it into place until the retaining clip engages correctly behind (inboard of) the

sun gear. Grasp the inner joint body firmly and check that the clip is properly engaged by trying to pull the driveshaft out of the sun gear.

23   Refit the right-hand driveshaft on 1.6 litre models, as described above.

24   On refitting the right-hand driveshaft on all other models, tighten the support bearing housing bolts to the specified torque setting.

25   Refit the hub carrier to the front suspension lower arm, refit the mounting plate and tighten the three nuts to their specified torque setting, also the suspension strut top mounting nuts (see Chapter 10.)

26   Refit the track rod outer balljoint to the hub carrier, tighten the retaining nut to the specified torque setting and fit a new split pin to secure it (see Chapter 10).

27   Refit the metal washer and driveshaft nut (photo), then refit the roadwheel and lower the car to the ground. Tighten the driveshaft nut to its specified torque setting (photo), then refit the soft washer and locking ring.

3.27A Refit metal washer, then driveshaft nut

3.27B Driveshaft nut torque setting is high – nut should be tightened with roadwheel refitted and car lowered to the ground

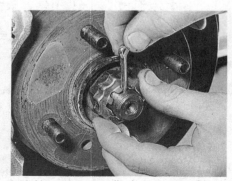

3.29 Always renew split pin on reassembly

28   On cars with steel roadwheels, fit a new split pin to secure the driveshaft nut, check that the roadwheel nuts are securely fastened, then refit the roadwheel trim or centre cap. Do not forget to refit the black plastic cap (if fitted).

29   On cars with light alloy roadwheels, jack the car up again and remove the roadwheel so that a new split pin can be fitted to secure the driveshaft nut (photo). Refit the black plastic cap (if fitted). Refit the roadwheel and its centre cover, lower the car to the ground and tighten the roadwheel nuts to the specified torque setting.

30   Refill the transmission with oil or fluid, then check the level. See Chapter 6 or 7, as appropriate.

---

4   Driveshafts – overhaul

---

1   Remove the driveshaft from the car. See Section 3 of this Chapter. **Do not** attempt to dismantle the outer joints with the driveshafts in the car; the risk of possible damage is too great.

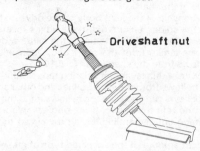

Fig. 8.6 Refitting outer constant velocity joint to driveshaft (Sec 4)

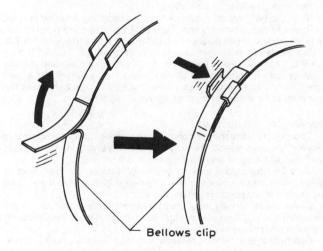

Fig. 8.8 Secure the clip end under the tags (Sec 4)

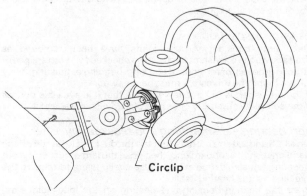

Fig. 8.10 Remove the circlip to release the inner joint spider (Sec 4)

2   Note that all bellows clips, circlips and retaining clips **must** be renewed as a matter of course, whenever they are distributed during removal and refitting.

3   Clean the driveshaft thoroughly before dismantling it and clamp it, between the two joints, in a large vice with padded jaws.

Outer joints – dismantling and reassembly

4   Remove the bellows clips, then slide the bellows off the joint and towards the middle of the shaft. Mark the relationship of the outer joint to the shaft.

5   Pull the outer joint off the driveshaft assembly while tapping it outwards with a mallet to force the retaining clip to contract into its groove, thus releasing the joint from the shaft. Slide the bellows off the shaft end and remove the retaining clip.

6   On refitting, wind a thin layer of insulating tape around the shaft's end to protect the bellows from the shaft splines and other sharp edges. Fit the new small bellows clip and slide the bellows on to the driveshaft. Remove the tape and fit the new retaining clip to the groove in the shaft end.

7   Fit the outer joint to the shaft and engage it with the shaft splines. If the original joint is re-used, align the marks on dismantling. Refitting the driveshaft nut to protect the joint outer threaded end, use a mallet to tap the outer joint on to the shaft until the retaining clip engages correctly behind the joint cage.

8   Pack the joint with the correct amount of the specified type of grease (supplied with the kit), twist the joint to ensure that all its recesses are filled and pack any surplus grease into the bellows.

9   Slide the bellows onto the outer joint, fit the new large bellows clip and tighten it as shown in Fig. 8.7, then bend back the end and secure it

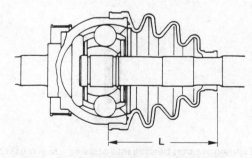

Fig. 8.7 Tightening a driveshaft bellows clip (Sec 4)

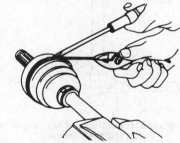

Fig. 8.9 Outer joint bellows set length (Sec 4)

L = 96.0 to 98.0 mm (3.78 to 3.86 in)

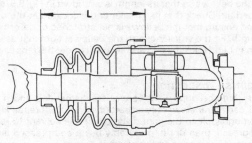

Fig. 8.11 Inner joint bellows set length (Sec 4)

L = 101.5 to 103.5 mm (4.00 to 4.07 in)

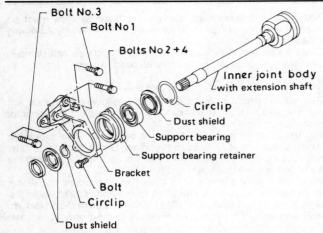

Fig. 8.12 Support bearing assembly – 1.8 and 2.0 litre models only
(Sec 4)

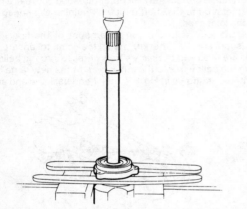

Fig. 8.13 Pressing support bearing and housing off inner joint's
extended shaft (Sec 4)

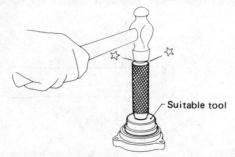

Fig. 8.14 Tapping support bearing into housing – tool must fit only
against bearing outer race (Sec 4)

under the tags as shown in Fig. 8.8.
10   Set the bellows so that its length is as shown in Fig. 8.9, and expel any trapped air. Check that its smaller end is located in the driveshaft groove and ensure that the bellows is not stretched or deformed when at this length. Fit the smaller clip to the bellows, tighten it as shown in Fig. 8.7, then bend back the end and secure it under the tags as shown in Fig. 8.8.

Outer joints – inspection

11   Note that the outer joint cannot be dismantled and if worn or damaged, can be renewed only as part of a driveshaft repair kit.
12   Thoroughly clean the joint using a suitable solvent to remove all traces of grease, then dry it, preferably using compressed air. Ensure that all traces of grease and solvent are removed.
13   Twisting and moving the joint as necessary, examine each of the balls for signs of pitting or wear, also the inner and outer ball tracks.

Check the splined section for signs of wear or damage and ensure that there are no signs of wear around the ball cage windows, also that there are no signs of cracking between balls.
14   Check that the joint's outer end is free from signs of wear or damage. Check particularly that the threaded and splined lengths are in good condition.
15   If the joint shows any sign of wear or damage it must be renewed.
16   Note that on later models a shield is pressed on to the joint to protect the wheel hub bearing from dirt or water. It may be necessary to transfer the shield (where fitted) to the replacement joint. Check that the shield is of the correct type for the new joint.
17   Carefully check the joint bellows, looking for signs of splits, cracking or other wear or damage. Renew the bellows if there is any doubt about its condition . It is available only with a repair kit which includes both bellows clips, a joint retaining clip and a quantity of the specified grease.

Inner joints – dismantling and reassembly

18   Remove the bellows clips, then slide the bellows off the joint and towards the middle of the shaft.
19   Mark the relationship of the joint body to the driveshaft, then pull the joint body off the spider; ensure that the spider's rollers remain in place. Mark the relationship of the spider to the shaft and use circlip pliers to remove the circlip from the shaft end. Then withdraw the spider and the bellows from the shaft (see Fig. 8.10).
20   On refitting, wind a thin layer of insulating tape around the shaft's end to protect the bellows from the shaft splines and other sharp edges. Fit the new small bellows clip and slide the bellows on to the driveshaft. Remove the tape and refit the spider. If the original spider is re-used, align the marks made on dismantling. Fit a new circlip to secure the spider.
21   Pack the correct amount of the specified type of grease (supplied with the repair kit) around the spider rollers and into the joint body. Fit the joint body over the spider. Where the original body is being re-used, align the marks made on dismantling.
22   Slide the bellows on to the joint body, expelling any trapped air, then fit a new larger bellows clip. Tighten the clip as shown in Fig. 8.7, then bend back the end and secure it under the tags as shown in Fig. 8.8.
23   Set the bellows so that its length is as shown in Fig. 8.11, then check that its smaller end is located in the driveshaft groove and that the bellows is not stretched or deformed when at this length. Fit a new smaller bellows clip, tighten it as shown in Fig. 8.7, then bend back the end and secure it under the tags as shown in Fig. 8.8.

Inner joints – inspection

24   Thoroughly clean the joint components, using a suitable solvent to remove all traces of grease, then dry it, preferably using compressed air. Ensure that all traces of grease and solvent are removed.
25   Examine the spider assembly closely, looking for damaged or missing rollers, worn splines or any other wear or damage. If any such signs are found the spider must be renewed.
26   Check the joint body for signs of wear or damage, particularly the spider roller tracks. Check also the splined section. Renew the joint body if it is worn or damaged in any way.
27   Carefully check the joint bellows, looking for signs of splits, cracking or other wear or damage. Renew the bellows if there is any doubt about its condition. It is available only with a repair kit which includes both bellows, clips, a circlip, a retaining clip (where necessary) and a quantity of the specified grease.

Driveshaft – inspection

28   Once both constant velocity joints have been removed as described above, the driveshaft itself can be checked for worn splines or retaining clip grooves, or for signs of cracking, bending or twisting. If any of these are found the driveshaft must be renewed.
29   If the driveshaft is to be renewed, note that it is available only as part of the complete assembly or as part of a driveshaft repair kit.

Support bearing – dismantling and reassembly

30   On all 1.8 and 2.0 litre models, first tap the dust shield gently off the right-hand driveshaft's inboard end, then prise the larger dust shield out of the bearing housing's inboard side. Use circlip pliers to remove the circlip set against the bearing itself.
31   Press the bearing housing and bearing off the inner joint's extended shaft section, as shown in Fig. 8.13.

32   Invert the assembly and use circlip pliers to remove the large circlip, then remove the dust shield. Using as a drift a socket or similar which bears only on the bearing's outer race, tap the bearing out of the housing.

33   On reassembly, pack the bearing with grease and tap it into the housing until the dust shield and a new large circlip can be refitted (Fig. 8.14). Ensuring that the bearing's inner race is fully supported, press the inner joint's extended shaft section into the bearing until a new smaller circlip can be refitted to its groove.

34   Refit the two dust shields to the bearing housing and to the driveshaft inboard end, respectively.

Support bearing – inspection

35   Note that none of the support bearing assembly's components are available separately (apart from the bearing bracket and bolts). If any are worn or damaged they can only be renewed as part of the right-hand inner joint repair kit. In spite of this, Nissan recommend that the bearing retaining circlips are renewed whenever they are disturbed.

36   To check the bearing itself, hold its inner race and spin the outer race, then try to feel for free play between the two. The bearing should spin smoothly and quietly, slowing down steadily with no sign of roughness and there should be no trace of free play between the inner and outer races. The bearing must be renewed if it is worn or damaged. If this does not coincide with the fitting of a replacement inner joint repair kit, it may be possible to obtain a replacement bearing from a bearing supplier. Make an accurate note of the bearing's outer and inner diameters and of its width and also of any manufacturer's marks or numbers, and take this to the supplier so that the correct item can be found.

37   All other components of the assembly should be checked for obvious signs of wear or damage and renewed if necessary.

5   Driveshaft bellows – removal and refitting

1   Remove the driveshaft from the car. See Section 3 of this Chapter.

2   To renew the inner joint bellows, release the bellows clips and slide back the bellows, then dismantle the joint and withdraw the bellows (see Section 4 of this Chapter).

3   If both inner and outer joints' bellows are to be renewed, the outer joint bellows clips can then be released and the bellows can be withdrawn along the length of the shaft. if this course is adopted, be careful on refitting to clean the shaft thoroughly and to protect the new bellows from any splines or sharp edges by wrapping a thin layer of insulating tape around the shaft at these points.

4   To renew the outer joint bellows alone, release the bellows clips and slide back the bellows, then dismantle the joint and withdraw the bellows (see Section 4 of this Chapter.)

5   On both inner and outer joints, clean out as much of the grease as possible, using a plastic or wooden spatula and old rags. Do not use solvents unless the joint is to be completely dismantled, so that it can be dried properly.

6   Check the joint components for signs of wear or damage. If any are found the joint must be renewed (see Section 4 of this Chapter).

7   On reassembly, pack the joint with the correct amount of the specified grease (supplied with the kit). Pack any surplus grease into the bellows. Refit the bellows and reassemble the joint as described in Section 4 of this Chapter.

8   Refit the driveshaft to the car (see Section 3 of this Chapter.)

6   Fault diagnosis – driveshafts

Symptom	Reason(s)
Vibration and/or noise, especially on tight turns	Worn outer constant velocity joint(s)
Vibration when accelerating	Worn inner constant velocity joint(s)
	Bent or distorted driveshaft(s)
	Worn support bearing (1.8 and 2.0 litre models)
Noise on taking up drive	Worn driveshaft or constant velocity joint splines
	Worn constant velocity joints
	Loose driveshaft nut

Note: *This Section is not intended to be an exhaustive guide to fault diagnosis but summarises the more common faults which may be encountered during a car's life. Consult a dealer for more specific advice*

Chapter 9 Braking system

Contents

Specifications

System type .... Hydraulically-operated diagonally-split dual circuit with pressure-reducing valve (early models) or pressure-proportioning valve (later models) for rear brake, vacuum servo-assisted. Disc brakes front and rear on Turbo models, disc brakes front and drum brakes rear on all other models. Cable-operated handbrake to rear wheels.

Hydraulic fluid type/specification .... Hydraulic fluid to FMVSS 116, DOT 3 or 4 (Duckhams Universal Brake and Clutch Fluid)

Front brakes
Type	Tokico CL28VA
Disc outside diameter	250 mm (9.843 in)
Disc minimum thickness	20 mm (0.787 in)
Disc maximum runout – total indicator reading at centre of pad swept area	0.07 mm (0.0028 in)
Brake pad friction material minimum thickness 'A' (see Fig. 9.13)	2.0 mm (0.079 in)
Caliper cylinder internal diameter	60.6 mm (2.386 in)

Rear drum brakes
Type:	
Up to September 1987	LT23A
September 1987 on...	LT23B
Drum internal diameter:	
Standard..	228.6 mm (8.999 in)
Maximum..	230.0 mm (9.055 in)
Drum maximum ovality	0.03 mm (0.0012 in)
Drum maximum radial runout – total indicator reading	0.05 mm (0.0020 in)
Drum maximum taper – at 45 mm (1.77 in) from inlet	0.04 mm (0.0016 in)
Brake shoe friction material minimum thickness 'A' (see Fig. 9.20)...........	1.5 mm (0.059 in)
Wheel cylinder make	Nabco or Tokico
Wheel cylinder internal diameter:	
Up to September 1987	20.638 mm (0.813 in)
September 1987 on...	22.225 mm (0.875 in)

Rear disc brakes

Type	Tokico CL11H
Disc outside diameter	258 mm (10.158 in)
Disc minimum thickness	9.0 mm (0.354 in)
Disc maximum runout – total indicator reading at centre of pad swept area	0.07 mm (0.0028 in)
Brake pad friction material minimum thickness	2.0 mm (0.079 in)
Caliper cylinder internal diameter	38.18 mm (1.503 in)

Master cylinder

Make	Nabco
Bore internal diameter:	
Primary	30.163 mm (1.188 in)
Secondary	23.813 mm (0.938 in)

Note: *Information not available for Turbo models from April 1989 on*

Vacuum servo unit

Type:	
Early models – up to Feb 1988 (T12) or May 1988 (T72)	Tokico G23 or Jidosha kiki M23
Later models	Jidosha kiki M195T (tandem type)
Diaphragm outside diameter:	
Early type	230.0 mm (9.055 in)
Late type – primary	205.0 mm (8.071 in)
Late type – secondary	180.0 mm (7.087 in)

Note: *Information not available for Turbo models from April 1989 on*

Brake pedal adjustments*

Pedal height 'H'	190 to 200 mm (7.480 to 7.874 in)
Pedal depressed height 'D' (minimum) – at applied pressure of 490 N (110 lbf) with engine running	100 mm (3.937 in)
Pedal free play 'A'	1.0 to 3.0 mm (0.039 to 0.118 in)
Stop-lamp switch threaded end to pedal stop clearance 'C'	0.3 to 1.0 mm (0.012 to 0.039 in)

* Refer to Fig. 9.3 for details

Handbrake adjustment

Number of clicks from released to applied positions at pulling force of 196 N (44 lbf):	
T12 models – drum rear brakes	9 to 11 clicks
T12 models – disc rear brakes	11 to 13 clicks
All T72 models	7 to 9 clicks

Torque wrench settings

	Nm	lbf ft
Roadwheel nuts	98 to 118	72 to 87
Pedal mounting bracket nuts and bolts	8 to 11	6 to 8
Pedal pivot bolt retaining nut	16 to 22	12 to 16
Stop lamp switch locknut	12 to 15	9 to 11
Vacuum servo unit input rod locknut	16 to 22	12 to 16
Vacuum servo unit-to-body/pedal bracket mounting nuts	8 to 11	6 to 8
Master cylinder-to-vacuum servo unit mounting nuts	8 to 11	6 to 8
Metal hydraulic pipe union nuts	15 to 18	11 to 13
Connector block mounting bolt – early models only	5 to 7	4 to 5
All bleed nipples	7 to 9	5 to 6.5
Pressure-reducing valve – early models only:		
Valve assembly-to-body mounting bolts	8 to 11	6 to 8
Valve-to-mounting bracket nut	8 to 11	6 to 8
Front brake caliper:		
Hub carrier-to-caliper mounting bracket bolts	72 to 97	53 to 71.5
Guide pin bolts	22 to 31	16 to 23
Flexible hose banjo bolt	17 to 20	12.5 to 15
Rear drum brake:		
Backplate to rear suspension strut bolts	38 to 52	28 to 38
Wheel cylinder mounting bolts	6 to 8	4.5 to 6
Rear brake caliper:		
Brake disc shield and adapter plate-to-rear suspension strut bolts	38 to 52	28 to 38
Adapter plate-to-caliper mounting bracket bolts	38 to 52	28 to 38
Guide pin bolts	22 to 31	16 to 23
Flexible hose banjo bolt	17 to 20	12.5 to 15
Handbrake:		
Adjuster locknut – early models only	3.1 to 4.3	2 to 3
Lever assembly mounting bolts	8 to 11	6 to 8
Cable mounting clamp bolts and nuts	8 to 11	6 to 8
Cable abutment-to-backplate bolts – later models only	Not available	Not available

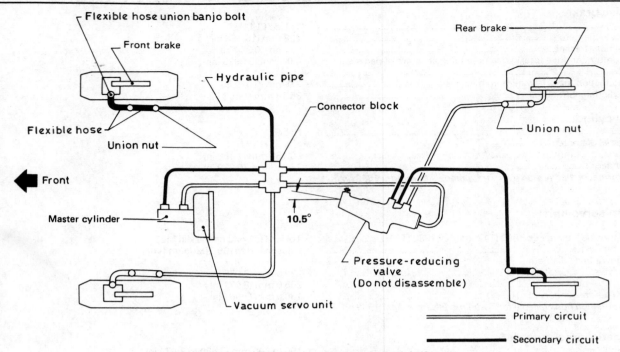

Fig. 9.1 Diagram of braking system – early models (Sec 1)

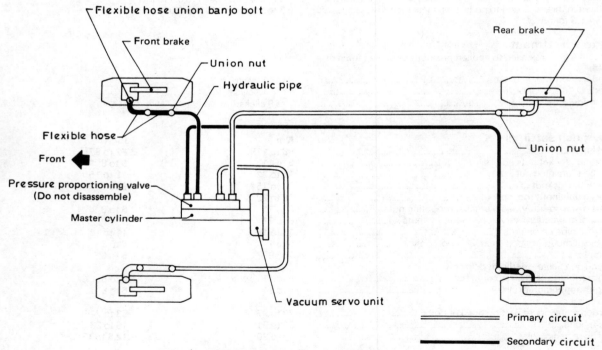

Fig. 9.2 Diagram of braking system – later models (Sec 1)

1   General description

The braking system is hydraulically-operated and incorporates a vacuum servo unit and master cylinder mounted on the right-hand side of the engine compartment bulkhead, and a brake disc and caliper assembly at each front wheel. At each rear wheel, a brake disc and caliper assembly is fitted on Turbo models, and a brake drum assembly on all other models. The master cylinder is of the tandem type and, with the connecting metal hydraulic pipes and flexible hoses, provides a diagonally-split dual circuit system. The primary circuit operates the left-hand front and right-hand rear brakes and the secondary operates the right-hand front and the left-hand rear brakes. Under normal conditions both circuits operate in unison, but in the event of hydraulic failure of one of the circuits full brake pressure will still be available at two of the brakes, thus allowing the car to be stopped in a stable manner, albeit at the expense of increased pedal movement.

To prevent the rear wheels locking, early models incorporate an inertia-sensitive (load-conscious) pressure-reducing valve which controls the pressure to the rear brakes. On later models, the master cylinder incorporates a pressure-conscious proportioning valve which shuts off when a predetermined pressure is reached and allows any further pressure increase to be transmitted only to the front brakes. This type can be identified by its double-barrelled configuration and by the four metal hydraulic pipes connected to it.

The vacuum servo unit uses intake (inlet) manifold depression (generated only while the engine is running) to boost the effort applied by the driver at the brake pedal and transmits this increased effort to the master cylinder pistons. The servo is direct-acting, with its input rod connected directly to the brake pedal, and is of the suspended-vacuum type. Basically it consists (on early models) of a metal chamber divided into front and rear sections by a piston, which is sealed by a diaphragm. On later models, a tandem type is used, which has two diaphragms, but the operating principle is the same.

The brake calipers, whether at the front or at the rear, are of the single-piston sliding type in which the main caliper body slides (or 'floats') on a mounting bracket that is rigidly attached to the suspension member. Full braking efficiency relies on the ability of the caliper body to slide easily on its mounting bracket, as well as on the condition of the pads and the piston, cylinder bore and seals.

The drum brakes fitted to the rear wheels of most models consist of a cast iron drum, which is an integral part of the rear hub and which rotates with the roadwheel and the backplate. Each drum assembly is bolted to the bottom of each suspension strut and carries the two brake shoes and their operating mechanism. As the brake shoe friction material wears, a spring-loaded ratchet in the self-adjuster strut assembly causes the strut to expand to take up the slack whenever shoe movement exceeds normal levels.

The handbrake is controlled by a lever assembly bolted to the floor next to the driver's seat and actuates the rear bracket through a front cable, a compensator assembly and two rear cables, one to each brake assembly.

In addition to the stop lamps, which are operated by a switch on the brake pedal bracket, there is in the instrument panel a stop/tail lamp bulb failure warning lamp (which lights when any of these bulbs is faulty), and a brake warning lamp which lights either when the handbrake is applied (operated by a plunger switch mounted at the base of the lever), or when the master cylinder reservoir fluid level falls to a dangerously low level (operated by a float-type switch in the master cylinder).

Note: *When servicing any part of the braking system, work carefully and methodically, and observe scrupulous cleanliness when overhauling any part of the hydraulic system. Always renew components (in axle sets where applicable) if in doubt about their condition and use only genuine Nissan replacement parts, or at least those of known good quality. Note the warnings given in 'Safety First' and at relevant points in this Chapter concerning the dangers of asbestos dust and hydraulic fluid.*

---

2 Routine maintenance

Note: *Hydraulic fluid is an effective paint stripper and will also attack plastics. If any is spilt, it should be washed off immediately using copious quantities of fresh water. When topping-up or renewing the fluid, always use a good quality fluid of the specified type and ensure that it comes from a freshly-opened sealed container. Hydraulic fluid is hygroscopic (it absorbs moisture from the air) – old fluid may be contaminated and unfit for further use.*

1   At the intervals given in *'Routine maintenance'* at the beginning of this manual a thorough inspection of all brake components should be carried out, using the following procedures as a guide.

Check the hydraulic fluid level

2   Check that the hydraulic fluid level in the brake master cylinder translucent reservoir is between the 'Max' and 'Min' lines marked on the reservoir. If the level is below the 'Min' line, top up to between the level lines using only good quality fluid of the specified type from a freshly opened container (photo).

3   If frequent topping-up is necessary, check carefully for signs of fluid leaks from the various components of the system. Any leaks found should be cured immediately by the renewal of the seal or component concerned.

4   Note that the fluid level should drop steadily in normal service as the brake friction material wears. Thus, while a steady lowering of the level is to be expected, any sudden changes require immediate attention.

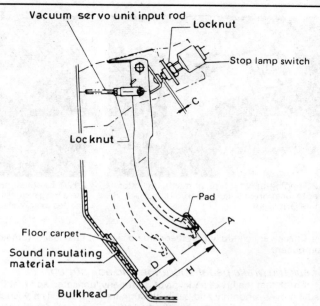

Fig. 9.3 Brake pedal adjustment details (Sec 2)

See Specifications for actual dimensions

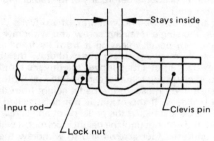

Fig. 9.4 Vacuum servo unit input rod end must be visible inside clevis after adjustment (Sec 2)

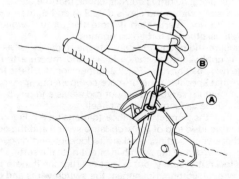

Fig. 9.5 Adjusting handbrake – early models (Sec 2)

A Locknut	B Adjuster

Note also that it is not necessary to top up to the 'Max' level line unless all brake pads and shoes (as applicable) have been renewed. It is quite sufficient to maintain the level above the 'Min' line as described so that there is no risk of air entering the system.

General check

5   Check carefully all visible components of the system and ensure that all are securely fastened and free from damage or deterioration of any sort. Check that the metal hydraulic pipes are free from damage or corrosion and that the flexible hoses are undamaged and correctly secured so that they are not chafing against any other component (see Section 9). Similarly, check the handbrake cables and lubricate the linkages and exposed cable inner wires.

2.2 Topping-up later type of master cylinder – note location of vacuum servo unit check valve (arrowed)

2.17A To adjust handbrake on later models, use a long extension bar to reach through bristles in console slot ...

2.17B ... so that adjuster can be turned with a deep socket spanner

6   Check very carefully that there are no signs of fluid leaks from any component.

Check the brake pedal operation and adjustment

7   Check that the brake pedal pivot is properly lubricated and that the pedal moves smoothly and easily through its full travel. The vacuum servo unit's operation can be checked, if required, as described in Section 4 of this Chapter.

8   The pedal height, once set, should not need resetting, but should be checked as a matter of course before any of the remaining adjustments are checked or altered.

9   Undo the three screws and withdraw the driver's door sill tread panel. Remove the single retaining screw and withdraw the footwell right-hand side trim panel, releasing it from its front retaining clip. Remove the single retaining screw and withdraw the throttle pedal step. Peel back the carpet, lifting it over the driver's footrest, until the flap in the sound insulating material can be lifted up. With reference to Fig. 9.3 (dimension 'H') measure the pedal height from the pedal pad centre to the bulkhead. If the height is not as specified, slacken the locknut at the clevis just below the pedal pivot and screw the vacuum servo unit input rod in or out until the height is correct. It will probably be necessary to undo the four screws and to withdraw the facia lower panel from below the steering column to provide sufficient access to reach the input rod.

10   When the pedal height is correct, check that the end of the input rod remains visible within the clevis (Fig. 9.4) and tighten the locknut securely, but do not overtighten it; note the torque wrench setting specified. Refit all other disturbed components.

11   To measure the pedal free play, lift the pedal as far as possible, then lower it until slight resistance is felt and measure the distance between the two positions; see Fig. 9.3 (dimension 'A'). If the free play is greater than that specified, one or more components are worn. Check primarily the vacuum servo unit's input rod clevis and pin, but also the pedal pivot and the vacuum servo unit itself.

12   Check that the correct clearance (dimension 'C' Fig. 9.3) exists between the threaded end of the stop-lamp switch and the pedal stop. To adjust the switch setting, slacken its locknut and disconnect the switch wires, then screw the switch in or out until the setting is correct. Tighten the locknut securely, but do not overtighten it; note the specified torque wrench setting. Reconnect the switch wires and check the operation of both stop-lamps.

13   Measure the brake pedal's depressed height (dimension 'D', Fig. 9.3) as a quick general check of the braking system's condition. With the engine running, apply the specified pressure to the brake pedal, then measure the distance from the pedal pad to the bulkhead. If the depressed height is any less than the minimum value specified, check the system for fluid leaks or damaged components such as the master cylinder, caliper or wheel cylinders, or carry out the bleeding procedure (Section 8) to remove any trapped air bubbles.

Check the handbrake operation and adjustment

14   Note that, since the rear brakes are of the self-adjusting type, the only adjustments to the handbrake mechanism that are required are to the cables themselves.

15   The handbrake should be capable of holding the parked car stationary, even on steep slopes, when applied with moderate force (see Specifications). The mechanism should be firm and positive in feel, with no trace of stiffness or sponginess from the cables, and should release immediately the handbrake lever is released. If the mechanism falls short of these conditions in any respect it should be checked immediately.

16   To check the setting, apply the handbrake firmly several times to establish correct shoe/pad-to-drum/disc clearance, then fully release the lever. Applying normal, moderate pressure, pull the handbrake lever to the fully-applied position and count the number of clicks required to do so. If there is any doubt about the setting use a spring balance to apply the exact pulling force specified. If the number of clicks heard is more or less than the specified range, then adjustment is required.

17   To adjust the handbrake cable assembly, first look down through the console slot on the left-hand side of the handbrake lever (prising apart the bristles to do so) and peel back the rubber flap covering the adjuster. On early models, the adjuster has a screwdriver slot at its upper end and is secured by a locknut. If a deep box spanner is not available to slacken and tighten the locknut with the console in place, the console must be removed first (as described in Chapter 11) so that the adjustment can be made using ordinary tools (see Fig 9.5). On later models, the adjustment is made using a box spanner or deep socket (photos) to turn a self-locking adjuster nut. With care, this can be achieved with the console in place. To make the adjustment, slacken the locknut (early models only) and tighten or slacken the adjuster or adjuster nut (as applicable) until the setting is correct.

18   When the setting is correct, tighten the adjuster locknut (early models only), apply the handbrake several times to settle the cables, then recheck the setting as described above.

19   Note that, if the handbrake's efficiency is suspect, raise the rear of the vehicle and check that the rear wheels are fully locked when the lever is in the applied position, and free to rotate easily when the lever is fully released. Check carefully the rear brake assemblies if necessary.

Check the brake pads and discs

20   Refer to Sections 12, 15, 23 and 26 of this Chapter.

Check the brake shoes and drums

21   Refer to Sections 18 and 21 of this Chapter

Renew the brake hydraulic fluid

22   The brake system's hydraulic fluid must be renewed at the specified interval to prevent its boiling point being reduced to an unsafe level by contamination from moisture and particles of dirt and foreign matter. Regular renewal of the hydraulic fluid will also prolong the life of the master cylinder and caliper/wheel cylinder components by minimising corrosion.

23   First read Section 8 of this Chapter and assemble the necessary equipment as well as a sufficient quantity (in new, still-sealed containers) of the specified type of fluid. Note the warnings given at the beginning of this Section.

24   Remove the master cylinder reservoir cap and examine the condition of the fluid. If it is dark and dirty, with a significant quantity of sludge at the bottom of the reservoir, syphon out the fluid and wipe out the reservoir using a lint-free cloth. Keep fluid spillage to a minimum and try to keep dirt out of the by-pass and inlet ports. Then top up to the 'Max' level with new fluid; this will prevent additional dirt from being flushed into the system.

25   To change the fluid, the manufacturer recommends that each

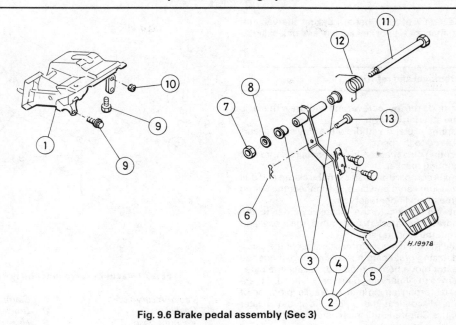

Fig. 9.6 Brake pedal assembly (Sec 3)

1	*Pedal mounting bracket*	5	*Pedal rubber pad*
2	*Pedal assembly*	6	*Spring clip*
3	*Pedal pivot bushes*	7	*Nut*
4	*Stop pad*		

8	*Washer*	11	*Pedal pivot bolt*
9	*Bolt*	12	*Return spring*
10	*Nut*	13	*Clevis pin*

bleed nipple in turn (following the sequence given in Section 8) is opened and the pedal is pumped gently until all the old fluid has been expelled, when the nipple can be tightened again. When all the old fluid has been removed, refill the master cylinder with clean fluid and again open each nipple in turn (following the sequence) and pump the pedal until new fluid emerges. When the complete system is refilled, carry out the bleeding procedure to remove any air bubbles.

26   Since the old fluid is invariably much darker in colour than the new, making it easy to distinguish the two, the recommended procedure can be speeded up as follows. Open the first bleed nipple in the sequence and pump the brake pedal gently until nearly all the old fluid has been emptied from the master cylinder reservoir. Top up to the 'Max' level with new fluid and continue until the new fluid remains in the reservoir and new fluid can be seen emerging from the bleed nipple. Work through all the remaining nipples in the sequence until new fluid can be seen at all of them. Be careful to keep the master cylinder reservoir topped up to above the 'Min' level at all times or air may enter the system and greatly increase the length of the task.

27   When the operation is complete, wash off all traces of spilt fluid, replace all bleed nipple dust caps and check the master cylinder reservoir fluid level. Check the operation of the brakes before taking the car on the road. If the pedal feels spongy air may still be present in the system and must be removed immediately.

Check the vacuum servo unit hose, connections and check valve

28   Tests to check the operation of the vacuum servo unit and of its check valve are given in Sections 4 and 7 of this Chapter. If there is any doubt about their condition both components should be checked immediately.

29   Check the condition of the large diameter vacuum hose linking the vacuum servo unit to the intake (inlet) manifold. This must be renewed if it is cracked, split, or damaged in any way. Check that the connections are securely fastened and the clamps in good condition.

---

3 Brake pedal – removal and refitting

1   Undo the four screws and withdraw the facia lower panel from below the steering column.

2   Extract the retaining spring clip and withdraw the clevis pin securing the vacuum servo unit's input rod to the pedal.

3   Release return spring pressure by unhooking the spring end that is looped over the pedal.

4   Unscrew the pedal pivot bolt nut and washer, remove the pivot bolt and withdraw the pedal, complete with bushes and return spring.

5   Carefully clean all components and renew any that are worn or damaged. Check particularly the return spring and the bearing surfaces of the pivot bushes and bolt.

6   Refitting is the reverse of the removal procedure, but apply a thin smear of the specified multi-purpose grease to the pedal pivot bearing surfaces and clevis pin before installation.

7   Referring to Section 2 of this Chapter, check the pedal height, free play and the stop lamp switch setting, and adjust them if required. Refit all disturbed carpets and trim panels.

---

4 Vacuum servo unit – checking

Note: *Do not attempt to dismantle the unit, to clean or renew the air filter or to adjust the output rod length. The unit is sealed and no components are available to make reconditioning viable.*

1   In normal use any failure of the vacuum servo unit will be evident to the driver, due to the increased pedal effort required to achieve normal braking. To test the unit if its performance is in doubt, park the car on level ground and release the handbrake, then proceed as follows.

2   Switch the engine off and destroy the vacuum in the unit by depressing the brake pedal several times. Check that there is no significant change in pedal travel after the first two or three strokes.

3   Apply normal pressure to the brake pedal and maintain it while the engine is started. If the unit is operating correctly, the pedal should move down slightly as vacuum is restored in the unit.

4   To check whether the unit is completely airtight, start the engine and run it for one or two minutes, then switch off the ignition. Depress the brake pedal slowly several times using the same, normal pressure at each stroke. If the unit is airtight, the pedal should go down to the normal depressed height on the first one or two strokes, but after that the depressed height should gradually rise as the vacuum is destroyed and the level of assistance decreases.

5   Finally start the engine again, apply normal pressure to the brake pedal and maintain it while the engine is switched off. There should be no change in pedal stroke for at least thirty seconds.

6   If the vacuum servo unit proves faulty as a result of the above tests it must be renewed, although it is worth checking first that the check

valve is not faulty (see Section 7 of this Chapter) or that the vacuum hose from the intake (inlet) manifold is not kinked, blocked or leaking.

5 Vacuum servo unit – removal and refitting

1   Working inside the car, undo the four screws and withdraw the facia lower panel from below the steering column.
2   Extract the retaining spring clip and withdraw the clevis pin securing the vacuum servo input rod to the pedal.
3   Unscrew the four mounting nuts that secure the vacuum servo unit to the bulkhead/pedal mounting bracket.
4   Working inside the engine compartment, slacken the clamp and pull the vacuum hose off the vacuum servo unit stub. Disconnect the wiring lead from the base of the master cylinder reservoir.
5   Unscrew the two nuts which secure the master cylinder to the vacuum servo unit, withdraw the bracket and move the hose and bracket assembly away from the working area.
6   Very carefully move the master cylinder forwards clear of the servo unit studs and output rod, taking great care not to kink or damage the metal hydraulic pipes. If extra movement is required, release the pipes from the clips securing them to the inner wing panel or bulkhead. If there is any risk of kinking or distorting any metal hydraulic pipe, or of damaging any component, disconnect the pipe(s) from the master cylinder (see Section 10 of this Chapter) until the master cylinder can be moved forwards or removed, as required.
7   When the master cylinder is clear of the vacuum servo unit, withdraw the unit from the car. Collect the gasket from the unit's bulkhead mating surface; renew the gasket if it is torn or damaged.
8   Refitting is the reverse of the removal procedure. Do not forget to refit the gasket and do not overtighten the servo unit or master cylinder mounting nuts; note the torque wrench settings specified. Refer also to Section 10 of this Chapter if any of the metal hydraulic pipes were disconnected from the master cylinder. Do not forget to bleed any air bubbles from the system and to wash off any spilt hydraulic fluid. Check the pedal heights and free play and the stop-lamp switch setting as described in Section 2 of this Chapter.

6 Vacuum servo unit check valve – removal and refitting

1   The vacuum servo unit one-way check valve is situated in the vacuum hose linking the servo unit with the intake (inlet) manifold and is secured by the bracket at the front of the servo unit. See photos 2.1 and 10.1.
2   Slacken the clamps securing the hose to each end of the valve and pull off the hoses. Note carefully which way round the valve is fitted. Slacken the clamp screw and push the valve out of the clamp.
3   Refitting is the reverse of the removal procedure. Ensure the valve is fitted with its tapered face towards the manifold (Fig. 9.8) and tighten all three clamps securely.

7 Vacuum servo unit check valve – testing

1   When testing the servo unit check valve, remember that its function is to allow air to flow in one direction only, **out** of the servo unit. If it allows air to flow in both directions, or in neither, it is faulty and must be renewed.
2   To test the valve, blow through it from the (square-cut) servo unit end; air should pass freely through the valve. Now suck hard on the same end; there should be no leakage at all back through the valve.

8 Brake hydraulic system – bleeding

1   The correct functioning of the brake hydraulic system is only possible after removing all air from the components and circuit; this is achieved by bleeding the system. Only clean, unused hydraulic fluid of the specified type may be used.

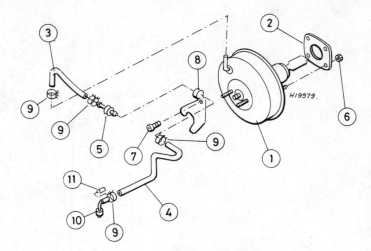

Fig. 9.7 Vacuum servo unit and hose (Secs 5 and 6)

1 Vacuum servo unit	7 Clamp screw
2 Gasket	8 Bracket
3 Vacuum hose	9 Hose clamp
4 Vacuum hose	10 Vacuum hose to manifold
5 Check valve	union
6 Nut	11 Plug (where fitted)

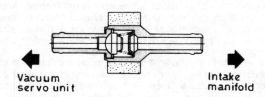

Fig. 9.8 Ensure the vacuum servo unit check valve is fitted the correct way round (Sec 6)

2   If there is any possibility of incorrect fluid being already in the system, the brake lines and components must be completely flushed with uncontaminated, correct fluid and new seals fitted to the components.
3   **Never** re-use hydraulic fluid which has been bled from the system.
4   During the procedure, do not allow the reservoir fluid level to drop below the 'Min' line.
5   Before starting work, check that all pipes and hoses are secure, unions tight, and bleed nipples closed. Take great care not to allow hydraulic fluid to come into contact with plastic or with the car paintwork, otherwise the finish will be seriously damaged. Wash off any spilled fluid immediately with cold water.
6   If hydraulic fluid has been lost from the master cylinder due to a leak in the system, ensure that the cause is traced and rectified before proceeding further.
7   There are a number of one-man, do-it-yourself, brake bleeding kits currently available from motor accessory shops. It is recommended that one of these kits is used wherever possible, as they greatly simplify the bleeding operation, and also reduce the risk of expelled air and fluid being drawn back into the system. If one of these kits is not available, it will be necessary to gather together a clean glass jar and a suitable length of plastic or rubber tubing which is a tight fit over the bleed nipples and a ring spanner to fit the nipples. The help of an assistant will also be required.
8   If the hydraulic system has only been partially disconnected and suitable precautions were taken to minimise fluid loss, it should only be necessary to bleed that part of the system (ie primary or secondary circuit).

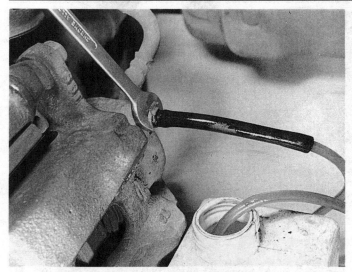

8.12 Bleeding air from hydraulic system at front brake caliper bleed nipple

9   If the complete system is to be bled, then it should be done in the following sequence.

Early models (single-barrel master cylinder with two metal hydraulic pipe unions):
    1) Pressure-reducing valve
    2) Left-hand rear brake
    3) Right-hand front brake
    4) Right-hand rear brake
    5) Left-hand front brake
Note: *In exceptionally difficult cases it may be necessary to bleed item 1 again after items 2 and 3 (the secondary circuit) and after items 4 and 5 (the primary circuit)*

Later models (double-barrel master cylinder with four metal hydraulic pipe unions):
    1) Left-hand rear brake
    2) Right-hand front brake
    3) Right-hand brake
    4) Left-hand front brake

Bleeding – basic (two-man) method
10   Clean the areas around all the nipples to be bled, then remove the dust cap from the first nipple in the sequence. Fit the spanner and tube to the nipple, place the other end of the tube in the jar and press in sufficient fluid to cover the end of the tube. Remove the master cylinder reservoir cap and top up the level to the 'Max' line. Refit the cap loosely, but remember to watch the fluid level and to keep it topped up throughout the bleeding procedure. Do not allow the level to fall below the 'Min' line at any time or there is a risk of further air entering the system.
11   Have the assistant fully depress the brake pedal several times to build up pressure, then maintain it on the final stroke.
12   While pedal pressure is maintained, unscrew the bleed nipple (approximately one turn) and allow the compressed fluid and air to flow into the jar (photo). The assistant should maintain pedal pressure, following it down to the floor if necessary and should not release it until instructed to do so. When the flow stops, tighten the bleed nipple again, release the pedal slowly and check the reservoir fluid level.
13   Repeat the steps given in paragraphs 11 and 12 until the fluid emerging from the bleed nipple is free from air bubbles. If the master cylinder has been drained and refilled and air is being bled from the first nipple in the sequence, allow approximately five seconds between cycles for the master cylinder passages to refill.
14   When no more air bubbles appear, tighten the bleed nipple securely, remove the tubing and spanner and refit the dust cap. **Do not** overtighten the bleed nipples; note the torque wrench setting specified.
15   Repeat the procedure on all the remaining nipples in the sequence until all air is removed from the system and the brake pedal feels firm again.

Bleeding – using a one-way valve kit
16   Follow the instructions supplied with the kit, as the procedure may vary slightly according to the type being used, but generally they are as follows.
17   Clean the area around the appropriate bleed nipple and remove its dust cap.
18   Attach the tube to the bleed nipple and open the nipple approximately one turn.
19   Depress the brake pedal with a smooth steady stroke, then slowly release it. The one-way valve in the kit will prevent expelled air and fluid from returning at the end of each pedal downstroke. Repeat this operation several times to be sure of ejecting all air from the system. Some kits incorporate a translucent container, which can be positioned so that the air bubbles can be seen flowing from the end of the tube.
20   Tighten the bleed nipple, remove the tube and refit the dust cap. Repeat these procedures on the remaining bleed nipples as necessary.

Bleeding – using a pressure-bleeding kit
21   These kits are also available from accessory shops, and are usually operated by air pressure from the spare tyre.
22   By connecting a pressurised, fluid-filled container to the master cylinder reservoir, bleeding is then carried out by simply opening each bleed nipple in turn and allowing the fluid to run out, rather like turning on a tap, until no air is visible in the expelled fluid.
23   By using this method, the large reservoir of hydraulic fluid provides a safeguard against air being drawn into the master cylinder during bleeding, which often occurs if the reservoir fluid level is not maintained.
24   Pressure bleeding is particularly effective when bleeding 'difficult' systems, or when bleeding the complete system at the time of routine fluid renewal.

All methods
25   When bleeding is completed, check and top up the fluid level in the master cylinder reservoir. Wash off any spilled fluid.
26   Check the feel of the brake pedal. If it feels at all spongy, air must still be present in the system, and further bleeding is required. Failure to bleed satisfactorily after a reasonable repetition of the bleeding operations may be due to worn master cylinder seals.
27   Discard hydraulic fluid which has been bled from the system. It is almost certain to be contaminated with moisture and air, making it unsuitable for further use. Clean fluid should always be stored in an airtight container, as it is hygroscopic (absorbs moisture readily). This lowers its boiling point, and could affect braking performance under severe conditions.

9   Hydraulic pipes and hoses – inspection, removal and refitting

1   The brake hydraulic system consists of a number of metal hydraulic pipes which run from the master cylinder (via, on early models, a connector block and the pressure-reducing valve) across the front of the engine compartment bulkhead and along the inner wing panels to the front brakes, or along the underbody to the rear brakes. Flexible hoses run from a bracket inside each wheel arch to the brake itself, to allow for suspension (and steering) movement (photos). Figs 9.1 and 9.2 show a schematic representation of the layout.
2   When checking the system, first look for signs of leakage at the pipe or hose unions, then examine the flexible hoses for signs of cracking, chafing or deterioration of the rubber. Bend them sharply between the fingers (but do not actually bend them double or the casing may be damaged) and check that this does not expose previously hidden cuts or splits. Check that the pipes and hoses are securely fastened in their clips or brackets (photo).
3   Carefully work along the length of the metal hydraulic pipes looking for dents or kinks, damage of any sort or corrosion. Corrosion should be polished off and if the depth of pitting is significant the pipe should be renewed.
4   If any pipe or hose is to be renewed, minimise fluid loss by removing the master cylinder reservoir cap and then tightening it down on to a piece of polythene to obtain an airtight seal. If a flexible hose is to be disconnected, unscrew the hydraulic pipe union nut before removing the spring clip which secures the hose to its mounting bracket.
5   To unscrew the union nuts, it is preferable to obtain a brake pipe spanner of the correct size. These are available from most large motor

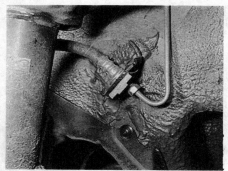

9.1A Metal hydraulic pipe-to-flexible hose junction at front wheel arch ...

9.1B ... and rear wheel arch – slacken union nut before releasing pipe and hose from bracket, if they are to be disconnected

9.2 Check that flexible hoses are secured correctly by spring clips

accessory shops. Failing this, a close-fitting open-ended spanner will be required, though if the nuts are tight or corroded their flats may be rounded-off if an open-ended spanner slips. In such a case a self-locking wrench is often the only way to unscrew a stubborn union, but it follows that the hydraulic pipe and damaged nuts must be renewed on reassembly. Always clean a union and surrounding area before disconnecting it. If disconnecting a component with more than one union (such as the bulkhead-mounted connector block on early models) make a careful note of the connections before disturbing any pipe.

6   If a hydraulic pipe is to be renewed, it can be obtained, cut to length and with the end flares and union nuts in place, from Nissan dealers. All that is then necessary is to bend it to shape, following the line of the original pipe, before it is fitted to the car. Alternatively, most motor accessory shops can make up hydraulic pipes from kits, but this requires very careful measurement of the original to ensure that the replacement is of the correct length. The safest answer is usually to take the old pipe to the shop as a pattern.

7   On refitting, do not overtighten the union nuts. The specified torque settings are not high and it is not necessary to exercise brute force to obtain a sound joint. When refitting flexible hoses, always renew the sealing washers on each side of a banjo union (where applicable) and tighten the banjo bolts to the specified torque settings.

8   Ensure that the pipes and hoses are correctly routed with no kinks and that they are secured in the clips or brackets provided (photo). After refitting, remove the polythene from the reservoir and bleed the hydraulic system as described in Section 8 of this Chapter. Wash off any spilt fluid and check carefully for fluid leaks.

9.8 Metal hydraulic pipes are secured to underbody by insulating clips, as shown

10   Master cylinder – removal and refitting

1   Remove the master cylinder reservoir cap (photo) and empty the hydraulic fluid from the reservoir, either by syphoning it out or by opening any convenient bleed nipple in the system and gently pumping the brake pedal to expel the fluid.

2   Unscrew the union nuts and disconnect the hydraulic pipes. Try to keep fluid spillage to a minimum and wash off any spilt fluid as soon as possible.

3   Disconnect the wiring lead from the base of the reservoir.

4   Unscrew the two nuts which secure the master cylinder to the vacuum servo unit, slacken the vacuum servo unit check valve clamp and swing the bracket upwards out of the way.

5   Withdraw the master cylinder from the vacuum servo unit studs and output rod.

6   Refitting is the reverse of the removal procedure. Refill the reservoir with new fluid and bleed the system, as described in Section 8 of this Chapter. If a new master cylinder has been fitted (or the original has been fully drained) start the bleeding procedure by disconnecting each hydraulic pipe union in turn and gently pumping the brake pedal until only clear hydraulic fluid emerges. Before commencing, place a container or some rag under the master cylinder to catch the ejected fluid. Work from front to rear (ie secondary circuit first). In very difficult cases, disconnect the hydraulic pipes and plug all of them, then uncover one while the pedal is depressed and plug it when the pedal is released so that fluid is forcibly drawn down from the reservoir. Tighten all pipe

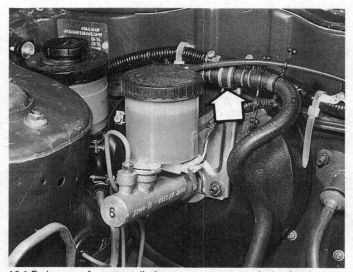

10.1 Early type of master cylinder – vacuum servo unit check valve arrowed

unions securely as soon as the master cylinder has been cleared of air and is pumping correctly, then proceed with the normal bleeding sequence.

7   When the full system has been cleared of air, check the master cylinder reservoir fluid level as described in Section 2 of this Chapter.

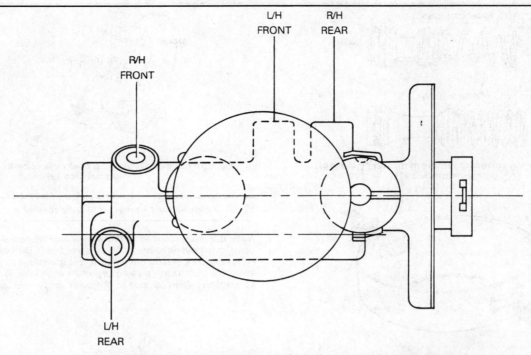

R/H
FRONT

L/H
FRONT

R/H
REAR

L/H
REAR

Fig. 9.9 Hydraulic pipe unions on later type of master cylinder (Sec 10)

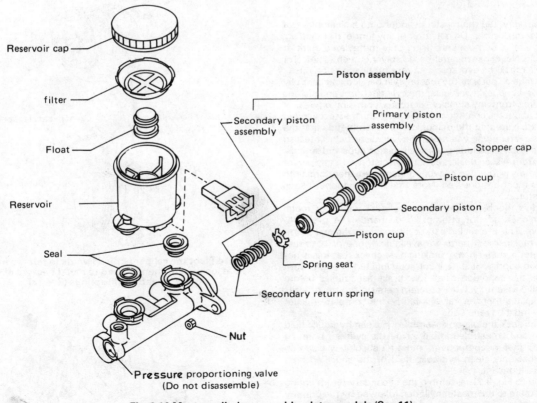

Reservoir cap

filter

Float

Reservoir

Seal

Piston assembly

Secondary piston
assembly

Primary piston
assembly

Stopper cap

Piston cup

Secondary piston

Piston cup

Spring seat

Secondary return spring

Nut

Pressure proportioning valve
(Do not disassemble)

Fig. 9.10 Master cylinder assembly – later models (Sec 11)

8   Wash off all spilt fluid and check for fluid leaks while full pressure is applied repeatedly to the brake pedal.

11   Master cylinder – overhaul

1   Remove the master cylinder as described in Section 10 of this Chapter, then clean it thoroughly.

2   Remove the filter and float from the reservoir, then prise it gently from the master cylinder body and remove the two seals. Discard the seals and obtain new ones for reassembly.

3   Prise the stopper cap from the rear end of the master cylinder. Obtain a new one if its locking tabs are damaged or missing.

4   Extract the primary and secondary piston assemblies, noting carefully the order of removal and the way in which the components are

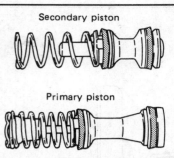

Secondary piston

Primary piston

Fig. 9.11 Showing correct assembly of master cylinder piston components (Sec 11)

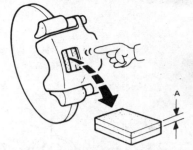

Fig. 9.13 Checking remaining thickness of brake pad friction material (Sec 12)

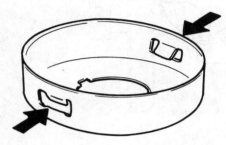

Fig. 9.12 Bend in stopper cap locking tabs at points shown (Sec 11)

12   Front brake pads – inspection and renewal

Note: *The dust produced by brake wear and deposited on brake components may contain asbestos (see 'Safety first!').* **Do not** *blow it out with compressed air and* **do not** *inhale it, it is hazardous to your health. Wipe away the dust using a clean dry cloth and work in a well-ventilated atmosphere. Then dispose of the cloth safely. Although some friction*

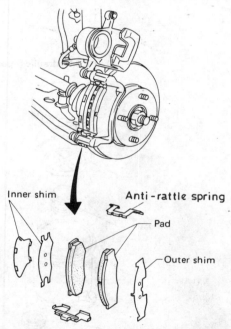

Inner shim   Anti-rattle spring

Pad

Outer shim

Fig. 9.14 Pivot the caliper body upwards to release front brake pads – note location of shim(s) fitted to metal backing of each pad, also anti-rattle springs (Sec 12)

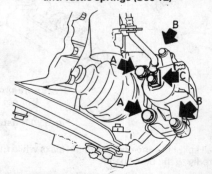

Fig. 9.15 Front brake caliper mountings (Secs 12, 13 and 14)

*A   Hub carrier-to-caliper
      mounting bracket bolts
B   Guide pin bolts*

*C   Flexible hose union banjo
      bolt*

assembled. If necessary, tap the master cylinder onto a clean block of wood to jar the assemblies free. Do not attempt any further dismantling.

5   Thoroughly clean all components using only methylated spirit or clean hydraulic fluid. Never use mineral-based solvents such as petrol or paraffin which will attack the hydraulic system's rubber components.

6   Carefully examine all parts of the master cylinder, looking carefully for signs of wear or damage. In particular the cylinder bores and pistons must be perfect, free from any signs of scratches, corrosion or wear. If there is any doubt about the condition of any part of the master cylinder, it must be renewed. Note that the manufacturer recommends that the piston assemblies are renewed whenever they are disturbed. Note also that the piston assemblies, including the seals, piston cups and springs, are only available from Nissan dealers as part of a piston kit. If any part of either piston assembly is found to be worn or damaged, therefore, both piston assemblies must be renewed. Note that a new stopper cap is included in the piston kit.

7   On later models (double-barrel master cylinder with four metal hydraulic pipe unions), do not attempt to dismantle the pressure-proportioning valve. This is a sealed part of the master cylinder assembly for which no replacement parts are available. If one or both rear wheels lock repeatedly under heavy braking, first check that this is not due to adverse road conditions or to incorrectly inflated or badly-worn tyres. Then check the condition of all four brake assemblies before suspecting the valve assembly. If the problem persists and the process of elimination indicates that the valve is faulty, the complete master cylinder assembly must be renewed.

8   On reassembly, soak the piston assemblies in clean hydraulic fluid before installation and smear clean fluid inside the cylinder bores. It should be stressed that all components must be absolutely clean on reassembly and that only clean hydraulic fluid of the specified type should be used as a lubricant.

9   With reference to Fig. 9.11, assemble the secondary return spring and piston and fit them to the master cylinder, followed by the primary return spring and piston. Take care not to distort the lips of the seals and piston cups as they enter their bores.

10   Fit the stopper cap to the master cylinder rear end, ensuring that its locking tabs are bent inwards to engage in the slots in the master cylinder body (see Fig. 9.12).

11   Fit the new seals to the master cylinder body inlet ports, then press the reservoir into them. Refit the float and filter.

12   Refit the master cylinder as described in Section 10 of this Chapter. Check carefully the operation of the braking system to be sure that it is completely satisfactory.

**Fig. 9.16 Exploded view of front brake caliper
(Secs 12, 13 and 14)**

1 Bolt
2 Washer
3 Piston
4 Dust cap
5 Bleed nipple
6 Bottom guide pin
7 Top guide pin
8 Guide pin bolt
9 Brake pads
10 Caliper body
11 Brake disc shield
12 Caliper mounting bracket
13 Rubber dust cover
14 Piston seal
15 Dust seal
16 Anti-rattle spring
17 Shim
18 Shim
19 Shim

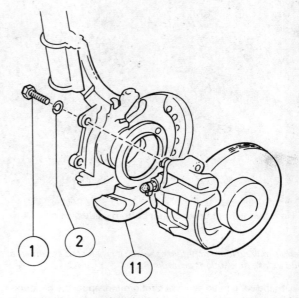
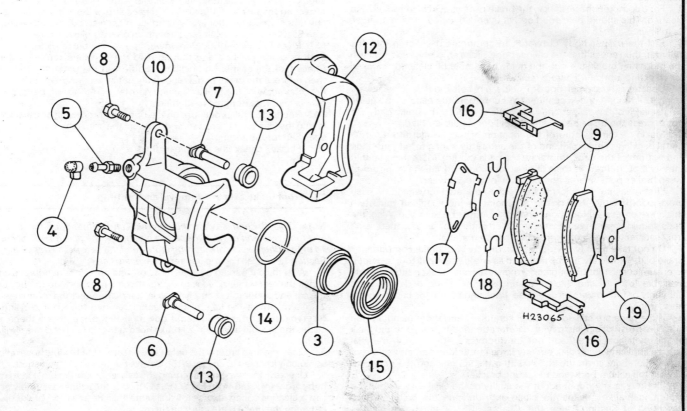

H23065

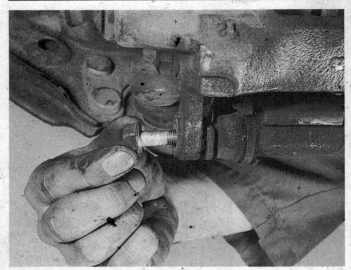

12.5 Unscrewing front brake caliper bottom guide pin bolt

12.6 Removing the outboard (fixed) brake pad – note location of shim(s) on pad metal backing

materials may no longer contain asbestos it is safest to assume that they do and to take precautions accordingly.

1   With the car parked on level, firm ground, apply the handbrake and chock the rear wheels. Slacken the roadwheel nuts, jack up the front of the car and support it securely on axle stands. Remove the roadwheel.

2   For a quick check, the thickness of friction material remaining on both brake pads can be measured through the slot in the brake caliper body (Fig. 9.13). If any pad's friction material is worn to the specified thickness or less, all four front brake pads must be renewed, as described below.

3   For a comprehensive check, the brake pads should be removed and cleaned. This should be carried out, at every specified service interval, as follows.

4   Pull the caliper body outwards to compress the piston into the cylinder, then check that the caliper body slides smoothly, and easily in the mounting bracket. If not, the guide pins must be cleaned, checked for wear and lubricated before reassembly.

5   Unscrew the caliper bottom guide pin bolt (photo), if necessary using a slim open-ended spanner to counterhold the head of the guide pin itself. Pivot the caliper body upwards to expose the brake pads. **Do not** depress the brake pedal until the caliper is reassembled.

6   Making a careful note of the location of the shim(s) fitted to the metal backing of each pad and of the anti-rattle spring fitted to the top and bottom of the pads, withdraw the pads (photo). Mark them so that they will be refitted in their original locations. Do not be tempted to swap brakes pads over to compensate for uneven wear.

7   First measure the thickness of friction material remaining on each brake pad. If either is worn at any point to the specified minimum thickness or less, all four front brake pads must be renewed. Also, the pads should be renewed if any are fouled with oil or grease; there is no truly satisfactory way of degreasing friction material.

8   Do not take risks by trying to save money with brake components. Brake pads should always be renewed as an axle set (ie all four together) to ensure consistent braking performance. For this reason they are only available from Nissan dealers as an axle set. If the pads are worn unevenly or fouled with oil or grease, trace and rectify the cause before reassembly.

9   If the pads are still serviceable, carefully clean them using a clean fine wire brush or similar, paying careful attention to the sides and back of the metal backing. Clean out the grooves in the friction material (where applicable) and pick out any large embedded particles of dirt of debris. Carefully clean the shims, anti-rattle springs and the pad locations in the caliper body and mounting bracket.

10   If there is any doubt about the ability of the caliper to slide in the mounting bracket, dismantle, clean and lubricate the guide pins as described in Section 14 of this Chapter. Check the brake disc as described in Section 15.

11   On reassembly, fit the anti-rattle springs to the caliper mounting bracket and apply a thin smear of silicone- or PBC (Poly Butyl Cuprysil)

based high-temperature brake grease to those surfaces which bear on the metal backing of each pad. Similarly, fit the shim(s) to the metal backing of the pads and apply a thin smear of the same grease to the edges and rear face only of each pad's metal backing. **Do not** allow grease to foul the friction material. Refit the pads to the caliper mounting bracket, ensuring that the friction material is against the disc.

12   If new pads have been installed, the piston must be pushed back into the cylinder to make room for them. Either use a G-clamp or similar tool, or use suitable pieces of wood as levers. Provided that the master cylinder reservoir has not been overfilled with hydraulic fluid, there should be no spillage, but keep a careful watch on the fluid level while retracting the piston. If the fluid level rises above the 'Max' line at any time the surplus should be syphoned off or ejected via a plastic tube (see Section 8 of this Chapter) through an opened bleed nipple.

13   Pivot the caliper body downwards over the brake pads, refit the bottom guide pin bolt and tighten it to the specified torque setting. Check that the caliper body slides smoothly in the mounting bracket, then depress the brake pedal repeatedly until the pads are pressed into firm contact with the brake disc and normal (non-assisted) pedal pressure is restored. Refit the roadwheel.

14   Repeat the full procedure on the opposite brake caliper assembly, lower the car to the ground and tighten the roadwheel nuts to the specified torque setting.

15   Finally, check the hydraulic fluid level. See Section 2 of this Chapter.

13   Front brake caliper – removal and refitting

Note: *This Section covers the removal and refitting of the caliper assembly as a single unit; if the caliper is to be overhauled, refer to Section 14 of this Chapter. Before starting work, read the note at the beginning of Section 12 concerning the dangers of asbestos dust.*

1   With the car parked on level, firm, ground apply the handbrake and chock the rear wheels. Slacken the roadwheel nuts, jack up the front of the car and support it securely on axle stands. Remove the roadwheel.

2   To minimise the loss of fluid, either remove the master cylinder reservoir cap and then tighten it down on to a piece of polythene, or clamp the flexible hose using a brake hose clamp, a G-clamp or a similar tool.

3   Clean the area around the union and unscrew the flexible hose union banjo bolt (marked 'C' in Fig. 9.15). Collect the two sealing washers.

4   Unscrew the two bolts securing the caliper mounting bracket to the hub carrier (marked 'A' in Fig. 9.15). Withdraw the caliper assembly and slip a clean wooden spacer (of the same thickness as the brake disc) between the brake pads to retain them.

5   Refitting is the reverse of the dismantling procedure. Tighten all bolts and nuts to the torque settings specified and ensure that the flexible hose is correctly routed before tightening the banjo bolt.

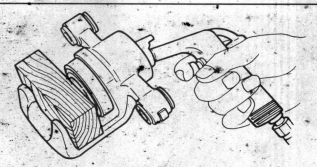

Fig. 9.17 Using compressed air to eject caliper piston (Sec 14)

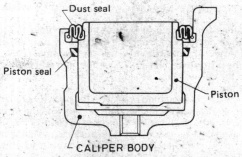

Fig. 9.18 Showing correct fitting of caliper piston seal and dust seal (Sec 14)

6   Bleed any air from the system as described in Section 8 of this Chapter, then check the master cylinder reservoir fluid level and top up if necessary (see Section 2).

14   Front brake caliper – overhaul

Note: *Before starting work, read the note at the beginning of Section 12 concerning the dangers of asbestos dust.*

Checking the caliper's action

1   If a fault occurs in the braking system (such as the car pulling to one side under braking), which lead one to suspect either of the front brake calipers, their sliding action and release can be checked as follows.
2   With the car parked on level, firm, ground apply the handbrake and chock the rear wheels. Slacken the roadwheel nuts, jack up the front of the car and support it securely on axle stands. Remove the roadwheel.
3   Remove the brake pads, as described in Section 12 of this Chapter, then attach a spring balance to one of the roadwheel studs and measure the hub bearing's turning torque as described in Section 4 of Chapter 10. This measurement, which should be within the specified range, should be recorded as force 'A'.
4   Refit the brake pads and caliper body, repeatedly depress the brake pedal until the pads are pressed into firm contact with the brake disc and normal (non-assisted) pedal pressure is restored, then apply the brake pedal firmly and maintain pressure for five seconds. Release pressure, rotate the brake disc through ten full turns and measure again the hub bearing's turning torque; let this second measurement be force 'B'.
5   Subtract 'A' from 'B' to calculate the amount of drag exerted on the brake disc by the caliper and pads. If this exceeds 103 N (23 lbf), dismantle the caliper as described below to check the caliper guide pins for wear. Renew them (and the rubber dust covers) if they are worn or damaged, otherwise clean them carefully and grease them on reassembly. Check also the brake pads, cleaning and greasing the edges of their metal backings as described in Section 12 of this Chapter.
6   Repeat the measurements as described in paragraphs 3 and 4 above. If the calculated brake drag is not reduced to less than that given, then either the caliper piston is sticking or seized in the caliper body or the piston seal is faulty. In this case the caliper must be completely dismantled and overhauled as described below.

Overhauling the caliper

7   With the car parked on level, firm, ground apply the handbrake and chock the rear wheels. Slacken the roadwheel nuts, jack up the front of the car and support it securely on axle stands. Remove the roadwheel.
8   To minimise the loss of fluid, either remove the master cylinder reservoir cap and then tighten it down on to a piece of polythene, or clamp the flexible hose using a brake hose clamp, a G-clamp or similar tool.
9   Clean the area around the union (photo) and unscrew the flexible hose union banjo bolt (marked 'C' in Fig. 9.15). Collect the two sealing washers.
10   Slacken both caliper guide pin bolts (using a slim open-ended spanner if necessary to counterhold the guide pins themselves), unscrew the bottom guide pin bolt and pivot the caliper body upwards.
11   Withdraw the brake pads, shims and anti-rattle springs as described in Section 12 of this Chapter.
12   Unscrew the top guide pin bolt and withdraw the caliper body from the mounting bracket. Extract the guide pins, if necessary by

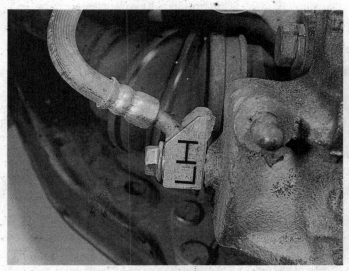

14.9 Clean union before disconnecting flexible hose from front brake caliper – LH stamped in union identifies hose for left-hand caliper

screwing their bolts into them and pulling on the head of each bolt using a self-locking wrench or similar. Peel off the rubber dust cover from each guide pin.
13   Unbolt the caliper mounting bracket from the hub carrier.
14   Place a small block of wood in the jaws of the caliper as shown in Fig. 9.17, then remove the piston, including the dust seal, by applying a jet of low-pressure compressed air, such as that from a tyre pump, at the fluid entry port.
15   Peel the dust seal off the piston and use a blunt instrument such as a knitting needle to extract the piston seal from the caliper cylinder bore.
16   Thoroughly clean all components using only methylated spirit or clean hydraulic fluid. Never use mineral-based solvents such as petrol or paraffin which will attack the hydraulic system's rubber components.
17   The caliper piston seal and dust seal, the guide pin dust covers and the bleed nipple dust cap are only available as part of a seal kit. Since the manufacturer recommends that the piston seal and dust seal are renewed whenever they are disturbed all of these components should be discarded and new ones fitted on reassembly as a matter of course. Do not try to save money by re-using seals etc.
18   Carefully examine all parts of the caliper assembly, looking for signs of wear or damage. In particular the cylinder bore and piston must be perfect, free from any signs of scratches, corrosion or wear. If there is any doubt about the condition of any part of the caliper it must be renewed, but note that if the caliper body or the mounting bracket are to be renewed, they are available only as part of the complete assembly.
19   The manufacturer states that minor scratches, rust etc may be polished away from the cylinder bore using fine emery paper, but that the piston must be renewed to cure such defects. The piston's surface is plated and must not be polished with emery or similar abrasives.
20   Check that the threads are in good condition in the caliper body and mounting bracket. Check that both guide pins are undamaged and (when cleaned) a reasonably tight sliding fit in the mounting bracket bores. Use compressed air to blow clear the fluid passages.

21   On reassembly, ensure that all components are spotlessly clean and dry.

22   Soak the new piston seal in clean hydraulic fluid and fit it to the groove in the cylinder bore, using the fingers only to manipulate it into place. Fit the new dust seal to the piston groove, smear clean hydraulic fluid over the piston and caliper cylinder bore and refit the piston. Press it fully into the caliper body (see Fig. 9.18), then fit the dust seal to the groove in the caliper body.

23   Refit the caliper mounting bracket to the hub carrier, tightening its mounting bolts to the specified torque setting. Fit a new rubber dust cover to each guide pin and apply a smear of silicone- or PBC (Poly Butyl Cuprysil) based high-temperature brake grease to the guide pins before refitting them to their bores. Refit the brake pads as described in Section 12 of this Chapter.

24   Fit the caliper body over the mounting bracket and brake pads, refit the guide pin bolts and tighten them to the specified torque setting. Check that the caliper slides smoothly on the mounting bracket.

25   Ensuring that the flexible hose is correctly routed without being twisted, connect it to the caliper again using two new sealing washers and tightening the union banjo bolt to the specified torque setting.

26   Bleed any air from the system as described in Section 8 of this Chapter, then depress the brake pedal repeatedly until the pads are pressed into firm contact with the brake disc and normal (non-assisted) pedal pressure is restored, Check the master cylinder reservoir fluid level and top up if necessary (see Section 2). Refit the roadwheel and lower the car to the ground, then wash off any spilt fluid and check for fluid leaks while an assistant applies full pressure to the brake pedal.

27   Repeat the full procedure on the opposite caliper – always overhaul both calipers together.

15   Front brake disc – inspection, removal and refitting

1   With the car parked on level, firm, ground apply the handbrake and chock the rear wheels. Slacken the roadwheel nuts, jack up the front of the car and support it securely on axle stands. Remove the roadwheel.

2   Slowly rotate the disc so that the full area of both sides can be checked. Light scoring is normal in the area swept by the brake pads, but if heavy scoring is found the disc must be renewed. The only alternative to this is to have the disc surface-ground until it is flat again, but this must not reduce the disc to less than the specified minimum thickness.

3   It is normal to find a lip of rust and brake dust around the disc's outside diameter; this can be scraped off if required. If, however, a lip has formed due to excessive wear of the brake pad's swept area then the disc's thickness must be measured using a micrometer. Take measurements at four places around the disc at the inside and outside of the pad swept area. If the disc has worn at any point to the specified minimum thickness or less, it must be renewed.

4   If the disc is thought to be warped, it can be checked for runout either using a dial gauge mounted on any convenient fixed point, while the disc is slowly rotated, or by using feeler gauges to measure, at several points all around, the clearance between the disc and a fixed point such as the caliper mounting bracket. Take measurements in the centre of the pad's swept area. Fasten the disc with the roadwheel nuts tightened (to the specified torque setting) on to suitable spacers. If the measurements obtained are at the specified maximum or beyond, the disc is excessively warped and should be renewed. It is worth checking first that the hub bearings are in good condition (see Section 4 of Chapter 10). Also try the effect of removing the disc, turning it through 180° to reposition it on the hub and then refitting it. If runout is still excessive, the disc must be renewed.

5   Check the disc for cracks, especially around the stud holes, and any other wear or damage. Renew it if any of these are found.

6   To remove a front brake disc, jack the car up and remove the roadwheel as described above. Unscrew the two bolts securing the caliper mounting bracket to the hub carrier, withdraw the caliper assembly and secure it out of harm's way without stretching or kinking the flexible hose. Remove the spring clip securing it to the suspension strut bracket if required. Place a clean spacer (of the same thickness as the disc) between the pads to prevent them being dislodged. Use chalk or paint to mark the relationship of the disc to the hub, then pull the disc off the roadwheel studs (photo). If the disc is stuck with corrosion it can be pushed off by evenly tightening two suitably-sized bolts into the threaded holes in the disc's centre.

15.6 Removing front brake disc – ensure hub/disc mating surfaces are clean on refitting

7   Refitting is the reverse of the removal procedure. Ensure that the mating surfaces of the hub and of the disc are clean and flat; align (if applicable) the marks made on removal. Use a suitable solvent to wipe any preservative coating from the disc before the brake caliper is refitted.

8   Note that to ensure even and consistent braking performance, both discs should be renewed at the same time, even if only one is faulty.

16   Front brake shield – removal and refitting

The shield can only be removed after the front suspension hub carrier has been removed from the car and the hub has been dismantled. Refer to Sections 3 and 4 of Chapter 10.

17   Pressure-reducing valve – removal and refitting

Note: Do not attempt to dismantle the valve or to 'adjust' it in any way. It is effectively a sealed unit, since no component parts are available separately. If the valve is damaged or blocked, or if it proves faulty, it must be renewed.

1   The pressure-reducing valve is fitted only to early models which have the single-barrel master cylinder with two metal hydraulic pipe unions. It is referred to by Nissan as a DLSV (Dual Load Sensing Valve).

2   The valve is situated behind the rear suspension crossmember (photo). It is bolted to a bracket which is attached to the underbody.

3   If one or both rear wheels lock repeatedly under heavy braking, first check that this is not due to adverse road conditions or to incorrectly inflated or badly-worn tyres, then check the condition of all four brake assemblies before suspecting the valve assembly. If the problem persists and the process of elimination indicates that the valve is faulty, the complete assembly must be renewed.

4   To remove the valve, minimise fluid loss by removing the master cylinder reservoir cap and then tightening it down on to a piece of polythene.

5   With the car parked on firm, level ground, apply the handbrake firmly and select first or reverse gear (manual transmission) or the 'P' position (automatic). Chock the front wheels, jack up the rear of the car and support it securely on axle stands.

6   Note carefully the location and routing of all hydraulic pipes connected to the valve, then unscrew the union nuts and disconnect each pipe in turn; be prepared to catch the spilt fluid. Unbolt the valve and withdraw it.

7   Refitting is the reverse of the removal procedure, noting the following points. Tighten the valve mounting bolts (and nuts, if applicable) to

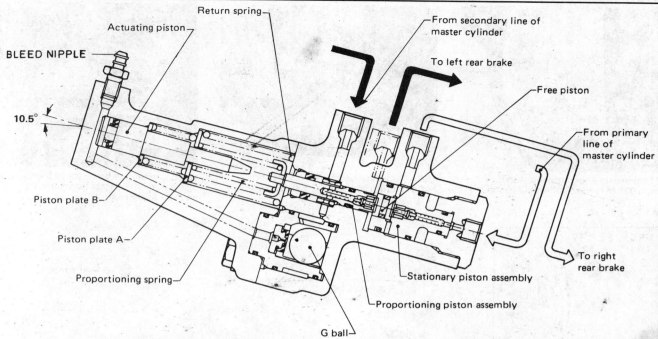

Fig. 9.19 Cross-section of pressure-reducing valve – early models only (Sec 17)

For reference only – do not attempt to dismantle

17.2 Pressure-reducing valve is fitted to early models only

the specified torque settings and ensure that each hydraulic pipe is connected to its correct union on the valve. Tighten the union nuts securely; noting the specified torque wrench settings. Lower the car to the ground.

8   Carry out the full bleeding procedure described in Section 8 of this Chapter to remove all traces of air from the system, but note that it may take several attempts (and a larger than usual amount of hydraulic fluid) to clear all the air from a new valve. This is one of the cases where a pressure-bleeding kit would be most useful.

9   Finally, check the master cylinder reservoir fluid level (Section 2), wash off any spilt fluid and check for fluid leaks at all disturbed unions while an assistant applies full pressure at the brake pedal.

18   Rear brake shoes – inspection and renewal

Note: *The dust produced by brake wear and deposited on brake components may contain asbestos (see 'Safety first!').* **Do not** *blow it out with*

compressed air and **do not** *inhale it; it is hazardous to your health. Wipe away the dust using a clean, dry cloth and work in a well-ventilated atmosphere. Dispose of the cloth safely. Although some friction materials may no longer contain asbestos it is safest to assume that they do and to take precautions accordingly.*

Do not try to save money by taking risks with brake components. Brake shoes should always be renewed as an axle set (ie all four together) to ensure consistent braking performance. For this reason they are only available from Nissan dealers as an axle set. If the shoes are worn unevenly, damaged, or fouled with oil or grease, trace and rectify the cause before reassembly.

1   Cars built from September 1987 on are all fitted with an inspection aperture in each rear brake backplate to permit the measurement of the amount of friction material remaining on the leading brake shoe (see Section 1), without removing the roadwheel and brake drum.

2   For a quick check, on these later models, prise out the rubber plug from the backplate front outer edge and insert a rod (such as a drill bit) 1.5 mm (0.06 in) in diameter into the aperture until it rests against the brake shoe friction material. If the friction material is worn to the thickness of the rod or less all four rear brake shoes must be renewed, as described below.

3   To check the rear brakes on earlier models, and to check them comprehensively on later models, the roadwheels and brake drums must be removed and the full procedure given below must be followed.

4   The rear brake drums are integral with the rear hubs. Removal therefore requires the dismantling of the hub bearings. On refitting, the hub bearings must be reassembled and adjusted. Proceed as described in Sections 13 and 12 of Chapter 10.

5   Very carefully remove all traces of brake dust from the brake drum

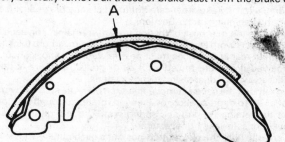

Fig. 9.20 Measuring remaining thickness of brake shoe friction material ('A') (Sec 18)

18.7 Depress retainer (arrowed) and turn through 90° to release anti-rattle spring

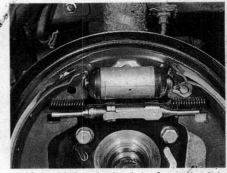

18.8A Note location of brake shoes and bottom return spring (early type shown) ...

18.8B ... withdraw brake shoes from wheel cylinder, then separate from return spring and self-adjuster strut

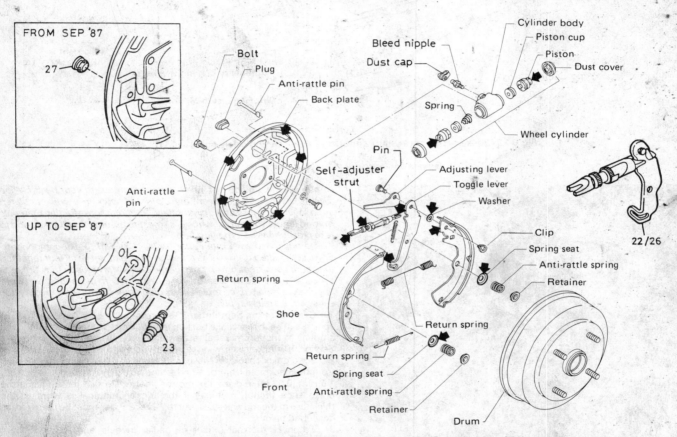

Fig. 9.21 Exploded view of rear drum brake assembly (Secs 18, 19 and 20)

Arrows indicate brake grease points – see text

and from the brake backplate assembly and shoes. Where possible, a clean dry cloth should be used, but if necessary a soft brush can be employed, provided that the loose dust is sucked away using a vacuum cleaner or similar. Take great care not to inhale any brake dust (see the note at the beginning of this Section).

6   Measure the thickness of friction material remaining on each brake shoe. If either is worn at any point to the specified minimum thickness or less, all four rear brake shoes must be renewed. The shoes should also be renewed if any are fouled with oil or grease as there is no truly satisfactory way of degreasing friction material.

7   To remove the shoes, remove first the anti-rattle springs by using a pair of pliers to depress each retainer and rotate it through 90° (photo); collect the retainer, spring and spring seat. The anti-rattle pin can be removed for safe keeping, if required.

8   Carefully note the exact fitted positions of the brake shoes, return springs and the handbrake operating linkage to ensure correct reassembly. Gently lever each shoe in turn, off the bottom anchor point and

unhook the bottom return spring (photos). Disconnect the handbrake cable from the toggle lever and collect the return spring fitted over the cable.

9   Gently slide both brake shoes downwards off the wheel cylinder pistons and withdraw them, complete with the handbrake operating linkage and self-adjuster strut. Do not depress the brake pedal until the brake has been reassembled.

10   Clean the backplate and apply a thin smear of silicone- or PBC (Poly Butyl Cuprysil) based high-temperature brake grease to all points of contact between the brake shoes and the backplate. Also apply it to the bottom anchor point, the wheel cylinder pistons and to the anti-rattle pins and spring seats. If the shoes are not renewed, check the handbrake operating linkage is working properly and is correctly lubricated.

11   Carefully peel back the wheel cylinder rubber dust covers and check that there are no signs of fluid leakage or other damage. Refer to Sections 19 and 20 of this Chapter if the wheel cylinder requires overhaul.

18.14 Rear brake shoes (later type, right-hand side shown) reassembled

12   To renew the brake shoes, slide them apart until the self-adjuster strut can be withdrawn, remove the top return spring, then prise off the retaining clip to release the handbrake operating linkage from the rear (trailing) shoe. Discard the retaining clip.

13   Transfer the handbrake operating linkage to the new rear (trailing) shoe, applying a thin smear of brake grease to the pivot pin and washer and fitting a new retaining clip to the pivot pin groove. Apply a thin smear of brake grease to the end forks and threads of the self-adjuster strut, then turn the serrated nut fully to retract the strut.

14   Being careful not to get grease on the brake shoe friction material, assemble both brake shoes, the self-adjuster strut and the top return spring on a flat surface then refit the assembly to the brake backplate and wheel cylinder. Refit the return spring to the handbrake cable and connect the cable to the toggle lever, then lever the brake shoe bottom ends onto the anchor point and refit the bottom return spring. Tap the shoes to centralise them within the backplate assembly (photo).

15   Refit the anti-rattle pins (if removed) passing them through the backplate and brake shoes from inside to outside, then refit the spring seats and spring. Compress the springs with the retainers, while holding the pins in place, then turn the retainers through 90° and release them to secure each assembly.

16   Adjust the brake shoe diameter to just less than that of the drum, refit the drum and adjust the hub bearings, refit the roadwheel and operate the handbrake several times to allow the self-adjuster strut to establish correct brake shoe-to-drum clearance. Refer to Sections 13 and 12 of Chapter 10 for details.

17   Repeat the full procedure on the opposite brake assembly, then check the hydraulic fluid level, as described in Section 2 of this Chapter.

19   Rear wheel cylinder – removal and refitting

Note: *Before starting work, read the note at the beginning of Section 18 concerning the dangers of asbestos dust*

1   Remove the brake drum – see Section 13 of Chapter 10.
2   Remove the brake shoes – see Section 18 of this Chapter.
3   Minimise the loss of fluid either by removing the master cylinder reservoir cap and then tightening it down on to a piece of polythene or by clamping the flexible hose using a brake clamp, a G-clamp or similar tool.
4   Clean the backplate around the wheel cylinder mounting bolts and hydraulic pipe union, then unscrew the union nut and disconnect the hydraulic pipe.
5   Unbolt the wheel cylinder and withdraw it from the backplate.
6   Refitting is the reverse of the removal procedure. Tighten the wheel cylinder mounting bolts to the specified torque setting. When the brake is reassembled, bleed any trapped air from the system as described in Section 8 of this Chapter, wash off any spilt fluid, then check the master

cylinder reservoir fluid level, as described in Section 2. Watch carefully for any signs of fluid leaks.

20   Rear wheel cylinder – overhaul

1   Remove the wheel cylinder from the car, as described in Section 19 of this Chapter.
2   Clean the unit thoroughly using only methylated spirit or clean hydraulic fluid. Never use mineral-based solvents such as petrol or paraffin, which will attack the hydraulic system's rubber components.
3   Peel off both rubber dust covers, then use paint or similar to mark one of the pistons and that end of the cylinder so that the pistons are not interchanged on reassembly. Withdraw both pistons and the spring.
4   Discard the rubber cups and dust covers. These should be renewed as a matter of course whenever the cylinder is dismantled and are available as a repair kit which also includes the bleed nipple dust cap. Carefully examine all other components, renewing any that show signs of wear, damage or corrosion. Note that the wheel cylinder fitted can be made by either Nabco or Tokico; since the components are not interchangeable always specify the cylinder's manufacturer when obtaining replacement parts.
5   In particular, check the cylinder bore and piston; these must be perfect and free from scratches, scoring or corrosion. Note that while the pistons are available separately, it is very unlikely that the cylinder bore will have survived undamaged if one of the pistons is sufficiently worn or damaged to require renewal. Owners are advised to renew the complete wheel cylinder assembly if there is any doubt about its condition.
6   On reassembly it should be stressed that all components must be absolutely clean and dry. The pistons, spring and cups should be fitted wet, using hydraulic fluid as a lubricant; soak them in clean fluid before installation.
7   Fit the cups to the pistons, ensuring that they are the correct way round and using only the fingers to manipulate them into position. Fit the first piston into the cylinder, taking care not to distort the cup. If the original pistons are being re-used, use the marks made on dismantling to ensure they are refitted in their original bores. Refit the spring and the second piston.
8   Apply a smear of rubber grease to the exposed end of each piston and to the dust cover sealing lips, then fit the dust covers to each end of the wheel cylinder.
9   Refit the wheel cylinder to the car, as described in Section 19 of this Chapter.
10   Repeat the full procedure on the opposite wheel cylinder. Always overhaul both wheel cylinders together, to ensure even, consistent braking performance.

21   Rear brake drum – removal, inspection and refitting

Note: *Before starting work, read the note at the beginning of Section 18 concerning the dangers of asbestos dust.*

1   The rear brake drums are integral with the rear hubs. Removal therefore requires the dismantling of the hub bearings. On refitting, the hub bearings must be reassembled and adjusted. Refer to Sections 13 and 12 of Chapter 10.
2   Carefully remove all traces of brake dust. Where possible, a clean

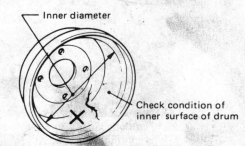

Inner diameter

Check condition of inner surface of drum

Fig. 9.22 Checking brake drums for wear or distortion (Sec 21)

dry cloth should be used, but if necessary a soft brush can be employed, providing that the loose dust is sucked away using a vacuum cleaner or similar. Take great care not to inhale any brake dust.

3   Scrub clean the outside of the brake drum and check it for obvious signs of wear or damage, such as cracks around the roadwheel studs. Renew the drum if necessary.

4   Examine carefully the drum's internal friction surface. Light scoring is normal, but if heavy scoring is found the drum must be renewed. It is usual to find a lip on the drum's inboard edge which consists of a mixture of rust and brake dust; this should be scraped away to leave a smooth surface. Finish by polishing the surface with fine (120 to 150 grade) emery paper. If, however, the lip is due to the friction surface being recessed by excessive wear, then the drum must be renewed.

5   If the drum is thought to be excessively worn, its internal diameter should be measured at several points (Fig. 9.22) using an internal micrometer. Take measurements in pairs, the second at right angles to the first, and compare the two to check for signs of ovality. Check also the difference between the inboard and outboard edges of the swept area to ensure that taper is within limits. It may be possible to have the drum refinished by skimming or grinding, provided that this does not enlarge it to the maximum specified diameter or greater. This is a task for the expert alone.

6   If one of the brake drums is sufficiently worn or damaged to justify renewal, both drums should be renewed at the same time, to ensure even and consistent braking performance.

7   On fitting a new brake drum, use a suitable solvent to remove any preservative coating that may have been applied to its interior.

22   Rear drum brake backplate – removal and refitting

Note: *Before starting work, read the note at the beginning of Section 18 concerning the dangers of asbestos dust.*

1   Remove the roadwheel and brake drum with reference to Section 13 of Chapter 10.

2   Remove the brake shoes as described in Section 18 of this Chapter.

3   Remove the wheel cylinder as described in Section 19 of this Chapter.

4   Release the handbrake cable from the backplate (early models) or unbolt and withdraw the cable (later models).

5   Unbolt the backplate from the suspension strut lower end.

6   On refitting, thoroughly clean the strut lower end and the backplate. Refit the backplate and tighten the mounting bolts to the specified torque setting. Refit the remainder of the assembly as described in the relevant Sections of this Chapter and of Chapter 10.

23   Rear brake pads – inspection and renewal

Note: *The dust produced by brake wear and deposited on brake components may contain asbestos (see 'Safety first!'). Do not blow it out with compressed air and do not inhale it; it is hazardous to your health. Wipe away the dust using a clean dry cloth, working in a well-ventilated atmosphere, then dispose of the cloth safely. Although some friction materials may no longer contain asbestos it is safest to assume that they do and to take precautions accordingly.*

Do not try to save money by taking risks with brake components. Brake pads should always be renewed as an axle set (ie all four together) to ensure consistent braking performance. For this reason they are only available from Nissan dealers as an axle set. If the pads are worn unevenly, or fouled with oil or grease, trace and rectify the cause before reassembly.

1   With the car parked on level, firm, ground, apply the handbrake and select first or reverse gear (manual transmission) or the 'P' position (automatic). Chock the front wheels. Slacken the roadwheel nuts, jack up the rear of the car and support it securely on axle stands. Remove the roadwheel and release the handbrake fully.

2   Unbolt the handbrake cable stay from the caliper (photo) and disconnect the cable and nipple from the lever. Remove the spring clip securing the flexible hose to the suspension strut bracket.

23.2 Unbolting handbrake cable stay from rear right-hand brake caliper

23.4 Pivot the caliper body upwards to expose pads – note location of shim on each pad's backing

23.6 Measuring thickness of brake pad friction material – renew all four pads if any are worn to limit

23.10 Use long-nosed pliers as shown to retract caliper piston – screw piston clockwise

23.11 Tighten caliper guise pin bolt to specified torque setting

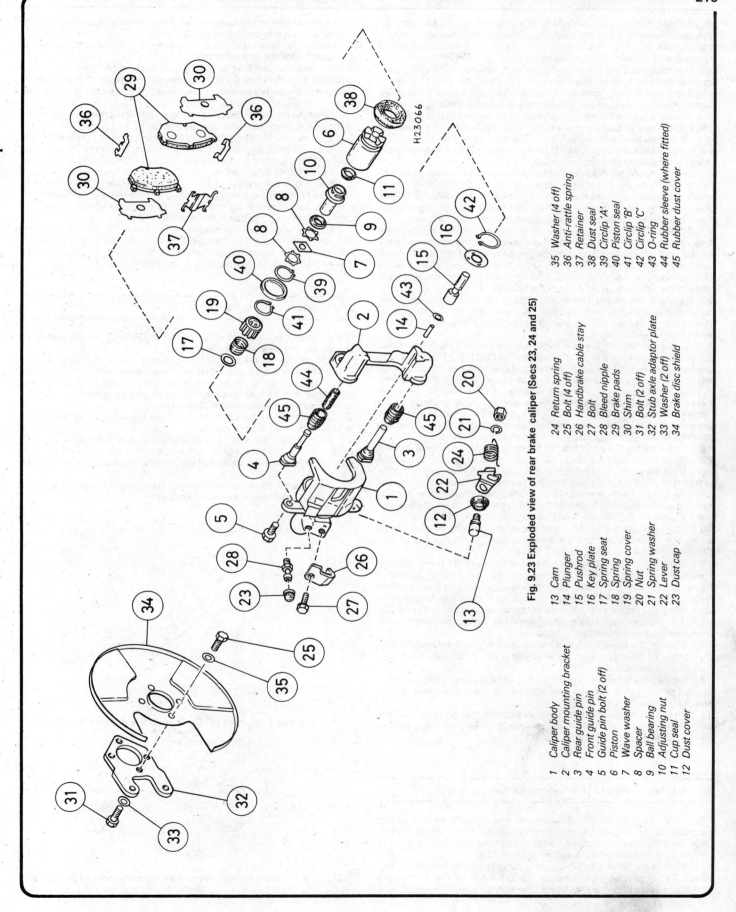

Fig. 9.23 Exploded view of rear brake caliper (Secs 23, 24 and 25)

1 Caliper body
2 Caliper mounting bracket
3 Rear guide pin
4 Front guide pin
5 Guide pin bolt (2 off)
6 Piston
7 Spacer
8 Wave washer
9 Ball bearing
10 Adjusting nut
11 Cup seal
12 Dust cover
13 Cam
14 Plunger
15 Pushrod
16 Key plate
17 Spring seat
18 Spring
19 Spring cover
20 Nut
21 Spring washer
22 Lever
23 Dust cap
24 Return spring
25 Bolt (4 off)
26 Handbrake cable stay
27 Bolt
28 Bleed nipple
29 Brake pads
30 Shim
31 Bolt (2 off)
32 Stub axle adaptor plate
33 Washer (2 off)
34 Brake disc shield
35 Washer (4 off)
36 Anti-rattle spring
37 Retainer
38 Dust seal
39 Circlip 'A'
40 Piston seal
41 Circlip 'B'
42 Circlip 'C'
43 O-ring
44 Rubber sleeve (where fitted)
45 Rubber dust cover

H23066

3   Pull the caliper body outwards to compress the piston into the cylinder, then check that the caliper body slides smoothly and easily in the mounting bracket. If not, the guide pins must be cleaned, checked for wear and lubricated before reassembly.

4   Unscrew the caliper rear guide pin bolt, if necessary using a slim open-ended spanner to counterhold the head of the guide pin itself. Pivot the caliper body upwards to expose the brake pads (photo). **Do not** depress the brake pedal until the caliper is reassembled.

5   Making a careful note of the location of the shim fitted to the metal backing of each pad and of the anti-rattle spring fitted to the front and rear of the pads, withdraw both pads. Mark them so that they will be refitted in their original locations. Do not be tempted to swap brake pads over to compensate for uneven wear.

6   First measure the thickness of friction material remaining on each brake pad, (photo). If either is worn at any point to the specified minimum thickness or less, all four rear brake pads must be renewed. Also, the pads should be renewed if any are fouled with oil or grease, as there is no truly satisfactory way of degreasing friction material.

7   If the pads are still serviceable carefully clean them using a clean, fine wire brush or similar, paying careful attention to the sides and back of the metal backing. Clean out the grooves in the friction material (where applicable) and pick out any large embedded particles of dirt or debris. Carefully clean the shims, anti-rattle springs and the pad locations in the caliper body and mounting bracket.

8   If there is any doubt about the ability of the caliper to slide in the mounting bracket, dismantle, clean and lubricate the guide pins as described in Section 25 of this Chapter. Check the brake disc as described in Section 26.

9   On reassembly, fit the anti-rattle springs to the caliper mounting bracket and apply a thin smear of silicone- or PBC (Poly Butyl Cuprysil) based high-temperature brake grease to those surfaces which bear on the metal backing of each pad. Remove, clean and lightly grease the retainer fitted to the caliper body. Similarly, fit the shim to the metal backing of each pad and apply a thin smear of the same grease to the edges and rear face only of each pad's metal backing. **Do not** allow grease to foul the friction material. Refit the pads to the caliper mounting bracket, ensuring that the friction material is against the disc.

10 If new pads have been fitted, the piston must be retracted into the cylinder to make room for them. Using long-nosed pliers fitted into the notches in the piston (photo), screw the piston clockwise (looking at the piston from the side of the car) until it is seated. Take care not to twist or damage the dust seal. Provided that the master cylinder reservoir has not been overfilled with hydraulic fluid, there should be no spillage, but keep a careful watch on the fluid level while retracting the piston. If the fluid level rises above the 'Max' level line at any time the surplus should be syphoned off or ejected via a plastic tube (see Section 8 of this Chapter) through the opened bleed nipple.

11 Pivot the caliper body downwards over the brake pads (rotating the piston so that the nearest of its notches fits over the peg on the pad backing), refit the rear guide pin bolt and tighten it to the specified torque setting (photo). Check that the caliper body slides smoothly in the mounting bracket, then depress the brake pedal repeatedly until the pads are pressed into firm contact with the brake disc and normal (non-assisted) pedal pressure is restored.

12 Connect the handbrake cable to the lever and bolt the cable stay to the caliper body, ensuring that the stay is correctly located by its pin. Refit the roadwheel.

13 Repeat the full procedure on the opposite brake caliper assembly, lower the car to the ground and tighten the roadwheel nuts to the specified torque setting.

14 Check the hydraulic fluid level, as described in Section 2 of this Chapter, then operate the handbrake several times until correct brake pad-to-disc clearance is established.

24 Rear brake caliper – removal and refitting

Note: *This Section covers the removal and refitting of the caliper assembly as a single unit. If the caliper is to be overhauled, refer to Section 25 of this Chapter. Before starting work, read the note at the beginning of Section 23 concerning the dangers of asbestos dust.*

1   With the car parked on firm, level ground apply the handbrake and select first or reverse gear (manual transmission) or the 'P' position (automatic). Chock the front wheels. Slacken the roadwheel nuts, jack

up the rear of the car and support it securely on axle stands. Remove the roadwheel and release the handbrake fully.

2   Unbolt the handbrake cable stay from the caliper and disconnect the cable end nipple from the lever.

3   To minimise the loss of fluid, either remove the master cylinder reservoir cap and then tighten it down on to a piece of polythene or clamp the flexible hose using a brake hose clamp, a G-clamp or a similar tool.

4   Clean the area around the union and unscrew the flexible hose union banjo bolt. Collect the two sealing washers.

5   Unscrew the two bolts securing the caliper mounting bracket to the stub axle adapter plate and withdraw the caliper assembly. Place a clean spacer (of the same thickness as the disc) between the pads to prevent them from being dislodged.

6   Refitting is the reverse of the removal procedure. Tighten all bolts and nuts to the torque settings specified. Ensure that the flexible hose is correctly routed before tightening the banjo bolt. Locate the handbrake cable stay on its pin before tightening its bolt.

7   Bleed any air from the system as described in Section 8 of this Chapter, then check the master cylinder reservoir fluid level and top up if necessary. Operate the handbrake several times until correct brake pad-to-disc clearance is established. See Section 2 of this Chapter.

25 Rear brake caliper – overhaul

Note: *Before starting work, read the note at the beginning of Section 23 concerning the dangers of asbestos dust*

1   With the car parked on level, firm ground, apply the handbrake and select first or reverse gear (manual transmission) or the 'P' position (automatic). Chock the front wheels. Slacken the roadwheel nuts, jack up the rear of the car and support it securely on axle stands. Remove the roadwheel and release the handbrake fully.

2   Unbolt the handbrake cable stay from the caliper and disconnect the cable end nipple from the lever.

3   To minimise the loss of fluid, either remove the master cylinder reservoir cap end then tighten it down on to a piece of polythene or clamp the flexible hose using a brake hose clamp, a G-clamp or a similar tool.

4   Clean the area around the union and unscrew the flexible hose union banjo bolt. Collect the two sealing washers.

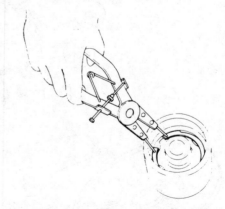

Fig. 9.24 Extracting circlip 'A' from the piston (Sec 25)

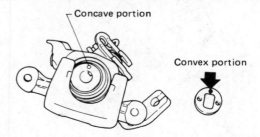

Fig. 9.25 Showing correct key plate alignment with caliper body (Sec 25)

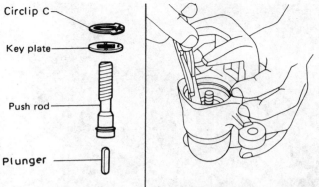

Circlip C
Key plate
Push rod
Plunger

Fig. 9.26 Refitting key plate and pushrod components to caliper body (Sec 25)

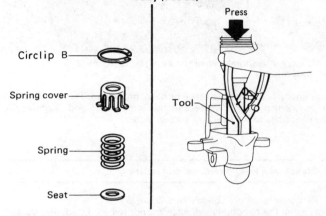

Circlip B
Spring cover
Spring
Seat
Press
Tool

Fig. 9.27 Refitting spring seat, spring and spring cover to caliper body (Sec 25)

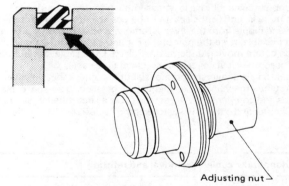

Adjusting nut

Fig. 9.28 Showing correct fitting of cup seal on adjusting nut (Sec 25)

5   Slacken both caliper guide pins bolts (using a slim open-ended spanner if necessary to counterhold the guide pins themselves), unscrew the rear guide pin bolt and pivot the caliper body upwards. Remove the brake pads, shims, and anti-rattle springs as described in Section 23 of this Chapter.
6   Unscrew the front guide pin bolt and withdraw the caliper body from the mounting bracket. Extract the guide pins, if necessary, by screwing their bolts into them and pulling on the head of each bolt using a self-locking wrench or similar. Peel the rubber dust cover off each guide pin, and the rubber sleeve that may be found on the front guide pin of some models. Unbolt the mounting bracket from the stub axle adaptor plate.
7   Clean the components to remove all external dust.
8   Using long-nosed pliers fitted into the notches in the piston, unscrew the piston anti-clockwise. Withdraw it from the caliper body and peel off the dust seal.
9   From inside the piston, use circlip pliers to extract circlip 'A' shown in Fig. 9.24, then remove the first spacer, the wave washer, the second

spacer, the ball bearing and the adjusting nut. Prise the cup seal off the adjusting nut.
10   From inside the caliper cylinder bore, use circlip pliers to extract circlip 'B' while using a suitable length of tubing to compress the spring cover against spring pressure. With the circlip removed from its groove, allow the spring to push out the components until pressure is relaxed, then withdraw the circlip, the spring cover, the spring and the spring seat.
11   Use circlip pliers to extract circlip 'C', then withdraw the key plate, the pushrod and the plunger. Prise the sealing O-ring off the pushrod.
12   Using a blunt instrument such as a knitting needle, extract the piston seal from the caliper cylinder bore.
13   Unhook the return spring from the handbrake lever, then prise the lever and cam assembly from the caliper body. Ensure that the short rod and pushrod have been removed before this is attempted.
14   Clamp the cam gently in a soft-jawed vice, unscrew the retaining nut and withdraw the spring washer, the return spring, the lever and the dust cover from the cam.
15   Thoroughly clean all components using only methylated spirit or clean hydraulic fluid. Never use mineral-based solvents such as petrol or paraffin, which will attack the hydraulic system's rubber components.
16   Discard all seals, cups, dust covers and other rubber components. These are all available as parts of a caliper seal kit and should be renewed as a matter of course whenever they are disturbed. Do not try to save money by re-using seals.
17   Carefully examine all parts of the caliper assembly, looking for signs of wear or damage. In particular, the cylinder bore and piston must be perfect, free from any signs of scratches, corrosion or wear. If there is any doubt about the condition of any part of the caliper it must be renewed, but note that if the caliper body or mounting bracket are to be renewed, they are only available as part of the complete assembly.
18   The manufacturer states that minor scratches, rust etc may be polished away from the cylinder bore using fine emery paper, but that the piston must be renewed to cure such defects. The piston's surface is plated and must not be polished with emery or similar abrasives.
19   Check that the threads are in good condition in the caliper body and mounting bracket. Check that both guide pins are undamaged and (when cleaned) a reasonably tight sliding fit in the mounting bracket bores. Use compressed air to blow the fluid passages clear.
20   On reassembly, ensure that all components are spotlessly clean and dry.
21   Fit the new dust cover to the cam and locate the lever correctly, on the cam flats, then refit the return spring, spring washer and nut. Tighten the nut securely, but do not overtighten it. Apply a smear of silicone- or PBC (Poly Butyl Cuprysil) based high-temperature brake grease to the cam before pressing the assembly into the caliper body. Check that the assembly is correctly installed and that the cam track aligns with the pushrod aperture when the lever is rotated. Hook the return spring over its stop and into the lever.
22   Soak the new piston seal in clean hydraulic fluid and fit it to the groove in the cylinder bore, using the fingers only to manipulate it into place.
23   Fit a new O-ring to the pushrod and apply a smear of rubber grease to the plunger and the pushrod. Assemble the plunger and pushrod and fit them to the caliper body. Refit the key plate so that its cutout fits over the squared section of the pushrod and its convex locating pip matches the concave depression in the caliper body, then secure the assembly by refitting circlip 'C'. See Figs 9.25 and 9.26.
24   Refit the spring seat, the spring and the spring cover, then compress the spring cover using a suitable length of tubing (see Fig. 9.27) while circlip 'B' is refitted to secure the assembly. Check the circlip is seated fully in its groove.
25   Fit the new cup seal to the adjusting nut, using only the fingers to manipulate it into position as shown in Fig. 9.28. Smear rubber grease over the cup seal lips and fit the adjusting nut into the piston. Pack the ball-bearing with brake grease and refit it, followed by a spacer, the wave washer and another spacer. Refit circlip 'A'.
26   Apply a smear of rubber grease to the inner and outer lips of the new dust seal and fit it to the piston. Smear clean hydraulic fluid over the piston and caliper cylinder bore, then refit the piston assembly and screw it in clockwise until it seats. Fit the dust seal to the caliper body.
27   Refit the caliper mounting bracket to the stub axle adaptor plate and tighten its mounting bolts to the specified torque setting. Fit a new rubber dust cover to each guide pin (do not forget to fit a new rubber sleeve to the front guide pin, where applicable) and apply a smear of silicone- or PBC (Poly Butyl Cuprysil) based high-temperature brake

grease to the guide pins before refitting them to their bores. Refit the brake pads as described in Section 23 of this Chapter.

28   Fit the caliper body over the mounting bracket and brake pads, refit the guide pin bolts and tighten them to the torque wrench settings specified. Check that the caliper slides smoothly on its mounting bracket.

29   Ensuring that the flexible hose is correctly routed without being twisted, connect it to the caliper again using two new sealing washers, and tightening the union banjo bolt to the specified torque setting.

30   Bleed any air from the system as described in Section 8 of this Chapter, then depress the brake pedal repeatedly until the pads are pressed into firm contact with the brake disc and normal (non-assisted) pedal pressure is restored. Check the master cylinder reservoir fluid as described in Section 2 of this Chapter.

31   Connect the handbrake cable to the lever and bolt the cable stay to the caliper body, ensuring that the stay is correctly located by its pin. Operate the handbrake several times until correct brake pad-to-disc clearance is established.

32   Have an assistant apply full pressure to the brake pedal, then check the caliper assembly for signs of fluid leaks. Wash off any spilt fluid and refit the roadwheel. Lower the car to the ground and tighten the roadwheel nuts to the specified torque setting.

33   Repeat the full procedure on the opposite caliper. Always overhaul both calipers together, to ensure even, consistent braking performance.

26   Rear brake disc – inspection, removal and refitting

1   With the car parked on firm level, ground, apply the handbrake and select first or reverse gear (manual transmission) or 'P' position (automatic). Chock the front wheels. Slacken the roadwheel nuts, jack up the rear of the car and support it securely on axle stands. Remove the roadwheel and release the handbrake fully.

2   Slowly rotate the disc so that the full area of both sides is checked. Light scoring is normal in the area swept by the brake pads, but if heavy scoring is found the disc must be renewed. The only alternative to this is to have the disc surface-ground until it is flat again, but this must not reduce the disc to less than the specified minimum thickness.

3   It is normal to find a lip of rust and brake dust around the disc's outside diameter; this can be scraped off if required. If, however, a lip has formed due to excessive wear of the brake pad's swept area then the disc's thickness must be measured using a micrometer. Take measurements at four places around the disc, at the inside and outside of the pad swept area. If the disc has worn at any point to the specified minimum thickness or less, it must be renewed.

4   If the disc is thought to be warped, it can be checked for runout either by using a dial gauge mounted on any convenient fixed point while the disc is slowly rotated, or by using feeler gauges to measure the clearance between several points all around the disc and a fixed point such as the caliper mounting bracket. Take measurements in the centre of the pads's swept area. If the measurements obtained are at the specified maximum or more, the disc is excessively warped and must be renewed. It is worth checking first that the hub bearings are in good condition and correctly adjusted – see Sections 12 and 13 of Chapter 10.

5   Check the disc for cracks, especially around the stud holes and any other signs of wear or damage. Renew it if any of these are found.

6   If one of the brake discs is sufficiently worn or damaged to justify renewal, both discs should be renewed at the same time, to ensure even and consistent braking performance.

7   Since the rear brake discs are integral with the rear hubs, removal requires the dismantling of the hub bearings. On refitting, the bearings must be reassembled and adjusted. Refer to Sections 13 and 12 of Chapter 10.

8   On fitting a new brake disc, use a suitable solvent to remove any preservative coating that may have been applied to it.

27   Rear brake disc shield – removal and refitting

1   Working as described in Section 13 of Chapter 10, jack up the rear of the car and remove the roadwheel, withdraw the brake caliper and the brake disc, then unbolt the brake disc shield and stub axle adaptor plate.

28.4 Unscrew handbrake lever mounting bolts (arrowed) to release lever assembly

2   Refitting is the reverse of the removal procedure. Thoroughly clean the shield, the adaptor plate and the strut lower end. Tighten the mounting bolts to the specified torque setting.

28   Handbrake lever – removal and refitting

1   Remove the centre console (see Chapter 11).

2   Slacken the handbrake adjuster locknut (where fitted) and slacken the adjuster as far as possible.

3   Disconnect the handbrake warning lamp switch wire.

4   Unbolt the handbrake lever assembly from the floor (photo).

5   If there is sufficient slack it will be possible to disconnect the front cable end nipple from the lever assembly, working inside the car. If this is not possible, raise the rear of the car and support it securely on axle stands before moving underneath. Pull back the cable sleeve from the lever assembly dust cover and disconnect the cable.

6   Refitting is a reverse of removal, but first check that the lever pawl and ratchet mechanism is adequately greased, also the cable end nipples and compensator. Adjust the cable as described in Section 2 of this Chapter and check the switch setting as described in Section 30.

29   Handbrake cables – removal and refitting

Front cable

1   Working inside the car, remove the centre console (if necessary) and slacken the cable adjustment fully (see Section 2 of this Chapter).

2   Raise the rear of the car and support it securely on axle stands. Working under the car, pull back the cable sleeve from the lever assembly dust cover and disconnect the cable from the lever assembly.

3   Unbolt the rear cable front clamp from the underbody and then disconnect both rear cables from the compensator (photo).

4   Refitting is the reverse of the removal procedure. If the original front cable is being refitted, clean it thoroughly and check the compensator swivels smoothly before covering it with a film of grease. If a new cable is being fitted, grease it carefully.

5   Adjust the handbrake cable as described in Section 2 of this Chapter.

Rear cables – drum rear brakes

6   Working inside the car, remove the centre console (if necessary) and slacken the cable adjuster fully (see Section 2 of this Chapter).

7   Raise the rear of the car and remove the brake drum (see Section 13 of Chapter 10.)

8   Using a pair of needle-nosed pliers, compress the return spring

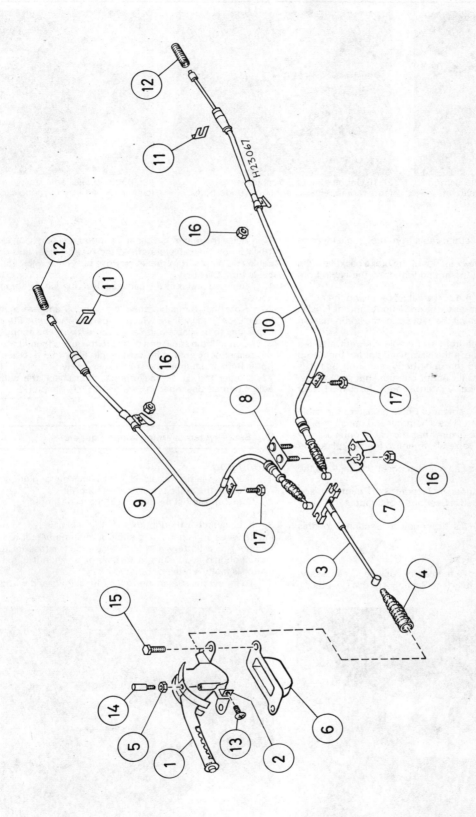

H23067

Fig. 9.29 Handbrake components (Secs 28 and 29)

1	Lever assembly	6	Dust cover	11 Cable spring clip (disc rear
2	Switch	7	Rear cable front clamp	brakes only)
3	Front cable	8	Clamp bracket	12 Return spring (drum rear
4	Rubber sleeve	9	Right-hand rear cable	brakes only)
5	Locknut (early models only)	10	Left-hand rear cable	13 Screw

14 Adjuster
15 Bolt (2 off)
16 Nut
17 Bolt

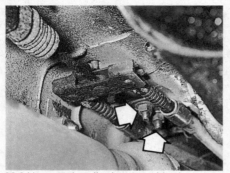

29.3 Unscrew handbrake rear cable clamp nuts (arrowed) to allow rear cables to be disconnected from compensator

29.10 Unbolt handbrake cable clamps (arrowed) to release cable from underbody

29.20 Handbrake cable stay, showing locating pin and cable spring clip (arrows)

fitted over the cable and disconnect the cable from the toggle lever on the brake backplate.

9   On early models, pull the cable outer out of the brake backplate. On later models unbolt the cable abutment and withdraw the cable from the backplate.

10   Work forwards along the length of the cable, removing the nut or bolt (as applicable) securing its clamps to the underbody (photo). Finally, unbolt the front clamp and disconnect the cable from the compensator. Withdraw the cable from the car.

11   On refitting, grease the cable front end nipple and refit it to the compensator then mount the cable in the clamp and tighten the clamp nuts. Route the cable back along the underbody, ensuring that it is correctly and smoothly routed, well clear of components such as the exhaust system and rear suspension. Tighten securely the clamp bolt or nut.

12   On early models, apply a thin smear of brake grease to the cable outer and press it into the backplate. Use a hammer and punch applied to the outer's flanged section to ensure that the cable outer is fully sealed. On later models, refit the cable abutment to the backplate and tighten the bolts securely.

13   Refit the return spring to the cable and connect the cable to the toggle lever.

14   Refit the brake drum as described in Section 13 of Chapter 10 and adjust the hub bearings as described in Section 12 of Chapter 10. Lower the car to the ground.

15   Adjust the handbrake cable as described in Section 2 of this Chapter.

Rear cables – disc rear brakes

16   Working inside the car, remove the centre console (if necessary) and slacken the cable adjustment fully (see Section 2 of this Chapter.)

17   Raise the rear of the car and support it securely on axle stands.

18   Unbolt the cable stay from the brake caliper and disconnect the cable end nipple from the lever. Prise out the spring clip to release the cable from the stay.

19   Remove and refit the cable as described in paragraphs 10 and 11 above.

20   Note that the cable stays are handed and are marked with the letter 'L' or 'R' to indicate which caliper they are to be fitted on. Refit the cable stay to the cable outer and secure it with the spring clip (photo).

21   Connect the cable end nipple to the lever, then fit the cable stay to the caliper body so that its locating pin fits into the recess in the caliper body. Refit and tighten the stay bolt securely.

22   Lower the car to the ground, then check the handbrake cable adjustment as described in Section 2 of this Chapter.

30   Brake system warning lamps – general

Stop-lamp

1   The stop-lamp circuit is controlled by a plunger-type switch mounted on the brake pedal bracket (photo).

2   Check and adjust the switch setting as described in Section 2 of this Chapter.

3   If the switch is thought to be faulty, it can be tested by disconnecting its wires and connecting either a multimeter (set to the resistance function) or a battery and bulb test circuit across its terminals. The switch should allow current to flow only when it is extended. If the switch is faulty it must be renewed.

4   To renew the switch, undo the four screws and withdraw the facia

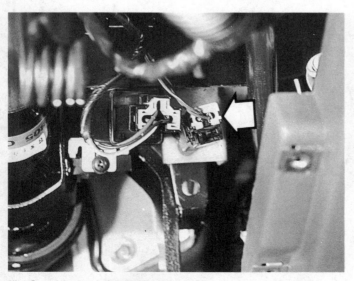

30.1 Stop-lamp switch is mounted on brake pedal bracket (arrow)

30.7 Handbrake lever switch is mounted on base of lever assembly

lower panel from below the steering column, unplug the switch's connector block, slacken the locknut and unscrew the switch. Refitting is the reverse of removal, but adjust the switch setting as described in Section 2.

Instrument panel warning lamps

5 The brake system warning lamps mounted in the instrument panel should illuminate whenever the ignition is switched on, as a check of the bulbs themselves and then go out when the engine is started. If the lamps do not light, check the bulbs as described in Chapter 12.

6 The stop tail lamp bulb failure warning lamp (where fitted) monitors the condition of the stop and tail lamp bulbs through a sensor which is mounted in the luggage compartment. On Saloon models it is found on the right-hand side, behind the wheel arch stiffener, while on Hatchback models it is on the left-hand side, in the corner in front of the rear lamp cluster. If the circuit is thought to be faulty, it can be checked as described in Chapter 12.

7 The brake warning lamp is controlled by the switch at the base of the handbrake lever assembly (photo) and by the switch in the base of the master cylinder fluid reservoir.

8 To check the handbrake lever switch, remove the centre console (see Chapter 11) and connect either a multimeter (set to the resistance function) or a battery and bulb test circuit between the switch's terminal

and its mounting bracket. The switch should allow current to flow as soon as the handbrake lever is raised sufficiently for the plunger to close the switch contacts. If the switch is faulty, try cleaning its contacts using fine abrasive paper before renewing it.

9 To renew the handbrake lever switch, remove the centre console (see Chapter 11), disconnect the switch's wire and remove its retaining screw. On refitting, check that the warning lamp is out when the handbrake lever is fully released and illuminates when the lever is raised by one or two clicks. If necessary, bend gently the switch mounting bracket until the setting is correct.

10 To check the master cylinder reservoir switch, unscrew the reservoir cap and remove the filter, then disconnect the wiring lead from the base of the reservoir. Connect a multimeter (set to the resistance function) or a battery and bulb test circuit across the switch terminals. Then check that the switch allows current to flow when the reservoir float is depressed to bridge the switch contacts. If the switch is faulty, it must be renewed.

11 To renew the master cylinder reservoir switch, empty the fluid from the reservoir (see Section 10 of this Chapter), disconnect the switch wiring lead and gently prise the switch from the reservoir base. Refitting is the reverse of the removal procedure, but note that if care has been taken not to allow air to enter the system, then bleeding will not be necessary.

31 Fault diagnosis – braking system

Symptom	Reason(s)
Brake pedal feels spongy	Air in hydraulic system Faulty master cylinder Weak flexible hose(s)
Excessive pedal travel	Incorrect pedal adjustment Faulty, sticking or seized brake caliper (disc brakes) Faulty self-adjuster strut (drum brakes) Faulty master cylinder Air in hydraulic system Primary or secondary hydraulic circuit failure Worn or incorrectly adjusted hub bearings Distorted or worn brake disc or drum
Pedal sinks to floor during sustained application	Hydraulic fluid leak – check first the caliper or wheel cylinder piston seals Master cylinder piston cups and/or seals leaking
Excessive pedal pressure required to stop car	Vacuum hose leaking or disconnected Faulty check valve Faulty vacuum servo unit Partially seized caliper or wheel cylinder Seized or worn brake caliper guide pins Brake pad or shoe friction material glazed, worn or contaminated, or (if recently renewed) of wrong grade New brake pad or shoe friction material not yet bedded in Primary or secondary hydraulic circuit failure
Car pulls to one side when brakes applied	Brake pad or shoe friction material contaminated with oil or grease (on opposite side) Partially seized caliper or wheel cylinder (on opposite side) Distorted or worn brake disc or drum Seized self-adjuster strut (drum brakes) Brakes overhauled on one side only Tyre fault – incorrect types fitted, incorrect tyre pressure or excessively worn tyres on one side Steering or suspension defect (see Chapter 10)
Rear wheels lock when brakes applied	Pedal pressure greater than required Adverse road conditions Tyres incorrectly inflated or badly worn Front brakes inefficient, or rear brakes grabbing Faulty pressure-reducing valve (early models) or master cylinder (later models)

Symptom	Reason(s)
Brakes grab	Brake pad or shoe friction material wet – apply brakes gently until they are dry Brake pad or shoe friction material worn out Distorted, cracked or worn brake disc or drum Brake components loose Hub bearings worn or incorrectly adjusted
Judder felt through brake pedal or steering wheel when brakes applied	Distorted, cracked or worn brake disc or drum, particularly at front Hubs distorted or hub bearings worn or incorrectly adjusted Brake pad or shoe friction material glazed, worn or contaminated. Worn brake caliper guide pins Brake components loose Steering or suspension defect (see Chapter 10) Wheel wobble or vibration (see Chapter 10)
Squealing noise when brakes applied	Brake pad or shoe friction material glazed Excessive brake dust in brake assembly Foreign matter caught between brake pads and disc Brake pad or shoe friction material (if recently renewed) of wrong grade
Brakes bind or drag	Partially seized caliper or wheel cylinder Handbrake incorrectly adjusted Seized handbrake cable or operating mechanism Master cylinder reservoir cap breather blocked Faulty master cylinder Metal hydraulic pipe(s) crushed or blocked; flexible hose(s) kinked or twisted Air in hydraulic system

Note: *This Section is not intended to be an exhaustive guide to fault diagnosis, but summarises the more common faults which may be encountered during a car's life. Consult a dealer for more specific advice.*

Chapter 10 Suspension and steering

Contents

Specifications

Front suspension
Type.. Independent, with MacPherson struts and coil springs, anti-roll bar

Rear suspension
Type.. Independent, with MacPherson struts and coil springs, transverse and trailing links, anti-roll bar

Front suspension struts
Piston rod diameter.. 22 mm (0.866 in)

Coil spring free length – nominal:

	Left-hand	Right-hand
Turbo engine models and all models with automatic transmission ...	339.5 mm (13.366 in)	348.0 mm (13.701 in)
All other models	331.5 mm (13.051 in)	339.5 mm (13.366 in)

Note: *Information applies to T12 and early T72 models only – not available for T72 models from May 1988 on*

Front hub bearings
Maximum endfloat at hub... 0.05 mm (0.002 in)

Bearing turning torque:

Nominal – at correct preload.. 0.3 to 2.5 Nm (0.2 to 1.8 lbf ft)

Measured at hub carrier – preload of 49 kN (4.9 Imp ton f) .... 2.0 to 17.7 N (0.4 to 3.9 lbf)

Measured at roadwheel stud – driveshaft nut fastened to specified torque setting .... 4.9 to 45.1 N (1.1 to 10.1 lbf)

Rear suspension struts

	Adjustable damping	Non- adjustable damping
Piston rod diameter..	22 mm (0.866 in)	20 mm (0.787 in)
Piston rod maximum warpage......................................	0.1 mm (0.004 in)	0.1 mm (0.004 in)
Inner cylinder inside diameter..................................	32.0 to 32.1 mm (1.260 to 1.264 in)	30.0 to 30.1 mm (1.181 to 1.185 in)
Inner cylinder maximum distortion	0.2 mm (0.008 in)	0.2 mm (0.008 in)
Fluid capacity..	325 cc (11.4 Imp fl oz)	330 cc (11.6 Imp fl oz)
Recommended fluid	Nissan Genuine Strut Fluid or equivalent	Nissan Genuine Strut Fluid or equivalent
Coil spring free length – nominal (T12 models, and T72 up to May 1988 only)	353.5 mm (13.917 in)	353.5 mm (13.917 in)

Rear hub bearings
Maximum endfloat – at hub .... Nil

Bearing maximum turning torque:	New grease seal	Used grease seal
Nominal	0.78 Nm (0.58 lbf ft)	0.64 Nm (0.47 lbf ft)
Measured at roadwheel stud	13.7 N (3.08 lbf)	10.8 N (2.43 lbf)

Steering – general
Type... Rack and pinion, manual or power assisted, depending on model
Steering wheel maximum free play.. 35 mm (1.38 in)
Steering column length – see Fig. 10.31....................................... 572.5 to 573.5 mm (22.539 to 22.579 in)
Steering gear maximum permissible movement .... 2 mm (0.079 in) in either direction

Manual steering gear
Number of turns lock-to-lock 4.5
Pinion average rotating torque .... 0.7 to 1.0 Nm (6.20 to 8.85 lbf in)
Rack protrusion at neutral position... 75 mm (2.95 in) beyond each side of gear housing

Power assisted steering system
Number of turns lock-to-lock – 15 in wheels................................. 2.8
Number of turns lock-to-lock – 14 in wheels................................. 3.0
Steering wheel maximum turning force.. 39 N (8.8 lbf)
Fluid normal operating temperature .... 60 to 80°C (140 to 176°F)
Fluid type/specification.. Dexron II type ATF (Duckhams D-Matic)
Fluid quantity – approximate .... 0.9 litre (1.6 Imp pints)
System maximum pressure .... 6865 kPa (995 psi) at engine idle speed

Power-assisted steering gear
Note: *The following information applies only to the Japanese-built steering gear fitted to T12 and early (before August 1988) T12 models.*
Manufacturer and type .... Yoshiwara PR24SA
Pinion average rotating torque .... 0.9 to 1.3 Nm (7.97 to 11.51 lbf in)
Pinion maximum rotating torque .... 1.9 Nm (16.81 lbf in)
Rack maximum sliding force .... 245 N (55 lbf)

Rack protrusion:	Pinion housing end	Opposite (left-hand) end
Rack protrusion at neutral position (cars with 14 in wheels – gear housing to rack end	62 mm (2.44 in)	75 mm (2.95 in)
Rack protrusion at neutral position (cars with 15 in wheels) – gear housing to rack spacer inboard edge	57 mm (2.24 in)	70 mm (2.76 in)

Wheel alignment and steering angles
Note: *All measurements are with car at kerb weight (see 'General dimensions, weights and capacities')*
Camber:
   Front... 0° 25′ negative to 1° 5′ positive
   Rear .... 1° 10′ negative to 0° 20′ positive
Castor:
   Early T12 models.. 1° 15′ to 2° 45′ positive
   Late T12 and all T72 models... 1° 20′ to 2° 50′ positive
Steering axis inclination (SAI) also known as kingpin inclination (KPI):
   T12 models... 13° 50′ to 15° 20′
   T72 models... 14° 15′ to 15° 45′
Toe setting – see Figs 10.38, 10.39 and 10.41:
   Front wheels – toe-in .... 1 to 3 mm (0.04 to 0.12 mm) or 0° 6′ to 0° 19′ (T12),
      0° 6′ to 0° 18′ (T72)
   Right-hand track rod length L .... 177.9 mm (7.004 in)
   Left-hand track rod length L .... 178.4 mm (7.024 in)
   Rear wheels – toe-out .... 2 to 6 mm (0.08 to 0.24 in) or 0° 12′ to 0° 37′
   Rear transverse link length A .... 50 to 55 mm (1.969 to 2.165 in)

Front wheel turning angles:	Inside wheel	Outside wheel
Toe-in turns...	22° 20′	20° 0′
Full lock – 14 in wheels......................................	38° to 42°	29° to 33°
Full lock – 15 in wheels......................................	34° to 38°	27° to 31°

Hub carrier steering lock stop bolt standard length – 14 in wheels.......... 24 mm (0.945 in)
Hub carrier steering lock stop bolt standard length – 15 in wheels.......... 31 mm (1.22 in)

Roadwheels
Type and size:
   Turbo engine models.. 6JJ x 15 light alloy
   Executive model (Oct 1989 on) .... Not available
   2.0 litre SGX and GSX models... 5½JJ x 14 light alloy
   All other models... 5J x 14 pressed steel, 5½JJ x 14 light alloy optional
Wheel maximum lateral runout.. 1.0 mm (0.039 in)

Tyres

Size:

Turbo engine models	195/60 R15 (86H)
Executive model (Oct 1989 on)	195/60 R14
2.0i GSX model	185/70 R14 (87T)
1.8 SLX and all 2.0 litre carburettor models	185/70 SR14
All other models	165 SR14 or 165 R14 (84S), 185/70 SR14 optional

Pressures:

	Front	Rear
165 SR14 or 165 R14 (84S) tyres	2.0 bar (29 psi)	2.0 bar (29 psi)
All other tyres	2.0 bar (29 psi)	1.8 bar (26 psi)

Note: *These pressures are specified for all loads and speeds and are for cold tyres (after car has been parked for at least 3 hours or driven no more than 1 mile (1.6 km).*

Pressures apply only to original equipment tyres and may vary if any other make or type is used. Check with the tyre manufacturer or supplier for correct pressures when alternative tyres are fitted.

Torque wrench setting

	Nm	lbf ft
Front suspension		
Strut top mounting nuts	31 to 42	23 to 31
Strut piston rod nut		
Adjustable damping	69 to 88	51 to 65
Non-adjustable damping	59 to 78	43.5 to 57.5
Strut-to-hub carrier clamp bolt nuts	112 to 124	83 to 91.5
Driveshaft nut	235 to 314	173 to 232
Lower arm balljoint retaining nut	71 to 86	52 to 63
Lower arm balljoint mounting plate nuts	76 to 109	56 to 80
Lower arm front pivot nut	88 to 118	65 to 87
Lower arm rear pivot clamp bolts	118 to 147	87 to 108
Lower arm mounting plate bolts	118 to 147	87 to 108
Anti-roll bar fasteners:		
Mounting clamp bolts	31 to 42	23 to 31
Connecting link-to-lower arm nuts	16 to 22	12 to 16
Connecting link-to-bar nuts	39 to 44	29 to 32.5
Rear suspension		
Strut top mounting nuts:		
T12 and early T72 models	31 to 42	23 to 31
Late (September 1988 on) T72 models	42 to 52	31 to 38
Strut piston rod nut:		
Adjustable damping	69 to 88	51 to 65
Non-adjustable damping	59 to 78	43.5 to 57.5
Strut gland nut	69 to 127	51 to 93.5
Strut bottom bracket mounting bolts	59 to 78	43.5 to 57.5
Rear hub bearing nut:		
To preload bearings only	25 to 34	18.5 to 25
Normal setting	9 to 12	6.5 to 9
Trailing link mountings (front and rear)	88 to 108	65 to 80
Transverse link pivot bolt nuts	88 to 118	65 to 87
Rear (adjustable) transverse link adjuster locknuts	78 to 98	57.5 to 72
Crossmember mounting nuts	88 to 108	65 to 80
Anti-roll bar fasteners:		
Connecting link-to-body clamp bolts	31 to 42	23 to 31
Connecting link retaining nut	16 to 22	12 to 16
Bar-to-connecting link clamp bolts	31 to 42	23 to 31
Bar-to-strut bottom bracket bolts	59 to 78	43.5 to 57.5
Roadwheels		
Roadwheel nuts	98 to 118	72 to 87
Steering		
Steering wheel nut	29 to 39	21 to 29
Steering column mounting bolts	9 to 14	6.5 to 10
Steering column pivot bolts	16 to 21	12 to 15.5
Rake-adjusting lever pivot bolt	8 to 11	6 to 8
Bulkhead aperture cover retaining nuts	3.4 to 4.4	2.5 to 3
Steering column lower joint pinch-bolts	24 to 29	17.5 to 21.5
Steering gear mounting clamp bolts	73 to 97	54 to 71.5
Track rod and inner balljoint assembly	78 to 98	57.5 to 72
Track rod outer balljoint locknut	37 to 46	27 to 34
Track rod outer balljoint retaining nut		
Stage 1	29 to 39	21.5 to 29
Stage 2	Tighten until split pin can be inserted (max torque of 49 Nm/36 lbf ft)	
Hub carrier steering lock stop bolt locknuts	54 to 72	40 to 53

Manual steering gear

Steering damper mounting bolts	26 to 38	19 to 28
Pinion nut	20 to 29	15 to 21.5
Pinion nut locknut	78 to 98	57.5 to 72
Slipper adjuster locknut	39 to 59	29 to 43.5

Power-assisted steering gear (Japanese-built)

Heat shield retaining screws	3.1 to 4.3	2 to 3
Fluid pipe union flare and banjo bolt	20 to 26	15 to 19
Fluid supply pipe sleeve nut at pinion housing	15 to 25	11 to 18.5
Return hose spigot at pinion housing	27 to 39	20 to 29
Slipper adjuster mounting bolts	16 to 21	12 to 15.5
Slipper adjuster locknut	10 to 15	7.5 to 11

Power-assisted steering system

Pump assembly pivot bolt at cylinder block	31 to 42	23 to 31
Pump drivebelt adjuster lockbolt	14 to 17	10 to 12.5
Pump drivebelt adjuster bracket bolts at water pump	16 to 20	12 to 15
Pump pulley nut	54 to 68	40 to 50
System hose unions at pump		
Supply hose union mounting bolts	14 to 18	10 to 13
Pump-to-steering gear hose banjo bolt	69 to 78	51 to 57.5
Pump-to-steering gear hose threaded coupling	29 to 49	21.5 to 36
Pump-to-steering gear hose banjo bolt at steering gear union	Not available	
Fluid reservoir mounting bolts	3.1 to 4.3	2 to 3

1 General description

Both front and rear suspension are independent, using MacPherson struts with coil springs. On some early turbo engine models the damping effect can be altered through three settings to suit the driver's preference.

On the front suspension, the roadwheel hub carriers are clamped to the bottom of each strut and are located, via a balljoint, by the suspension lower arms. The lower arms pivot on rubber bushes and are secured by mounting plates which are bolted to the body. An anti-roll bar is bolted to the body via rubber bushes and joined to both suspension lower arms by ball-jointed connecting links.

On the rear suspension, each strut carries the roadwheel stub axle at its lower end and is located laterally by two parallel, transverse links. These are pivoted on a central crossmember that is secured to the body by four nuts. The rear transverse links are adjustable for length. Fore-and-aft location is provided by a trailing link that is pivoted from the body. An anti-roll bar is bolted to the body via rubber bushes and connecting links and is connected to each strut/stub axle assembly.

Steering is by rack and pinion. Some 1.6 litre models have a manual system, but all others are fitted with a variable-effect ZF-type power-assisted system. This system includes an eccentric-vane pump that is mounted on the rear of the cylinder block and is belt-driven from the crankshaft, a bulkhead-mounted fluid reservoir and the related fluid supply hoses and pipes. The steering column is adjustable for rake and is of the collapsible, energy-absorbing, type to protect the driver in the event of an accident. The steering gear, which is clamped in two rubber bushes to the front of the bulkhead, is connected by track rods with inner and outer balljoints to the steering arms extending rearwards from the hub carriers.

2 Routine maintenance

1 At the intervals given in *'Routine maintenance'* at the beginning of this manual, a thorough inspection of all suspension and steering components should be carried out, using the following procedures as a guide.

Power-assisted steering system – fluid level and lines

2 The fluid level should be checked only when it is cold, and with the engine switched off. Check that the fluid level is between the 'Max' and 'Min' level lines on the reservoir body.

3 If topping-up is necessary, clean the area around the reservoir filler cap and unscrew the cap. Top up to the 'Max' level line using only good quality fluid of the specified type (photo). Refit the cap and tighten it securely.

4 Make a close inspection of each metal pipe or flexible hose running between the fluid reservoir, the power steering pump and the steering gear. Check for any signs of fluid leaks, for securely fastened connections and mountings, and for chafing, cracks, wear or other damage, or deterioration of any sort.

5 To check the system under pressure, start the engine and turn the steering several times from lock to lock until the fluid is warmed up (60 to 80°C/140 to 176°F). With the engine running at idle speed, hold the steering wheel for no more than 5 seconds at each full-lock position and carefully check for any sign of fluid leakage. **Note:** *If the steering is held in either full-lock position, with the engine running, for more than 15 seconds the system pressure may build up to the point where the gear or pump components may be damaged. The system pressure can be checked if required, but this is a task only for a Nissan dealer who has the necessary equipment.*

6 If any leaks are noticed they must be repaired as soon as possible. If a leak is spotted at one of the metal fluid pipe connections, try slackening the union nut through one turn only, then re-tighten it (to the specified torque setting, if possible). Do not simply overtighten any of the connecting unions in an attempt to cure fluid leaks. Any other component must be renewed that is found to be worn, damaged or leaking.

Power-assisted steering system – drivebelt

7 Check the condition and tension of the power steering and water pump drivebelt as described in Chapter 2.

Check the steering gear and linkage

8 Apply the handbrake, jack up the front of the car and support it securely on axle stands.

9 Visually inspect the steering gear rubber gaiters and the rubber dust covers over the track rod outer balljoints. Renew any component showing signs of grease or fluid leakage, wear or damage; refer to the relevant Section of this Chapter for renewal procedures. On cars with power-assisted steering, check carefully for signs of fluid leakage from the gear or gaiters which might indicate the failure of one of the gear's fluid seals.

10 On cars with manual steering, check that the steering damper is securely fastened on its mountings and that there are no signs of fluid leakage from the unit itself or of any damage to it.

11 On all cars check that the steering column lower joint pinch-bolts are tight, that the steering gear mounting bolts are securely fastened and that the track rod outer balljoint retaining nuts are tight, with the split pins correctly fitted.

12 Check the steering gear mounting rubbers. If a turning force

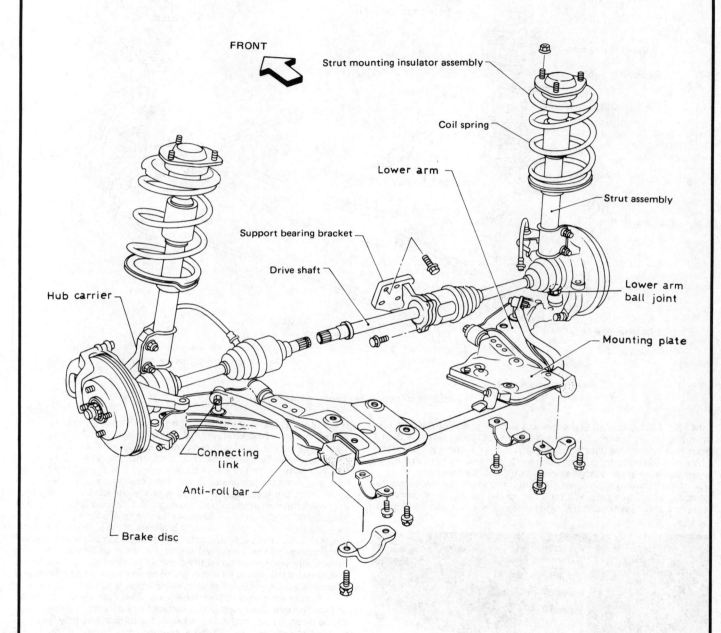

FRONT

Strut mounting insulator assembly

Coil spring

Lower arm

Strut assembly

Support bearing bracket

Drive shaft

Lower arm ball joint

Hub carrier

Mounting plate

Connecting link

Anti-roll bar

Brake disc

Fig. 10.1 Front suspension components (Sec 1)

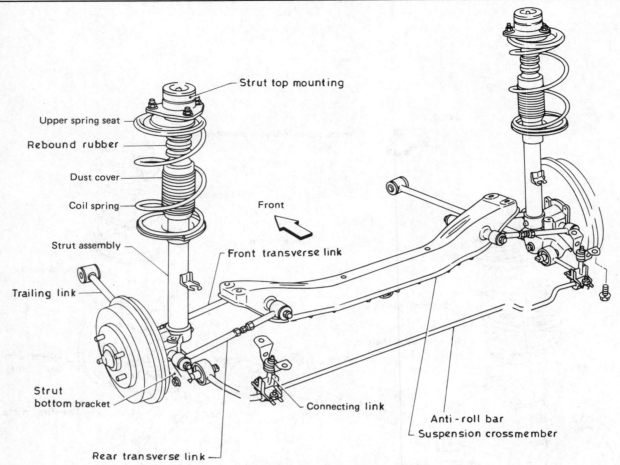

Strut top mounting

Upper spring seat

Rebound rubber

Dust cover

Coil spring

Strut assembly

Trailing link

Strut
bottom bracket

Front

Front transverse link

Connecting link

Anti-roll bar
Suspension crossmember

Rear transverse link

Fig. 10.2 Rear suspension components (Sec 1)

of 49 N (11 lbf) is applied to the steering wheel (ignition off) with the car standing on dry tarmac, the steering gear should move no more than 2 mm (0.08 in) in either direction, in relation to the car body. If it does, and the mounting bolts are correctly fastened, then both mounting rubbers must be renewed, as described in Section 28 of this Chapter.

13   Check the condition of the steering components by measuring the steering wheel free play. With the car parked on dry, level tarmac or concrete and its wheels in the straight-ahead position (see Section 20)

2.3 Use only good quality fluid of specified type when topping-up power steering fluid reservoir

check that there is no more than 35 mm (1.38 in) free play at the steering wheel rim. Some free play is normal, due to design tolerances within the steering gear itself, but if excessive free play is found the cause must be found and rectified immediately. Check that the steering wheel is securely fastened to the steering column and that the column mountings are correctly tightened. Check the steering column lower joint pinch-bolts, the steering gear mountings and the track rod outer ball-joint retaining nuts as described in paragraph 11 above. If the excessive free play is not due to loose fasteners it must be caused by wear in the steering column joints, the track rod balljoints or the steering gear itself. Check the track rod outer balljoints as described below. Examination of the steering column joints will reveal any wear or damage. In both causes, any wear must be rectified by the renewal of the component concerned. If the gear itself is thought to be worn it must be overhauled or renewed (as applicable), as soon as possible – see Section 30.

14   To check the track rod outer balljoints, lower the car to the ground and watch them closely while an assistant turns the steering wheel back and forth; any wear should be obvious in the form of free play between the track rod end and the hub carrier steering arms. Note that some early models may be fitted with a spring-loaded type of balljoint (identifiable by the cup-shaped top surface, opposite to the tapered stud) in which free play up to a maximum of 1.3 mm/0.05 in, measured in a vertical direction only, between the stud and its housing is normal. **Do not** confuse this free play with that produced by worn balljoints. If a balljoint is found to be worn or damaged it must be renewed. Note that Nissan recommend that the later type of balljoint (with a flat top surface) is renewed as a pair, even if only one is worn.

Check the suspension, roadwheels and tyres

15   With the car standing on its wheels on level ground, bounce it at each corner to test the performance of the suspension struts. If each strut is working properly the body will return once to its normal position and then stop. If the body oscillates more than once with weak damping and signs of uncontrolled movement the strut is probably suspect and

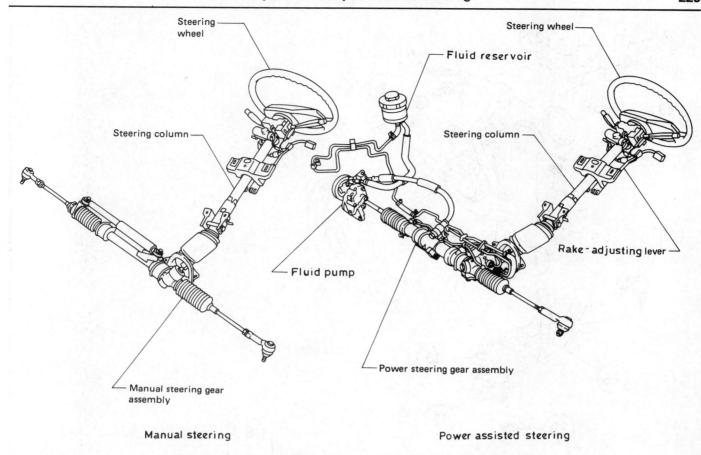

Manual steering   Power assisted steering

Fig. 10.3 Steering system components – early left-hand drive type shown (Sec 1)

should be renewed, especially if the car's handling has deteriorated. While bouncing the car, listen carefully for any groans, squeaks, rattles or creaks from the suspension components, which will require further investigation when the car is jacked up.

16   Apply the handbrake, jack up the front of the car and support it securely on axle stands.

17   Visually inspect all front suspension components, looking for obvious signs of wear, damage or loose mountings. Check the rubber dust covers over the suspension lower arm balljoint. Renew the balljoint if the cover is cracked, split or if it shows any signs of grease leakage. Similarly, check the suspension strut for oil leaks.

18   Grasp the roadwheel at the 12 o'clock and 6 o'clock positions and try to rock it. If any free play is evident, check first the tightness of the roadwheel nuts, then the driveshaft nut (see Chapter 8). If these are correctly secured, repeat the check with an assistant applying firm pressure to the brake pedal. If the movement is eliminated or significantly reduced it is likely that the hub bearings are worn. If not, then there is wear in one or more of the suspension components, particularly the suspension lower arm balljoints.

19   Spin the wheel hard and listen carefully. If the wheel rotates smoothly and easily with no signs of noise and if it slows down and stops with no sign of jerkiness the bearings are in good condition. If there is any doubt about their condition they should be renewed as detailed in Section 4 of this Chapter.

20   Using a large screwdriver or a flat bar, check for wear in the suspension bushes and mounting points by carefully levering against them to check for free play. Note that some free play is to be expected from rubber bushes, but excessive wear should be obvious. If free play is found, check first the tightness of the mounting nuts or bolts, using a torque wrench if possible. Any worn components should be renewed as described in the relevant Sections of this Chapter. When checking the suspension lower arm balljoint, ensure that its split pin is correctly fitted to secure the retaining nut. Check the strut top and bottom mountings, the lower arm bushes and mounting plate, the anti-roll bar mountings and connecting links as well as the lower arm balljoints.

21   Lower the car to the ground and select first or reverse gear (manual transmission) or the 'P' position (automatic). Chock the front wheels, jack up the rear of the car and support it on axle stands. Release the handbrake for the rear hub bearing checks.

22   Check the condition and security of all rear suspension components, first visually and then physically, as described in paragraphs 17 and 20 above. Check the crossmember mountings, the trailing and transverse link mountings and bushes, the anti-roll bar mountings, bushes and connections and the strut mountings.

23   Check the rear hub bearings as described in paragraphs 18 and 19 above, but note that if free play is found the bearing adjustment should be checked and reset, if necessary, before the bearings themselves are thought to be faulty (see Section 12).

24   When the suspension checks are complete, lower the car to the ground and check the tyre tread wear. If there is any sign of abnormal wear, or if the car's steering and handling have deteriorated in any way, the wheel alignment and steering angles should be checked as soon as possible (see Section 36).

25   Finally, check the roadwheels themselves, referring to Section 37 for further details. Check for obvious signs of cracks, wear or damage, particularly around the stud holes and the rims. Check that the roadwheel nuts are securely fastened, to the specified torque setting. Check that the balance weights are secure; if any are missing or if the wheels are thought to be out of balance, have them balanced as soon as possible.

Tyres

26   With reference to Section 37 for further details, check all five tyres for signs of tread wear or damage. Remove any stones, nails or other objects from the tread, check the sidewalls and tread for deep cuts, bulges or other damage and check the tyre pressures. Ensure that a sound cap is fitted to each valve. If a tyre repeatedly loses pressure, do not forget to check that the valve is not leaking before suspecting a puncture. If any of the tyres require renewal, puncture repair or other

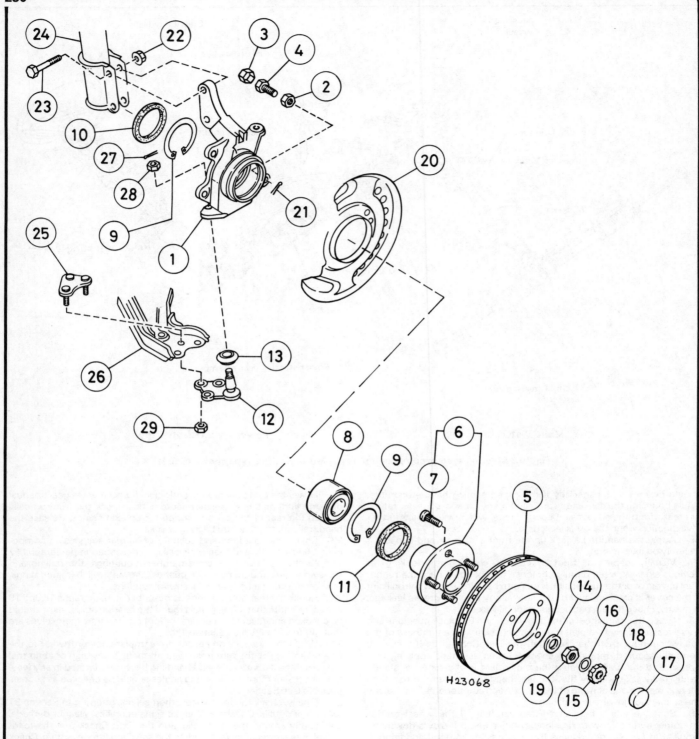

Fig. 10.4 Exploded view of front hub and bearings (Secs 3 and 4)

1	Hub carrier	9	Circlip
2	Locknut	10	Inboard grease seal
3	Plastic cup	11	Outboard grease seal
4	Steering lock stop bolt	12	Lower arm balljoint
5	Brake disc	13	Balljoint rubber dust cover
6	Hub	14	Metal washer
7	Roadwheel stud	15	Locking ring
8	Hub bearing assembly	16	Soft washer

17	Black plastic cap, (where fitted)	24	Suspension strut
18	Split pin	25	Lower arm balljoint mounting plate
19	Driveshaft nut	26	Suspension lower arm
20	Brake disc shield	27	Split pin
21	Split pin (where fitted)	28	Balljoint retaining nut
22	Nut	29	Nut
23	Clamp bolt		

H23068

professional attention ensure that this is done as soon as possible, in the interests of safety.

3 Front hub carrier – removal and refitting

1   With the car standing on its wheels, apply the handbrake firmly and select first or reverse gear (manual transmission) or the 'P' position (automatic).

Cars with steel roadwheels

2   Remove the roadwheel trim or prise off the centre cap. Withdraw the black plastic cap (if fitted) from the driveshaft end, then extract the driveshaft nut split pin. Remove the locking ring and soft washer. Using a suitable socket, a strong T-bar and a long extension tube, slacken the driveshaft nut, but do not unscrew it yet.

3   Slacken the roadwheel nuts, then jack up the front of the car and support it on axle stands. Remove the roadwheel, then unscrew the driveshaft nut and remove the metal washer.

Cars with light allow roadwheels

4   Slacken the roadwheel nuts, then jack up the front of the car and support it on axle stands. Remove the roadwheel, withdraw the black plastic cap (if fitted) from the driveshaft end, then extract the driveshaft nut split pin and remove the locking ring and soft washer.

5   Enlist the aid of an assistant to prevent hub rotation by applying firm pressure to the brake pedal, then use a suitable socket, a strong T-bar and a long extension tube to unscrew the driveshaft nut. Remove the metal washer. If brake pressure proves incapable of preventing hub rotation, temporarily refit the roadwheel (having removed its centre cover), lower the car to the ground and then slacken the driveshaft nut. Jack up the car again and support it on axle stands before removing the roadwheel, the driveshaft nut and the metal washer.

All cars

6   Extract the split pin and unscrew the track rod outer balljoint retaining nut, then separate the balljoint from the hub carrier, using a universal balljoint separator tool if necessary.

7   With reference to Chapter 9, unscrew the two bolts securing the brake caliper mounting bracket to the hub carrier, withdraw the caliper assembly and secure it out of harm's way without stretching or kinking the flexible brake hose. Remove the spring clip securing it to the suspension strut bracket if required. Place a clean spacer (of the same thickness as the disc) between the pads to prevent them being dislodged, then remove the brake disc.

8   Open the bonnet and slacken, by one or two turns only, each of the three suspension strut top mounting nuts.

9   At the bottom of the hub carrier, remove the three nuts, then withdraw the mounting plate and sharply tug the hub carrier outwards off the driveshaft splines. It may be necessary to use a soft-faced mallet (having first refitted the driveshaft nut to protect the shaft's threaded end) to tap the driveshaft out of the hub.

10   Remove the two nuts and bolts clamping the hub carrier to the suspension strut then remove the hub carrier from the car.

11   Remove and refit the hub and bearings, if required, as described in Section 4 of this Chapter.

12   Remove and refit the suspension lower arm balljoint, if required, as described in Section 5 of this Chapter.

13   The brake disc shield can be removed, if required, only after the hub and bearings have been dismantled. It is pressed on to the carrier centre boss and can be prised or tapped off if care is taken not to damage or bend it. Mark its position relative to the carrier **before** removal so that it can be refitted correctly.

14   **Do not** disturb the steering lock stop bolt unless it is absolutely necessary. If it or the hub carrier are renewed, screw the bolt in to the specified length (see Fig. 10.42), then tighten the locknut securely and refit the plastic cap and (where fitted) the split pin. When the car has been lowered to the ground again, check the front wheel turning angles (see Section 36 of this Chapter).

15   On reassembly, refit the hub carrier to the suspension strut, fit the two bolts from front to rear, then tighten the retaining nuts to the specified torque setting.

16   Having refitted (if it was removed) the suspension lower arm balljoint to the hub carrier, tap the hub carrier assembly on to the driveshaft splines, then refit the balljoint mounting plate and tighten the three nuts to the specified torque setting.

17   Tighten the suspension strut top mounting nuts to the specified

torque setting.

18   Refit the track rod outer balljoint to the hub carrier, tighten the retaining nut to the specified torque setting and fit a new split pin to secure it.

19   Refit the brake disc to the hub, withdraw the spacer from between the brake pads and refit the brake caliper as described in Chapter 9. Tighten the two bolts to the specified torque setting.

20   Refit the metal washer and driveshaft nut, then refit the roadwheel and lower the car to the ground. Tighten the driveshaft nut to its specified torque setting, then refit the soft washer and locking ring.

21   On cars with steel roadwheels, fit a new split pin to secure the driveshaft nut, check that the roadwheel nuts are securely fastened, then refit the roadwheel trim or centre cap; do not forget to refit the black plastic cap (if fitted).

22   On cars with light alloy roadwheels, jack the car up again and remove the roadwheel so that a new split pin can be fitted to secure the driveshaft nut. Refit the black plastic cap (if fitted). Refit the roadwheel and its centre cover, lower the car to the ground and tighten the roadwheel nuts to the specified torque setting.

23   It may be necessary to have the wheel alignment and steering angles checked – see Section 36 of this Chapter.

4 Front hub and bearings – removal and refitting

1   Remove the hub carrier from the car (see Section 3 of this Chapter).

2   Clamp the hub carrier in a large vice and use a hammer and a metal tube of suitable diameter to drive the hub out of the carrier as shown in Fig. 10.5. The bearing's outboard inner race and outboard grease seal will remain on the hub. Remove the brake disc shield from the hub carrier, if required.

3   Using a suitable puller as shown in Fig. 10.6, draw the bearing's outboard inner race off the hub, then prise off the outboard grease seal.

Fig. 10.5 Removing the hub from the hub carrier (Sec 4)

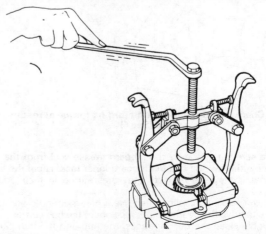

Fig. 10.6 Using a puller to remove the hub bearing outboard inner race (Sec 4)

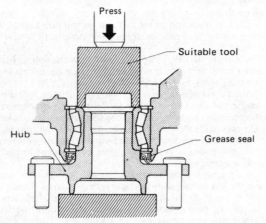

Fig. 10.7 Refitting the hub carrier to the hub and bearings (Sec 4)

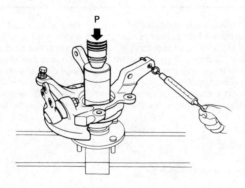

Fig. 10.8 Checking front hub bearing turning torque at hub carrier (Sec 4)

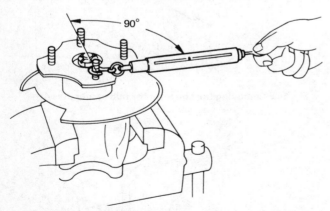

Fig. 10.9 Checking front hub bearing turning torque at roadwheel stud (Sec 4)

4   Using a screwdriver, lever the inboard grease seal from the hub carrier, then withdraw the bearing inboard inner race. Label the inner races so that if they are re-used, they are refitted in their original locations.

5   Extract the retaining circlips, then use a hammer and a socket of suitable size to drive the bearing outer race out of the hub carrier.

6   Thoroughly clean the bearing races, the hub and the hub carrier. Check all components for signs of wear or damage and renew them if necessary. Check particularly that the bearing rollers and races are free

from signs of scoring, pitting or flaking. Renew the bearings if there is any doubt about their condition. The grease seals and split pin should be renewed as a matter of course whenever they are disturbed.

7   If the roadwheel studs are to be renewed, they can be pressed out of the hub flange. Do not tap them out without supporting the flange fully, or the studs and hub may be broken. Note that the studs and hub are stamped with the letter 'N' or 'R'. If replacement parts are required ensure that they are marked with the same letter so that they are correctly matched.

8   On reassembly, refit the first circlip to the hub carrier inboard groove, then use the hammer and socket to tap the bearing outer race into the hub carrier until it seats against the circlip. Refit the second circlip.

9   Pack both bearing inner races with the specified type of grease, and fit them into the bearing outer race. If the original bearings are being re-used, ensure that each inner race is refitted in its original location.

10   Smear the sealing lips with grease and tap the outboard grease seal into the hub carrier.

11   Place the hub on a block of wood and lower the hub carrier over it. Using a hammer and a socket which bears only on the bearing inner race, tap the carrier assembly on to the hub (Fig. 10.7).

12   To check that the bearing is correctly installed, measure its turning torque, which should be in the range specified when the bearing is correctly preloaded.

13   If a press is available, apply a preload pressure of 49 kN (4.9 Imp tonf) to the bearing inner race. Spin the hub carrier several turns in each direction then measure the turning torque by means of a spring balance attached to the suspension strut top clamping bolt hole (see Fig. 10.8); the measurement obtained should be within the range specified.

14   If a press is not available, temporarily refit the hub carrier assembly to the car so that the driveshaft nut can be tightened to the specified torque setting to preload the bearings. Alternatively, the driveshaft can be removed and fitted to the hub carrier, which can be clamped in a vice for the test. Spin the hub several turns in each direction, then measure the turning torque by means of a spring balance attached to one of the roadwheel studs (see Fig. 10.9); the measurement obtained should be within the range specified.

15   In either case an incorrect reading indicates faulty or badly installed bearings or incorrect preload.

16   When the hub is correctly seated on the bearings, smear its sealing lips with grease and tap the inboard seal into the hub carrier; its outer

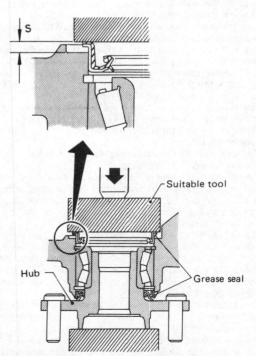

Fig. 10.10 Fitting inboard grease seal to hub carrier (Sec 4)

Protrusion S should be no more than 3.5 mm (0.14 in)

flange should be no more than 3.5 mm (0.14 in) proud of the hub carrier shoulder (see Fig. 10.10).

17   Refit the hub carrier to the car, as described in Section 3 of this Chapter.

5   Front suspension lower arm balljoint – removal and refitting

1   With the car standing on its wheels, apply the handbrake firmly and select first or reverse gear (manual transmission) or the 'P' position (automatic).

Cars with steel roadwheels

2   Remove the roadwheel trim or prise off the centre cap. Withdraw the black plastic cap (if fitted) from the driveshaft end, then extract the driveshaft nut split pin. Remove the locking ring and soft washer. Using a suitable socket, a strong T-bar and a long extension tube, slacken the driveshaft nut, but do not unscrew it yet.

3   Slacken the roadwheel nuts, then jack up the front of the car and support it on axle stands. Remove the roadwheel, then unscrew the driveshaft nut and remove the metal washer.

Cars with light alloy roadwheels

4   Slacken the roadwheel nuts, then jack up the front of the car and support it on axle stands. Remove the roadwheel, withdraw the black plastic cap (if fitted) from the driveshaft end, then extract the driveshaft nut split pin and remove the locking ring and soft washer.

5   Enlist the aid of an assistant to prevent hub rotation by applying firm pressure to the brake pedal, then use a suitable socket, a strong T-bar and a long extension tube to unscrew the driveshaft nut. Remove the metal washer. If brake pressure proves incapable of preventing hub rotation, temporarily refit the roadwheel (having removed its centre cover), lower the car to the ground and then slacken the driveshaft nut. Jack up the car again and support it on axle stands before removing the roadwheel, the driveshaft nut and the metal washer.

All cars

6   Extract the split pin and unscrew the track rod outer balljoint retaining nut, then separate the balljoint from the hub carrier, using a universal balljoint separator tool if necessary.

7   Open the bonnet and slacken, by one or two turns only, each of the three suspension strut top mounting nuts.

8   At the bottom of the hub carrier, remove the three nuts, withdraw the mounting plate and sharply tug the hub carrier outwards off the driveshaft splines. It may be necessary to use a soft-faced mallet (having first refitted the driveshaft nut to protect the shaft's threaded end) to tap the driveshaft out of the hub.

9   Taking care not to stretch or kink the flexible brake hose, move the strut and hub carrier clear of the driveshaft end, then extract the balljoint retaining nut split pin and unscrew the retaining nut.

10   Using a universal balljoint separator tool if necessary, remove the balljoint from the hub carrier.

11   Renew the balljoint if its movement is sloppy or if it is too stiff, if its rubber dust cover is cracked, perished or showing signs of grease leakage, or if the unit shows any other sign of wear or damage.

12   Note that while the rubber dust covers are available separately, a replacement should be fitted only if it is absolutely certain that the balljoint itself is fit for further use. Ensure that the balljoint is packed with grease before fitting the new cover.

13   Note that while as a general rule the balljoint should show no signs of free play either in the direction of rotation or in the vertical direction (measured between the stud and its housing) some early models may be fitted with a spring-loaded type of balljoint (identifiable by its cup-shaped bottom surface). This type is intended to have vertical free play of 0.1 to 1.0 mm (0.004 to 0.039 in) when a force of 981 N (220 lbf) is exerted on the stud. In practice however, unless the facilities are available to measure this with the required accuracy, it can be assumed that if any free play is evident on close inspection, the balljoint is worn out and must be renewed; this is certainly the case with the later type of balljoint (with a flat bottom surface).

14   On reassembly, degrease the tapers of the balljoint stud and the hub carrier, then press the balljoint firmly into the hub carrier while the retaining nut is refitted and tightened to the specified torque setting. Fit a new split pin to secure the nut.

15   Tap the hub carrier and strut on to the driveshaft splines, then refit the balljoint mounting plate and tighten the three nuts to the specified torque setting (photo).

5.15 Tighten lower arm balljoint mounting plate nuts to specified torque setting – note later type of balljoint shown

16   Tighten the suspension strut top mounting nuts to the specified torque setting.

17   Refit the track rod outer balljoint to the hub carrier, tighten the retaining nut to the specified torque setting and fit a new split pin to secure it.

18   Refit the metal washer and driveshaft nut, then refit the roadwheel and lower the car to the ground. Tighten the driveshaft nut to its specified torque setting, then refit the soft washer and locking ring.

19   On cars with steel roadwheels, fit a new split pin to secure the driveshaft nut, check that the roadwheel nuts are securely fastened, then refit the roadwheel trim or centre cap; do not forget to refit the black plastic cap (if fitted).

20   On cars with light alloy roadwheels, jack the car up again and remove the roadwheel so that a new split pin can be fitted to secure the driveshaft nut. Refit the black plastic cap (if fitted). Refit the roadwheel and its centre cover, lower the car to the ground and tighten to the specified torque setting the roadwheel nuts.

21   It may be necessary to have the wheel alignment and steering angles checked – see Section 36 of this Chapter.

6   Front suspension strut and spring – removal and refitting

1   Open the bonnet and slacken by one or two turns only, each of the three suspension strut top mounting nuts (photo). Remove, where necessary, the roadwheel trim and slacken the roadwheel nuts.

2   Apply the handbrake, jack up the front of the car and support it securely on axle stands. Remove the roadwheel.

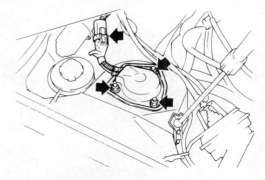

Fig. 10.11 Adjustable damping suspension strut – top mounting nuts and actuator wiring connector arrowed (Sec 6)

6.1 Front suspension strut top mounting nuts

6.10 Tighten the suspension strut-to-hub carrier clamp bolt nuts to the specified torque setting

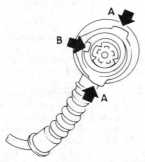

Fig. 10.12 Adjustable damping suspension strut top cover – squeeze together at points 'A' to remove, using point 'B' as a guide on refitting (Sec 6)

3   Remove the spring clip and release the brake flexible hose from the suspension strut bracket.
4   Unscrew the retaining nuts and remove the two bolts clamping the hub carrier to the suspension strut.
5   On cars with non-adjustable suspension, unscrew the three suspension strut top mounting nuts and withdraw the strut from under the front wing. Collect the strut top cover and gasket (where fitted).
6   On cars with adjustable suspension, follow the strut actuator's wiring lead back to its connector and disconnect it (see Fig. 10.11). Unscrew the three suspension strut top mounting nuts and hold the strut in place while the actuator wiring lead is disconnected from the strut piston rod by squeezing together the top cover at the points 'A' shown in Fig. 10.12. Collect the top cover and gasket (where fitted) and withdraw the strut from under the front wing.
7   On reassembly, thoroughly clean the underwing area and hub

carrier around the strut mounting points.
8   On cars with non-adjustable suspension, refit the gasket (where fitted) and the strut top cover, then offer up the strut to the wing and hub carrier. Refit the three top mounting nuts, then push the two bottom clamping bolts through from front to rear and refit the retaining nuts.
9   On cars with adjustable suspension, offer up the strut to the wing and hub carrier, ensuring that the top mounting studs are positioned as shown in Fig. 10.13. Have an assistant hold it up under the wing while the gasket (where fitted) is installed and the top cover is connected to the strut piston rod using the square cut-out (point 'B', Fig. 10.12) as a guide. Refit the three top mounting nuts, push the two bottom clamping bolts through from front to rear, refit the retaining nuts and connect the strut actuator's wiring lead to the wiring loom.
10   On all cars, tighten the strut top mounting nuts and bottom clamp bolts (photo) to the specified torque setting.
11   Refit the brake hose to the suspension strut bracket and secure it with the spring clip.
12   Refit the roadwheel and lower the car to the ground.
13   It may be necessary to have the wheel alignment and steering angles checked (see Section 36 of this Chapter).

7   Front suspension strut and spring – overhaul

Note: *Coil spring compressors are required to compress the strut spring safely before the piston rod nut is unscrewed. Do not attempt to undo this nut with the strut in place on the car.*
1   Remove the suspension strut and spring from the car, as described in Section 6 of this Chapter. Thoroughly clean the strut assembly.
2   Place a metal bar between two of the top mounting's studs to

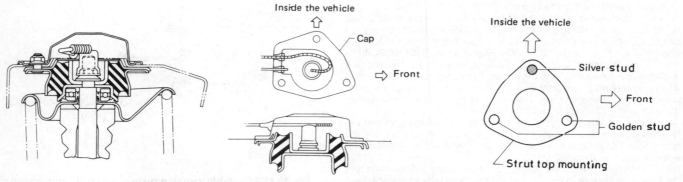

Fig. 10.13 Details of adjustable damping suspension strut top mounting (Sec 6)

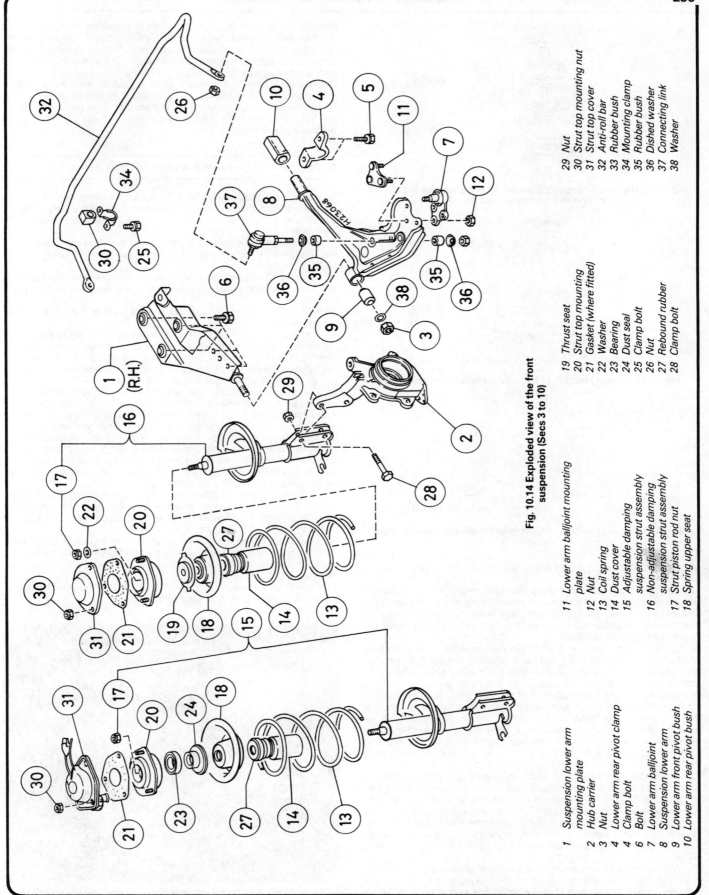

Fig. 10.14 Exploded view of the front suspension (Secs 3 to 10)

1 Suspension lower arm mounting plate
2 Hub carrier
3 Nut
4 Lower arm rear pivot clamp
6 Clamp bolt
7 Bolt
8 Lower arm balljoint
9 Suspension lower arm
10 Lower arm front pivot bush
10 Lower arm rear pivot bush

11 Lower arm balljoint mounting plate
12 Nut
13 Coil spring
14 Dust cover
15 Adjustable damping suspension strut assembly
16 Non-adjustable damping suspension strut assembly
17 Strut piston rod nut
18 Spring upper seat

19 Thrust seat
20 Strut top mounting
21 Gasket (where fitted)
22 Washer
23 Bearing
24 Dust seal
25 Clamp bolt
26 Nut
27 Rebound rubber
28 Clamp bolt

29 Nut
30 Strut top mounting nut
31 Strut top cover
32 Anti-roll bar
33 Rubber bush
34 Mounting clamp
35 Rubber bush
36 Dished washer
37 Connecting link
38 Washer

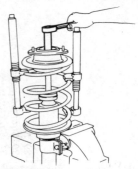

Fig. 10.15 Use coil spring compressors to compress spring before unscrewing piston rod nut (Sec 7)

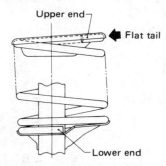

Fig. 10.16 Correct position of front suspension strut coil spring (Sec 7)

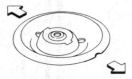

Fig. 10.17 Correct position of front suspension strut spring upper seat (Sec 7)

prevent it from rotating, then slacken, but do not remove yet, the piston rod nut.

3   Fit spring compressors (available from most motor accessory shops) as shown in Fig. 10.15 to each side of the spring and tighten them evenly to compress the spring until there is no pressure on the spring upper seat or the strut top mounting; it should be possible to rotate the top mounting easily by hand.

4   Unscrew the piston rod nut and remove the washer (where fitted). Withdraw the top mounting and (as applicable) the bearing and dust seal or the thrust seat, followed by the spring upper seat. Remove the spring and withdraw the rebound rubber and dust cover.

5   Visually inspect all components of the strut and renew any that are showing obvious signs of wear or damage. Check particularly the top mounting components for cracks or distortion, or deterioration of the rubber in the top mounting itself. Check the spring for cracks, damage or excessive sagging. If either of the front suspension springs requires renewal, note that it is good practice to renew both together as a matched pair.

6   Check the strut's damping action by mounting it upright in a vice and moving the piston rod fully up and down; firm, even, resistance should be felt in both directions. If the damping is weak or if the strut shows signs of oil leaks at any point, or if the piston rod is bent, scored or damaged, the complete strut must be renewed, as individual components are not available to permit repairs. Again, it is good practice to consider both front suspension struts a matched pair when renewing either.

7   Note that suspension struts must be stored in an upright position. If a strut is to be fitted after a long period of storage, mount it upright in a vice and move the piston rod fully up and down several times to prime

the damper passages and restore full damping action.

8   Reassembly is the reverse of the dismantling procedure, noting the following points. Pull the piston rod out to its full extent and ensure the spring is correctly compressed before refitting it. Position the spring and spring upper seat as shown in Figs. 10.16 and 10.17 and ensure that the thrust seat (or bearing and dust seal, as applicable) is correctly located on the piston rod and the spring upper seat. Tighten the piston rod nut to the specified torque setting and remove the spring compressors.

9   Refit the suspension strut and spring to the car, as described in Section 6 of this Chapter.

8   Front suspension lower arm – removal and refitting

1   Apply the handbrake firmly, jack up the front of the car and support it on axle stands. If better access is required, remove the roadwheel.

2   Unscrew the three nuts securing the balljoint mounting plate to the lower arm.

3   Unscrew the nuts securing the anti-roll bar connecting link to the lower arm and to the anti-roll bar, then remove the connecting link (see Section 10 of this Chapter).

4   Unscrew the nut securing the lower arm's front pivot then remove the two bolts and withdraw the metal clamp securing its rear pivot (photo).

5   Slide the arm forward clear of the front pivot and the anti-roll bar, then withdraw it.

6   Thoroughly clean the arm and the underbody areas around its mountings, removing all traces of dirt or underseal, then check it carefully for cracks, distortion or any other signs of wear or damage. Do not forget to check the clamp and the mounting fasteners. Renew any component that is found to be worn or damaged.

7   Check the pivot bushes and renew them if they are cracked, worn, split or perished. To remove the rear bush , grip it in a vice and work the lower arm out of it; an application of penetrating fluid will help to release it if necessary. Fit the new bush using liquid soap or petroleum jelly as a lubricant. The front pivot bush must be removed and installed using a press, although it may be possible to achieve the required result using a strong bench vice and sockets or pieces of tubing. Soak the old bush in penetrating fluid before attempting removal and use liquid soap or petroleum jelly as a lubricant on fitting the new bush.

8   Refitting is a reversal of the removal procedure, noting the following points. With all components assembled loosely on their mountings, align the anti-roll bar connecting link as described in Section 10 of this Chapter.

9   Lower the car to the ground so that all its weight is back on its wheels, rock it to settle the suspension, then tighten all disturbed nuts and bolts to the specified torque settings, being careful to tighten evenly the rear pivot clamp bolts.

10   It will be necessary to have the wheel alignment and steering angles checked (see Section 36 of this Chapter.)

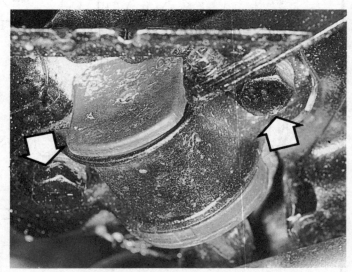

8.4 Front suspension lower arm rear pivot – clamp bolts arrowed

9 Front suspension lower arm mounting plate – removal and refitting

1   Apply the handbrake firmly, jack up the front of the car and support it on axle stands.
2   Remove the anti-roll bar (see Section 10 of this Chapter.)
3   Remove the appropriate suspension lower arm (see Section 8 of this Chapter.)
4   The procedure now varies according to which mounting plate is being removed.

Left-hand mounting plate
5   Unscrew the five (remaining) bolts securing the mounting plate to the car's body. Withdraw the plate and thoroughly clean it, and also the underbody around its mountings.
6   Check the plate for cracks or distortion and for damage of any sort to the lower arm front pivot; renew it if necessary.
7   Refitting is the reverse of the removal procedure. Tighten all mounting bolts and nuts to their specified torque settings, as described in the relevant Sections.

Right-hand mounting plate
8   Unbolt both engine compartment undershields.
9   Remove the engine mounting longitudinal member (see Chapter 1.)
10   Unscrew the five (remaining) bolts securing the mounting plate to the car's body. Withdraw the plate and thoroughly clean it, and also the underbody around its mountings.
11   Check the plate for cracks and for damage of any sort to the lower arm front pivot; renew it if necessary.
12   On refitting fit the plate to the underbody and tighten the mounting bolts to the specified torque setting.
13   Refit the engine mounting longitudinal member and secure the engine front and rear mountings as described in Chapter 1.
14   Refit the engine compartment undershields.
15   Refit the suspension lower arm and anti-roll bar. Tighten the mounting bolts and nuts to the specified torque settings, as described in the relevant Sections of this Chapter.

10 Front anti-roll bar and connecting links – removal and refitting

1   Apply the handbrake firmly, jack up the front of the car and support it on axle stands. If better access is required, remove the roadwheel.
2   Unscrew the nuts securing the anti-roll bar connecting links to the anti-roll bar itself and to each front suspension lower arm.
3   Unbolt the two mounting clamps (photo) and withdraw the anti-roll bar, then collect the connecting links. Thoroughly clean all components before inspection.

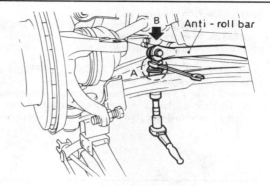

View from B

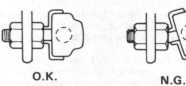

O.K.   N.G.

Fig. 10.18 Correct fitting of front anti-roll bar connecting links (Sec 10)

4   Check the anti-roll bar and mountings for signs of wear or damage. In particular check all rubber bushes for signs of cracks, splits or perishing and renew them if necessary. Check the connecting link balljoints for signs of grease leakage, stiffness or free play and renew the complete link if required.
5   On refitting, first clean the areas around the mounting points on the underbody and suspension lower arms. Use liquid soap or petroleum jelly as a lubricant when refitting the rubber bushes.
6   Refit the connecting links to the lower arms, noting that the balljoint stud projects rearwards and that the link passes downwards through a dished washer (concave surface downwards), a rubber bush, the lower arm, a second rubber bush and a second dished washer (concave surface upwards) before the retaining nut is refitted. Tighten the nut loosely at this stage.
7   Enlist the aid of an assistant to manage the other end of the anti-roll bar and refit the bar to the car. Secure it first to both connecting link balljoint studs, align the rubber bushes, then fit the bar against the underbody and refit both clamps. Tighten the clamp bolts firmly and evenly, but not to the full torque setting at this stage.
8   Using an open-ended spanner on the connecting link hexagon, rotate each link until it is square to the anti-roll bar, then moderately

10.3 Front anti-roll bar mounting clamp

10.11 Front anti-roll bar connecting link to suspension lower arm tighten both nuts at each link (see Fig. 10.18.)

9   Lower the car to the ground. When all its weight is on the road-wheels, rock the car to settle the suspension components.

10   Tighten the anti-roll bar clamp bolts evenly to the specified torque setting.

11   At each connecting link (photo), use an open-ended spanner applied to its hexagon to hold the link square to the anti-roll bar while the link-to-lower arm retaining nut is screwed up to the (upper) end of the link threads and then tighten to its specified torque setting. Finally, tighten the link-to-(anti-roll) bar retaining nut to the specified torque setting.

11   Adjustable suspension damping system – general

1   Early turbo engine models are fitted with suspension struts which have damping characteristics that can be altered through three settings, via a facia-mounted switch, to suit the driver's preference.

2   The system comprises an actuator motor mounted at the top of each of the four struts, a control unit mounted under the driver's seat and the facia switch.

3   Refer to the relevant Sections of this Chapter for details of strut removal and refitting and (where possible) overhaul. Refer to Chapter 12 for details of the electrical components of the system

12   Rear hub bearings – adjustment

1   With the car parked on firm, level ground apply the handbrake firmly and select first or reverse gear (manual transmission) or the 'P' position (automatic).

2   Where necessary, remove the roadwheel trim then slacken the roadwheel nuts. Chock the front wheels, jack up the rear of the car and support it securely on axle stands. Remove the roadwheel and release the handbrake.

3   Prise off the grease cap from the centre of the brake drum or disc, extract the split pin and remove the locking ring (photo). Check that all visible components are well greased.

4   Tighten the hub bearing nut to the torque setting specified to preload the bearings, then rotate the brake drum or disc back and forth several times to seat the bearings. Check that the nut is still fastened to the specified torque setting.

5   Slacken the hub bearing nut just enough to unload the bearings without introducing any brake drum or disc endfloat.

6   Tighten the hub bearing nut to the normal torque setting specified, then rotate the brake drum or disc back and forth several times to seat the bearings and check again that the nut is still fastened to the normally specified torque setting.

7   Fit the locking ring to the hub bearing nut so that a new split pin can be fitted to secure the nut (photo). **If necessary,** the nut may be slackened through **no more than** 15° to permit the fitting of the locking ring and split pin.

8   To check the setting, measure the timing torque, using a spring balance attached to one of the roadwheel studs (the principle of this procedure being shown in Fig. 10.9). First check that there is no dragging resistance from the brake components and spin the brake drum or disc several times in both directions. The reading obtained should be no more than that specified. Note that the condition of the grease seal has a considerable effect on the results.

9   Check also that there is no brake drum or disc endfloat, particularly if the turning torque reading obtained was very low.

10   If the turning torque is within limits with no discernible endfloat, the bearings are correctly adjusted. Half-fill the grease cap with the specified type of grease, spread the ends of the split pin correctly (photo) and tap the grease cap squarely into place. Refit the roadwheel and lower the car to the ground, then apply the handbrake.

11   If the turning torque is above the specified force, or if brake drum or disc endfloat is evident, repeat the full adjustment procedure until the bearings are correctly adjusted. If this is not possible, overhaul the hub and bearings to discover the fault (see Section 13 of this Chapter).

12.3 To adjust rear hub bearing, prise off grease cap, extract split pin, then withdraw locking ring to reach bearing nut

12.7 To correctly secure bearing nut, refit locking ring and spread new split pin ends as shown

13   Rear hub and bearings – removal and refitting

All models

Note: *The dismantling of the rear hub and bearings will require the removal of the brake drum or disc. Refer to the relevant Sections of Chapter 9 for full information on the removal and refitting of the various braking system components that is involved in this operation.*

1   With the car parked on level ground, apply the handbrake firmly and select first or reverse gear (manual transmission) or the 'P' position (automatic).

2   Where necessary, remove the roadwheel trim, then slacken the roadwheel nuts. Chock the front wheels, jack up the rear of the car and support it securely on axle stands.

3   Remove the roadwheel and release the handbrake.

4   The procedure now varies slightly according to the type of rear brake fitted.

Drum brake – removal

5   Prise off the grease cap from the centre of the brake drum, extract

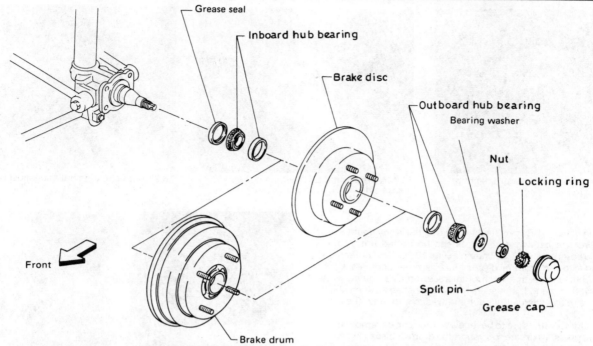

Fig. 10.19 Exploded view of rear hub and bearings (Secs 12 and 13)

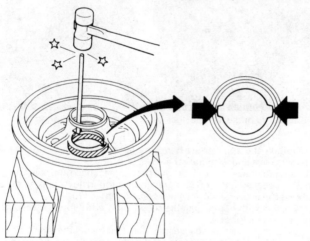

Fig. 10.20 Driving out the rear hub bearing outer races (Sec 13)

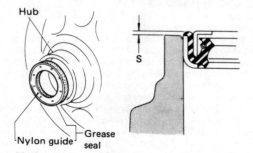

Fig. 10.21 Fitting rear hub bearing grease seal (Sec 13)

Protrusion S should be o to 0.5 mm (0 to 0.02 in)

the split pin and withdraw the locking ring.
6   Unscrew the hub bearing nut and withdraw the bearing washer.
7   Pull the drum towards you and then push it back enough to be able
to withdraw the outboard bearing inner race (photo). Identify the inner
race so that it is correctly refitted.

8   Pull the drum off the stub axle and use a clean dry cloth to remove all
traces of brake dust from its interior. Note that brake dust may contain
asbestos, so take care not to inhale any dust and never use compressed
air to blow it off.
9   If the drum binds on the brake shoes, first check that the handbrake
is fully released, then remove the rubber plug from the brake backplate
and use a screwdriver to turn the serrated nut so that the self-adjuster
strut retracts until the drum can be withdrawn. If this is necessary,
examine the drum interior friction surface and check that a lip has not
formed on the inboard edge. If such a lip is a mixture of rust and brake
dust it can be scraped away to leave a smooth surface. If, however, the
lip is due to the drum being heavily grooved it may be necessary to
renew the drum (see Chapter 9.)

Disc brake – removal
10   Disconnect the handbrake cable from the caliper, then release the
flexible brake hose from the suspension strut by removing its retaining
spring clip. Remove the two bolts securing the caliper mounting bracket
to the stub axle adaptor plate and withdraw the caliper assembly.
Secure the caliper out of harm's way without stretching or kinking the
brake hose. Place a clean spacer (of the same thickness as the disc)
between the pads to prevent them being dislodged.
11   Prise off the grease cap from the centre of the brake disc, extract
the split pin and withdraw the locking ring.
12   Unscrew the hub bearing nut and withdraw the bearing washer.
13   Pull the disc towards you and then push it back enough to be able
to withdraw the outboard bearing inner race. Identify the inner race so
that it is correctly refitted.
14   Pull the disc off the stub axle and use a clean dry cloth to remove all
traces of brake dust. Note that brake dust may contain asbestos, so take
care not to inhale any dust and never use compressed air to blow it off.

All models – inspection
15   Prise the grease seal out of the brake drum or disc inboard end and
withdraw the inboard bearing inner race. Do not confuse the outboard
and inboard inner races.
16   Thoroughly clean all the components and renew any that show
obvious signs of wear or damage, except for the grease seal and split pin
which must be renewed as a matter of course whenever they are
disturbed.
17   Check the brake surfaces of the drum or disc as described in
Chapter 9.
18   Check that the bearing rollers and races are free from signs of

13.7 Removing rear hub outboard bearing inner race

13.22A When refitting bearing washer, grease side which fits against bearing

13.22B Refit bearing nut and adjust bearings

scoring, pitting or flaking. Renew the bearings if there is any doubt about their condition. The bearing outer races can be drifted out, using a hammer and a soft metal drift, as shown in Fig. 10.20. New outer races can be drifted into the drum or disc using a hammer and a socket of suitable size, but ensure that each outer race remains square to its housing during fitting and that it seats firmly against its locating shoulder. Alternatively, use a large bolt, nut and washers to draw the races into position.

19   If the roadwheel studs are to be renewed they can be removed and refitted using a press. Take care to support the drum or disc fully around the stud, to prevent the risk of damage.

20   On reassembly, liberally pack both bearing inner races with the specified type of grease, refit the inboard inner race to the hub and use a hammer and a block of wood to tap a new grease seal into place. Note that the seal's white nylon guide must face inboard and that the seal must be just proud of the hub centre boss, as shown in Fig. 10.21. Lightly grease the seal lips and the stub axle bearing surfaces.

Drum brake – refitting

21   First measure the brake shoe outer diameter along the 3-9 o'clock line and turn the adjuster serrated nut until this measurement is 0.35 to 0.55 mm (0.014 to 0.022 in) less than the drum inside diameter. Ensure that the backplate rubber plug is refitted.

22   Refit the brake drum to the stub axle. Pack the outboard bearing inner race with grease and refit it. Grease the bearing washer on one side and refit it with the greased side against the bearing, then refit the hub bearing nut (photos).

23   Adjust the rear hub bearings as described in Section 12 of this Chapter (paragraph 4 onwards). Half-fill the grease cap with the specified type of grease before refitting it.

24   Operate the handbrake several times to allow the self-adjuster strut to establish correct brake shoe-to-drum clearance.

Disc brake – refitting

25   Refit the brake disc to the stub axle. Pack the outboard bearing inner race with grease and refit it. Grease the bearing washer on one side and refit it with the greased side against the bearing, then refit the hub bearing nut.

26   Adjust the rear hub bearings as described in Section 12 of this Chapter (paragraph 4 onwards). Half-fill the grease cap with the specified type of grease before refitting it.

27   Refit the brake caliper, connect the handbrake cable again and secure the flexible brake hose to the suspension strut (photo) – see Chapter 9.

---

14   Rear suspension strut and spring – removal and refitting

1   First work inside the car to reach the suspension strut top mounting nuts.

2   Note that while on Saloon models it may appear easier to reach the strut top mounting nuts from inside the luggage compartment, in practice access is restricted and it may be difficult to reach the front mounting nut (photos). Owners are advised to proceed as follows.

3   Working as described in the relevant Sections of Chapter 11, remove the rear seat base and back cushions, unclip their top covers

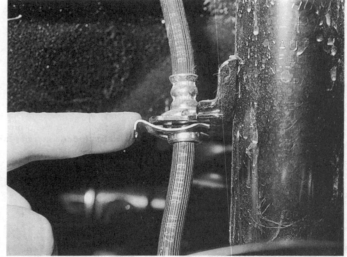

13.27 Secure brake flexible hose to strut bracket with spring clip

and unbolt the speakers (where fitted), then release the parcel shelf retaining clips and withdraw the shelf.

4   On Hatchback models, remove the rear seat base and carefully prise up the speaker grille or storage tray surround (as applicable), then remove the rear seat side cushions (see Chapter 11.)

5   On cars with non-adjustable suspension, withdraw the suspension strut top cover (photo).

6   On cars with adjustable suspension, first follow the strut actuator's wiring lead back to its connector and disconnect it, then disconnect the strut top cover from the strut piston rod by squeezing together the top cover at the points shown in Fig. 10.23.

7   On all cars, slacken each of the three suspension strut top mounting nuts by one or two turns only.

8   Working as described in Section 13 of this Chapter, jack up the rear of the car, then remove the roadwheel and the brake drum or disc.

9   On cars with drum rear brakes, disconnect the handbrake cable and remove the spring clip securing the brake hose and pipe to the suspension strut. Unbolt the brake backplate from the suspension strut lower end, then secure the complete brake assembly out of harm's way without stretching, kinking or damaging the brake hose or pipe. There is no need to disturb any of the hydraulic system components. Refer to the relevant Sections of Chapter 9 for full details.

10   On cars with disc rear brakes, the brake disc shield and caliper mounting adapter plate can be unbolted, if required, from the suspension strut lower end.

11   On all cars, slacken both trailing link mounting bolts, remove the rear mounting bolt and pull the link downwards clear of the suspension strut lower end.

12   Unbolt the bracket from the bottom of the suspension strut, leaving it attached to the anti-roll bar.

13   Slacken both transverse link pivot bolt retaining nuts, remove the outboard pivot bolt and pull both links downwards clear of the suspension strut lower end.

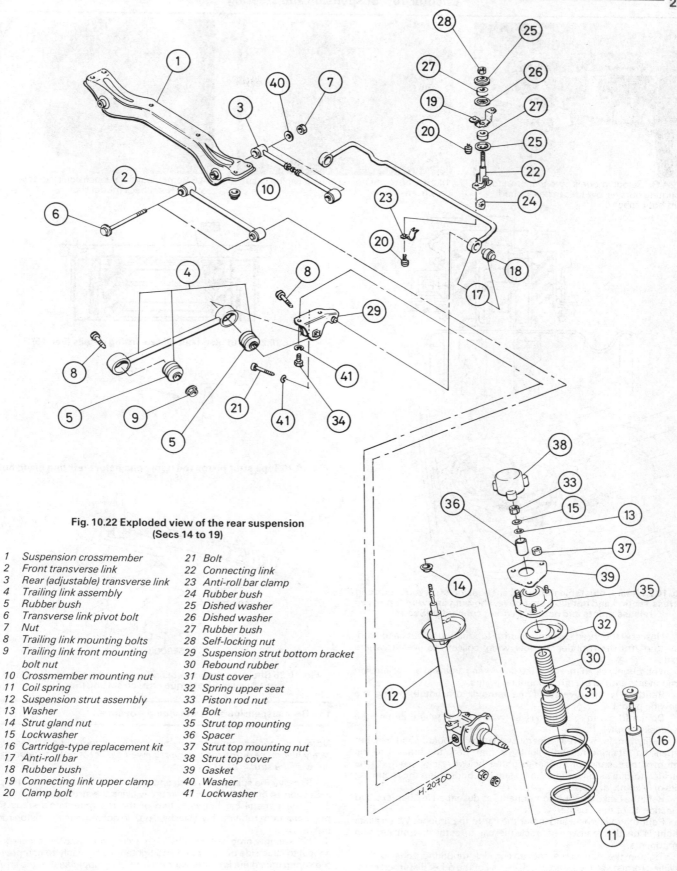

**Fig. 10.22 Exploded view of the rear suspension
(Secs 14 to 19)**

1 Suspension crossmember
2 Front transverse link
3 Rear (adjustable) transverse link
4 Trailing link assembly
5 Rubber bush
6 Transverse link pivot bolt
7 Nut
8 Trailing link mounting bolts
9 Trailing link front mounting
   bolt nut
10 Crossmember mounting nut
11 Coil spring
12 Suspension strut assembly
13 Washer
14 Strut gland nut
15 Lockwasher
16 Cartridge-type replacement kit
17 Anti-roll bar
18 Rubber bush
19 Connecting link upper clamp
20 Clamp bolt

21 Bolt
22 Connecting link
23 Anti-roll bar clamp
24 Rubber bush
25 Dished washer
26 Dished washer
27 Rubber bush
28 Self-locking nut
29 Suspension strut bottom bracket
30 Rebound rubber
31 Dust cover
32 Spring upper seat
33 Piston rod nut
34 Bolt
35 Strut top mounting
36 Spacer
37 Strut top mounting nut
38 Strut top cover
39 Gasket
40 Washer
41 Lockwasher

H.20700

14.2A On Saloon models, two rear strut top mounting nuts (arrowed) can be reached from boot space ...

14.2B ... but front nut (arrowed) can be seen only from above

14.5 Removing rear suspension strut top cover – Hatchback model shown

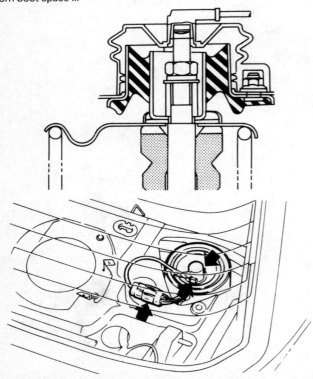

Fig. 10.23 Rear (adjustable damping) suspension strut top mounting – cross-section and details from above, showing arrowed top cover release points and actuator wiring connector (Sec 14)

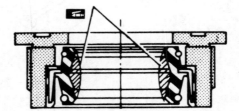

Fig. 10.24 Strut gland nut oil seal fitting details (Sec 15)

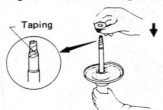

Fig. 10.25 Tape strut piston rod upper end before refitting gland nut (Sec 15)

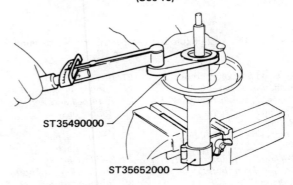

ST35490000

ST35652000

Fig. 10.26 Showing special tools necessary to tighten strut gland nut to specified torque wrench setting (Sec 15)

14   Unscrew the three suspension strut top mounting nuts and withdraw the strut from under the rear wing; collect the gasket (where fitted).

15   Thoroughly clean the strut, the underwing area and all suspension components around the strut mounting points.

16   Refitting is the reverse of the removal procedure, noting the following points.

17   Do not forget to refit the gasket (where fitted) when refitting the suspension strut.

18   Refit, from front to rear, the transverse link outboard pivot bolt, but tighten the retaining nut only lightly at first. Refit the bracket to the bottom of the suspension strut and tighten the two retaining bolts to the specified torque setting. Refit the trailing link but tighten the mounting bolts only lightly at first.

19   Refit the brake and hub components as described in Chapter 9 and in Section 13 of this Chapter.

20   Refit the roadwheel and lower the car to the ground. When all its weight is on the roadwheels, rock the car to settle the suspension components.

21   Tighten the transverse and trailing link mounting bolts to their specified torque settings, and check that all of the other disturbed components are correctly secured.

22   The rear wheel alignment should be checked and adjusted if necessary (see Section 36 of this Chapter.)

15   Rear suspension strut and spring – overhaul

Note: *Coil spring compressors are required to compress the strut spring safely before the piston rod nut is unscrewed. Do not attempt to undo the nut with the strut in place on the car.*

1   Remove the suspension strut and spring from the car, as described in Section 14 of this Chapter. Thoroughly clean the strut assembly.

2   Place a metal bar between two of the top mounting's studs to prevent it from rotating, then slacken, but do not remove the piston rod nut.

3   Fit spring compressors (available from most motor accessory shops) to each side of the spring and tighten them evenly to compress the spring until there is no pressure on the spring upper seat or the strut top mounting; it should be possible to rotate the top mounting by hand easily.

4   Unscrew the piston rod nut and withdraw the washers, spacer, top

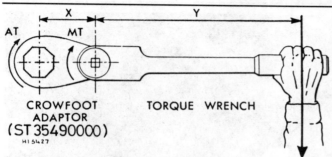

Fig. 10.27 Method of calculating metered torque when using special crowfoot adaptor (Sec 15)

MT = Metered torque (set on torque wrench)

AT = Actual torque

X = Effective length of adaptor (= 0.1 in/0.3 ft for tool specified)

Y = Effective length of torque wrench

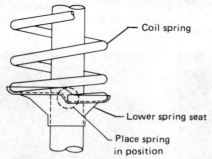

Fig. 10.28 Correct position of rear suspension strut coil spring (Sec 15)

mounting, upper spring seat and the (compressed) spring. Slide the rebound rubber and dust cover off the strut.

5   Visually inspect all components of the strut and renew any that are showing obvious signs of wear or damage. Check particularly the top mounting components for cracks or distortion, or deterioration of the rubber in the top mounting itself. Check the spring for cracks, damage or excessive sagging. If either of the rear suspension springs requires renewal, note that it is good practice to renew both together, as a matched pair.

6   Check the strut's damping action by mounting it upright in a vice and moving the piston rod fully up and down. Firm, even resistance should be felt in both directions. If the damping is weak or if the strut shows signs of oil leaks at any point, or if the piston rod is bent, scored or damaged, the strut requires overhaul.

7   Note that it is good practice to consider both rear suspension struts as a matched pair; both should be overhauled or renewed at the same time, even if only one is faulty.

8   Before attempting strut overhaul, owners should seek the advice of a Nissan dealer, Depending on the faults found several options are open; the complete strut assembly can be renewed, or the damping components alone can be overhauled. In the latter case, either a shock absorber

repair kit or a cartridge-type replacement can be used installed, either professionally or by the home mechanic.

9   To overhaul the strut first mount it upright in a vice and push the piston rod fully to the bottom of its stroke, then unscrew the gland nut.

10   If the strut is leaking from the gland nut seal and if it is not of the cartridge type, then the leak can be cured by fitting a gland seal kit which is available separately. See paragraphs 16 and 17 below.

11   Withdraw the piston rod and the cartridge (if fitted) or the rod, guide and inner cylinder, and collect or mop up the spilt fluid. Invert the strut outer tube to tip out any remaining fluid, then clean the tube and check it for wear or damage, particularly if it has shown signs of oil leaks; if the outer tube is damaged the strut must be renewed.

12   If a cartridge-type replacement is being used, carefully slide it into the strut outer tube and secure it by fitting the new gland nut (without oil seal), supplied with the cartridge kit. Tighten the gland nut to the specified torque setting (see paragraph 17 below.) Refit the spring and the top mounting components.

13   If the original (non-cartridge type) components are being examined, first clean them thoroughly, then check each for obvious signs of wear or damage. If the damping is weak or if the piston rod is scored or bent then all components should be renewed as a matter of course. Components can be checked for wear by direct measurement, if the facilities are available.

14   On reassembly, ensure that all components are absolutely clean and dry.

15   Assemble the piston rod, guide and inner cylinder and refit them to the outer tube. Press the piston rod fully into the outer tube and mount the strut assembly upright in a vice. Pour in the exact specified amount of recommended strut fluid; any variation in quantity or type of fluid will affect the strut's damping performance. Very gently move the piston rod to dislodge any air bubbles.

16   Before refitting the gland nut, push the piston rod fully into the strut outer tube, check that the rod is clean, then wrap a thin layer of insulating tape around its upper end to protect the gland seal lips from the sharp threads and locating shoulders. Apply a smear of grease to the gland seal lips and refit it (see Figs. 10.24 and 10.25).

17   When tightening the gland nut to the specified torque setting, note that the figure given is the true (actual) torque for the nut. To obtain this figure, a torque wrench has to be used with a special crowfoot-type adaptor shown in Fig. 10.26 (Nissan part no. ST35490000) and, because the torque is applied to the adaptor rather than the nut, a formula must be used so that the indicated (metered) torque set on the torque wrench can be related to the true torque. Referring to Fig. 10.27, the metered torque is calculated as follows:

$$MT = \frac{AT \times Y}{Y + X}$$

18   If the special tool is not available, the nut can be tightened by fitting a ring or open-ended spanner to it and applying a measured turning force by hooking a spring balance to the spanner's outer end. To calculate the force required, measure the distance from the nut centre to the balance's point of attachment. Bear in mind that a torque setting of 72.5 lbf ft (for example) is a turning force of 72.5 lbf, when applied at the end of a lever (the spanner) 1 ft long, so the applied force should be decreased proportionally for a longer spanner (eg a force of 48 lbf should be applied for a spanner 18 in long and vice versa for a shorter spanner.

19   When the gland nut is tightened, prepare the rebuilt strut (not the cartridge type) for use by holding the strut upright and pulling the piston rod fully out then inverting it and pushing the piston rod fully in. Repeat

L.H. side

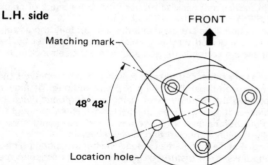

R.H. side

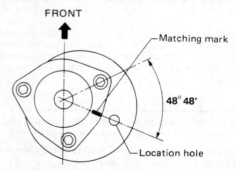

Fig. 10.29 Correct locations of rear suspension strut spring upper seats and top mountings (Sec 15)

16.2A Rear suspension trailing link front mounting (arrowed)

16.2B Trailing link rear end is bolted to suspension strut bottom bracket (arrowed)

this several times to prime the damper passages and bleed out any air bubbles.

20   Note that suspension struts must be stored in an upright position. If a strut is to be fitted after a long period of storage, mount it upright in a vice and move the piston rod fully up and down several times to restore full damping action.

21   Reassembly is the reverse of the dismantling procedure, noting the following points. Pull the piston rod out to its full extent and ensure the spring is correctly compressed before refitting it. Position the spring, spring upper seat and top mounting as shown in Figs. 10.28 and 10.29. Tighten the piston rod nut to the specified torque setting and remove the spring compressors.

22   Refit the suspension strut and spring to the car, as described in Section 14 of this Chapter.

16   Rear suspension trailing link and bushes – removal and refitting

1   With the car standing on its wheels on firm level ground, apply the handbrake firmly and select first or reverse gear (manual transmission) or the 'P' position (automatic). Chock the front wheels, jack up the rear of the car and support it on axle stands.

2   Unbolt the trailing link front and rear mountings (photos) then withdraw the trailing link.

3   Thoroughly clean the link and the area around its mounting points, then check for obvious signs of wear or damage. If the link itself is cracked, rusted or distorted it must be renewed complete with its bushes.

4   If the bushes are worn, compacted or perished they must be renewed. If possible, prepare for this by soaking the link end and bush overnight in penetrating fluid. Both bushes must be removed and installed using a press, although it may be possible to achieve the required result using a strong bench vice and sockets or pieces of tubing. Use liquid soap or petroleum jelly as a lubricant on fitting the new bush.

5   On refitting, the front mounting bolt retaining nut must be towards the outside. Tighten the bolts only lightly at first, then lower the car to the ground and rock it to settle the suspension components when all its weight is on its wheels. Tighten the mounting bolts to the specified torque setting.

17   Rear anti-roll bar and connecting links – removal and refitting

1   With the car standing on its wheels on firm, level ground, apply the handbrake firmly and select first or reverse gear (manual transmission) or the 'P' position (automatic). Chock the front wheels, jack up the rear of

17.2 Rear anti-roll bar is bolted to each suspension strut bottom bracket

the car and support it on axle stands.

2   Unscrew the bolt securing the anti-roll bar to the bracket at the bottom of each rear suspension strut (photo).

3   Unbolt the anti-roll bar clamps (photo) and withdraw the bar from under the car.

4   If required, the connecting links can be unbolted from the underbody.

5   Thoroughly clean all components, then check each for signs of wear or damage. In particular, check all rubber bushes for signs of cracks, splits or perishing and renew them if necessary.

6   If the connecting links are dismantled, note carefully the arrangement of the special dished washers which retain the rubber bushes. Ensure that these are correctly refitted and renew the self-locking nuts (if fitted).

7   If the bushes at each end of the anti-roll bar are to be renewed, they must be removed and installed using a press, although it may be possible to achieve the required result using a strong bench vice and sockets or pieces of tubing. Soak the bar end bushes overnight in penetrating fluid before attempting removal and use liquid soap or petroleum jelly as a lubricant on fitting the new bushes.

8   On refitting, first clean the areas around the bar mounting points. If the connecting links were disturbed, tighten the bolts securing their upper clamps to the underbody to the specified torque, but leave the link retaining nut slack.

17.3 Rear anti-roll bar connecting link to body

18.2 Remove both transverse link pivot bolt nuts (arrowed) to release rear (adjustable) transverse link

9   Enlist the aid of an assistant to manage the other end of the anti-roll bar and refit it to the car. First refit, and tighten loosely, the bolts securing each end of the bar to the bracket at the bottom of each rear suspension strut.

10   Aligning the bushes with the clamps, position the bar against the links and refit the clamps (slotted ends to the rear). Tighten the clamp bolts evenly and lightly.

11   Lower the car to the ground and rock it to settle the suspension components when all its weight is on its wheels.

12   Tighten the anti-roll bar-to-strut bottom bracket bolts, the bar clamp bolts (noting that these must be tightened evenly) and the connecting link retaining nuts to the specified torque setting (where a figure is given.)

18   Rear suspension transverse links – removal and refitting

Note: *Of the two transverse links on each side of the rear suspension, only the rearmost (adjustable) links can be removed without some preliminary dismantling work. To remove the front links either the fuel tank must be removed first (see Chapter 3) or the rear suspension crossmember must be removed completely and then dismantled (see Section 19 of this Chapter) or dismounted and lowered sufficiently to permit the removal of the link inboard pivot bolt.*

1   With the car standing on its wheels on firm, level ground, apply the handbrake firmly and select first or reverse gear (manual transmission) or the 'P' position (automatic). Chock the front wheels, slacken the rear roadwheel nuts,then jack up the rear of the car and support it on axle stands. Remove the roadwheel.

2   Unscrew both link pivot bolt retaining nuts (photo).

3   Remove the rear (adjustable) link.

4   Remove the link outboard pivot bolt.

5   If the rear suspension crossmember is to be removed or lowered, note that it may prove easier to remove the exhaust system rear section first (see Chapter 3) and the rear anti-roll bar (see Section 17 of this Chapter).

6   As soon as adequate working space is available, remove the link inboard pivot bolt and the front link.

7   Check the links and bushes for any signs of wear or damage and renew them if necessary. The bushes are not available separately, so a complete link must be renewed if either of its bushes are worn.

8   **Do not** disturb unnecessarily the setting of the rear (adjustable) link. If a new link is fitted, check that it is at the specified setting. (Section 36 of this Chapter.)

9   On refitting, thoroughly clean all components and the areas around their mounting points. Refitting is the reverse of the removal procedure, noting the following points. Tighten the crossmember mounting nuts to the specified torque setting. The transverse link pivot bolts must be fitted from front to rear and their nuts should be tightened to the

specified torque setting only when the car has been lowered to the ground so that all its weight is on its wheels. Rock the car to settle the suspension components before tightening.

10   It will be necessary to have the wheel alignment and steering angles checked (see Section 36 of this Chapter) on completion.

19   Rear suspension crossmember – removal and refitting

1   With the car standing on its wheels on firm, level ground, apply the handbrake firmly and select first or reverse gear (manual transmission) or the 'P' position (automatic). Chock the front wheels, slacken the rear roadwheel nuts, then jack up the rear of the car and support it on axle stands. Remove both roadwheels.

2   Unscrew all four transverse link pivot bolt retaining nuts. Remove the link outboard pivot bolts and, if necessary, the rear (adjustable) link. Mark each link clearly so that it can be refitted in its original position.

3   Slacken the bolt securing each end of the rear anti-roll bar to the bracket at the bottom of the suspension struts, remove the anti-roll bar clamps and allow the bar to hang down.

4   Either remove the exhaust system rear section (see Chapter 3), or release its mountings so that it hangs down clear of the crossmember.

5   Unscrew the four mounting nuts and withdraw the crossmember, complete with the transverse links. Remove the links, as described in Section 18 of this Chapter.

6   Thoroughly clean the crossmember and suspension components as well as the underbody areas around all mounting points.

7   Check the crossmember for cracks or distortion, especially around its mounting points and the transverse link pivots. Check the crossmember mounting stud threads for signs of wear or damage. If either the crossmember or the underbody show signs of rusting, the affected area must be cleaned back to bare metal and treated before being repainted (see Chapter 11). If extensive repairs are required, the crossmember should be renewed. For underbody repairs, seek professional advice.

8   Refitting is the reverse of the removal procedure, referring to the relevant Sections of this Chapter and to Chapter 3. Do not forget to refit the transverse links to the crossmember (adjustable links to the rear, pivot bolt fitted from front to rear) **before** fitting the crossmember to the body. Tighten the crossmember mounting nuts to the specified torque setting.

9   When the suspension is reassembled, lower the car to the ground and rock it to settle the suspension components when all its weight is on its wheels. Tighten to the specified torque setting the transverse link pivot bolt retaining nuts, the anti-roll bar clamp bolts and strut mounting bolts.

10   It will be necessary to have the wheel alignment and steering angles checked (see Section 36 of this Chapter) on completion.

20 Steering wheel – removal and refitting

Removal and refitting

1   Park the car on level ground with the roadwheels in the straight-ahead position and check that the steering wheel is in the neutral position (see below).
2   Disconnect the battery negative lead.
3   Remove the spoke cover or horn pad. On cars with the two-horn push, two-spoke wheel it is possible merely to prise out the square cover from the centre of the wheel to gain access to the steering wheel retaining nut, but access is much easier if the complete spoke cover is removed by unscrewing the two screws (accessible from the facia side of the steering wheel) which secure the spoke cover to the spokes. Disconnect the horn push wires to release the cover. On all other cars, carefully prise the horn pad off the centre of the steering wheel and disconnect the horn push wires to release the pad (photo).
4   Check that the steering wheel and column are marked in relation to each other (photo). A cast arrow (early models) or punch mark (later models) on the steering wheel should align exactly with a punch mark in the steering column. If no marks are found use a felt-tip pen or similar to make your own.
5   Unscrew the steering wheel retaining nut (photo) and remove (where fitted) the spring washer.
6   Grasp the steering wheel rim firmly and rock the wheel to jar it free, then pull it off the steering column splines. It is permissible to thump the wheel firmly from behind with the palms of the hands, but do not hammer the wheel or column, or use excessive force. On some cars the wheel centre is fitted with two tapped holes so that a small two-legged puller can be used to draw the steering wheel safely off the column.
7   On refitting, thoroughly clean and degrease the splines and tapered mating surfaces of the steering wheel and column. Apply a thin smear of multi-purpose grease to both mating surfaces of the direction indicator self-cancelling components and, on steering wheels with a central horn pad, to both faces of the horn push contacts.
8   Fit the steering wheel to the column, aligning the marks made or noted on removal (photo). This should leave the wheel in the neutral position (see below), with its spokes in the lower half of the wheel. Ensure that the direction indicator self-cancelling components are correctly engaged.
9   Refit the spring washer (where fitted) and the nut. Tighten the nut to the specified torque setting. Connect the horn push wires and refit the spoke cover or horn pad, then reconnect the battery.

Steering wheel neutral position

10   The steering wheel neutral position is when the steering wheel is located square to the facia (ie with the 'Nissan' emblem parallel to the instrument panel) with the spokes in the lower half of the wheel and the roadwheels are in the straight-ahead position.
11   If adjustment should be required, first check that the roadwheels are in the straight-ahead position and that the track rods are of the correct specified length (see Section 36 of this Chapter). Also check that the steering gear is exactly in its neutral position (using the pinion housing alignment marks on later models) and that the steering column lower joint is correctly installed. Finally, check that the steering wheel and column reference marks align exactly. This procedure should be

20.3 Remove horn pad and disconnect horn push wires ...

followed whenever the steering system is dismantled.
12   If the neutral position has altered, it can only be due to steering components that have been distorted or damaged, worn, or incorrectly assembled. These should be checked carefully before unnecessary adjustments are made.
13   If adjustment proves necessary, it can be made by re-positioning the wheel on the steering column splines. If the correct position falls between two splines it is permissible to make a small adjustment at the track rods, as described in Section 36 of this Chapter. Ensure that as one track rod is shortened the other is extended by exactly the same amount to preserve the correct steering angles and wheel alignment.

21 Steering column lock/ignition switch – removal and refitting

1   Disconnect the battery negative terminal.
2   Release the rake locking lever and pull the steering wheel and column to the lowest position.
3   Undo the four screws and withdraw the facia lower panel from below the steering column (photos).
4   Undo the four screws and unclip the steering column bottom shroud. Where applicable, disconnect the ignition switch illuminating bulb's wire. Remove the ignition switch surround and the steering column top shroud (photos).
5   Disconnect the ignition switch wiring connector.
6   Centre-punch the shear-head bolts which secure the lock to the column and drill off the bolt heads. New bolts will be required on refitting (photo).

20.4 ... note or make alignment marks between steering wheel and column (early type shown) ...

20.5 ... then unscrew retaining nut to release steering wheel

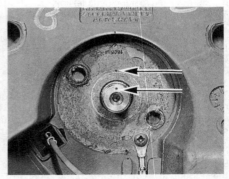

20.8 Align marks (arrowed – later type shown) on refitting steering wheel

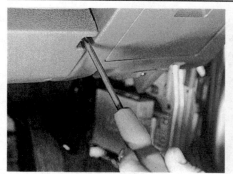

21.3A Remove four screws ...

21.3B ... and withdraw facia lower panel from beneath steering column

21.4A Remove four screws (remaining three arrowed) ...

21.4B ... then unclip steering column bottom shroud ...

21.4C ... and disconnect (where fitted) ignition switch illuminating bulb wire

21.4D ... then withdraw steering column top shroud

7   Remove the lock clamp, then withdraw the lock from the column.

8   If the lock is to be re-used, unscrew the remains of the shear-head bolts using a self-locking wrench or similar on the exposed ends.

9   The ignition switch can be detached, if required, by removing the retaining screws.

10   On refitting, position the lock assembly on the column and tighten the bolts lightly. Check that the lock operates correctly, with its tongue passing smoothly into the steering column cut-out. If necessary, reposition the lock slightly.

11   Tighten the new shear-head bolts evenly until their heads shear off. The remainder of the reassembly procedure is a reverse of removal.

22   Steering column – removal and refitting

1   Ensure that the roadwheels are in the straight-ahead position.

2   Disconnect the battery negative terminal and unlock the steering.

3   Remove the steering wheel (see Section 20 of this Chapter.)

4   Remove the steering column lower joint (see Section 24 of this Chapter.)

5   Release the rake locking lever and pull the steering column to the lowest position.

6   Undo the four screws and withdraw the facia lower panel from below the steering column.

7   Undo the four screws and unclip the steering column bottom shroud. Where applicable, disconnect the ignition switch illuminating bulb's wire. Remove the ignition switch surround and the steering column top shroud.

8   Disconnect the ignition switch wiring connector. Remove the retaining screws (where fitted) and slide out the steering column stalk switches, disconnect the wiring and remove them. Disconnect the horn wire(s) (photos).

9   Move aside the carpet or insulating material and unscrew the three nuts which secure the bulkhead aperture cover to the bulkhead. Remove the retaining screw and withdraw the flasher unit.

10   Unscrew the two bolts which secure the column upper mounting

21.6 Ignition switch/steering lock assembly is secured to column by shear-head bolts

to the bulkhead bracket; note the sliding plate fitted at each bolt hole (photo).

11   Unscrew the two bolts securing the column bottom mounting (photo) and withdraw the column from the car.

12   Refitting is a reverse of the removal procedure, but loosely assemble the column mountings and lower joint pinch-bolts and check that there is no undue stress on the column itself before tightening them to their specified torque settings. Note that alignment marks are provided to ensure that the bulkhead aperture cover is correctly located on the column jacket tube before its clamp and retaining nuts are fastened.

13   When reassembly is complete, jack up the front of the car and turn the steering from lock to lock to check that it is functioning correctly;

Fig. 10.30 Exploded view of steering column
(Secs 22 and 23)

1 Column assembly
2 Circlip
3 Plain washer
4 Lockwasher
5 Rake-adjusting lever
6 Clip
7 Column upper mounting
8 Sliding plate
9 Pivot bolt
10 Cover
11 Retainer
12 Spacer
13 Bulkhead aperture cover
14 Clamp
15 Lever pivot bolt
16 Stopper
17 Steering column
18 Jacket tube
19 Steering column lower joint
20 Pinch-bolt
21 Column upper mounting bolt
22 Column bottom mounting bolt
23 Nut
24 Lockwasher
25 Washer

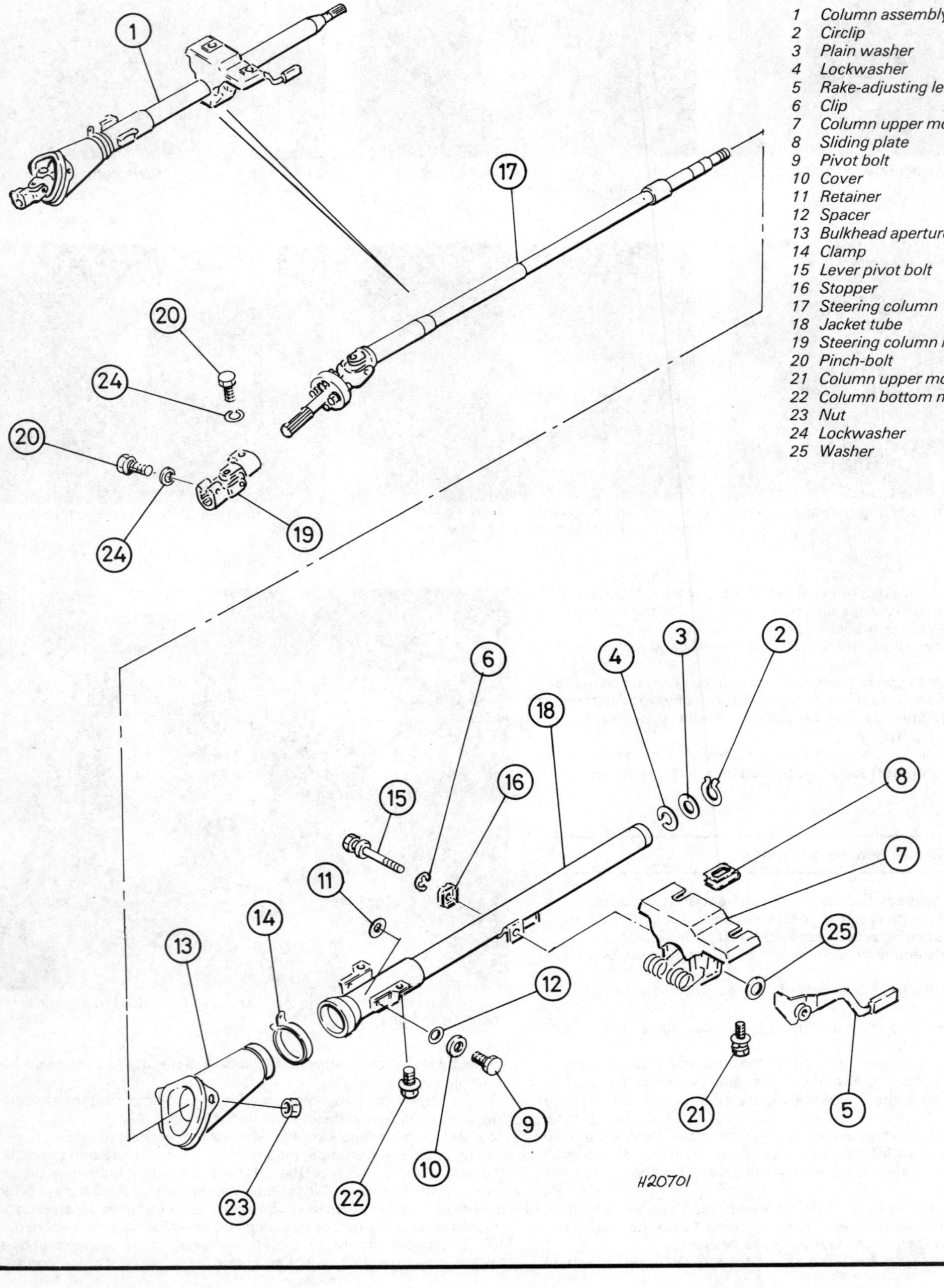

H20701

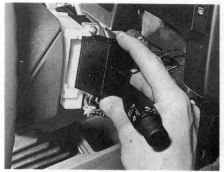

22.8A Slide out steering column stalk switches and disconnect wires ...

22.8B ... then disconnect horn wire(s)

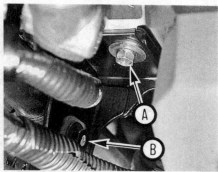

22.10 Steering column upper mounting bolt 'A' and rake-adjusting lever pivot bolt 'B'

22.11 Steering column bottom mounting bolts (arrowed) – pivot bolts for rake-adjusting mechanism also visible (flasher unit removed)

23.6 Showing correct fitted position of rake-adjusting mechanism spring

check carefully that the column is not binding or the steering stiff or restricted in movement.

14   Finally, check that the rake-adjusting mechanism works properly and that there is no trace of steering column movement when the locking lever is fastened.

23 Steering column – overhaul

1   Remove the steering column from the car, as described in the previous section of this Chapter.
2   Slacken the clamp and withdraw the bulkhead aperture cover.

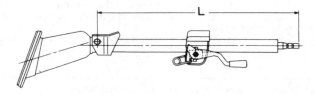

Fig. 10.31 Steering column length when undamaged (Sec 23)

L = 572.5 to 573.5 mm (22.539 to 22.579 in)

Remove the stalk switch base by removing its clamp screw (where fitted), then pressing it down, rotating it half a turn and withdrawing it.
3   Before further dismantling, check for excessive free play between the column and jacket tube, which might indicate worn bearings, or for signs of stiffness when rotating the column in the jacket tube, which might indicate that either or both of them is distorted or damaged. If the car has been involved in a front-end collision, measure the column's length (see Fig. 10.31). If the column is shorter than the specified length it must be renewed. Note that while the column and jacket tube are available separately, the bearings are only available as part of the jacket tube.
4   Remove the circlip, the plain washer and the lockwasher from the column upper end, then withdraw the column from the jacket tube.
5   Clean all components and check for obvious signs of wear or damage.
6   The rake-adjusting mechanism and pivot can be dismantled if required. On reassembly, ensure the spring is correctly refitted (photo) and grease the pivot bolt (as well as the slot into which it is fitted) before refitting it. Depress the lever through an angle of 13 to 16° from the locked position and tighten the bolt to the specified torque setting. Do not forget to check the mechanism when the steering column is refitted.
7   On reassembly, apply multi-purpose grease to the bearings and bearing surfaces of the column and jacket tube. Fit the column into the jacket tube and refit the lockwasher and plain washer. Fit the circlip, with its rounded surface downwards, to secure the assembly, then refit the bulkhead aperture cover and tighten its clamp loosely. Refit the stalk switch base to the top of the column, ensuring its locating protrusion engages with the hole in the column.

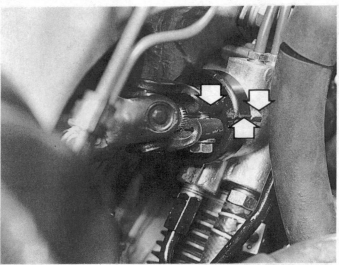

24.2 On later models, steering gear is in neutral position if lower joint slit, pinion cap mark and gear housing marks (arrowed) are all aligned

24.9 When refitting, joint longer section (arrowed) should be uppermost and joint slit should align with reference marks, as shown

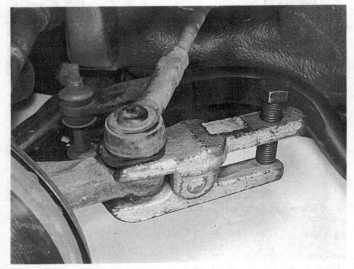

25.5A Using a universal balljoint separator tool to release track rod outer balljoint ...

25.5B ... from hub carrier steering arm – note early type of balljoint shown

24 Steering column lower joint – removal and refitting

1   Ensure that the roadwheels are in the straight-ahead position and that the steering wheel is in the neutral position (see Section 20 of this Chapter.)
2   Check for reference marks between the pinion shaft, the housing cap and the pinion housing. These should be present on all later models (photo) and should align when the steering gear is exactly in its neutral position. If no marks can be found, use paint or similar to make your own marks, especially between the cap and the housing. Note that on some models the steering column, lower joint and pinion may have a broad master spline to ensure exact alignment. Again, paint can be used to make reference marks as a guide to correct refitting.
3   Unscrew and remove both lower joint pinch-bolts.
4   Lift the joint upwards off the pinion splines, then slide it downwards off the steering column splines. If it is tight, gently prise the joint slits apart with a screwdriver.
5   Check the joint for wear or damage, and renew it and its pinch-bolts if necessary.
6   On refitting, first check that the steering wheel is aligned correctly on the steering column and that the wheel is in the neutral position.
7   Refit the lower joint (longer joint section uppermost) to the steering column so that the pinch-bolt hole is exactly square to the slot cut in the

column splines; the pinch-bolt should be an easy fit in the joint. On later models, aligning the master spline should automatically find the correct position, while on earlier models, the paint marks made on removal should help to ensure correct refitting.
8   Check that the steering gear is exactly in its neutral position and that the reference marks between the pinion shaft, the housing cap and the pinion housing (noted or made on removal) are aligned exactly.
9   Refit the lower joint to the pinion shaft, ensuring that its slit aligns exactly with the reference mark on the housing cap (photo). On later models, aligning the master spline should automatically find the correct position, while on earlier models the paint marks made on removal should help to ensure correct refitting.
10   Check that both the steering wheel and the steering gear are still in their respective neutral positions, then check that both lower joint pinch-bolts are an easy fit.
11   Refit both lower joint pinch-bolts and tighten them to the specified torque setting.

25 Track rod outer balljoint – removal and refitting

1   With the car standing on its wheels, apply the handbrake firmly and select first or reverse gear (manual transmission) or the 'P' position (automatic).

2   Remove the roadwheel trim, (where necessary) and slacken the roadwheel nuts.

3   Jack up the front of the car and support it on axle stands. Remove the roadwheel.

4   If the balljoint is to be re-used, use a straight-edge and a scriber or similar to mark its relationship to the track rod. Unscrew the balljoint locknut by one quarter of a turn.

5   Extract the split pin and unscrew the balljoint retaining nut. Then separate the balljoint from the hub carrier, using if necessary a universal balljoint separator tool (photos).

6   Counting the exact number of turns necessary to do so, unscrew the balljoint from the track rod. Note that the depth of track rod thread in the balljoint should be at least 25 mm (0.98 in).

7   Carefully clean the balljoint and the track rod threads.

8   Renew the balljoint if its rubber dust cover is cracked, split or perished or if its movement is either sloppy or too stiff. Check also for other signs of damage such as worn threads.

9   On refitting, screw the balljoint on to the track rod by the number of turns noted on removal. This should, of course, bring the balljoint to within a quarter of a turn from the locknut, with the alignment marks that were made (if applicable) on removal lined up. Note that the depth of track rod thread in the balljoint should be at least 25 mm (0.98 in).

10   Degrease the tapers of the balljoint stud and the hub carrier, then press the balljoint firmly into the hub carrier while the retaining nut is refitted and tightened to the specified torque setting. Fit a new split pin to secure the nut.

11   If the car is to be driven to have the wheel alignment and steering angles checked, tighten the balljoint locknut securely, refit the road-wheel and lower the car to the ground. Otherwise refit the roadwheel, lower the car to the ground and check the wheel alignment and steering angles (Section 36 of this Chapter), then tighten the locknut securely.

26   Track rod and inner balljoint – removal and refitting

Note: *On later T72 models with UK-built power-assisted steering gear, the track rod and inner balljoint assemblies are not available separately. If either is worn, damaged or faulty it can be repaired only by the renewal of the complete steering gear (see Sections 28 and 30 of this Chapter.)*

On all cars with manual steering, and T12 and early T72 models with Japanese-built power-assisted steering gears, the track rod and inner balljoint assemblies can be removed and refitted (given suitable tools) when the steering gear is in place on the car. Access is, however, limited and owners may prefer to remove the steering gear from the car (see Section 28 of this Chapter) so that the operation can be carried out on the bench.

1   With the car standing on its wheels, apply the handbrake firmly and select first or reverse gear (manual transmission) or the 'P' position (automatic).

2   Remove the roadwheel trim (where necessary) and slacken the roadwheel nuts.

3   Jack up the front of the car and support it on axle stands. Remove the roadwheel.

4   Remove the track rod outer balljoint, as described in Section 25 of this Chapter. Carefully clean the track rod and unscrew the balljoint locknut.

5   The procedure now varies according to the steering system and side being serviced.

Manual steering (left-hand side)

6   Remove or slacken the clips and slide the balljoint dust cover (where fitted) outwards along the track rod.

7   Use paint or similar to mark the relationship of the rubber gaiter to the steering gear housing, then remove or slacken its clips and slide the gaiter inwards along the housing until it is clear of the steering damper bracket.

8   Turn the steering wheel fully to the right. Prise up the lockplate ears and unscrew the track rod and inner balljoint with one spanner while holding the rack steady with a second spanner. Collect the lockplate and steering damper bracket.

9   Renew the track rod and inner balljoint as a single assembly if the balljoint's movement is either sloppy or too stiff. Do not attempt to dismantle them further. Renew the lockplate as a matter of course

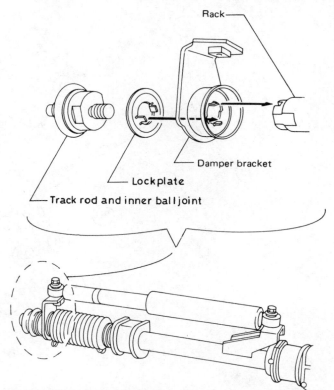

Fig. 10.32 Showing correct fitting of lockplate and steering damper bracket to rack end – manual steering gear, left-hand side (Sec 26)

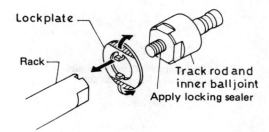

Fig. 10.33 Showing correct fitting of lockplate to rack end – manual steering gear, right-hand side, power-assisted steering gear, both sides (Sec 26)

whenever it is disturbed.

10   On reassembly, thoroughly clean all components and degrease the threads of the inner balljoint and of the rack. Refit the gaiter, dust cover and clips. Pack the balljoint with the specified grease.

11   Refit the steering damper bracket to the rack end, followed by the new lockplate. Ensure that their locating tabs engage correctly with each other and with the rack (Fig. 10.32).

12   Applying a few drops of locking compound to the threads, screw the track rod and inner balljoint into the rack. Tighten them securely, to the specified torque setting if possible.

13   Lock the inner balljoint and track rod by bending two parts of the lockplate on to opposite flats, then use a fine file to smooth down any burrs or rough edges.

14   Refit the gaiter and (if fitted) the balljoint dust cover, and secure them with their clips as described in Section 27 of this Chapter.

Manual steering (right-hand side) and power-assisted steering (both sides)

15   Use paint or similar to mark the relationship of the rubber gaiter to the steering gear housing, disconnect the breather tube (where fitted), then remove or slacken the clips and slide the gaiter outwards along the track rod.

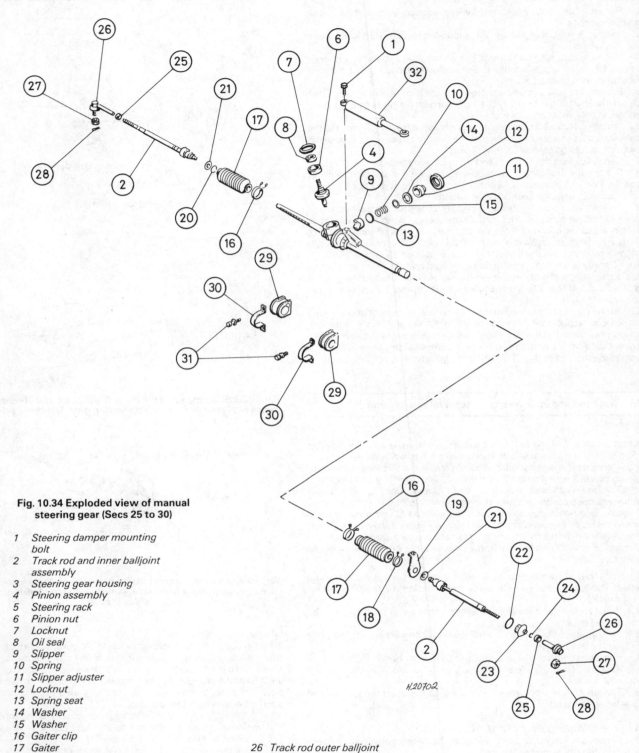

Fig. 10.34 Exploded view of manual steering gear (Secs 25 to 30)

1 Steering damper mounting bolt
2 Track rod and inner balljoint assembly
3 Steering gear housing
4 Pinion assembly
5 Steering rack
6 Pinion nut
7 Locknut
8 Oil seal
9 Slipper
10 Spring
11 Slipper adjuster
12 Locknut
13 Spring seat
14 Washer
15 Washer
16 Gaiter clip
17 Gaiter
18 Gaiter clip
19 Steering damper bracket
20 Gaiter clip
21 Lockplate
22 Dust cover clip
23 Dust cover
24 Dust cover clip
25 Track rod outer balljoint locknut

26 Track rod outer balljoint
27 Track rod outer balljoint retaining nut
28 Split pin
29 Steering gear mounting rubber
30 Steering gear mounting clamp
31 Clamp bolt
32 Steering damper

H.20702

16   Prise up the lockplate ears and unscrew the track rod and inner balljoint with one spanner while holding steady the rack with a second spanner. Collect the lockplate and, on turbo engine models only, the rack spanner.

17   Renew the track rod and inner balljoint as a single assembly if the balljoint's movement is either sloppy or too stiff. Do not attempt to dismantle them further. Renew the lockplate as a matter of course whenever it is disturbed.

18   On reassembly, thoroughly clean all components and degrease the threads of the inner balljoint and of the rack. Refit the gaiter and clips to the track rod. Pack the balljoint with the specified grease.

19   Fit the new lockplate to the rack end, ensuring that its locating tabs engage correctly with the rack. On turbo engine models, do not forget to refit the spacer between the rack end and the lockplate (Fig. 10.33).

20   Applying a few drops of locking compound to the threads, screw the inner balljoint and track rod into the rack. Tighten them securely, to the specified torque setting if possible.

21   Lock the inner balljoint and track rod by bending two parts of the lockplate on to opposite flats, then use a fine file to smooth down any burrs or rough edges.

22   Refit the gaiter and secure it with its clips (see Section 27 of this Chapter.)

All models

23   Refit the track rod outer balljoint and roadwheel, lower the car to the ground and check the wheel alignment and steering angles (see Section 25 of this Chapter.)

27 Steering gear rubber gaiters – removal and refitting

Note: *While this task is possible, with suitable tools, when the steering gear is in place on the car, access is limited and owners may prefer to remove the steering gear from the car (see Section 28 of this Chapter) so that the operation can be carried out on the bench.*

1   With the car standing on its wheels, apply the handbrake firmly, and select first or reverse gear (manual transmission) or the 'P' position (automatic).

2   Remove the roadwheel trim (where necessary) and slacken the roadwheel nuts.

3   Jack up the front of the car and support it on axle stands. Remove the roadwheel.

4   Remove the track rod outer balljoint, as described in Section 25 of this Chapter. Carefully clean the track rod and unscrew the balljoint locknut.

5   The procedure now varies according to the steering system and side being serviced.

Manual steering (left-hand side)

6   Remove or slacken the clips and slide the balljoint dust cover outwards along the track rod.

7   Use paint or similar to mark the relationship of the rubber gaiter to the steering gear housing, then remove or slacken the clips and slide the gaiter inwards along the housing until it is clear of the steering damper bracket.

8   Turn the steering wheel fully to the right and disconnect the inner balljoint and track rod from the steering rack (see Section 26 of this Chapter.)

9   Slide the gaiter off the gear housing and check it for cracks, splits, tears or any other signs of damage. Similarly remove and check the dust cover. Renew them if they are worn, damaged or leaking. Renew the clips as a matter of course whenever they are disturbed.

10   On reassembly, clean the gear housing and track rod. Use liquid soap or petroleum jelly as a lubricant when fitting the dust cover to the track rod. Fit the gaiter and clips to the gear housing and refit the track rod and inner balljoint to the rack (see Section 26 of this Chapter.)

11   Apply a smear of suitable sealant to the gaiter's mating surface on the gear housing and position the gaiter correctly on the housing and on the steering damper bracket; if applicable, align the marks made on removal. Slide the dust cover into place and secure both gaiter and cover by fitting new clips.

12   If the gaiter clips consist of a length of wire with a loop at each end they are installed as follows. Wrap the clip twice around the gaiter groove so that the looped ends are at the rear (when the steering gear is installed in the car). Pass a screwdriver or similar through the loops and twist them together through 4 to 4½ turns while pulling firmly. **Do not** overtighten the clips. Bend the twisted end neatly out of the way so that it cannot foul any other component or rub on the gaiter.

Manual steering (right-hand side) and power-assisted steering (both sides)

13   Use paint or similar to mark the relationship of the rubber gaiter to the steering gear housing, disconnect the breather tube (if fitted), then remove or slacken the clips and slide the gaiter outwards off the track rod.

14   Check the gaiter for cracks, splits or tears and renew it if it shows these or any other signs of damage or leakage. Renew the clips as a matter of course whenever they are disturbed.

15   On reassembly, clean the gear housing and track rod and be very careful not to damage the gaiter as it is installed. Do not forget to grease the inner balljoint.

16   Apply a smear of suitable sealant to the gaiter's mating surface on the gear housing (both systems) and track rod (power-assisted steering only). Slide the gaiter into place, aligning the marks made on removal, if applicable, and secure it by fitting new clips. If the clips are of the wire type, fit them as described in paragraph 12 above.

All models

17   Refit the track rod outer balljoint and roadwheel, lower the car to the ground and check the wheel alignment and steering angles (see Section 25 of this Chapter.)

28 Steering gear – removal and refitting

Manual steering system

1   With the car standing on its wheels, apply the handbrake firmly and select first or reverse gear (manual transmission) or the 'P' position (automatic).

2   Remove the roadwheel trim (where necessary) and slacken the roadwheel nuts.

3   Jack up the front of the car and support it on axle stands. Remove both roadwheels.

4   Disconnect the track rod outer balljoints from the hub carrier steering arms (see Section 25 of this Chapter.)

5   Rotate the steering wheel to the neutral position, then remove the ignition key so that the steering is locked.

6   Remove the steering column lower joint, ensuring that alignment marks are made or noted, as described in Section 24 of this Chapter.

7   Unscrew the four steering gear mounting bolts and collect the two clamps.

8   Withdraw the steering gear through the aperture at the rear of either wheel arch. Renew the mounting rubbers if they are worn or damaged.

9   Refitting is the reverse of the removal procedure. Ensure that all nuts and bolts are fastened securely, to the specified torque settings. Check the wheel alignment and steering angles (see Section 36 of this Chapter.)

Power-assisted steering system

10   Carry out the preliminary dismantling procedures described in paragraphs 1 to 6 above.

11   Using a brake hose clamp, a G-clamp or similar tool, clamp the short length of flexible tubing which is connected to a spigot on the steering gear pinion housing, slacken the clip and pull the tubing off the spigot. Mop up any spilt fluid, remembering that it may be hot enough to cause injury.

12   Again, using a brake hose clamp, a G-clamp or similar tool, clamp the large-diameter pressure hose connecting the pump to the union mounted just in front of the steering gear, then trace the metal supply pipe from that union to the steering gear pinion housing and unscrew the long sleeve nut (photo). Be prepared to catch any spilt fluid.

13   The clamps securing this pump-to-gaiter supply hose union (and pressure switch, where fitted) is retained by four bolts. Two are removed from above, working inside the engine compartment. Working underneath the car, unscrew the two retaining screws to release the

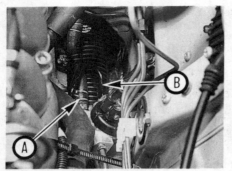

28.12 Removing power-assisted steering gear – disconnect fluid return hose A and supply pipe B from steering gear pinion housing

28.13A Remove two clamp bolts (arrowed) from above

28.13B Work underneath car to remove heat shield from above exhaust – note steering gear mounting bolts (seen with engine removed, for clarity) ...

28.13C ... then remove two lower clamp bolts (arrowed) to release clamp

28.15 Steering gear right-hand lower mounting clamp bolt (from below)

28.16 Withdrawing steering gear

heat shield from above the exhaust system flexible section, then remove the other two clamp bolts (photos).

14   Returning to the engine compartment, dismantle the clamp, disconnect the supply pipe from the steering gear pinion housing and secure the assembly clear of the steering gear. Collect the sealing O-ring from the pinion housing aperture and discard it.

15   Unscrew the four steering gear mounting bolts (photo) and collect the two clamps.

16   Withdraw the steering gear through the aperture at the rear of either wheel arch (photo). Renew the mounting rubbers if they are worn or damaged.

17   Refitting is the reverse of the removal procedure. Always renew any sealing O-rings or gaskets found at the fluid pipe or hose unions and check that all nuts and bolts are fastened securely, to the specified torque settings. Top up the fluid reservoir and bleed any air from the system, as described in Section 35 of this Chapter. Check the wheel alignment and steering angles, as described in Section 36.

29   Steering gear – in-car checks

1   Owners tracing the cause of a suspected fault in the steering system should note the following checks, which are additional to those given in Section 2 of this Chapter.

Checking the rack slipper adjustment

2   First check that the tyres are in good condition and inflated to the correct pressure, also that the brakes are not binding.

3   Drive the car along a flat, level road and check that it continues to move in a straight line when the steering wheel is released from the neutral position.

4   Next carefully check that the steering wheel returns to the neutral position when it is released from a slightly (approx 20°) rotated position on either side of neutral.

5   If the response is slow or stiff, first check the rack slipper adjustment, as described in the relevant part of Section 30 of this Chapter.

Note that the adjuster is not accessible when the steering gear is installed in the car, therefore the gear must be removed first (see Section 28 of this Chapter.)

Checking the steering wheel turning force (power-assisted steering only)

6   First check that the fluid level and pump drivebelt tension are correct, that the tyres are in good condition and that they are inflated to the correct pressures.

7   With the car parked on dry, level, tarmac or concrete, start the engine and turn the steering several times from lock to lock until the fluid is warmed up (60 to 80°C/140 to 176°F). Rotate the steering wheel one full turn (360°) in either direction from the neutral position, then attach a spring balance to the steering wheel rim and measure the force required to rotate the wheel further in that direction with the engine at idle speed.

8   If the force measured exceeds that specified there is a fault in the system. The hydraulic system can be checked only by measuring its operating pressure, which is a task for a Nissan dealer who has the necessary equipment. The gear itself can be checked only by removing it from the car (see Section 28 of this Chapter) and measuring the pinion rotating torque and rack sliding force as described in the relevant part of Section 30. If the steering gear proves to be faulty it must be renewed as a complete unit.

30   Steering gear – overhaul

Manual steering gear

Note: *Before attempting to overhaul the steering gear, check the price and availability of individual components and the price of a new or reconditioned unit, as gear overhaul may not be viable on economic grounds alone. Also, read through the procedure concerned and check that the special tools and facilities required are available.*

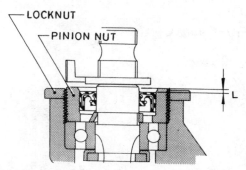

Fig. 10.35 Showing correct fitting of pinion nut oil seal – manual steering gear (Sec 30)

Depth L = 1.5 ± 0.3 mm (0.059 ± 0.012 in)

1   Remove the steering gear from the car (see Section 28 of this Chapter.)
2   Thoroughly clean the steering gear assembly, prepare a clean working area and observe scrupulous cleanliness throughout the overhaul.
3   Remove both track rod and inner balljoint assemblies and the rubber gaiters (see Sections 26 and 27.) Mark clearly the left- and right-hand components so that they cannot be interchanged on refitting.
4   Unbolt the steering damper. Check it for obvious signs of wear, damage or fluid leakage. Pump it through its full stroke and check that the damping is firm and even in both directions. If the damper is damaged, leaking or ineffective it must be renewed.
5   Slacken the locknut and unscrew the slipper adjuster, then withdraw both washers, the spring and spring seat and the slipper itself.
6   With the rack centred in the neutral position (ie protruding an equal amount from each side of the gear housing), check that alignment marks are made or noted between the pinion shaft and the pinion housing. Slacken the locknut, then unscrew the pinion nut using Nissan tool KV4810200. If this is not available, a serviceable copy can be made by obtaining a length of tubing of suitable diameter and wall thickness and cutting away four segments from one end to leave four pegs which will fit fully into the pinion nut slots. Drill the other end of the tubing to accept a tommy bar, or weld an old socket to it.
7   Withdraw the pinion assembly. Slide off the pinion nut and extract the oil seal from its centre. Discard the oil seal, which must be renewed as a matter of course whenever the assembly is disturbed. **Do not** attempt to dismantle the pinion assembly any further.
8   Withdraw the rack from the gear housing.
9   Thoroughly clean all components and renew any that show obvious signs of wear or damage. Roll the rack on a sheet of plate glass or similar flat surface to check that it is not bent or distorted, then check the teeth of the rack and of the pinion. Check the pinion bearing and rack bearing surfaces for signs of wear. Renew as a matter of course all oil seals, sealing washers and O-rings, the gaiter clips and track rod inner balljoint lockplate.
10   On reassembly, thoroughly lubricate all components with the specified multi-purpose grease.
11   Grease the rack and insert it from the pinion housing end. Set it to the neutral position, with an equal amount (75 mm/2.9 in) protruding from each end of the steering housing.
12   Fill the pinion housing with grease and pack the pinion assembly with grease, then hold the rack steady and insert the pinion, meshing its teeth with those of the rack. Ensure that the alignment marks made or noted on removal between the pinion shaft and the housing are exactly in line, so that the steering gear is correctly set in the neutral position.
13   Refit the pinion nut, applying a few drops of locking compound to its threads, and tighten it securely, to the specified torque setting if possible. Do not allow any locking compound to drop into the pinion bearing. Refit and tighten the pinion nut locknut to its specified torque setting.
14   Grease the sealing lips and press a new oil seal into the pinion nut until it is exactly at the specified depth (see Fig. 10.35.) Check that the rack and pinion components are correctly installed by moving the rack

once or twice from side to side. It should slide smoothly and easily while the pinion rotates. Centre the rack again, as described in paragraph 11 above.
15   Grease and refit the slipper, followed by the spring seat, the spring, both washers and the adjuster and its locknut; apply a few drops of locking compound to the adjuster's threads before installing it.
16   Check that the slipper is correctly seated against the rack by tightening the adjuster to a torque setting of 4.9 Nm (3.6 lbf ft), then move the rack fully from side to side and centre it again. Check that the adjuster is still fastened to the same torque setting and repeat the procedure if necessary. Next slacken the adjuster and re-tighten it to a torque setting of 0.2 Nm (0.1 lbf ft), then again move the rack fully from side to side and centre it.
17   In order to set the slipper correctly, some means must be devised of measuring the pinion's rotating torque. The Nissan tools for this task are a torque wrench and adaptors, No. ST3127S00 and an adaptor for the pinion shaft, No. KV48101100. If these are not available, refit the steering column lower joint to the pinion shaft and use the pinch-bolt to clamp a strip of metal into the joint's slit so that the strip projects radially outwards from the shaft. Mark the strip at a distance of 1 in from the shaft centre and attach a spring balance (capable of reading sensitively over a range of 1 to 10 lbs) to the strip at that point. By holding the balance at right angles to the strip at all times the force can be measured (in lbf in) that is required to rotate the pinion.
18   Rotate the pinion half a turn (180°) anti-clockwise from the neutral position, then measure the torque while turning it slowly clockwise through one full turn. Find the point at which the rotating torque is greatest, then slacken the adjuster and re-tighten it **by hand only** until it just touches the slipper. Hold the adjuster steady and tighten the locknut to the specified torque setting. **Do not** overtighten the adjuster.
19   To check the setting, return the pinion to the neutral position, then rotate it 100° (ie just over one quarter of a turn) anti-clockwise and carefully measure the rotating torque while turning the pinion slowly clockwise through 200° (ie just over half a turn). The **average** value (ie half the sum of the maximum and minimum forces measured) should be in the range specified, while the maximum permissible fluctuation between maximum and minimum forces should be 0.4 Nm (3.54 lbf in). Repeat if necessary to obtain an accurate reading.
20   Repeat the check, this time rotating the pinion through an angle of 500° each side of the neutral position (ie 500° anti-clockwise, then 1000°, or 2¼ turns, clockwise) The **average** value should still be in the range specified, but the maximum permissible fluctuation can be up to 0.6 Nm (5.31 lbf in).
21   If the average of the rotating torque measured is not within the range specified, first of all reset the slipper adjustment (refer to paragraph 18 above) and measure the rotating torque again to ensure that an accurate setting is obtained and that the reading is correct.
22   If the rotating torque is still incorrect and is too low, renew the slipper spring.
23   If the rotating torque is still incorrect and is too high, slacken the adjuster in small steps, measuring the rotating torque at each alteration, until the correct average is obtained.
24   Refit the track rod and inner balljoint assemblies and the rubber gaiters (see Section 26 and 27 of this Chapter.) Refit the steering damper and tighten its mounting bolts to the specified torque setting.
25   Refit the steering gear to the car (see Section 28 of this Chapter.)

Power-assisted steering gear

Note: *The overhaul of the power-assisted steering gear is considered to be beyond the scope of the home mechanic and is therefore not described. The task requires a considerable degree of skill and a number of special tools and other equipment and owners should also note the following factors:*

(a)   Nissan specifically forbid the dismantling of the steering gear and advise that the complete steering gear is renewed, regardless of the nature of any faults found
(b)   The only individual components of the (Japanese-built) steering gear that are available separately are the various oil and fluid seals, and the gear cannot therefore be overhauled or repaired if it is worn, damaged or faulty. This is especially true of the UK-built gear, which is available only as a single unit, with the trackrod and inner balljoint assemblies.

26   To renew the steering gear, renew it from the car as described in Section 28 of this Chapter, then withdraw both rubber gaiters as

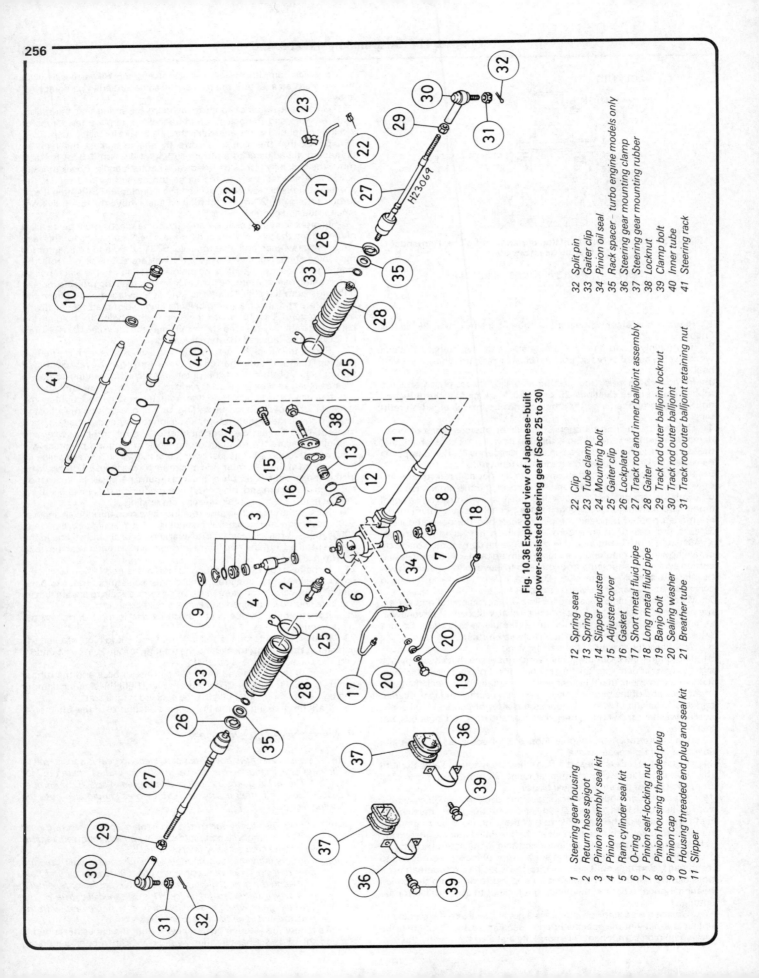

Fig. 10.36 Exploded view of Japanese-built power-assisted steering gear (Secs 25 to 30)

1   Steering gear housing
2   Return hose spigot
3   Pinion assembly seal kit
4   Pinion
5   Ram cylinder seal kit
6   O-ring
7   Pinion self-locking nut
8   Pinion housing threaded plug
9   Pinion cap
10 Housing threaded end plug and seal kit
11 Slipper

12 Spring seat
13 Spring
14 Slipper adjuster
15 Adjuster cover
16 Gasket
17 Short metal fluid pipe
18 Long metal fluid pipe
19 Banjo bolt
20 Sealing washer
21 Breather tube

22 Clip
23 Tube clamp
24 Mounting bolt
25 Gaiter clip
26 Lockplate
27 Track rod and inner balljoint assembly
28 Gaiter
29 Track rod outer balljoint locknut
30 Track rod outer balljoint
31 Track rod outer balljoint retaining nut

32 Split pin
33 Gaiter clip
34 Pinion oil seal
35 Rack spacer – turbo engine models only
36 Steering gear mounting clamp
37 Steering gear mounting rubber
38 Locknut
39 Clamp bolt
40 Inner tube
41 Steering rack

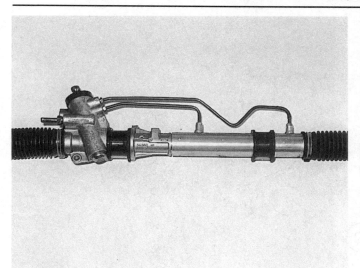

30.37 The UK-built power-assisted steering gear – do not attempt overhaul

described in Section 27 and (where possible) both track rod and inner balljoint assemblies as described in Section 26. Mark clearly the left- and right-hand components so that they cannot be interchanged on reassembly. Install the new steering gear, following the reverse of the removal procedure.

27   Owners tracing the cause of a steering fault should note that the gear's performance can be checked, as described below. Both checks require that the steering gear is removed from the car and mounted in a soft-jawed vice; be careful to avoid damaging the aluminium gear housing.

28   Unscrew the union flare nuts or banjo bolt (as applicable) and remove both metal fluid pipes, making careful notes as to their connections and routing for reference on removal. Move the rack slowly back and forth a few times and collect the fluid which will be expelled.

29   To set the gear's neutral position, place the rack so that it protrudes exactly the specified amount on each side of the gear housing. On turbo engine models, (15 in wheels) measure from the housing to the inboard edge of each rack spacer. Reference marks should be noted or made between the pinion shaft and the pinion housing, across the pinion caps.

30   To measure the rack's sliding force, empty the gear of fluid as described above and set it to the neutral position. Push the rack 5 mm (0.2 in) to one side, attach a spring balance to the opposite track rod outer balljoint and measure the force required to pull the rack 10 mm (0.4 in) in that direction (ie back through the neutral position).

31   If the force measured is significantly higher than the maximum specified, the steering gear is worn or damaged in some way and must be renewed. If the difference is marginal it is worth trying the effect of slipper adjustment (see below) before renewing the rack.

32   To measure the pinion's rotating torque, empty the gear of fluid as described above and set it to the neutral position. The basic procedure is as described in paragraphs 17 and 19 above but note that the pinion shaft adaptor should now be Nissan tool no. KV48100700. Also, while the **average** value is measured and calculated in the same way, the **maximum** force measured at any time should not exceed the specified figure. Repeat if necessary to obtain an accurate reading.

33   If the **average** of the rotating torque measured is not within the range specified, adjust the slipper setting as described below. If the **maximum** force measured exceeds that specified above, the steering gear is worn or damaged in some way and must be renewed. This is especially true if the rack sliding force is also too high.

34   To adjust the slipper setting, set the gear to the neutral position and slacken the adjuster locknut. Tighten the adjuster to a torque setting of 4.9 Nm (3.6 lbf ft), then move the rack fully from side to side and return it to the neutral position. Check that the adjuster is still fastened to the same torque setting and repeat the procedure, if necessary. Next slacken the adjuster and re-tighten it to a torque setting of 0.05 to 0.20 Nm (0.04 to 0.15 lbf ft). Apply a coat of sealant to the threads and base flange of the locknut and tighten it to the specified torque setting. Move the rack fully from side to side and return it to the neutral position, then re-measure the pinion's rotating torque.

35   If the average of the rotating torque is still incorrect and is too low, renew the slipper spring. Slacken the slipper adjuster locknut, remove the two mounting bolts and withdraw the assembly, complete with the gasket, spring, spring seat and the slipper itself. Check the slipper for wear or damage and renew it if necessary. On reassembly, grease the slipper components and renew the cover gasket. Set the slipper adjustment as described above and re-measure the pinion's rotating torque.

36   If the average of the rotating torque is still incorrect and is too high, slacken the adjuster in small steps, measuring the rotating torque at each alteration, until the correct average is obtained.

37   Note that the Fig. 10.36 refers to the Japanese-built steering gears fitted to T12 and early T72 models; the UK-built steering gear fitted to later T72 models (photo) is basically similar.

---

31   Power-assisted steering pump drivebelt – removal, refitting and adjustment

Refer to Chapter 2, Section 7.

---

32   Power-assisted steering pump – removal and refitting

1   On carburettor-engined models, the air filter assembly can be removed, if required for better access, as described in Chapter 3.

2   Using a brake hose clamp, a G-clamp or similar tool, clamp the large diameter pressure hoses running from the fluid reservoir to the pump and from the pump to the steering gear union. Slacken the clip and pull the reservoir-to-pump hose off its spigot. Unscrew the threaded coupling, while holding the coupling centre nut to prevent the hose twisting, and disconnect the pump-to-gear hose from the pump union. Plug or cover both hose ends to prevent the entry of dirt.

3   Slacken the pump pivot and adjuster nut and lockbolt, swivel the pump towards the engine and remove the drivebelt from the pump pulley.

4   Remove the pivot bolt and adjuster lockbolt, then withdraw the pump from the engine. Remove the two mounting bolts to release the adjuster bracket, if required.

5   Refitting is the reverse of the removal procedure. Adjust the drivebelt tension as described in Chapter 2. Top up the fluid reservoir and bleed any air from the system as described in Section 35 of this Chapter.

---

33   Power-assisted steering pump – overhaul

Note: *The power-assisted steering pump should* **not** *be overhauled by the home mechanic; the operation requires extreme cleanliness and a considerable degree of skill and experience. Furthermore, Nissan state that the pump should be dismantled only to renew the pulley or to cure fluid leaks. As a result, only the various seals are available separately. If the car has covered a high mileage and the pump is thought to be worn or damaged, the complete assembly must be renewed. To renew the pump or the pulley, proceed as follows.*

1   Remove the pump from the car (see Section 32 of this Chapter.)

2   Carefully clamp the pulley across a soft-jawed vice, tightening the vice by just enough to hold the pulley while the retaining nut is unscrewed. Collect the washer and remove the pump from the pulley.

3   If the pump shows signs of fluid leakage from any of its unions, mating surfaces or the pump shaft oil seal, take the unit to a Nissan dealer for repair. As stated above, if the pump is damaged or thought to be worn, it must be renewed, complete with its mounting bracket.

4   On refitting, tighten all nuts and bolts to the specified torque settings.

---

34   Power-assisted steering system pressure switch, pipes and reservoir – inspection, removal and refitting

1   The system incorporates the fluid reservoir (rubber-mounted between the front suspension right-hand strut and the bulkhead) from which a large- diameter pressure hose runs to the pump supply union on

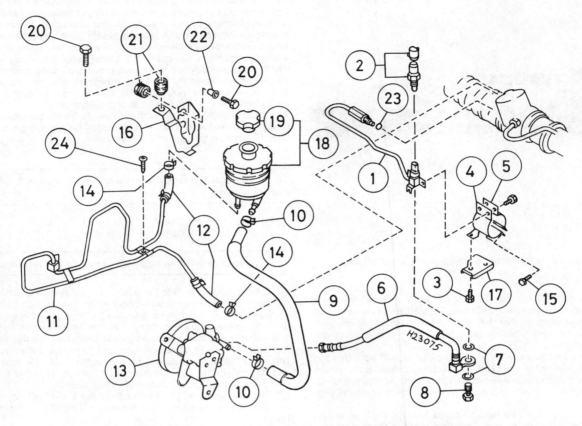

Fig. 10.37 Power-assisted steering system pipes and reservoir (Sec 34)

1	Metal fluid pipe – steering gear bracket to pinion housing	6 Pressure hose – pump to steering gear union	11 Metal return pipe – steering gear to reservoir	18 Reservoir assembly
2	Pressure switch (where fitted)	7 Sealing washer	12 Fluid hose	19 Reservoir filler cap
3	Heat shield screw	8 Banjo bolt	13 Fluid pump	20 Bolt
4	Clamp front half	9 Pressure hose – reservoir to pump supply union	14 Clip	21 Mounting rubber bush
5	Clamp rear half	10 Hose clip	15 Bolt	22 Spacer

1 Metal fluid pipe – steering
    gear bracket to pinion
    housing
2 Pressure switch (where
    fitted)
3 Heat shield screw
4 Clamp front half
5 Clamp rear half

6 Pressure hose – pump to
    steering gear union
7 Sealing washer
8 Banjo bolt
9 Pressure hose – reservoir to
    pump supply union
10 Hose clip

11 Metal return pipe – steering
    gear to reservoir
12 Fluid hose
13 Fluid pump
14 Clip
15 Bolt
16 Mounting bracket
17 Heat shield

18 Reservoir assembly
19 Reservoir filler cap
20 Bolt
21 Mounting rubber bush
22 Spacer
23 O-ring
24 Screw

the pump itself. The pressurised delivery from the pump runs from the pump's banjo union via a large-diameter pressure hose to a union in front of the steering gear (which is fitted with a pressure switch on early carburettor engine and turbo engine models) and from there via a metal pipe to the steering gear pinion housing. Two further metal pipes run from the steering gear pinion housing to points on the gear housing tube, on each side of the rack's ram cylinder.
2 The return from the steering gear pinion housing to the reservoir is by a long metal pipe which is mounted on the inner wing panel and connected at each end by a short length of flexible tubing.
3 Refer to 'Routine maintenance' for details of inspection procedures.
4 To remove the reservoir, syphon its fluid into a clean container, unbolt it from the inner wing and slacken the clips securing the supply and return flexible hoses. Disconnect the hoses and withdraw the reservoir, then cover or plug the hose ends to prevent the entry of dirt. Refitting is the reverse of the removal procedure. Fill the system with fluid and bleed out any trapped air as described in Section 35 of this Chapter.
5 Before any other part of the system is disturbed, ensure that the engine is switched off and that the fluid has cooled down. On carburettor engine models, the air filter assembly can be removed, if required for better access, as described in Chapter 3. Always clean the area around any union before disconnecting it.
6 To minimise fluid loss before disturbing any part of the system either drain the fluid completely (see below) or clamp the flexible hoses using a brake hose clamp, a G-clamp or similar tool. Alternatively,

disconnect the hose or pipe and plug both uncovered apertures as soon as possible, which will also prevent the entry of dirt into the system. Refill the system and bleed out trapped air (Section 35) on completion of the work.
7 To drain the fluid, disconnect the short length of flexible tubing from the steering gear pinion housing and allow the fluid to drain into a suitable container using a cardboard chute to minimise spillage. The process can be speeded up by connecting a length of plastic tubing to the steering gear spigot and running its other end into the container. Start the engine and run it at no more than idle speed while turning the steering wheel from lock to lock until all the fluid is expelled. Stop the engine as soon as the system is empty of fluid, or the pump may be damaged.
8 To renew the reservoir-to-pump supply hose or either of the short lengths of flexible tubing at each end of the gear-to-reservoir return pipe, syphon the fluid from the reservoir (where applicable) and slacken the clips securing each end, then work the hose or tubing off its spigots. On refitting, ensure that the hose or tubing is correctly routed and fully seated on both spigots before fastening the clips.
9 To renew the pump-to-steering gear union flexible hose, first either drain the system or clamp the reservoir-to-pump supply hose, then disconnect the hose from the pump by unscrewing the threaded coupling. Do not disturb the pump banjo union unnecessarily. If it is disturbed, the sealing washers must be renewed and the union must be positioned on refitting at an angle of 45° to a line running through the banjo bolt centre, parallel with the pump shaft, before the banjo bolt is

34.9 Move aside exhaust system and remove heat shield to reach pump-to- steering gear hose bottom banjo union (arrowed)

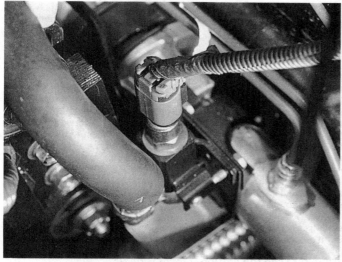

34.10 Where fitted, disconnect pressure switch before removing supply pipe

tightened. Working underneath the car, unscrew the retaining nuts and separate the exhaust system at the joint in front of its flexible section, then disconnect the mounting behind the flexible section so that the system can be moved far enough out of the way for the heat shield to be removed and the hose bottom end banjo bolt to be unscrewed (photo). Renew the sealing washers and exhaust gasket on refitting and tighten all bolts to the specified torque settings.

10   To renew the metal pipe running from the union in front of the steering gear to its pinion housing, first either drain the system or clamp the pump- to-steering gear union flexible hose. Working underneath the car, separate and move aside the exhaust system so that the heat shield can be removed and the flexible hose bottom end banjo union bolt can be unscrewed as described in paragraph 9 above. Disconnect the pressure switch, where fitted (photo), and unscrew the two bolts securing the union to the steering gear clamp. Unscrew the long sleeve nut securing the pipe to the pinion housing, then withdraw the pipe. On refitting, renew all seals, gaskets and sealing washers disturbed and tighten all bolts to the specified torque setting. Refill the system with fluid and bleed out any trapped air as described in Section 35 of this Chapter.

11   To renew either of the metal fluid pipes fitted to the steering gear,

unscrew the union nuts, preferably using a brake pipe spanner of the correct size, which will be available from most large motor accessory shops. Failing this, a close-fitting open-ended spanner will be required. However, if the nuts are tight or corroded their flats may be rounded-off if an open-ended spanner slips. On refitting, do not overtighten the union nuts; the specified torque settings are not high and it is not necessary to exercise brute force to obtain a sound joint. Where a banjo-type union is used, always renew the sealing washers whenever they are disturbed.

12   To renew the long metal gear-to-reservoir return pipe, disconnect the flexible tubing from each end (see paragraph 8 above) then unbolt the pipe from the inner wing. Note that the pipe acts as a rudimentary fluid cooler and must therefore be kept as clean as possible at all times.

13   To test the pressure switch, where fitted, disconnect the switch wires and connect a multimeter (set to the resistance function), or a battery and bulb test circuit, across its terminals. No continuity (ie infinite resistance) should be indicated. Start the engine and run it at no more than idle speed, then have an assistant turn the steering wheel fully from left to right lock. When a set pressure (actually 1961 to 2942 kPa/284 to 427 psi) is exceeded, at full lock, the switch contacts will close to show no resistance. If not, the switch is faulty and must be renewed.

14   To renew the switch, proceed as described in paragraphs 5 and 6 above, then disconnect the switch wires and unscrew it. On refitting, apply a smear of sealant to the switch threads and tighten securely before reconnecting it. Mop up the spilt fluid, top up the reservoir and bleed out any trapped air.

35   Power-assisted steering fluid – filling and bleeding

1   When refilling, use only good quality fluid of the specified type.

2   Check the reservoir fluid level as described in Section 2 of this Chapter.

3   The system should be bled if the level ever falls so low that air enters the system (as shown by air bubbles in the reservoir fluid or pronounced clicking or buzzing noises from the fluid pump) or if it is required after component renewal. First switch off the engine, then remove the reservoir filler cap and top up to the 'Max' level line.

4   Apply the handbrake, jack up the front of the car and support it securely on axle stands.

5   Quickly turn the steering wheel several times from lock to lock, ensuring that it touches the lock stops only lightly, then re-check the reservoir fluid level and top up.

6   Repeat the cycle of operating the steering and then topping-up until the reservoir fluid level no longer drops, then start the engine and run it at no more than idle speed. Turn the steering wheel ten times from lock to lock, as described in paragraph 5 above, then stop the engine, allow the fluid level to settle and top up if necessary. Repeat as often as necessary until the reservoir fluid level no longer drops.

7   When the level has stabilised, lower the car to the ground and run it for a few miles to warm up the fluid and system components thoroughly and to expel any remaining air. Stop the engine, allow the fluid to cool down completely, then top up if necessary to the 'Max' level line.

36   Wheel alignment and steering angles – checking and adjusting

1   Accurate wheel alignment is essential to provide positive steering and handling characteristics, and to prevent excessive tyre wear. Before considering the steering/suspension geometry, check that the tyres are in good condition and correctly inflated, the wheels are not buckled, and the steering linkage and suspension joints are in good order, without slackness or wear. The car must be parked on level ground and be at its kerb weight (see 'General dimensions, weights and capacities').

2   Wheel alignment consists of five factors:

Camber is the angle at which the roadwheels are set from the vertical when viewed from the front or rear of the car. Positive camber is the angle (in degrees) that the wheels are tilted outwards at the top from the vertical; negative camber is when the wheels are tilted inwards at the top. Camber is not adjustable.

Castor is the angle between the steering axis and a vertical line when

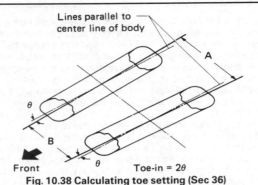

Fig. 10.38 Calculating toe setting (Sec 36)

Toe-in (front wheels) = $A - B$
Toe-out (rear wheels) = $B - A$

Note: If measuring angles, those specified are total values

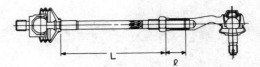

Fig. 10.39 Track rod basic setting (Sec 36)

Right-hand side length L = 177.9 mm (7.004 in)
Left-hand side length L = 178.4 mm (7.024 in)
Both sides length l = 25 mm (0.98 in) minimum

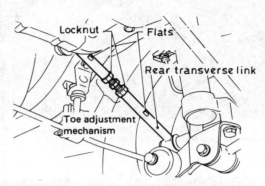

Fig. 10.40 Details of rear suspension toe setting components (Sec 36)

viewed from each side of the car. Positive castor is indicated when the steering axis is inclined towards the rear of the car at its upper end. Castor is not adjustable.

Steering axis inclination or SAI (also known as kingpin inclination or KPI), is the angle, when viewed from the front or rear of the car, between an imaginary vertical line drawn through the centre of the front wheel and an imaginary line drawn through the centres of the front suspension strut top mounting and the fork suspension lower arm balljoint. It is not adjustable.

Toe is the amount by which the distance between the front inside edges of the roadwheel rims differs from that between the rear inside edges, measured at hub centre height. If the distance at the front is less than at the rear, the wheels are said to 'toe-in'. If the distance at the front inside edges is greater than at the rear, the wheels 'toe-out'. On the front wheels, toe-in is adjusted by varying the length of the track rods, while on the rear wheels toe-out is adjusted by varying the length of the rear (adjustable) transverse links.

Turning angles are the differences in the angle of rotation, seen from above the car, between the inside and outside front wheels when measured at full lock and at 20° rotation of the outside wheel (toe-out in turns). The basic setting is adjusted by varying the length of the hub carrier steering lock stop bolts.

3   Due to the special measuring equipment necessary to check the wheel alignment and steering angles and the skill required to use it properly, the checking and adjustment (where possible) of these settings is best left to a Nissan dealer or similar. Alternatively many tyre-fitting shops now possess sophisticated checking equipment. Apart from the front and rear toe settings and the turning angles basic setting, all other steering and suspension angles are set in production and are not adjustable. If these angles are checked and found to be outside specification, then either the body or suspension components are damaged or distorted, or wear has occurred in the bushes at the mounting points.

Checking the toe setting – front and rear wheels

4   First obtain some means of measuring the toe setting; two methods are normally available to the home mechanic. The first is to use a gauge (sometimes known as a tracking gauge) which can measure the distance between the front and rear inside edges of the roadwheels. A home-made version can be fabricated from a length of steel tubing, cranked to clear the engine/transmission or suspension components, with a long bolt and locknut at one end. The second is to use a scuff plate, in which the roadwheel is rolled across a moveable plate which records any deviation, or scuff, of the tyre relative to the straight-ahead position as it moves across the plate. Both types are available in relatively inexpensive forms from accessory outlets to enable checking and adjustment to be carried out at home.

5   For accurate checking, the car must be at its kerb weight, the tyre pressures must be correct and the car must be parked on level ground so that it is level both front to rear and side to side. Rock the car at front and rear to settle the suspension, then check that the roadwheels are in the straight-ahead position. The steering wheel should be in the neutral position, as should the steering gear. In the latter case, check carefully that the rack protrudes the specified amount on each side of the gear housing (see Section 30).

6   Move the car backwards several feet, then push it forwards again. Follow the equipment manufacturer's instructions for the equipment being used to check the setting.

7   If a gauge is being used, first measure the distance between the inside edges of the roadwheel rims, at hub centre height at the rear of the wheels; call this dimension 'A'. Now push the car forwards so that the wheels rotate exactly 180° (half a turn) and measure the distance again, but now at hub centre height at the front of the wheels; call this dimension 'B'. The measurement would be much more accurate if it were to be repeated twice more, at points spaced 120° apart around the wheel rim, and the average of the three readings taken as the setting.

8   To calculate the toe-in for the front wheels refer to Fig. 10.38 and subtract dimension 'B' from dimension 'A'. To calculate the toe-out for the rear wheels, subtract dimension 'A' from dimension 'B'. The toe setting calculated should be within the specified range.

9   If adjustment is required proceed as described below.

Adjusting the toe setting – front wheels

10   If adjustment is required, first check that both track rods are at the specified basic setting (see Fig. 10.39). If there is any discrepancy, this should be taken into account during adjustment.

11   Slacken both track rod outer balljoint locknuts and apply open-ended spanners to the flats, either of the outer balljoint or of the track rod itself, to hold them while the locknut is unscrewed. If the threads are corroded, apply penetrating fluid before starting adjustment. Release the steering gear rubber gaiter (or dust cover) outboard clip and check that the gaiter or dust cover is free to rotate on the track rod.

12   Alter the length of **both** track rods **by exactly the same amount** by screwing them into the outer balljoints (to decrease toe-in) or out of the outer balljoints (to increase toe-in). Alter the setting by one-quarter of a turn only at a time, then re-check it as described above and repeat if necessary. Hold the outer balljoints vertically upright with an open-ended spanner while adjustment is made.

13   When the setting is correct, tighten the track rod outer balljoint locknuts securely, to the specified torque setting if possible. Check that the steering gear rubber gaiter or dust cover is not twisted (and apply sealant to its mating surface, on power-assisted steering gear) before fastening its clip. Check finally that both track rods are the same length and that the steering wheel is still in the neutral position. If not, the adjustment has not been made equally on both sides and problems will be encountered with tyre scrubbing in turns. The only solution is to return to the track rod basic setting and start the procedure again from paragraph 5 onwards.

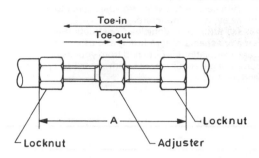

Fig. 10.41 Rear (adjustable) transverse link basic setting (Sec 36)

Length A = 50 to 55 mm (1.969 to 2.165 in)

Adjusting the toe-setting – rear wheels

14   If adjusting is required, first check that both rear (adjustable) transverse links are at the specified basic setting (Fig. 10.41). If there is any discrepancy between the two the rear suspension and body should be checked carefully for damage or distortion.

15   Slacken fully both adjuster locknuts on each link. Do not allow the link to twist on its mounting bush. Instead, hold the inboard or outboard link section by applying an open-ended spanner to the flats provided while the appropriate locknut is slackened. If the threads are corroded, apply penetrating fluid before starting adjustment.

16   Alter the length of **both** transverse links **by exactly the same amount** by screwing the adjusters into the inboard and outboard link sections (to shorten the link and increase toe-out) or out of them (to decrease toe-out). Alter the setting by one-quarter of a turn at a time, then re-check it as described above and repeat if necessary.

17   When the setting is correct, tighten all locknuts securely, to the specified torque setting if possible. Ensure that the link sections are held securely with an open-ended spanner while the locknuts are tightened.

Checking and adjusting the front wheel turning angles

18   These angles can be checked using only a pair of scuff plates. If these are available, prepare the car as described in paragraphs 5 and 6 above and push it forwards on to the scuff plates until the front roadwheels are seated squarely on the centre of each.

19   Turn the steering wheel first one way, until the outside wheel is at an angle of 20°, then check the angle of the inside wheel. Next turn the steering wheel the other way, back through the neutral position, and repeat the check in that direction.

20   Turn the steering wheel to full lock and measure the wheel angles. On cars with power-assisted steering, start the engine and run it at no more than idle speed, then have an assistant use a spring balance attached to the steering wheel rim to apply a turning force of 98 to 147 N (22 to 33 lbf) while the angles are noted. Turn the steering wheel to the opposite lock and repeat the check in that direction.

21   If the angles are incorrect at full lock, check that the hub carrier steering lock stop bolts are at the specified basic setting (see Fig. 10.42) and that each bolt's plastic cap is in place and in good condition; renew the caps if necessary. Slacken the locknuts and screw the bolts in or out as necessary, by one-quarter of a turn at a time, re-checking the angles at each adjustment.

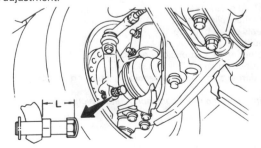

Fig. 10.42 Hub carrier steering lock stop bolt basic setting (Sec 36)

Turbo engine models (15 in wheels) L = 31 mm (1.221 in)
All other models (14 in wheels) L = 24 mm (0.945 in)

22   Note that both bolts should be the same length and should not vary from the basic setting. If difficulty is encountered in achieving the correct setting, slacken the clips and peel back both steering gear rubber gaiters, then check that the rack protrudes the specified amount on each side of the gear housing when the steering gear is in the neutral position. On T12 and early T72 turbo engine models with Japanese-built power-assisted steering gear, check that the spacers are correctly installed at each end of the rack (see Section 30 of this Chapter.)

23   If the angles are correct at full lock but not at the part-lock position, or if there is any discrepancy between the measurements obtained at either check on each side of the car, then one or more components of the steering linkage, front suspension or body are damaged or distorted. Have the car checked as soon as possible by a Nissan dealer.

37   Wheels and tyres – general care and maintenance

Wheels and tyres should give no real problems in use provided that a close eye is kept on them with regard to excessive wear or damage. To this end, the following points should be noted.

Ensure that tyre pressures are checked regularly and maintained correctly. Checking should be carried out with the tyres cold and not immediately after the vehicle has been in use. If the pressures are checked with the tyres hot, an apparently high reading will be obtained owing to heat expansion. Under no circumstances should an attempt be made to reduce the pressures to the quoted cold reading in this instance, or effective underinflation will result.

Underinflation will cause overheating of the tyre owing to excessive flexing of the casing, and the tread will not sit correctly on the road surface. This will cause a consequent loss of adhesion and excessive wear, not to mention the danger of sudden tyre failure due to heat build-up.

Overinflation will cause rapid wear of the centre part of the tyre tread coupled with reduced adhesion, harsher ride, and the danger of shock damage occurring in the tyre casing.

Regularly check the tyres for damage in the form of cuts or bulges, especially in the sidewalls. Remove any nails or stones embedded in the tread before they penetrate the tyre to cause deflation. If removal of a nail *does* reveal that the tyre has been punctured, refit the nail so that its point of penetration is marked. Then immediately change the wheel and have the tyre repaired by a tyre dealer. Do *not* drive on a tyre in such a condition. In many cases a puncture can be simply repaired by the use of an inner tube of the correct size and type. If in any doubt as to the possible consequences of any damage found, consult your local tyre dealer for advice.

Periodically remove the wheels and clean any dirt or mud from the inside and outside surfaces. Examine the wheel rims for signs of rusting, corrosion or other damage such as cracks around the stud holes. Light alloy wheels are easily damaged by 'kerbing' whilst parking, and similarly steel wheels may become dented or buckled. Renewal of the wheel is very often the only course of remedial action possible.

The balance of each wheel and tyre assembly should be maintained to avoid excessive wear, not only to the tyres but also to the steering and suspension components. Wheel imbalance is normally signified by vibration through the vehicle's bodyshell, although in many cases it is particularly noticeable through the steering wheel. Conversely, it should be noted that wear or damage in suspension or steering components may cause excessive tyre wear. Out-of-round or out-of-true tyres, damaged wheels and wheel bearing wear/maladjustment also fall into this category. Balancing will not usually cure vibration caused by such wear.

Wheel balancing may be carried out with the wheel either on or off the vehicle. If balanced on the vehicle, ensure that the wheel-to-hub relationship is marked in some way prior to subsequent wheel removal so that it may be refitted in its original position.

General tyre wear is influenced to a large degree by driving style – harsh braking and acceleration or fast cornering will all produce more rapid tyre wear. Interchanging of tyres may result in more even wear, but this should only be carried out where there is no mix of tyre types on the vehicle. However, it may be worth bearing in mind that if this is completely effective, the added expense is incurred of replacing a complete set of tyres simultaneously, which may prove financially restrictive for many owners.

Front tyres may wear unevenly as a result of wheel misalignment.

The front wheels should always be correctly aligned according to the settings specified by the vehicle manufacturer.

Legal restrictions apply to the mixing of tyre types on a vehicle. Basically this means that a vehicle must not have tyres of differing construction on the same axle. Although it is not recommended to mix tyre types between front axle and rear axle, the only legally permissible combination is crossply at the front and radial at the rear. When mixing radial ply tyres, textile braced radials must always go on the front axle, with steel braced radials at the rear. An obvious disadvantage of such mixing is the necessity to carry two spare tyres to avoid contravening the law in the event of a puncture.

In the UK, the Motor Vehicles Construction and Use Regulations apply to many aspects of tyre fitting and usage. It is suggested that a copy of these regulations is obtained from your local police if in doubt as to the current legal requirements with regard to tyre condition, minimum tread depth, etc.

38 Fault diagnosis – suspension and steering

Note: *Before diagnosing suspension or steering faults, ensure that the trouble is not due to overloading (or uneven loading), to incorrect tyre pressures, a mixture of tyre types, or binding brakes. If checking a power-assisted steering system for faults, always check first that the pump drivebelt is correctly adjusted and that the reservoir fluid is topped-up to the correct level and is free from air bubbles. After this, faults on such a system should be referred to a Nissan dealer who has the special test equipment required to check the system properly.*

Symptom	Reason(s)
Car wanders or pulls to one side	Incorrect wheel alignment Wear in front suspension or steering components Wear in rear suspension components Weak suspension struts Faulty tyre or incorrect tyre pressures Accident damage to body, suspension or steering components
Steering stiff and heavy (manual steering)	Incorrect wheel alignment Steering column or rack bent or damaged Seized steering or front suspension balljoint(s) Damaged suspension strut Faulty tyre or incorrect tyre pressures
Steering stiff and heavy (power-assisted steering)	Pump drivebelt slipping or broken Low fluid level Pump or steering gear defective Incorrect wheel alignment Steering column or rack bent or damaged Seized steering or front suspension balljoint(s) Damaged suspension strut Faulty tyre or incorrect tyre pressures
Excessive play in steering	Worn steering or suspension joints Worn steering column lower joint Worn steering gear or slack gear mountings
Excessive pitching or rolling	Weak suspension struts Worn anti-roll bar mountings
Wheel wobble and vibration	Roadwheel nuts loose Roadwheels out of balance, damaged or distorted Tyres faulty, damaged or incorrectly fitted Worn steering or suspension joints Weak suspension struts Worn hub bearings
Excessive or uneven tyre wear	Incorrect tyre pressures Incorrect wheel alignment Roadwheels out of balance Driver abuse Wear in steering or suspension components Weak suspension struts Accident damage to body suspension or steering components

Note: *This Section is not intended to be an exhaustive guide to fault diagnosis but summarises the more common faults which may be encountered during a car's life. Consult a dealer for more specific advice.*

Chapter 11 Bodywork and fittings

Contents

Specifications

Torque wrench settings

	Nm	lbf ft
Bonnet hinge bolts:		
T12 models	16 to 21	12 to 15.5
T72 models	21 to 26	15.5 to 19
Bonnet lock mounting bolts:		
T12 models	22 to 29	16 to 21.5
T72 models	21 to 26	15.5 to 19
Front bumper mounting bolts (T12 models)	16 to 21	12 to 15.5
Front bumper mounting nuts (T12 models)	9.1 to 11.8	6.5 to 8.5
Front bumper mounting nuts and bolts (T72 models)	13 to 16	9.5 to 12
Rear bumper mounting nuts and bolts (T12 models)	16 to 21	12 to 15.5
Rear bumper mounting nuts (T72 models)	13 to 16	9.5 to 12
Rear bumper mounting bolts (T72 models)	21 to 26	15.5 to 19
Boot lid hinge arm bolts	5.1 to 6.5	4 to 5
Tailgate hinge nuts and bolts:		
T12 models	18 to 24	13 to 17.5
T72 models	13 to 16	9.5 to 12
Boot lid latch and striker mounting bolts	5.1 to 6.5	4 to 5
Tailgate latch mounting bolts:		
T12 models	18 to 24	13 to 17.5
T72 models	13 to 16	9.5 to 12
Tailgate striker mounting bolts	11 to 15	8 to 11
Door hinge mounting bolts	29 to 37	21.5 to 27
Door striker mounting screws	13 to 16	9.5 to 12
Door latch and handle mounting screws and nuts	5.1 to 6.5	4 to 5
Front seat mounting bolts	25 to 31	18.5 to 23
Seat belt mounting bolts	24 to 31	17.5 to 23
Air conditioning compressor mounting bolts	44 to 54	32.5 to 40

1   General description

Note: *Always disconnect the battery negative lead before disconnecting any item of electrical equipment encountered during work on the body and fittings*

The bodyshell is of monocoque construction, using high-tensile sheet steel to produce a substantially-built body of four-door Saloon or five-door Hatchback configuration. Extensive use is made of a zinc chromate coating to prevent rust; followed by the careful application of several layers of paint. Box sections and other inaccessible areas are coated with rust-inhibiting wax, sealant is used at spot welds and hinge mountings and the underbody is sprayed with underseal. In addition, areas such as the sills are given a stoneguard coating.

Extensive use is made of plastics for components such as the (polypropylene) bumpers, the radiator grille and wheel trims, as well as for much of the interior trim.

Interior fittings are to a high standard, with even the basic level models being well equipped. A wide range of features is fitted according to the particular models' specification, including air conditioning and leather upholstery on the Executive models.

In December 1987, the model range was revised to include a general uprating of specification. In May 1988 the T72 models (which had entirely replaced the Japanese-built T12 models early in 1988) were give a minor facelift which was largely confined to fitting a different radiator grille and larger front and rear bumpers. Also, the front direction indicator lamps were reduced in size and recessed into the bumper.

2   Maintenance – bodywork and underframe

The general condition of a car's bodywork is the one thing that significantly affects its value. Maintenance is easy but needs to be regular. Neglect, particularly after minor damage, can lead quickly to further deterioration and costly repair bills. It is important also to keep watch on those parts of the car not immediately visible, for instance the underside, inside all the wheel arches and the lower part of the engine compartment.

The basic maintenance routine for the bodywork is washing – preferably with a lot of water, from a hose. This will remove all the loose solids which may have stuck to the car. It is important to flush these off in such a way as to prevent grit from scratching the finish. The wheel arches and underframe need washing in the same way to remove any accumulated mud which will retain moisture and tend to encourage rust. Paradoxically enough, the best time to clean the underframe and wheel arches is in wet weather when the mud is thoroughly wet and soft. In very wet weather the underframe is usually cleaned of large accumulations automatically and this is a good time for inspection.

Periodically, except on cars with a wax-based underbody protective coating, it is a good idea to have the whole of the underside of the car steam cleaned, engine compartment included, so that a thorough inspection can be carried out to see what minor repairs and renovations are necessary. Steam cleaning is available at many garages and is necessary for removal of the accumulation of oily grime which sometimes is allowed to become thick in certain areas. If steam cleaning facilities are not available, there are one or two excellent grease solvents available, such as Holts Engine Cleaner or Holts Foambrite, which can be brush applied. The dirt can then be simply hosed off. Note that these methods should not be used on cars with wax-based underbody protective coating or the coating will be removed. Such cars should be inspected annually, preferably just prior to winter, when the underbody should be washed down and any damage to the wax coating repaired using Holts Undershield. Ideally, a completely fresh coat should be applied. It would also be worth considering the use of such wax-based protection for injection into door panels, sills, box sections, etc, as an additional safeguard against rust damage where such protection is not provided by the car manufacturer.

After washing paintwork, wipe off with a chamois leather to give an unspotted clear finish. A coat of clear protective wax polish, like the many excellent Turtle Wax polishes, will give added protection against chemical pollutants in the air. If the paintwork sheen has dulled or oxidised, use a cleaner/polisher combination such as Turtle Extra to restore the brilliance of the shine. This requires a little effort, but such dulling is usually caused because regular washing has been neglected. Care needs to be taken with metallic paintwork, as special non-abrasive

cleaner/polisher is required to avoid damage to the finish. Always check that the door and ventilator opening drain holes and pipes are completely clear so that water can be drained out. Bright work should be treated in the same way as paint work. Windscreens and windows can be kept clear of the smeary film which often appears by the use of a proprietary glass cleaner like Holts Mixra. Never use any form of wax or other body or chromium polish on glass.

3   Maintenance – upholstery and carpets

Mats and carpets should be brushed or vacuum cleaned regularly to keep them free of grit. If they are badly stained, remove them from the car for scrubbing or sponging and make quite sure they are dry before refitting. On Executive models, the leather upholstery should be cleaned only if necessary, using mild soap (such as saddle soap) or a proprietary leather cleaner. **Do not** use strong soaps, detergents or chemical cleaners. If the leather is very stained, seek the advice of a Nissan dealer. On all other models, the seats and interior trim panels can be kept clean by wiping with a damp cloth and Turtle Wax Carisma. If they do become stained (which can be more apparent on light coloured upholstery) use a little liquid detergent and a soft nail brush to scour the grime out of the grain of the material. Do not forget to keep the headlining clean in the same way as the upholstery. When using liquid cleaners inside the car, do not over-wet the surfaces being cleaned. Excessive damp could get into the seams and padded interior causing stains, offensive odours or even rot. If the inside of the car gets wet accidentally it is worthwhile taking some trouble to dry it out properly, particularly where carpets are involved. *Do not leave oil or electric heaters inside the car for this purpose.*

4   Maintenance – hinges, locks and door latches

1   Oil the hinges of the bonnet, boot lid or tailgate, and doors with a few drops of light oil at regular intervals.
2   At the same time lightly lubricate the bonnet release mechanism, the door latches and the boot/tailgate latch, striker and lock (photo).
3   **Do not** attempt to lubricate the steering lock or any of the seat belt retractor assemblies.

5   Maintenance – seat belts

1   All models are fitted with three-point lap and diagonal inertia reel seat belts at both front and at the rear outer seats. The rear centre seat has a two-point lap-type belt which is fixed (ie not inertia reel).
2   Maintenance is limited to regular inspection of the belts for signs of fraying or other damage. Also check the operation of the buckles and

4.2 Lubricate the bonnet release mechanism and door locks

retractor mechanisms and ensure that all mounting bolts are securely tightened. Note that the bolts are shouldered so that the belt anchor points are free to rotate.

3   If there is any sign of damage, or any doubt about a belt's condition, it must be renewed. If the car has been involved in a collision, any belts in use at the time must be renewed as a matter of course and all other belts should be checked carefully.

4   Use only warm water and non-detergent soap to clean the belts. Never use any chemical cleaners, strong detergents, dyes or bleaches. Keep the belts fully extended until they have dried naturally; do not apply heat to dry them.

6   Minor body damage – repair

The photographic sequences on pages 270 and 271 illustrate the operations detailed in the following sub-sections.
Note: *For more detailed information about bodywork repair, the Haynes Publishing Group publish a book by Lindsay Porter called The Car Bodywork Repair Manual. This incorporates information on such aspects as rust treatment, painting and glass fibre repairs, as well as details on more ambitious repairs involving welding and panel beating.*

Repair of minor scratches in bodywork

If the scratch is very superficial, and does not penetrate to the metal of the bodywork, repair is very simple. Lightly rub the area of the scratch with a paintwork renovator like Turtle Wax New Color Back, or a very fine cutting paste like Holts Body + Plus Rubbing Compound, to remove loose paint from the scratch and to clear the surrounding bodywork of wax polish. Rinse the area with clean water.

Apply touch-up paint, such as Holts Dupli-Color Color Touch or a paint film like Holts Autofilm to the scratch using a fine paint brush; continue to apply fine layers of paint until the surface of the paint in the scratch is level with the surrounding paintwork. Allow the new paint at least two weeks to harden; then blend it into the surrounding paintwork by rubbing the scratch area with a paintwork renovator or a very fine cutting paste, such as Holts Body + Plus Rubbing Compound or Turtle Wax New Color Back. Finally, apply wax polish from one of the Turtle Wax range of wax polishes.

Where the scratch has penetrated right through to the metal of the bodywork, causing the metal to rust, a different repair technique is required. Remove any loose rust from the bottom of the scratch with a penknife, then apply rust inhibiting paint, such as Turtle Wax Rust Master, to prevent the formation of rust in the future. Using a rubber or nylon applicator fill the scratch with bodystopper paste like Holts Body + Plus Knifing Putty. If required, this paste can be mixed with cellulose thinners, such as Holts Body + Plus Cellulose Thinners, to provide a very thin paste which is ideal for filling narrow scratches. Before the stopper-paste in the scratch hardens, wrap a piece of smooth cotton rag around the top of a finger. Dip the finger in cellulose thinners, sych as Holts Body + Plus Cellulose Thinners, and then quickly sweep it across the surface of the stopper-paste in the scratch; this will ensure that the surface of the stopper-paste is slightly hollowed. The scratch can now be painted over as described earlier in this Section.

Repair of dents in bodywork

When deep denting of the car's bodywork has taken place, the first task is to pull the dent out, until the affected bodywork almost attains its original shape. There is little point in trying to restore the original shape completely, as the metal in the damaged area will have stretched on impact and cannot be reshaped fully to its original contour. It is better to bring the level of the dent up to a point which is about $\frac{1}{8}$ in (3 mm) below the level of the surrounding bodywork. In cases where the dent is very shallow anyway, it is not worth trying to pull it out at all. If the underside of the dent is accessible, it can be hammered out gently from behind, using a mallet with a wooden or plastic head. Whilst doing this, hold a suitable block of wood firmly against the outside of the panel to absorb the impact from the hammer blows and thus prevent a large area of the bodywork from being 'belled-out'.

Should the dent be in a section of the bodywork which has a double skin or some other factor making it inaccessible from behind, a different technique is called for. Drill several small holes through the metal inside the area – particularly in the deeper section. Then screw long self-tapping screws into the holes just sufficiently for them to gain a good purchase in the metal. Now the dent can be pulled out by pulling on the protruding heads of the screws with a pair of pliers.

The next stage of the repair is the removal of the paint from the damaged area, and from an inch or so of the surrounding 'sound' bodywork. This is accomplished most easily by using a wire brush or abrasive pad on a power drill, although it can be done just as effectively by hand using sheets of abrasive paper. To complete the preparation for filling, score the surface of the bare metal with a screwdriver or the tang of a file, or alternatively, drill small holes in the affected area. This will provide a really good 'key' for the filler paste.

To complete the repair see the Section on filling and re-spraying.

Repair of rust holes or gashes in bodywork

Remove all paint from the affected area and from an inch or so of the surrounding 'sound' bodywork, using an abrasive pad or a wire brush on a power drill. If these are not available a few sheets of abrasive paper will do the job just as effectively. With the paint removed you will be able to gauge the severity of the corrosion and therefore decide whether to renew the whole panel (if this is possible) or to repair the affected area. New body panels are not as expensive as most people think and it is often quicker and more satisfactory to fit a new panel than to attempt to repair large areas of corrosion.

Remove all fittings from the affected area except those which will act as a guide to the original shape of the damaged bodywork (eg headlamp shells etc). Then, using tin snips or a hacksaw blade, remove all loose metal and any other metal badly affected by corrosion. Hammer the edges of the hole inwards in order to create a slight depression for the filler paste.

Wire brush the affected area to remove the powdery rust from the surface of the remaining metal. Paint the affected area with rust inhibiting paint like Turtle Wax Rust Master; if the back of the rusted area is accessible treat this also.

Before filling can take place it will be necessary to block the hole in some way. This can be achieved by the use of aluminium or plastic mesh, or aluminium tape.

Aluminium or plastic mesh or glass fibre matting, such as the Holts Body + Plus Glass Fibre Matting is probably the best material to use for a large hole. Cut a piece to the approximate size and shape of the hole to be filled, then position it in the hole so that its edges are below the level of the surrounding bodywork. It can be retained in position by several blobs of filler paste around its periphery.

Aluminium tape should be used for small or very narrow holes. Pull a piece off the roll and trim it to the approximate size and shape required, then pull off the backing paper (if used) and stick the tape over the hole; it can be overlapped if the thickness of one piece is insufficient. Burnish down the edges of the tape with the handle of a screwdriver or similar, to ensure that the tape is securely attached to the metal underneath.

Bodywork repairs – filling and re-spraying

Before using this Section, see the Sections on dent, deep scratch, rust holes and gash repairs.

Many types of bodyfiller are available, but generally speaking those proprietary kits which contain a tin of filler paste and a tube of resin hardener are best for this type of repair, like Holts Body + Plus or Holts No Mix which can be used directly from the tube. A wide, flexible plastic or nylon applicator will be found invaluable for imparting a smooth and well contoured finish to the surface of the filler.

Mix up a little filler on a clean piece of card or board – measure the hardener carefully (follow the maker's instructions on the pack) otherwise the filler will set too rapidly or too slowly. Alternatively, Holts No Mix can be used straight from the tube without mixing, but daylight is required to cure it. Using the applicator apply the filler paste to the prepared area; draw the applicator across the surface of the filler to achieve the correct contour and to level the filler surface. As soon as a contour that approximates to the correct one is achieved, stop working the paste – if you carry on too long the paste will become sticky and begin to 'pick up' on the applicator. Continue to add thin layers of filler paste at twenty-minute intervals until the level of the filler is just proud of the surrounding bodywork.

Once the filler has hardened, excess can be removed using a metal plane or file. From then on, progressively finer grades of abrasive paper should be used, starting with a 40 grade production paper and finishing with 400 grade wet-and-dry paper. Always wrap the abrasive paper around a flat rubber, cork, or wooden block – otherwise the surface of the filler will not be completely flat. During the smoothing of the filler surface the wet-and-dry paper should be periodically rinsed in water. This will ensure that a very smooth finish is imparted to the filler at the final stage.

At this stage the 'dent' should be surrounded by a ring of bare metal, which in turn should be encircled by the finely 'feathered' edge of the good paintwork. Rinse the repair area with clean water, until all of the dust produced by the rubbing-down operation has gone.

Spray the whole repair area with a light coat of primer, either Holts Body + Plus Grey or Red Oxide Primer – this will show up any imperfections in the surface of the filler. Repair these imperfections with fresh filler paste or bodystopper, and once more smooth the surface with abrasive paper. If bodystopper is used, it can be mixed with cellulose thinners to form a really thin paste which is ideal for filling small holes. Repeat this spray and repair procedure until you are satisfied that the surface of the filler, and the feathered edge of the paintwork are perfect. Clean the repair area with clean water and allow to dry fully.

The repair area is now ready for final spraying. Paint spraying must be carried out in a warm, dry, windless and dust free atmosphere. This condition can be created artificially if you have access to a large indoor working area, but if you are forced to work in the open, you will have to pick your day very carefully. If you are working indoors, dousing the floor in the work area with water will help to settle the dust which would otherwise be in the atmosphere. If the repair area is confined to one body panel, mask off the surrounding panels; this will help to minimise the effects of a slight mis-match in paint colours. Bodywork fittings (eg chrome strips, door handles etc) will also need to be masked off. Use genuine masking tape and several thicknesses of newspaper for the masking operations.

Before commencing to spray, agitate the aerosol can thoroughly, then spray a test area (an old tin, or similar) until the technique is mastered. Cover the repair area with a thick coat of primer; the thickness should be built up using several thin layers of paint rather than one thick one. Using 400 grade wet-and-dry paper, rub down the surface of the primer until it is really smooth. While doing this, the work area should be thoroughly doused with water, and the wet-and-dry paper periodically rinsed in water. Allow to dry before spraying on more paint.

Spray on the top coat using Holts Dupli-Color Autospray, again building up the thickness by using several thin layers of paint. Start spraying in the centre of the repair area and then, with a side-to-side motion, work outwards until the whole repair area and about 2 inches of the surrounding original paintwork is covered. Remove all masking material 10 to 15 minutes after spraying on the final coat of paint.

Allow the new paint at least two weeks to harden, then, using a paintwork renovator or a very fine cutting paste such as Turtle Wax New Color Back or Holts Body + Plus Rubbing Compound, blend the edges of the paint into the existing paintwork. Finally, apply wax polish.

Plastic components

With the use of more and more plastic body components by the vehicle manufacturers (eg bumpers, spoilers, and in some cases major body panels), rectification of more serious damage to such items has become a matter of either entrusting repair work to a specialist in this field, or renewing complete components. Repair of such damage by the DIY owner is not really feasible owing to the cost of the equipment and materials required for effecting such repairs. The basic technique involves making a groove along the line of the crack in the plastic using a rotary burr in a power drill. The damaged part is then welded back together by using a hot air gun to heat up and fuse a plastic filler rod into the groove. Any excess plastic is then removed and the area rubbed down to a smooth finish. It is important that a filler rod of the correct plastic is used, as body components can be made of a variety of different types (eg polycarbonate, ABS, polypropylene).

Damage of a less serious nature (abrasions, minor cracks etc) can be repaired by the DIY owner using a two-part epoxy filler repair material like Holts Body + Plus or Holts No Mix which can be used directly from the tube. Once mixed in equal proportions (or applied direct from the tube in the case of Holts No Mix), this is used in similar fashion to the bodywork filler used on metal panels. The filler is usually cured in twenty to thirty minutes, ready for sanding and painting.

If the owner is renewing a complete component himself, or if he has repaired it with epoxy filler, he will be left with the problem of finding a suitable paint for finishing which is compatible with the type of plastic used. At one time the use of a universal paint was not possible owing to the complex range of plastics encountered in body component applications. Standard paints, generally speaking, will not bond to plastic or rubber satisfactorily, but Holts Professional Spraymatch paints to match any plastic or rubber finish can be obtained from dealers. However, it is now possible to obtain a plastic body parts finishing kit which consists of a pre-primer treatment, a primer and coloured top

coat. Full instructions are normally supplied with a kit, but basically the method of use is to first apply the pre-primer to the component concerned and allow it to dry for up to 30 minutes. Then the primer is applied and left to dry for about an hour before finally applying the special coloured top coat. The result is a correctly coloured component where the paint will flex with the plastic or rubber, a property that standard paint does not normally possess.

---

7   Major body damage – repair

Where serious damage has occurred, or large areas need renewal due to neglect, it means that complete new sections or panels will need welding in, and this is best left to professionals. If the damage is due to impact, it will also be necessary to check completely the alignment of the bodyshell, and this can only be carried out successfully using special jigs. If the body is left misaligned, it is primarily dangerous as the car will not handle properly, and secondly, uneven stresses will be imposed on the steering, suspension, and possibly transmission, causing abnormal wear, or complete failure, particularly to such items as the tyres.

---

8   Bonnet – removal and refitting

1   The help of an assistant will be necessary for these operations. First, with the bonnet propped open, place a thick pad of cloth beneath each rear corner of the bonnet to protect the paintwork.
2   Disconnect the windscreen washer tubing.
3   Mark around the hinge plates on the underside of the bonnet with a pencil.
4   Support the bonnet on the shoulders and lower the stay.
5   Working with one person at each side, unscrew the hinge bolts and lift the bonnet from the vehicle (photo). It may be found that the hinge plates are stuck to the bonnet by the strong sealing compound used, in which case it will be necessary to cut the compound away before loosening the bolts.
6   Refitting is a reversal of removal, using new sealing compound. Do not fully tighten the bolts until the bonnet has been closed and checked for alignment with the surrounding bodywork. Refer to Section 9 for adjustments possible with the bonnet lock.
7   The bonnet front and rear rubber sealing strips are each attached by plastic clips which can be prised out using a screwdriver or similar. The rear sealing strip is also secured, where necessary, by double-sided adhesive tape or adhesive.
8   The bonnet front mouldings are each secured by three screws at their rear edges and by double-sided adhesive tape at the front.
9   The bonnet air intake is secured by three nuts and sealing washers.

8.5 Always have an assistant to help with bonnet removal

Fig. 11.1 Bonnet lock and release cable (Sec 9)

1 Release cable
2 Bonnet lock
3 Bolt
4 Washer
5 Cable tie
6 Clip
7 Clip
8 Bonnet grille
9 Clip
10 Nut
11 Bonnet front moulding
12 Captive nut
13 Insulating material
14 Clip stud
15 Screw
16 Rubber finisher
17 Screw

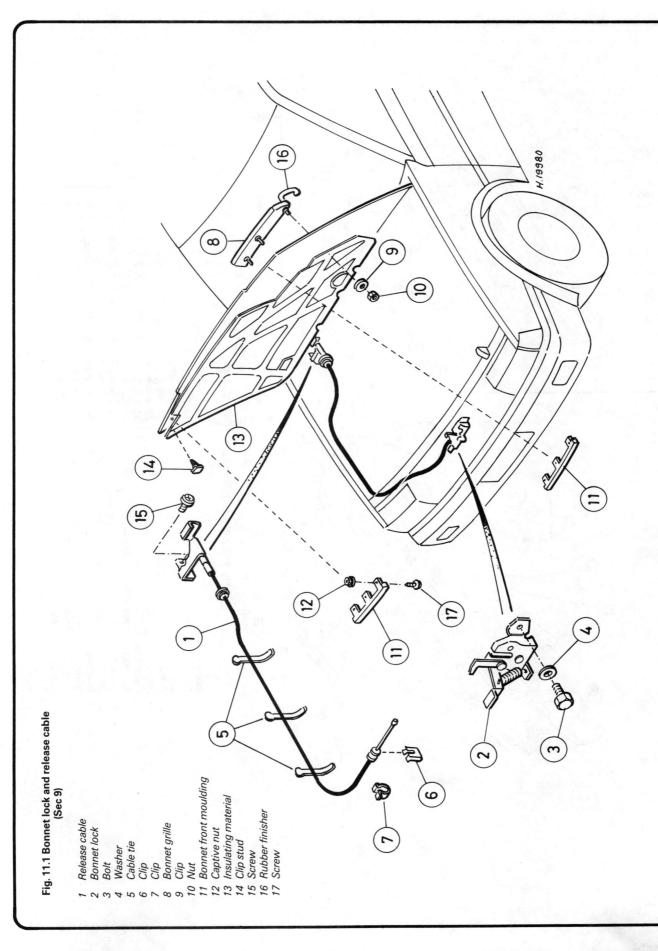

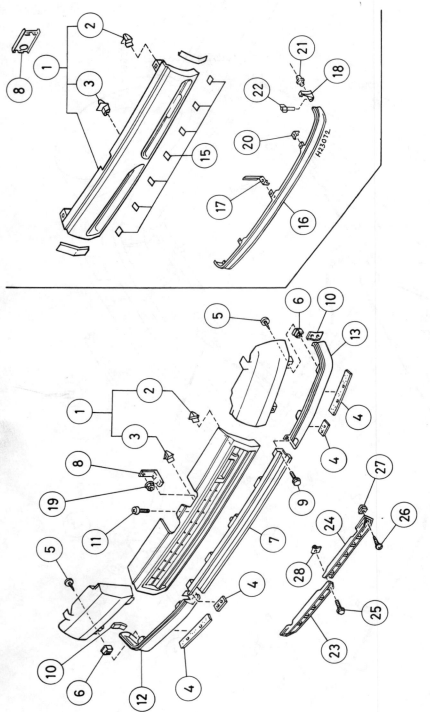

Fig. 11.2 Radiator grille and trim panels (Sec 10)

1 Radiator grille
2 Clip
3 Clip
4 Adhesive pad
5 Screw
6 Captive nut
7 Trim panel centre section – early models
8 Bracket
9 Screw
10 Moulding
11 Screw
12 Trim panel right-hand section
13 Trim panel left-hand section
14 Rubber mounting
15 Rubber mounting

16 Trim panel – later models
17 Bracket
18 Moulding
19 Nut
20 Bracket
21 Clip
22 Cover
23 Lower grille right-hand section – early
   models
24 Lower grille left-hand section – early
   models
25 Bolt
26 Screw
27 Captive nut
28 Captive nut

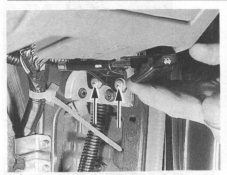

9.4 Bonnet release lever and mounting screws (arrowed)

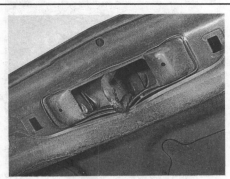

9.8A Bonnet lock striker

9.8B Bonnet support buffers

9 Bonnet lock and release cable – removal, refitting and adjustment

1   Open the bonnet and mark around the bonnet lock with a pencil, then unbolt the lock from the body front panel. Release the clip and disconnect the cable.
2   Release the cable from any securing clips or ties along its length and tie a long length of string to its end nipple.
3   Working inside the car, undo its three screws and withdraw the driver's door sill tread panel. Remove the single retaining screw and withdraw the footwell right-hand side trim panel, releasing it from its front retaining clip.
4   Unscrew the bonnet release lever mounting screws (photo) and carefully pull the cable back through the inner wing panel and bulkhead. Untie the string as soon as the cable is clear.
5   Refitting is the reverse of the removal procedure. Use the string to gently pull the cable back into position. Ensure that the cable is smoothly routed, with no kinks or sharp turns. Position the lock so that it matches the pencilled marks and check that the lock works properly.
6   There is no adjustment as such for the release cable.
7   To adjust the lock setting, first remove the radiator grille (see Section 10 of this Chapter.)
8   Slacken the lock mounting bolts and position the lock so that its primary (main) latch engages centrally on the bonnet striker when the bonnet is 1.0 to 1.5 mm (0.039 to 0.059 in) below the level of each wing. Tighten down the bonnet support buffers, if necessary, to permit this (photos). Tighten the lock mounting bolts securely, then recheck carefully the operation of the primary and secondary (safety) latches.
9   The secondary latch hook should overhang the bonnet lip by at least 5 mm (0.20 in) and should be retained securely by its spring.
10   Finally, screw the bonnet support buffers in or out until they hold the bonnet squarely at the height of the wings. The buffer free height should be approximately 13 mm (0.5 in).
11   Refit the radiator grille and interior trim panels.

10 Radiator grille(s) and trim panels – removal and refitting

1   Where applicable, remove the headlamp cleaner wiper arms (Chapter 12).
2   The grille is secured by a number of special clips, one at each corner and one (or two) in the centre. Where their slotted heads are accessible from the front, release the clips by rotating them through 45° using a screwdriver (see Fig. 11.3), otherwise, they must be released from behind using pliers (photo).
3   On refitting, it may prove easier to assemble the clips on the grille before offering the grille up to its mountings (photo). Press the clips into place and rotate them to lock them, where necessary. **Do not** use excessive force, or the grille and its mounting brackets will be damaged.
4   The two-piece grille built into the front apron panel of some models (before May 1988) is secured by a bolt at the centre and a screw at each end. All are threaded into captive nuts fitted in the apron panel.
5   To remove the trim panel(s) fitted between the radiator grille,

headlamps and front bumper, first remove the radiator grille, then proceed as follows.
6   On cars built before May 1988, remove the two screws, one at each end of the panel (slotted) centre section, and withdraw the centre section. The two end sections are now secured only by pieces of double-sided adhesive tape on their top and bottom surfaces and at their outer ends.
7   On cars built after May 1988, remove the three hexagon-headed screws securing the panel at its centre and to each headlamp, then prise each end forwards out of the wing panel grommet (photos).
8   Refitting is the reverse of the removal procedure. Degrease the relevant areas thoroughly before applying new pieces of adhesive tape.

11 Spoilers – removal and refitting

Turbo (early models) – front

1   Turbo models built before May 1988 are fitted with a three-piece urethane front air spoiler (see Fig. 11.4).
2   Each side section is retained by four screws (three in the wheel arch and one underneath) and by two nuts at the front end. In some cases double-sided adhesive tape may also be used.
3   To remove the spoiler centre section, first remove both side sections, then release the spoiler retaining clips (Fig. 11.5). Remove the retaining screws and unbolt the mounting brackets to release the centre section from the body front panel.
4   Refitting is the reverse of the removal procedure. Ensure that the relevant areas are thoroughly degreased before applying new pieces of adhesive tape.

Turbo – rear

5   On Saloon models, open the boot lid and use pliers to release the spoiler retaining clips, then unscrew the mounting nuts (Fig. 11.6). Withdraw the spoiler from the top of the boot lid, noting the double-sided adhesive tape that secures it.
6   On Hatchback models, open the tailgate and remove its interior trim panel (see Section 33 of this Chapter) then unscrew the retaining screw at each end of the spoiler and the nuts at its centre (Fig. 11.7). Release the retaining clips and withdraw the spoiler from the tailgate, noting the double-sided adhesive tape that secures it.
7   Refitting is the reverse of the removal procedure, but note that a special primer must be applied in an even coat to the spoiler before applying new pieces of adhesive tape. Seek the advice of a Nissan dealer to obtain a suitable product. Degrease the boot/tailgate surface thoroughly before refitting the spoiler.

Rotate 45°
to remove.

Fig. 11.3 Releasing the radiator grille clips (Sec 10)

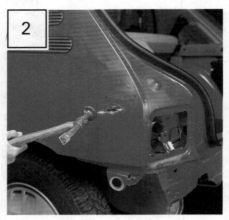

1

This photographic sequence shows the steps taken to repair the dent and paintwork damage shown above. In general, the procedure for repairing a hole will be similar; where there are substantial differences, the procedure is clearly described and shown in a separate photograph.

2

First remove any trim around the dent, then hammer out the dent where access is possible. This will minimise filling. Here, after the large dent has been hammered out, the damaged area is being made slightly concave.

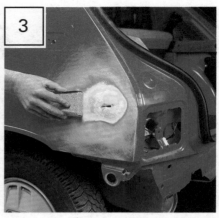

3

Next, remove all paint from the damaged area by rubbing with coarse abrasive paper or using a power drill fitted with a wire brush or abrasive pad. 'Feather' the edge of the boundary with good paintwork using a finer grade of abrasive paper.

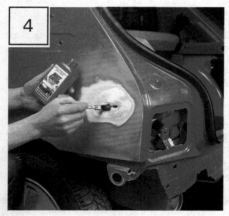

4

Where there are holes or other damage, the sheet metal should be cut away before proceeding further. The damaged area and any signs of rust should be treated with Turtle Wax Hi-Tech Rust Eater, which will also inhibit further rust formation.

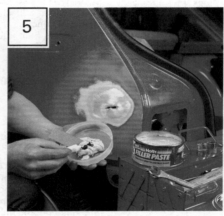

5

For a large dent or hole mix Holts Body Plus Resin and Hardener according to the manufacturer's instructions and apply around the edge of the repair. Press Glass Fibre Matting over the repair area and leave for 20-30 minutes to harden. Then ...

5A

... brush more Holts Body Plus Resin and Hardener onto the matting and leave to harden. Repeat the sequence with two or three layers of matting, checking that the final layer is lower than the surrounding area. Apply Holts Body Plus Filler Paste as shown in Step 5B.

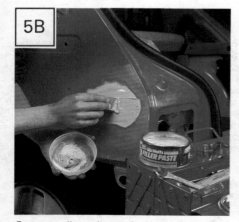

5B

For a medium dent, mix Holts Body Plus Filler Paste and Hardener according to the manufacturer's instructions and apply it with a flexible applicator. Apply thin layers of filler at 20-minute intervals, until the filler surface is slightly proud of the surrounding bodywork.

5C

For small dents and scratches use Holts No Mix Filler Paste straight from the tube. Apply it according to the instructions in thin layers, using the spatula provided. It will harden in minutes if applied outdoors and may then be used as its own knifing putty.

6

Use a plane or file for initial shaping. Then, using progressively finer grades of wet-and-dry paper, wrapped round a sanding block, and copious amounts of clean water, rub down the filler until glass smooth. 'Feather' the edges of adjoining paintwork.

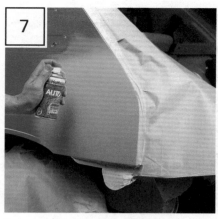

7 Protect adjoining areas before spraying the whole repair area and at least one inch of the surrounding sound paintwork with Holts Dupli-Color primer.

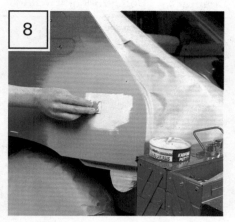

8 Fill any imperfections in the filler surface with a small amount of Holts Body Plus Knifing Putty. Using plenty of clean water, rub down the surface with a fine grade wet-and-dry paper – 400 grade is recommended – until it is really smooth.

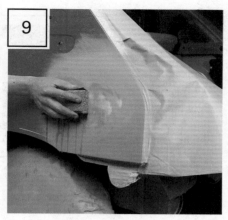

9 Carefully fill any remaining imperfections with knifing putty before applying the last coat of primer. Then rub down the surface with Holts Body Plus Rubbing Compound to ensure a really smooth surface.

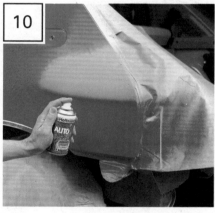

10 Protect surrounding areas from overspray before applying the topcoat in several thin layers. Agitate Holts Dupli-Color aerosol thoroughly. Start at the repair centre, spraying outwards with a side-to-side motion.

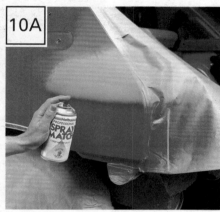

10A If the exact colour is not available off the shelf, local Holts Professional Spraymatch Centres will custom fill an aerosol to match perfectly.

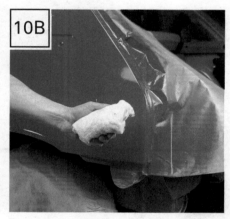

10B To identify whether a lacquer finish is required, rub a painted unrepaired part of the body with wax and a clean cloth.

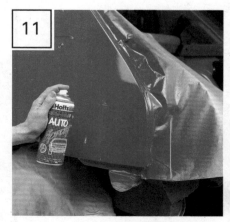

11 If *no* traces of paint appear on the cloth, spray Holts Dupli-Color clear lacquer over the repaired area to achieve the correct gloss level.

12 **13** The paint will take about two weeks to harden fully. After this time it can be 'cut' with a mild cutting compound such as Turtle Wax Minute Cut prior to polishing with a final coating of Turtle Wax Extra.

14 When carrying out bodywork repairs, remember that the quality of the finished job is proportional to the time and effort expended.

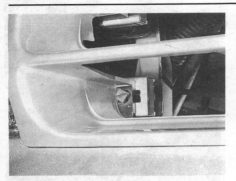

10.2A Radiator grille retaining clips must be released from in front ...

10.2B ... or behind

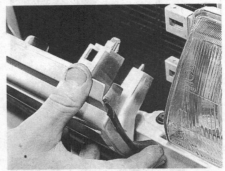

10.3 Refitting the radiator grille with clips in place – do not use excessive force

10.7A Removing radiator grille trim panel – remove screws (one shown) ...

10.7B ... and prise panel ends out of wing grommets (later cars only)

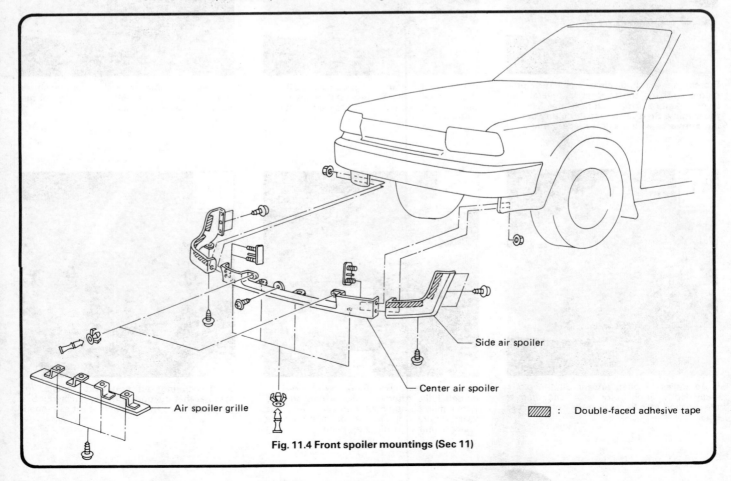

Side air spoiler

Center air spoiler

Air spoiler grille

▨ : Double-faced adhesive tape

Fig. 11.4 Front spoiler mountings (Sec 11)

Removal:

Push

Push

Installation:

Fig. 11.5 Front spoiler clip details (Sec 11)

Executive models

8   Apart from the three screws evident at each wheel arch, there is no information available on the mountings of the Executive models' front and rear spoilers.

Front apron panel – all other (early) models

9   Cars built before May 1988 are fitted with an apron panel at the bottom of the body front panel.

10   First remove the two-piece grille (see Section 10 of this Chapter.)

11   The apron panel is secured by nuts at each end and by screws along its length. Remove these to release the panel from the wings and body front panel. Refitting is the reverse of removal.

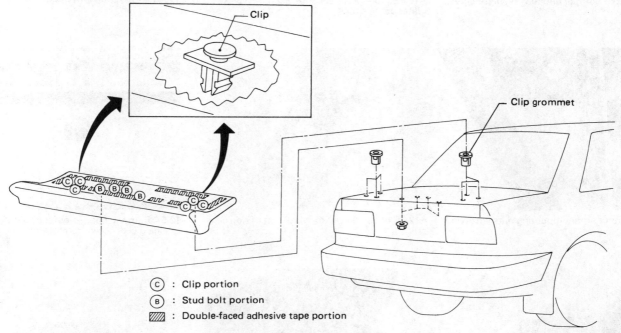

ⓒ : Clip portion
Ⓑ : Stud bolt portion
▨ : Double-faced adhesive tape portion

Fig. 11.6 Rear spoiler mountings – Saloon (Sec 11)

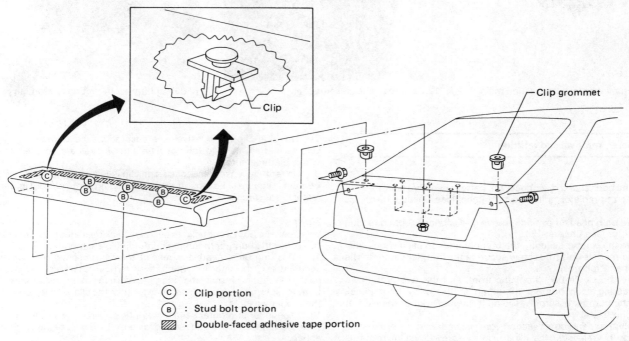

ⓒ : Clip portion
Ⓑ : Stud bolt portion
▨ : Double-faced adhesive tape portion

Fig. 11.7 Rear spoiler mountings – Hatchback (Sec 11)

12.4A Front bumper end to wing panel screw

12.4B Front bumper centre securing screw – later models only

12.5A Front bumper mounting bolt (arrowed)

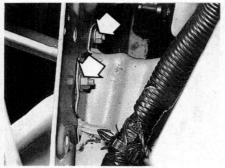

12.5B Front bumper mounting nuts (arrowed)

12.5C Slide bumper forwards out of side clips

12.6A Bumper inner-to-outer section retaining clip – seen from below

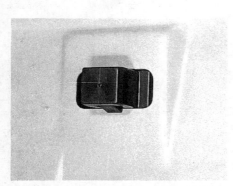

12.6B Bumper inner-to-outer section main retaining clip

12.7 Bumper side clip outer half

12.9 Rear bumper mounting reinforcing plate – Saloon

12 Bumpers – removal and refitting

Front

1   Open the bonnet and disconnect the battery negative lead.
2   Remove the radiator grille and trim panel (see Section 10 of this Chapter.)
3   Remove both headlamps and remove or disconnect both direction indicator lamps (see Chapter 12.)
4   Remove the screws securing the bumper ends to each wing panel and, on later models only, the screw securing the bumper centre to the body front panel (photos).
5   Remove the single bolt (from the front) and the two nuts (from behind) securing each bumper mounting to the body front panel. Withdraw the bumper assembly, sliding it forwards out of the clips at each end (photos).
6   The polypropylene outer section can be separated from the steel inner section by releasing the clips using a screwdriver or pliers as appropriate (photos).

7   The side clip outer halves are secured to the bumper by three screws and are handed (photo). The inner halves are secured to the wings by three nuts.
8   On refitting, ensure that each side clip is fully engaged and that the bumper is square to its mountings before sliding it into place. Tighten all fasteners securely.

Rear

9   Open the boot lid or tailgate and peel back the carpet or interior trim to expose the bumper mounting reinforcing plate (photo).
10   Working underneath the rear of the car, unscrew the two nuts securing each bumper mounting, then remove the four nuts (two at each mounting) inside the luggage compartment. Withdraw the bumper assembly, sliding it backwards out of the clips at each end. Note the rubber washers.
11   The inner and outer sections can be separated and the side clip halves can be removed and refitted, as described in paragraphs 6 and 7 above.
12   Refitting is as described in paragraph 8 above.

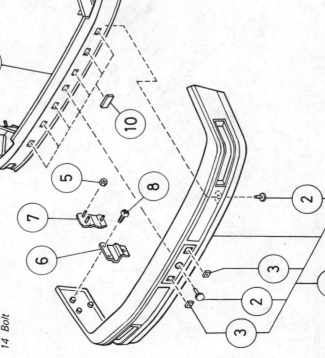

Fig. 11.8 Front bumper (Sec 12)

1 Outer section
2 Clip
3 Captive nut
4 Steel inner section
5 Nut
6 Side clip outer half
7 Side clip inner half
8 Screw
9 Nut
10 Spacer
11 Spacer – later models
12 Screw – later models
13 Captive nut
14 Bolt

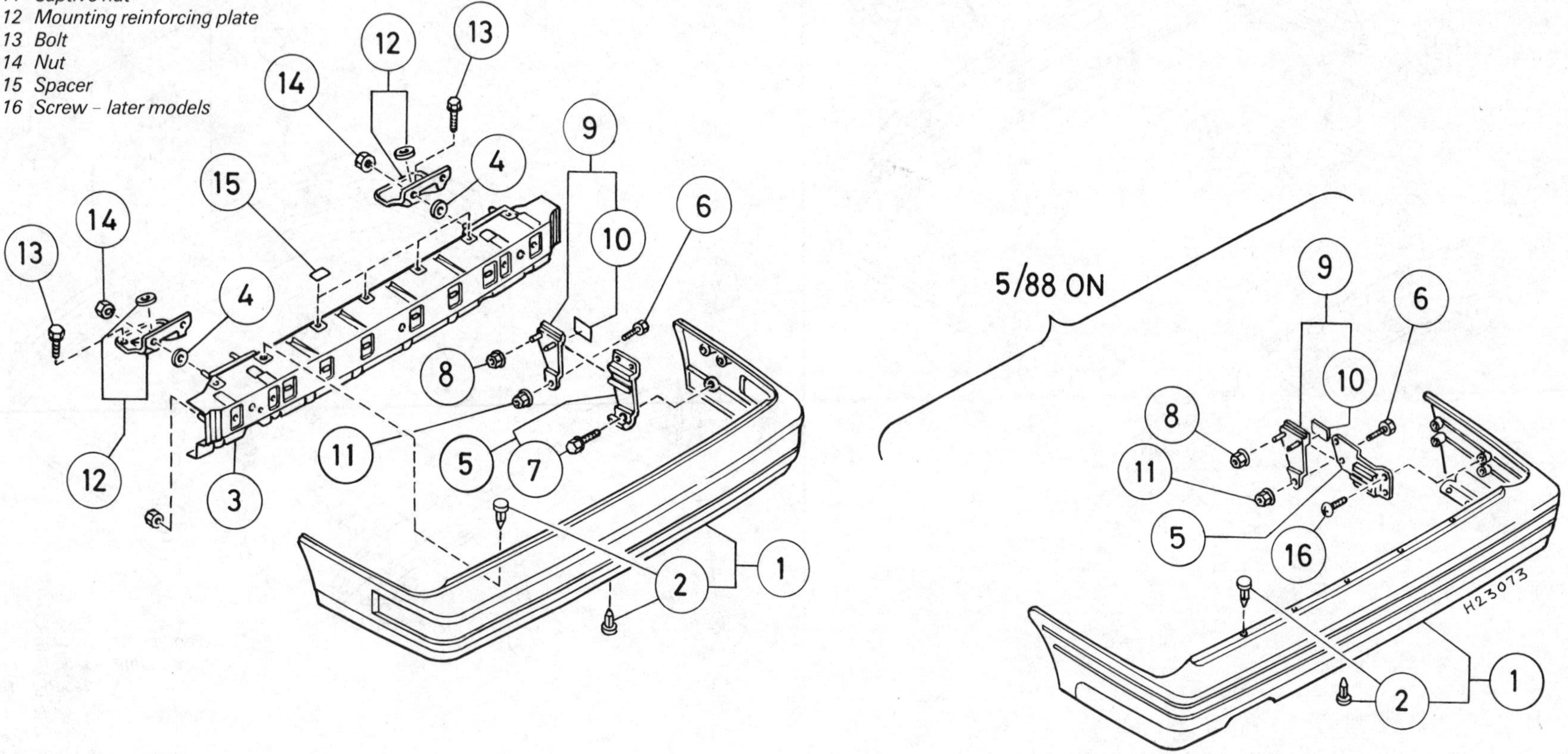

Fig. 11.9 Rear bumper (Sec 12)

1 Outer section
2 Clip
3 Steel inner section
4 Rubber washer
5 Side clip outer half
6 Screw
7 Bolt – early models
8 Nut
9 Side clip inner half
10 Rubber pad – right-hand side
11 Captive nut
12 Mounting reinforcing plate
13 Bolt
14 Nut
15 Spacer
16 Screw – later models

5/88 ON

H29.013

Rear bumper trim panel

13   The trim panel fitted between the bumper and each rear lamp cluster can be removed as follows.

14   On Saloon models, remove the rear bumper then peel back the interior trim rear panel to expose the lamp cluster and trim panel mountings.

15   Unscrew the retaining nuts and remove the clips to release the panel.

16   On Hatchback models, note that the rear bumper and the lamp cluster (see Chapter 12) must be removed before the trim panel can be withdrawn. This will expose the panel retaining screws. The remainder of the removal procedure is as described above for Saloon models.

17   Refitting is the reverse of the removal procedure.

13   Front wing – removal and refitting

1   Remove the front bumper (see Section 12 of this Chapter.)

2   Remove the front spoiler or apron panel, as applicable (see Section 11 of this Chapter.)

3   Remove the retaining screws and withdraw the wing stay(s).

4   Raise the front of the car and remove the roadwheel.

5   Release the retaining clips and remove the fixing screws, then withdraw the mudflap (where fitted) and the anti-chipping protector strip from the wheel arch rear lip and remove the wheel arch liner from inside the wing.

6   Remove, if required, the underwing shield (four bolts and two plastic clips) and the air intake (inlet) duct (fuel injection models only) which is secured by a screw at each end and four clips at its upper end. Remove the direction indicator side repeater lamp (see Chapter 12).

7   Remove the row of wing fixing bolts from the top edge and from the front and rear of the wing.

8   Cut along the mastic joints and then remove the wing.

9   Before fitting the new wing, clean the mating flanges on the body and apply a fresh bead of suitable mastic.

10   Fit the wing and tighten the screws and bolts.

11   Apply protective coating under the wing and refinish the outer surface to match the body colour.

12   Refit the remaining components using a reversal of the removal procedure.

14   Mudflaps and undershields – removal and refitting

Front mudflaps

1   The front mudflaps, where fitted, are each secured by three screws threaded into plastic captive nuts.

Rear mudflaps

2   The rear mudflaps, where fitted, are each secured by four screws threaded into plastic clips or captive nuts.

Underwing shields

3   Each underwing shield is secured by four hexagon-headed screws (the front one of which also secures the engine compartment under-shield) and by two plastic clips (photo).

4   While the shields can be withdrawn with the roadwheels in place, access is much easier if the car is raised and the roadwheel removed.

Engine compartment undershields

5   The engine compartment undershields are secured by bolts threaded into the body front panel and engine mounting longitudinal member, and by hexagon-headed screws threaded into the inner wing panel. Note that one each of the latter also secures the underwing shield.

6   The left-hand shield is secured by five bolts or screws, the right-hand shield by six.

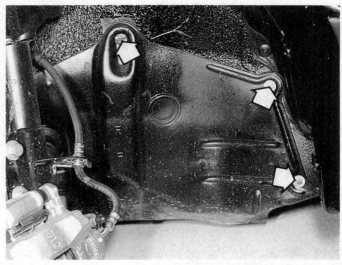

14.3 Underwing shield mounting points (three shown)

15   Body side fittings – removal and refitting

Body side moulding

1   The moulding sections (where fitted) are attached to the front wings by double-sided adhesive tape and to the doors and rear wings by double-sided adhesive tape and sealant.

2   Replacement sections are attached by double-sided adhesive tape.

3   Removal and refitting requires that the moulding and body panels are heated to a temperature of 30 to 40°C (86 to 104°F) using a hot-air gun. This obviously required great care if damage is to be avoided and should therefore be left to an expert. Owners who wish to carry out the work themselves should proceed as follows.

4   Heat the full length of the section to be removed evenly, then concentrate on one end. Raise the end of the section, cutting the bonding agent if necessary, then work along the section until it is released.

5   On refitting, remove all traces of old bonding agent and very thoroughly degrease the body panel's contact surface. Heat both the panel and the moulding to the specified temperature and press the moulding into place.

Roof drip channel – Saloon

6   Open the doors and remove the three screws securing each of the front and rear door pillar strips. Withdraw them, noting how each fits over the centre strip, then gently prise the centre strip off the roof edge.

7   Refitting is the reverse of the removal procedure. Press the centre strip into position using only firm hand pressure, then refit the door pillar strips, noting that each must overlap the centre strip by approximately 10 mm (0.39 in).

Roof drip channel – Hatchback

8   Open the front door and remove the three screws securing the door pillar strip.

9   Withdraw the door pillar strip, noting how it fits over the centre strip, then carefully prise the centre strip and clips off the roof edge until it can be withdrawn from the rear quarter window moulding.

10   On refitting, space the clips evenly along the centre strip (there should be approximately seven clips), then slide the strip into the window moulding for a distance of approximately 10 mm (0.39 in). Press the strip into position, seating the clips with firm hand pressure. Refit the door pillar strip so that it overlaps the centre strip by approximately 10 mm (0.39 in).

Ventilation system exhaust vents

11   Open the boot lid or tailgate and remove the interior trim panels to expose the vent mountings.

12   Unscrew the four nuts from inside the luggage compartment and withdraw the air duct. Withdraw the vent from the outside, noting the single washer (later models only), the deflector (Saloon only) and the rubber seal.

15.18 Fuel filler flap opener retaining nut

18.4 Boot lid mounting bolts on hinge arm

13   Refitting is the reverse of the removal procedure.

Wheel arch anti-chipping strips

14   Protective strips are fitted to the rear edge of each front wheel arch and to the front edge of each rear wheel arch.
15   The front wheel arch strips are each secured by four screws, the rear wheel arch strips are each secured by seven screws.

Side skirts – Executive models

16   Apart from the three screws evident at each wheel arch, there is no information on the mountings of the Executive models' side skirts.

Fuel filler flap

17   Open the fuel filler flap and unscrew the two screws securing the flap hinge. Withdraw the flap.
18   Where applicable, unscrew the retaining nut and press the flap opener back into the luggage compartment (photo).
19   Unscrew the four retaining nuts, then reach up inside the wheel arch and tap the flap base out from behind. Note the filler neck grommet and packing piece.
20   Refitting is the reverse of the removal procedure.

---

16   Windscreen, rear window/tailgate glass and rear quarter windows – removal and refitting

---

1   These areas of fixed glass, (the rear quarter glass applying to Hatchbacks only), are secured into the body apertures by direct bonding, and attempts at removal and refitting by the home mechanic are definitely not recommended.
2   Special primers and sealant are required, together with spacers, and therefore the work is best left to a specialist.
3   It should be noted that after a repair of this type the car must not be driven over rough surfaces until the sealant is completely cured. The period for curing varies according to the ambient temperature and humidity, but as a general guide four days in the summer and eleven days in the winter should be sufficient for windscreens and Hatchback tailgate glass. For Saloon rear windows eight days (summer) and twenty-two days (winter) will be required. Note that some time should be allowed for curing before fitting an interior mirror using an adhesive patch.
4   A toughened-glass windscreen is fitted to 1.6L models as standard equipment; all other models are fitted with laminated glass windscreens.

---

17   Sunroof – general

---

1   A sunroof was available as an optional extra on some models up to

December 1987, when it became standard equipment on all except the Premium models (introduced early in 1989).
2   The sunroof is electrically-operated on all models except the later 1.6LS models, which use a manually-operated version of the same assembly.
3   Sunroofs fitted to cars built before May 1988 are Japanese-built, but after this a UK-built assembly was installed. The UK-built sunroof is featured in the accompanying illustration, the earlier version being broadly similar.
4   The sunroof is maintenance-free, but any adjustment or removal and refitting of the component parts should be entrusted to a dealer, due to the complexity of the unit and the need to remove much of the interior trim and headlining to gain access. The latter operation is involved, and requires care and specialist knowledge to avoid damage.
5   See Chapter 12 for details of the electrically-operated sunroof circuit components.

---

18   Boot lid (Saloon) – removal and refitting

---

1   The help of an assistant will be necessary for these operations. First, with the boot lid open, place a thick pad of cloth beneath each front corner to protect the paintwork.
2   Disconnect the wiring from the number plate illuminating lamps and release it from the clips securing it to the boot lid.
3   Mark around the hinge arms on the underside of the boot lid with a pencil.
4   Have an assistant support the lid, then unbolt the hinge arms (photo) and lift the boot lid from the car.
5   If necessary, the boot lid torsion bars may be removed using a hooked, padded, lever to release them. The hinge arms may also be removed by extracting the wire spring clip that secures the outer end of each hinge pin and removing the pins.
6   Refitting is a reversal of removal, but apply a little grease to the hinge pins. Do not fully tighten the hinge arm bolts until the boot lid has been closed and checked for alignment with the surrounding bodywork. Refer to Section 22 for adjustments possible with the striker.
7   To remove the boot lid handle panel, open the boot, unscrew the panel retaining nuts and release the plastic clips. Withdraw the panel, noting the sealing washers. Refitting is the reverse of removal.
8   No information is available on the mountings of the moulded emblems (where fitted).

---

19   Tailgate (Hatchback) – removal and refitting

---

1   The help of an assistant will be necessary for these operations, First, with the tailgate open, place a thick pad of cloth on the roof of the car beneath the top corners of the tailgate.

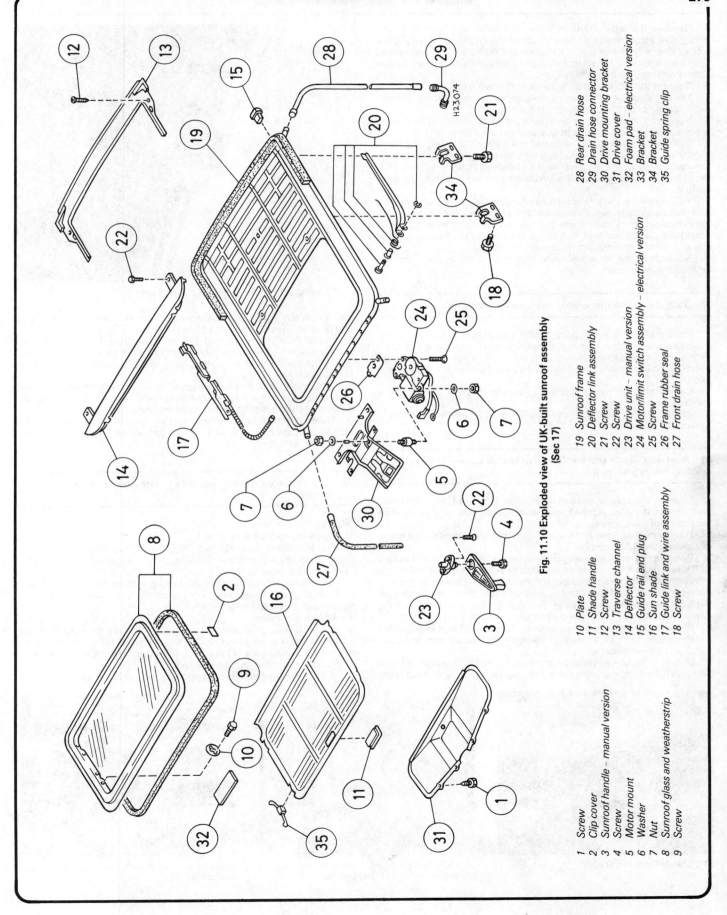

Fig. 11.10 Exploded view of UK-built sunroof assembly (Sec 17)

1 Screw
2 Clip cover
3 Sunroof handle – manual version
4 Screw
5 Motor mount
6 Washer
7 Nut
8 Sunroof glass and weatherstrip
9 Screw

10 Plate
11 Shade handle
12 Screw
13 Traverse channel
14 Deflector
15 Guide rail end plug
16 Sun shade
17 Guide link and wire assembly
18 Screw

19 Sunroof frame
20 Deflector link assembly
21 Screw
22 Screw
23 Drive unit – manual version
24 Motor/limit switch assembly – electrical version
25 Screw
26 Frame rubber seal
27 Front drain hose

28 Rear drain hose
29 Drain hose connector
30 Drive mounting bracket
31 Drive cover
32 Foam pad – electrical version
33 Bracket
34 Bracket
35 Guide spring clip

H23074

2   Remove the left-hand door pillar trim panel and disconnect the wiring connector plugs, then tie a length of string to them. Prise out the rubber sleeve from the top of the pillar and withdraw the wiring lead from the pillar. Untie the string, leaving it in the pillar. Disconnect the rear screen washer pipe from the tailgate.
3   Support the tailgate, then disconnect the two struts.
4   Mark around the hinges on the tailgate with a pencil, then unscrew the hinge nuts and lift the tailgate from the car.
5   If required, the hinges can be removed if the roof trim and headlining are detached at the rear edge to give access to the bolts.
6   Refitting is a reversal of removal, but before tightening the hinge nuts to the tailgate, close it to check for correct alignment. The tailgate may be moved within the limits of the elongated holes to achieve this, but the striker will then need adjustment to ensure smooth positive closure.
7   To remove the tailgate handle panel, open the tailgate and remove its interior trim panel (see Section 33 of this Chapter), then unscrew the panel retaining nuts and release the plastic clips. Withdraw the panel, noting the sealing washers. Refitting is the reverse of removal; use the string to draw the wiring down through the pillar.
8   No information is available on the mountings of the moulded emblems (where fitted).

20   Tailgate strut (Hatchback) – removal and refitting

1   Open the tailgate and support it with a piece of wood.
2   Release each strut from its mountings by raising the spring clips with a small screwdriver, then pulling the strut off the ball-stands. Do not raise the clips more than 4 mm (0.16 in) if the strut is to be re-used (photo).
3   Do not attempt to dismantle a strut, and dispose of it safely. It contains gas under pressure.
4   To refit a strut, position it over the ball-studs. Push on each end in turn until it snaps home.

21   Boot lid/tailgate and fuel filler flap opener cable – removal, refitting and adjustment

1   Operate the opener to release the filler flap and boot lid/tailgate, then remove the door sill tread panel and the door pillar trim panels (see Section 33 of this Chapter.)
2   Prise back the carpet to expose the opener lever, then unbolt it and disconnect the cable (photo).
3   Remove the rear seat base cushion (see Section 34 of this Chapter.)
4   Prise up the retaining clips and lift the floor carpet sufficiently to withdraw the cable from its clips. It may also be necessary to remove the rear door sill tread panel and to prise up a section of weatherstrip. If the cable is trapped as it passes over the left-hand rear wheel arch, remove also the rear seat back cushion(s).
5   Remove the luggage compartment left-hand and rear interior trim panels (see Section 33) to expose the fuel filler flap opener and boot lid/tailgate striker (photos).
6   Unscrew the opener retaining nut from inside the flap aperture (see Section 15) and withdraw the cable and opener assembly. Pull the cable

20.2 Raising spring clip to release tailgate strut

through to the luggage compartment, release the clips and unbolt the end bracket, then disconnect it from the striker.
7   Refitting is the reverse of the removal procedure. Do not use excessive force or allow the cable to be kinked or trapped at any point. Check the operation of the boot/tailgate lock and adjust it if necessary (see Section 22).
8   The cable itself can be adjusted by slackening its end bracket mounting bolts and moving the brackets within the limits of their slotted holes until the correct free play is obtained (see Section 22).
9   Note that when the striker lever is in the 'Cancel' position the remote opener is inoperative; the lock can be opened only from the outside using the master key.

22   Boot lid/tailgate latch and striker – removal, refitting and adjustment

Striker
1   Open the boot lid or tailgate.
2   On Hatchback models not fitted with the remote fuel filler flap/tailgate opener, prise out the two clips and remove the access panel to expose the striker (photo).
3   On all other models, remove the luggage compartment rear interior trim panel (see Section 33), then unbolt the cable end bracket and disconnect the cable (where fitted).
4   Unbolt the striker.
5   On refitting, tighten the mounting bolts loosely then position the striker so that it engages squarely in the centre of the latch and so that the boot lid or tailgate is held flush with the surrounding bodywork. Tighten the mounting bolts securely.
6   Adjust the opener cable (where fitted) by moving its end bracket

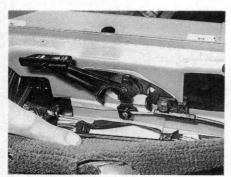

21.2 Opener lever and cable

21.5A Remove luggage compartment trim panel to expose fuel filler opener

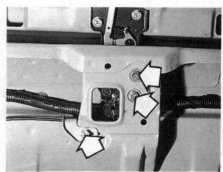

21.5B Boot lid latch and opener cable mounting bolts

Fig. 11.11 Boot lid/tailgate and fuel filler flap opener cable (Sec 21)

1 Latch
2 Striker
3 Opener lever
4 Opener cable
5 Opener retaining nut
6 Clip
7 Clip
8 Lever cover
9 Grommet
10 Lock striker (where fitted)
11 Spring clip
12 Clamp
13 Cable tie
14 Screw
15 Screw
16 Screw
17 Bolt

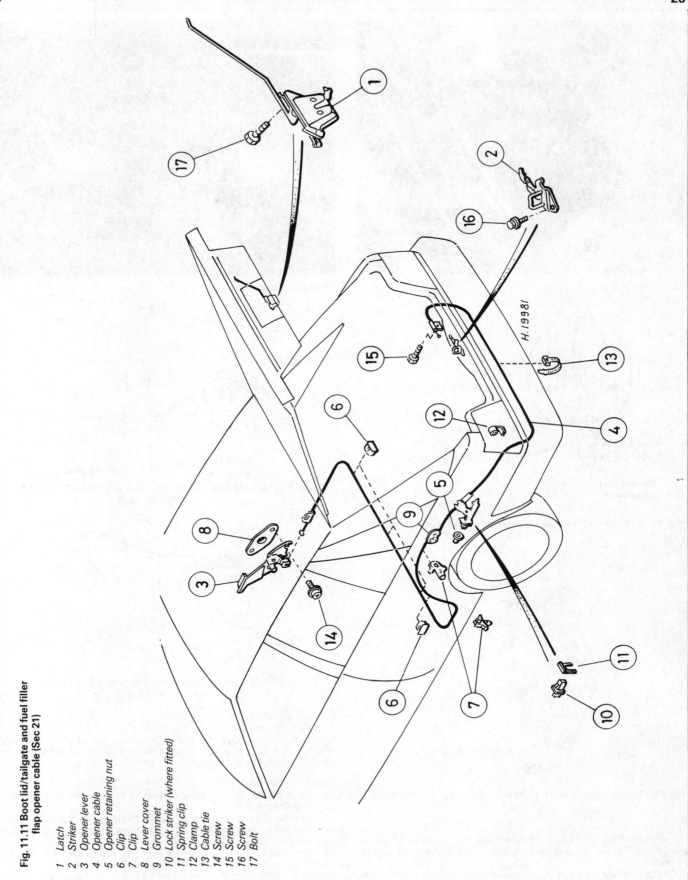

22.2 Tailgate striker

22.11 Tailgate latch

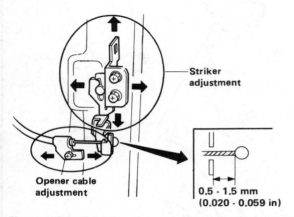

Fig. 11.12 Boot lid striker and opener cable adjustment – Saloon
(Sec 22)

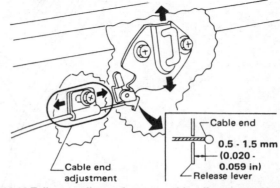

Fig. 11.13 Tailgate striker and opener cable adjustment – Hatchback
(Sec 22)

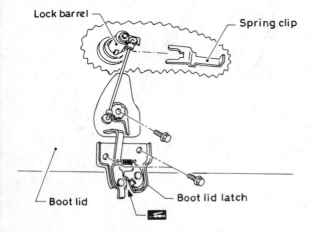

Fig. 11.14 Boot lid latch and lock barrel – Saloon (Secs 22 and 23)

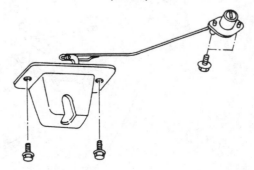

Fig. 11.15 Tailgate latch and lock barrel – Hatchback
(Secs 22 and 23)

Latch – Saloon
8   Open the boot lid and unbolt the latch (Fig. 11.14).
9   On refitting, ensure that the latch is engaged correctly with the bellcrank and that it engages centrally on the striker when the boot lid is closed. Tighten the bolts securely.

Latch – Hatchback
10   Open the tailgate and remove the interior trim panel (see Section 33 of this Chapter.)
11   Release the clip securing the lock rod to the latch, then unbolt the latch and withdraw it (photo). Fig. 11.15 shows the latch and lock barrel assembly.
12   On refitting, lightly grease the latch and rod end, check that the latch engages centrally on the striker when the tailgate is closed, then tighten the bolts securely. Connect the lock rod to the latch and refit the clip.

until the specified free play is achieved (see Fig. 11.12 or 11.13, as appropriate). Tighten the bolt securely and carefully check the cable's operation.
7   Check carefully the fit of the boot lid/tailgate and ensure that the lock works properly.

23.5 Tailgate lock barrel mounting screws (arrowed)

24.1 Fuel filler flap lock barrel

23 Boot lid/tailgate lock barrel – removal and refitting

Saloon

1   Open the boot lid and disconnect the rod from the lock barrel by releasing the clip. Extract the spring clip to release the lock.
2   Refitting is the reverse of removal. Apply a smear of grease to both ends of the rod and refit the clips to secure it.
3   Check that the bellcrank is free to rotate. Dismantle it and apply a smear of grease if it is stiff (see Fig. 11.14).

Hatchback

4   Open the tailgate and remove the interior trim panel (see Section 33 of this Chapter.)
5   Remove the clip securing the lock rod to the latch or lock barrel (as applicable), then remove the mounting screws and withdraw the lock (photo).
6   Refitting is the reverse of removal. Apply a smear of grease to both ends of the rod, refit the clip to secure it and tighten the screws securely.

24 Fuel filler flap lock barrel – removal and refitting

1   Open the fuel filler flap and prise out the spring clip to release the lock (photo). Note that the lock striker is also retained by a spring clip.
2   Refitting is the reverse of removal.

25 Door – removal, refitting and adjustment

1   Open the door and remove its interior trim panel (see Section 33 of

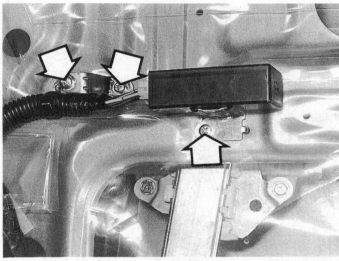

25.1 Remove power window amplifier and armrest bracket to release condensation barrier

this Chapter.) Remove and disconnect the loudspeaker, then disconnect and remove (where fitted) the power window amplifier and the armrest bracket. Peel off the polythene condensation barrier (photo).
2   Identify the connectors for refitting, then disconnect all wiring leads from the electrical components fitted and withdraw the wiring from the door.

25.3 Front door check link and pin

25.5 Rear door upper hinge

25.7 Front door striker

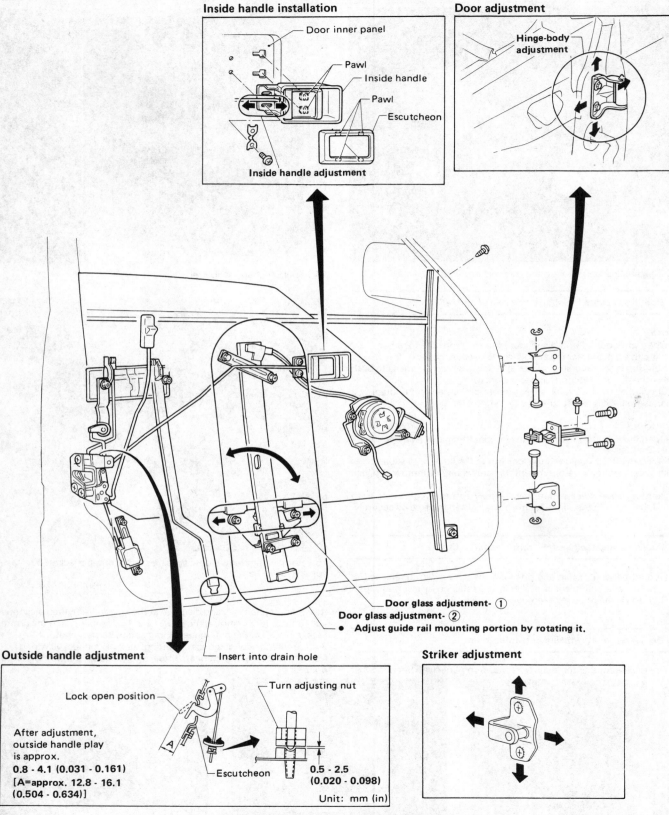

Inside handle installation

- Door inner panel
- Pawl
- Inside handle
- Pawl
- Escutcheon

Inside handle adjustment

Door adjustment

Hinge-body adjustment

Outside handle adjustment

Lock open position

After adjustment, outside handle play is approx.
0.8 - 4.1 (0.031 - 0.161)
[A=approx. 12.8 - 16.1 (0.504 - 0.634)]

- Turn adjusting nut
- Escutcheon
- **0.5 - 2.5 (0.020 - 0.098)**

Unit: mm (in)

Door glass adjustment- ①
Door glass adjustment- ②
• Adjust guide rail mounting portion by rotating it.

Insert into drain hole

Striker adjustment

Fig. 11.16 Front door components (Secs 25 to 29)

3   Disconnect the check link by driving out the pin upwards (photo).
4   Support the door on blocks of wood.
5   Extract the circlips and drive out the hinge pins, noting that the heads face each other between the hinges (photo).

6   Lift the door from the car. If necessary the hinges may be unbolted from the door pillars.
7   Refitting is a reversal of removal, but lubricate the hinge pins and check link pin with a little grease. Check that the door is positioned

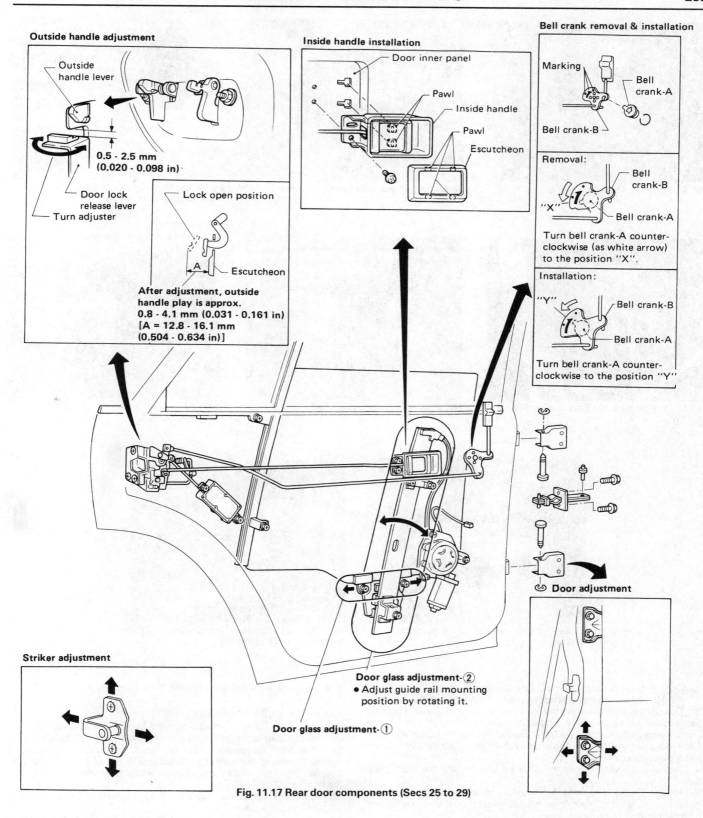

Outside handle adjustment

- Outside handle lever
- 0.5 - 2.5 mm (0.020 - 0.098 in)
- Door lock release lever
- Turn adjuster

Lock open position

A — Escutcheon

After adjustment, outside handle play is approx. 0.8 - 4.1 mm (0.031 - 0.161 in) [A = 12.8 - 16.1 mm (0.504 - 0.634 in)]

Inside handle installation

- Door inner panel
- Pawl
- Inside handle
- Pawl
- Escutcheon

Bell crank removal & installation

- Marking
- Bell crank-A
- Bell crank-B

Removal:
- Bell crank-B
- "X"
- Bell crank-A

Turn bell crank-A counter-clockwise (as white arrow) to the position "X".

Installation:
- "Y"
- Bell crank-B
- Bell crank-A

Turn bell crank-A counter-clockwise to the position "Y"

Striker adjustment

Door glass adjustment-②
● Adjust guide rail mounting position by rotating it.

Door glass adjustment-①

Door adjustment

Fig. 11.17 Rear door components (Secs 25 to 29)

centrally in the body aperture, and if necessary loosen the hinge bolts and reposition them. Check that the door lock engages the striker smoothly, and if necessary loosen the hinge bolts and reposition them. Check that the door lock engages the striker smoothly, and if necessary loosen the cross-head screws and reposition the striker within the elongated holes (photo).

26   Door latch, striker and handles – removal and refitting

Door latch

1   Open the door and ensure that the window is fully raised, then

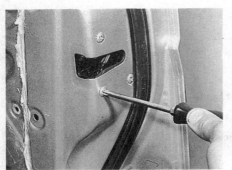

26.4A Remove mounting screws ...

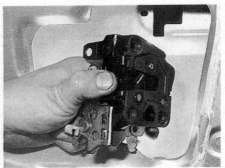

26.4B ... to release door latch assembly

26.10 Door outside handle rod clip and mounting nuts (arrowed)

26.15 Door outside handle rod adjusting nut (arrowed)

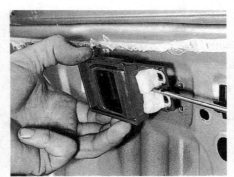

26.20 Removing door inside handle

26.21 Adjust handle position before finally tightening screws

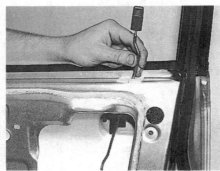

26.23 Removing front door inside lock knob and rod

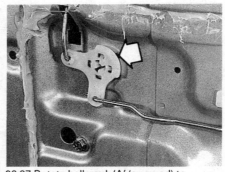

26.27 Rotate bellcrank 'A' (arrowed) to release bellcrank assembly

remove the door interior trim panel (see Section 33 of this Chapter.)

2   Peel back the polythene condensation barrier to reach the latch.

3   Disconnect from the latch the rods connecting it to the door outside (front doors only) and inside handles, the inside lock knob, the lock barrel (front doors only) and, if fitted, the central locking switch or actuator. Each rod is secured by a spring clip which must be released before the rod is disconnected.

4   Remove the latch mounting screws and withdraw the latch (photos).

5   Refitting is the reverse of the removal procedure. Apply a smear of grease to the latch components and rod ends. Adjust the rods (where possible) as described below.

Door striker

6   Open the door and mark around the striker with a pencil.

7   Remove the mounting screws and withdraw the striker, noting the shim behind it.

8   On refitting, adjust the striker position (if necessary) as described in

Section 25, paragraph 7, then tighten the screws securely.

Outside handle – front door

9   Open the door and ensure that the window is fully raised, then remove the door interior trim panel (see Section 33 of this Chapter.)

10   Peel back the corner of the polythene condensation barrier and release the clip to disconnect the handle rod from the handle (photo).

11   Where fitted, unplug the keyhole illuminating bulb's switch from the handle.

12   Peel back the access plug or patch to expose the handle mounting nut nearest to the latch.

13   Unscrew the two handle mounting nuts, collect the lock barrel stay and both washers, then withdraw the handle from the outside of the door.

14   Refitting is the reverse of the removal procedure. Apply a smear of grease to the handle pivots and rod end, then check the handle adjustment.

15   When correctly adjusted, the front door outside handle should

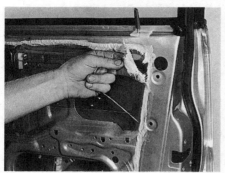
27.2 Peel back polythene condensation barrier to reach lock mountings

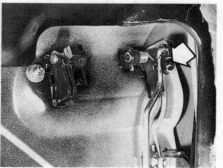
27.3A Lock barrel stay is secured by outside handle nut (arrowed) ...

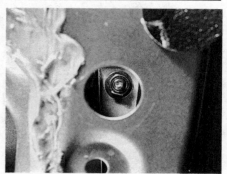
27.3B ... and is accessible via aperture shown – note adhesive patch

27.4A Remove spring clip to release lock barrel ...

27.4B ... and withdraw lock barrel and rod

have free play of between 0.8 to 4.1 mm (0.032 to 0.161 in) before it starts to engage the latch. Its total movement, to the (latch) fully-opened position should be between 12.8 to 16.1 mm (0.504 to 0.634 in). Adjustment is made by turning the plastic adjusting nut at the latch end of the handle's rod (photo). Adjustment should be correct when there is 0.5 to 2.5 mm (0.020 to 0.098 in) free play between the nut and the latch lever. (see Fig. 11.16.)

Outside handle – rear door
16   Apart from the fact that there is no link rod between the handle and the latch and no illuminating bulb or lock barrel stay, removal and refitting is as described in paragraphs 9 to 14 above.
17   The rear door outside handle adjustment should be as described in paragraph 15 above, but adjustment is actually made by turning the latch adjuster, (see Fig. 11.17.)

Inside handle
18   Open the door and ensure that the window is fully raised, then remove the door interior trim panel (see Section 33 of this Chapter.)
19   Peel back the corner of the polythene condensation barrier. Release the clip securing the handle's rod end to the latch and disconnect the rod.
20   Mark around the handle with a pencil, remove its two retaining screws and withdraw the handle (see Fig. 11.16 or 11.17), releasing the rod from its guide clip (photo).
21   On refitting, connect the rod to the latch and press it into its guide clip, then refit the handle. Tighten the two screws loosely, then slide the handle in its slotted holes until all but the barest minimum of free play is eliminated. Tighten the screws fully (photo).

Inside lock knob – front door
22   Open the door and ensure that the window is fully raised, then remove the door interior trim panel (see Section 33 of this Chapter.)
23   Peel back the corner of the polythene condensation barrier and release the clip securing the knob rod to the latch. Withdraw the knob and rod (photo).
24   Refitting is the reverse of the removal procedure. Apply a smear of grease to the rod end.

Inside lock knob – rear door
25   Open the door and ensure that the window is fully raised, then remove the door interior trim panel (see Section 33 of this Chapter.)
26   Peel down the polythene condensation barrier and release the clip to disconnect the bellcrank rod from the latch.
27   Rotate anti-clockwise (to position 'X', Fig. 11.17) the black plastic bellcrank 'A' until the bellcrank assembly can be withdrawn from the door, (photo). Disconnect the knob rod from the bellcrank, release the bellcrank rod from its guide clip and withdraw them.
28   Refitting is the reverse of the removal procedure. Apply a smear of grease to the rod ends and rotate bellcrank 'A' anti-clockwise to position 'Y'.

27 Front door lock barrel – removal and refitting

1   Open the door and ensure that the window is fully raised, then remove the door interior trim panel (see Section 33 of this Chapter.)
2   Peel back the corner of the polythene condensation barrier (photo) and withdraw the central locking system lock/unlock switch (driver's door only, where fitted). Release the clip to disconnect the lock rod from the latch.
3   Peel back the access plug or patch and slacken (or fully unscrew) the nut securing the door outside handle and the lock barrel stay. Withdraw the stay from the lock barrel (photos). Where fitted, disconnect the keyhole illuminating bulb wiring.
4   Prise out the spring clip to release the lock barrel and withdraw the lock barrel from the outside of the door (photos).
5   Refitting is the reverse of the removal procedure. Apply a smear of grease to the rod end and pivot.

28 Door window glass and regulator – removal and refitting

Window glass
1   Open the door and remove its interior trim panel (see Section 33 of this Chapter.)

28.3 Armrest bracket and power window amplifier

28.5 Door window glass mounting bolts (arrowed)

28.6 Front door window glass front sash mounting bolt (arrowed)

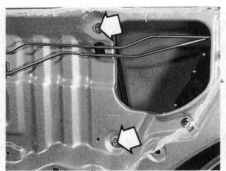

28.7 Rear door window glass rear sash mounting bolts (arrowed)

28.8 Removing front door window glass

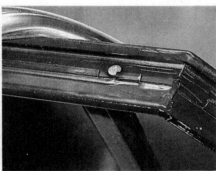

28.9 Rear door rear sash top mounting screw

28.12A Front door regulator channel top mounting bolts (arrowed)

28.12B Rear door regulator channel top mounting bolts (arrowed)

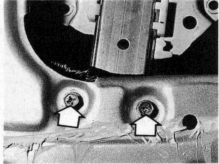

28.12C Regulator channel bottom mounting bolts (arrowed)

2   Remove and disconnect the loudspeaker.
3   Disconnect and remove (where fitted) the power window amplifier and the armrest bracket (photo).
4   Peel off the polythene condensation barrier.
5   Temporarily refit the window regulator (manual windows), or connect the power window switch and amplifier (power window), then lower the window until its mounting bolts appear in the aperture in the door inner panel (photo).
6   On front doors, slacken the single bolt securing the front sash lower end (photo).
7   On rear doors, slacken the two bolts securing the rear sash lower end (photo).
8   Unbolt the window glass from the regulator and withdraw it, tilting it to clear the door frame (photo).
9   On rear doors, the fixed quarter glass can be removed, after the window glass has been withdrawn, by unbolting the rear sash and lifting out the glass. The sash is retained by the two bolts at its lower end and by a single screw at its upper end, through the door frame, peel back the weatherstrip to expose the screw (photo).

10   Refitting is the reverse of the removal procedure, but apply a little grease to the regulator mechanism and adjust the position of the sash within its elongated bolt hole(s) until the glass slides smoothly and easily through its full travel.

Regulator
11   Remove the window glass, as described above.
12   Remove the regulator channel top and bottom mounting bolts (photos).
13   On manual windows, remove the regulator mechanism mounting bolts (photo).
14   On power windows, disconnect the motor wiring and remove the motor mounting bolts (photos).
15   Manoeuvre the regulator assembly (photo) out of the door.
16   Refitting is the reverse of the removal procedure. Apply a little grease to the regulator mechanism and refit it, tightening the mounting bolts only loosely at first. Refit the window glass and move it several times through its full travel, adjusting the position of the regulator

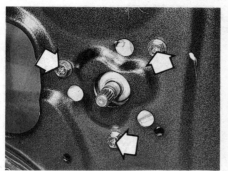

28.13 Manual window regulator mechanism mounting bolts (arrowed)

28.14A Disconnecting the power window motor wiring

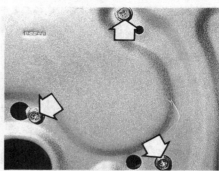

28.14B Front door power window motor mounting bolts (arrowed)

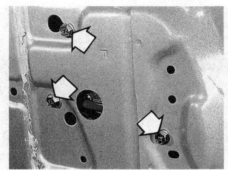

28.14C Rear door power window motor mounting bolts (arrowed)

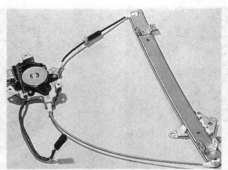

28.15 Door window regulator assembly – power window type

channel and the sash within their elongated bolt holes until the glass slides smoothly and easily. Tighten all the bolts securely.

29 Central locking system – general

1   The four passenger compartment doors (not the boot lid/tailgate) can be locked on some models by a central locking system.
2   The system allows all four doors to be locked by turning the driver's door key or depressing the driver's door inside lock knob. Turning the driver's door key to unlock will unlock all four doors, but raising the driver's door inside lock knob will unlock only that door.
3   Operating the main lock/unlock switch (number 1 switch) in the driver's door armrest will lock or unlock all doors except the driver's.
4   Refer to Chapter 12 for details of the system's electrical components.

30 Power windows – general

Some models are fitted with electrically-operated windows. Refer to Chapter 12 for details of the system's components.

31 Mirrors – removal and refitting

Exterior mirror – manual

1   Prise out the plastic cover from the corner finisher plate on the front door, then remove the screw and withdraw the plate (photos).
2   Remove the three screws (photo), then withdraw the mirror from the door noting the bracket hooked under the door edge.
3   Refitting is a reversal of removal.

Exterior mirror – electric

4   Remove the door interior trim panel as described in Section 33 of this Chapter. This will of course require the removal of the triangular cover and corner finisher plate.
5   Peel back the polythene condensation barrier as necessary to gain access to the mirror wiring multi-plug, then disconnect it (photo).
6   Undo the three mirror retaining screws (photo) and withdraw the mirror from the door.
7   Refitting is the reverse sequence to removal (photos).

Interior mirror – roof-mounted

8   On early models, remove the single screw securing the mirror stalk to its base. The base may be detached from the roof if required by removing its retaining screw(s).
9   On T12 models built after January 1988, prise the plastic cover off the mirror stalk and remove the three screws securing the mirror stalk to its base. Remove the complete assembly. The base can be detached if required by removing the screw and clip.

Interior mirror – windscreen mounted

10   T72 models built after May 1988 are fitted with a mirror that is attached to the windscreen itself by an adhesive patch. **Do not** disturb the patch unless absolutely necessary and note that the patches themselves may not be available separately from Nissan dealers. If this is the case, try dealers in other makes (Ford and Rover, for example, supply patches separately), accessory shops or windscreen repair specialists. Removal and refitting are as follows.
11   Remove the mirror from the windscreen by 'sawing' through the adhesive bond with a piece of nylon cord.
12   Clean the mirror base and the mounting area on the windscreen with methylated spirit. Both items must be **perfectly** clean, and the windscreen must be at room temperature (20°C/68°F approx).
13   If a separate patch is being used, fit it according to the instructions supplied and remove **all** traces of the old patch from the mirror base. Generally the windscreen and mirror base mounting areas must be **absolutely** clean and must be warmed as described below.
14   Warm the mirror base and patch to 50° to 70°C (122° to 158°F).

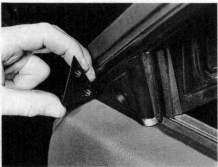
31.1A Prise out triangular cover ...

31.1B ... and remove single screw ...

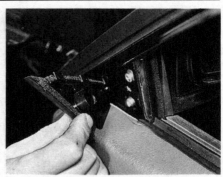
31.1C ... to release exterior mirror/door corner finisher plate

31.2 Manual exterior mirror mounting screws

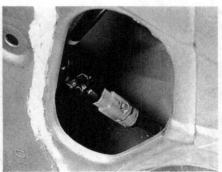
31.5 Electric exterior mirror connector plug

31.6 Removing electric exterior mirror mounting screws

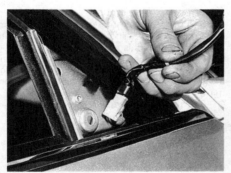
31.7A Refit electrical lead inside door

31.7B Ensure bracket engages correctly under door edge (arrowed)

Immediately remove the backing paper from the patch and press the mirror firmly onto the mounting area. Hold it in position for at least two minutes, and do not attempt to adjust the mirror for at least an hour.

15   Beware of using proprietary adhesives to attach the mirror to the windscreen: not all are suitable and some may leave residues which are difficult to remove, while others (such as the modern 'superglues') may actually cause the windscreen to crack.

32 Exterior mirror glass – renewal

1   Replacement glasses are available for the exterior mirrors, but note that exactly the correct glass must be obtained; they are handed, and those fitted to electric remote control mirrors incorporate heating elements.

2   To remove a cracked glass, first put on proper hand and eye protection.

3   Using a 700 to 1500 W heat gun, warm up the glass base's retaining

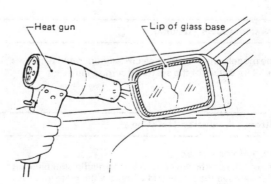
Fig. 11.18 Softening glass base retaining lip to release exterior mirror glass (Sec 32)

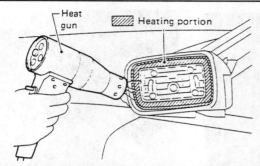

Fig. 11.19 Warm shaded area before installing new glass (Sec 32)

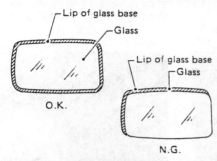

Fig. 11.20 Lip must cover glass edges evenly (Sec 32)

lip all around the edge of the glass until the lip is softened (see Fig. 11.18).

4   Using a screwdriver or stiff scraper inserted under the retaining lip, prise the glass out of the base. Start at the vertical edge furthest away from the car and take care not to damage the heating element wires. **Do not** use excessive force.

5   Thoroughly clean those base surfaces which will accept the replacement glass's adhesive strips.

6   Warm the retaining lip again and the edge of the replacement glass (Fig. 11.19), then remove the protective covering from the glass's adhesive strips and insert the glass under the retaining lip at one end. Work the glass into place until its edges are covered evenly by the retaining lip, (Fig. 11.20) but be careful, as it is possible to crack the new glass or damage its base.

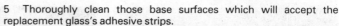

33   Interior trim panels and fittings – removal and refitting

Door panel

1   On front doors only, prise out the small triangular plastic cover from the front corner finisher plate, remove the screw and withdraw the plate (photo).

2   Where manual windows are fitted, use a length of bent wire to hook out the regulator handle wire clip (pass the wire down behind the handle and press back the plastic washer) until the handle can be withdrawn. Remove the plastic washer (photos).

3   Where fitted, remove the screws securing the step lamp lens, withdraw the lamp body and unplug the connector to release its wiring (photos).

4   On rear doors only, remove the ashtray, unscrew the retaining screw and withdraw the ashtray surround (photo).

5   Unclip the door inside handle escutcheon from the handle (photo) – see Fig. 11.16 or 11.17.

6   On T72 models built after May 1988, prise out the cover plug from the grab handle upper end and remove the retaining screw, then prise out the clip from the lower end and slacken the retaining screw. Withdraw the grab handle (photos).

7   Where power windows are fitted, remove the switch from the armrest by prising it up at the front and sliding it forwards until the wiring connector can be unplugged (photos).

8   On T12 models, and early T72 models, prise out the cover plug from

33.1 Removing front door corner finisher plate

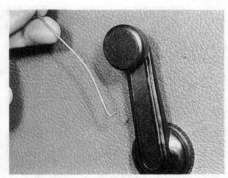

33.2A Pass length of bent wire down regulator handle ...

33.2b ... to release wire clip from regulator shaft groove

33.2C Remove regulator handle plastic washer

33.3A Remove doorstep lamp lens ...

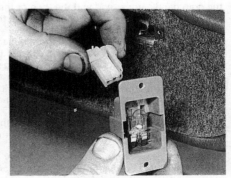

33.3B ... and disconnect wiring lead from lamp

33.4 Ashtray surround is secured by a single screw

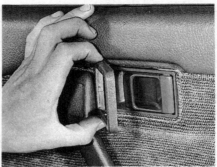
33.5 Removing door inside handle escutcheon

33.6A Removing grab handle (later T72 models) – prise out cover plug ...

33.6B ... and remove retaining screw ...

33.6C ... then prise out armrest clip ...

33.6D ... and slacken retaining screw ...

33.6E ... to release grab handle

33.7A Prise up power window switch at front, slide forwards ...

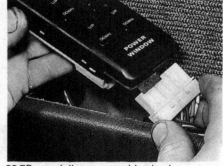
33.7B ... and disconnect wiring lead

the grab handle upper end and the (two or three, as applicable) cover plugs from the armrest lower edge. Remove the retaining screws and withdraw the grab handle/armrest assembly.

9   Using a suitable flat tool (such as a wide-bladed screwdriver) or your fingers, release the clips securing the panel to the door around the panel's front, rear and bottom edges by prising the panel out, or sharply pulling it out, in the vicinity of each clip. Release the clip in the centre of the panel, then lift the panel upwards to unclip it along its upper edge, lift it over the inside lock knob and withdraw it (photos).

10   Renew any broken clips.

11   Fittings such as door storage pockets, speaker grilles etc can be released by removing the retaining screws or releasing the clips from behind the panel.

12   Before disturbing the armrest or ashtray brackets, note carefully which way round each is fitted so that they are correctly refitted and align with their respective holes in the interior trim panel (see photos 25.1 or 28.3).

13   Refitting is the reverse of the removal procedure. When refitting the manual window regulator handle, position the clip as shown in photo 33.2b and press it into place on the regulator driveshaft.

Tailgate panel (Hatchback)

14   Open the tailgate and use a suitable flat tool (such as a wide-bladed screwdriver) to prise out the four clip studs along the panel's bottom edge.

15   Gently pull the panel away from the tailgate to release the (approximately six) clips securing it.

16   Gripping the panel by its raised shoulders, pull the upper locating tongue out of the tailgate glass weatherstrip. Renew any broken clips.

17   Refitting is the reverse of the removal procedure.

Door sill tread panel

18   Remove the retaining screws (photo) and lift away the panel.

Footwell trim panel

19   Remove the door sill tread panel.

20   On the right-hand side, remove the single retaining screw and

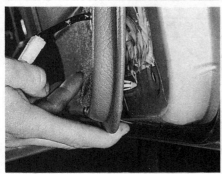

33.9A Release retaining clips around panel edges ...

33.9B ... then lift panel upwards to withdraw

33.18 Removing driver's door sill tread panel retaining screws

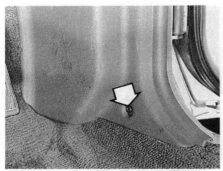

33.20 Footwell right-hand trim panel retaining screw (arrowed)

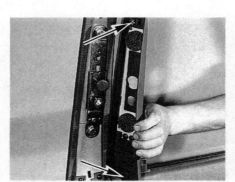

33.23 Door centre pillar upper trim panel is secured by two clips (arrowed)

33.24 Removing lower trim panel retaining screws

withdraw the panel, releasing it from its front retaining clip (photo). On the left-hand side, remove the two screws and withdraw the panel.
21   Refitting is the reverse of the removal procedure.

Door centre pillar trim panel
22   Unbolt the front seat belt top anchorage (see Section 35 of this Chapter.)
23   Gently prise the upper trim panel away from the pillar to release its two clips (photo).
24   Remove the two screws at the top of the lower trim panel (photo).
25   Either remove both door sill tread panels or slacken their screws so that they can be lifted sufficiently to release the lower trim panel ears.
26   Gently prise the lower trim panel away from the pillar to release its four clips (photo), then disengage it from the seat belt.
27   Refitting is the reverse of the removal procedure.

Windscreen pillar trim panel
28   Open the door and prise off the bearing, if necessary, along the length of the panel.
29   Gently prise the panel away from the pillar to release its retaining clips.

Rear quarter trim panel – Saloon
30   Remove the rear seat back (see Section 34 of this Chapter.)
31   Unbolt the rear seat belt top anchorage (see Section 35 of this Chapter.)
32   Prise the door edge beading, if necessary, off the panel, and prise up the three clip studs along the panel's rear edge.
33   Gently prise the panel away from the pillar to release its retaining clips.

Tailgate/door pillar trim panel – Hatchback
34   Remove the rear seat back (see Section 34 of this Chapter.)
35   Unbolt the rear seat belt top anchorage (see Section 35 of this Chapter.)
36   Prise the rear door and tailgate edge beading, if necessary, off the panel.

37   Remove the screw from the panel's top corner and prise up the retaining clip studs from its lower front corner and rear edge.
38   Gently prise the panel away from the door pillar at its front edge to release the retaining clips, then withdraw it, unhooking the metal clips along its rear edge.

Luggage compartment panels – Saloon
39   Remove the rear seat back (see Section 34 of this Chapter.)
40   Lift the luggage compartment carpet, prising up the clip studs along its front edge.
41   Remove the edge beading from the rear seat aperture, unbolt the rear seat belt anchorages and remove the luggage compartment lamp and jack cover (photo).
42   Work around the edge of each side trim panel, releasing the retaining clips and screws until the panel can be removed.
43   To remove the rear panel, remove both side panels or release their rear ends, then prise off the bearing along the panel's upper edge and remove the rear lamp cluster access panels.
44   Work around the panel releasing the retaining clips until the panel can be removed.

Luggage compartment panels – Hatchback
45   Open the tailgate and remove the parcel shelf.
46   Remove the rear seat base, fold the seat back cushions forwards and remove the side cushions (see Section 34 of this Chapter.)
47   Lift the luggage compartment carpet, releasing the clip studs and folding it forwards over the seat back cushions.
48   Prise up the two retaining clip studs and withdraw the access panel over the tailgate striker, prise the edge beading (if necessary) away from the rear panel's upper edge and withdraw the jack cover and rear lamp cluster access panels from the panel.
49   Work around the edge of the rear panel, removing the retaining screws along its bottom edge and releasing the clip studs at all other points, until the panel can be withdrawn.
50   To remove the side panels, first remove the rear panel, then remove the retaining screws and withdraw the speaker/storage tray mountings.

33.26 Disengage trim panel from seat belt via slot

33.41 Removing rear seat aperture edge beading – note metal clips securing trim panel

33.55A Glovebox lid is pivoted on two hinge pins ...

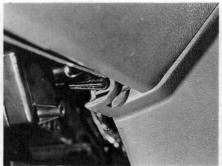

33.55B ... which are fitted as shown

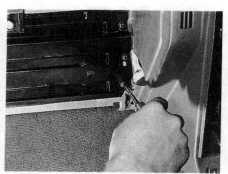

33.56A Remove retaining screws ...

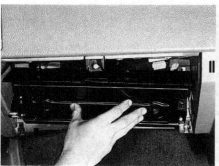

33.56B ... to release glovebox front panel

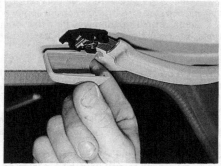

33.57 Passenger grab handle mounting

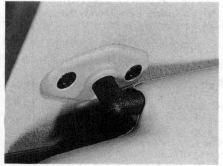

33.58 Sunvisor pivot retaining screws

51   Work around the edge of the panel, removing the retaining screws and prising up the clip studs until the panel can be withdrawn.

Parcel shelf – Saloon
52   Remove the rear seat back (see Section 34 of this Chapter.)
53   Unclip the speaker top covers (where fitted) and remove the screws and nuts to release the speakers and their bases.
54   Gently prise up the parcel shelf to release the clip studs and withdraw it, disengaging it from the seat belts.

Glovebox
55   Withdraw the hinge pin at each bottom corner of the glovebox lid, then open the lid and withdraw it (photos).
56   The glovebox front panel is retained by a number of screws along its top and side edges (photos).

Passenger grab handles
57   Prise off the cover at each end of the handle and unscrew the two retaining bolts to release it (photo).

Sunvisor
58   Remove the retaining screws (photo) to release the pivot from the roof, unclip the sunvisor from its holder and withdraw it.

Headlining
59   The removal and refitting of the headlining is an involved operation which requires considerable skill and experience if it is to be carried out without damage. It is a task for the expert alone and should not be attempted by the home mechanic.

---

34 Seats – removal and refitting

Front seats
1   Operate the adjuster and move the seat fully rearwards.

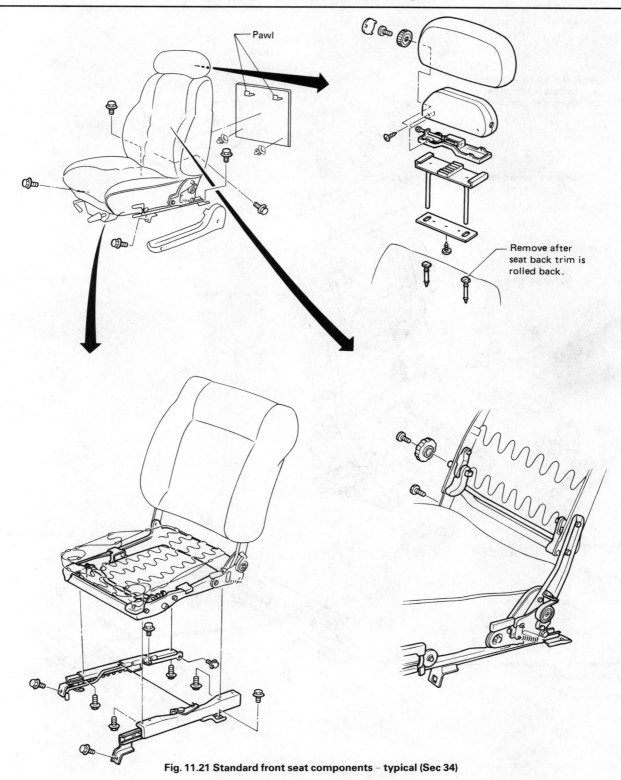

Pawl

Remove after
seat back trim is
rolled back.

Fig. 11.21 Standard front seat components – typical (Sec 34)

2   Unscrew the bolts securing the front of the runners to the floor (photo).

3   Move the seat fully forwards, then remove the plastic covers and unscrew the rear bolts (photos).

4   Lift the seat from inside the car, disconnecting the wiring leads (where fitted), where the seat is of the heated type.

5   Refitting is a reversal of removal.

Rear seats – Saloon

6   Remove the base cushion by pulling sharply upwards at each front corner to remove the wire legs from the retainers, then slide it forwards to release the rear legs (photo).

7   On models without a fold-through rear seat back, to remove the seat back the base cushion must be removed first (see paragraph 6). Remove the two screws securing the wire leg at the bottom of each end, then

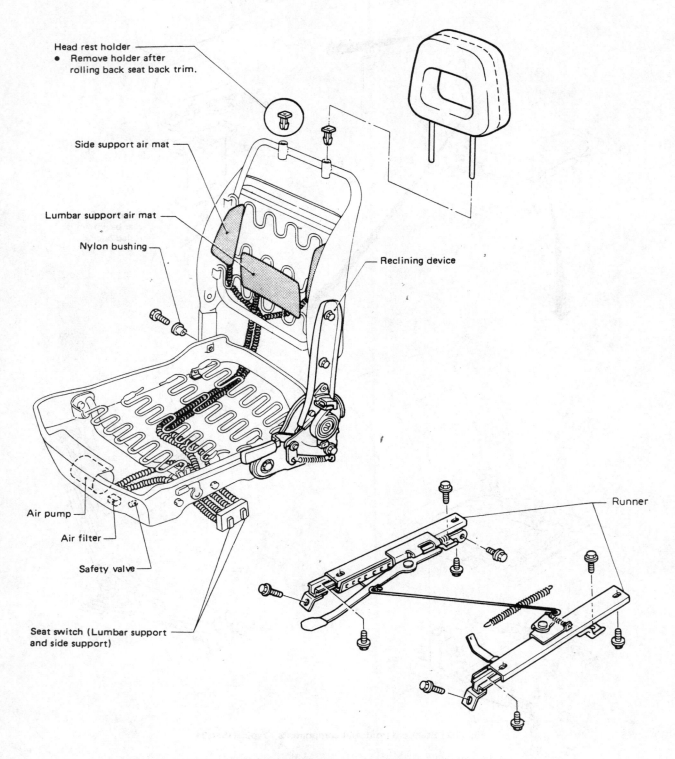

Head rest holder
● Remove holder after rolling back seat back trim.

Side support air mat

Lumbar support air mat

Nylon bushing

Reclining device

Air pump

Air filter

Safety valve

Seat switch (Lumbar support and side support)

Runner

Fig. 11.22 Power support front seat components – LHD shown (Sec 34)

push the seat back sharply upwards to release the three wire legs on its upper edge from their retainers in the parcel shelf. The seat back panel can then be prised gently out to release the clip studs securing it.

8   On models with a fold-through rear seat, first remove the base

cushion (see paragraph 6), then pull forwards the seat back cushions.

9   Prise up the clip studs securing the seat back cushion covers to the luggage compartment floor (photo).

10   Fold back the covers to expose the seat back cushion hinges,

34.2 Front seat runner front mounting bolt

34.3A Front seat runner rear mounting bolt and cover

34.3B Note front seat runner stopper bolts screwed into central tunnel

34.6 Rear seat base cushion front corner wire leg and retainer

34.9 Rear seat back cushion cover is secured by clip studs

34.10A Unbolting rear seat back cushion from hinge

34.10B Disengage rear seat back cushion from central hinge pin

34.11A Removing seat back lower finisher clip stud ...

34.11B ... to release finishers

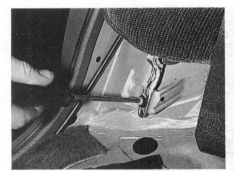

34.12A Main seat back is secured by a screw at the bottom of each end ...

34.12B ... by screws at each end of bottom rail ...

34.12C ... and middle of bottom rail ...

34.13 ... and by three wire legs into parcel shelf retainers

34.17A Remove speaker grille to reach side cushion top retaining screw

34.17B Side cushion bottom retaining screw

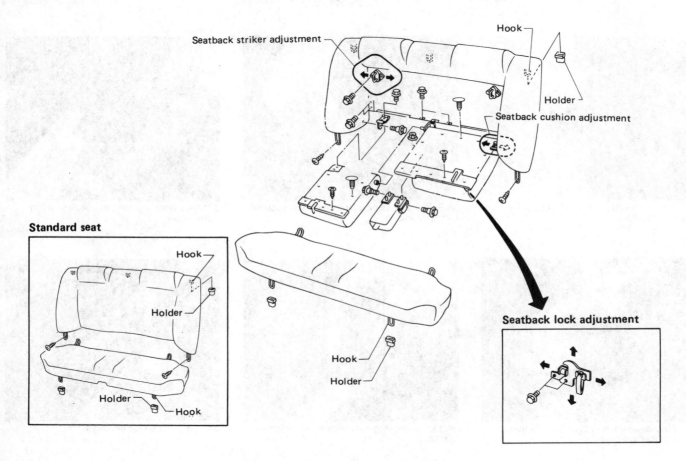

Fig. 11.23 Rear seat components – Saloon (Sec 34)

unbolt the cushions and remove them (the left-hand cushion incorporating the centre armrest) (photos).
11   Prise out the clip studs securing the seat back lower finishers and remove both finishers (photos).
12   Remove the screws securing the wire leg at the bottom of each end of the seat back and the three hexagon-headed screws securing the seat back bottom rail to the floor (photos).
13   Push the seat back sharply upwards to release the three wire legs on its upper edge from their retainers in the parcel shelf (photo).
14   Refitting is the reverse of removal.

Rear seats – Hatchback
15   Open the tailgate and remove the parcel shelf.
16   Remove the seat base cushion as described in paragraph 6 above.
17   Carefully prise up each speaker grille/storage tray (as applicable) to release the four retaining clips, then remove the screws securing the top and bottom ends of each side cushion and push each cushion sharply

upwards to unhook it (photos).
18   Remove the carpet retainer strip from the back of each seat back cushion; each strip is retained by three screws. Prising up the clip studs to release them, remove the carpet from the seat back and fold it into the luggage compartment.
19   Unbolt each outer recliner/hinge assembly from the floor and withdraw the seat back cushions.
20   Refitting is the reverse of removal.

---

35   Seat belts – removal and refitting

Front seat belts
1   Prise off the plastic cover and unbolt the belt top anchorage (photo).
2   Remove the door centre pillar trim panels (see Section 33 of this Chapter.)

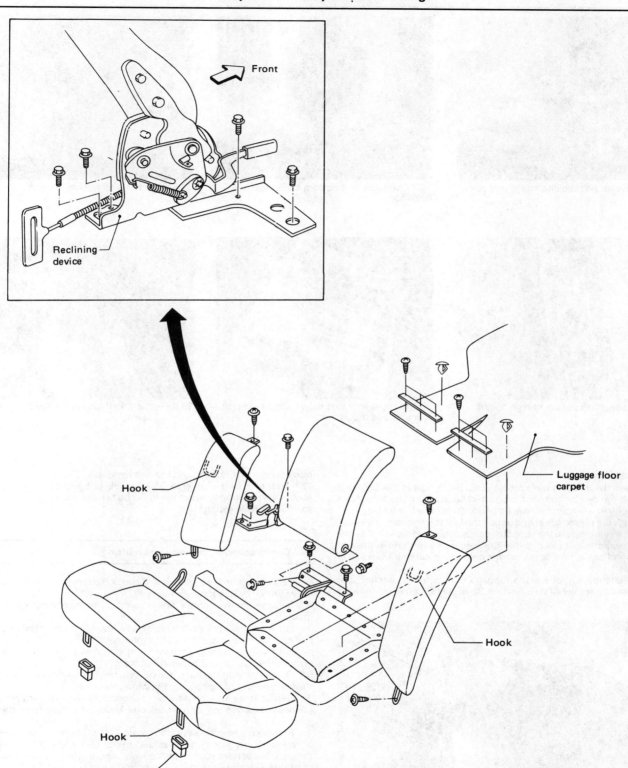

Reclining device

Front

Hook

Luggage floor carpet

Hook

Hook

Holder

Fig. 11.24 Rear seat components – Hatchback (Sec 34)

3 Prise off its plastic cover and unbolt the belt bottom anchorage, then remove the retaining screw and withdraw the retractor mechanism. The retractor cover can be unclipped from the pillar if required (photo).
4 The buckle can be unbolted from the seat base, if required (photo).
5 Where fitted, the top anchorage height adjuster can be unbolted

from the pillar after the belt anchorage and upper trim panel have been removed (photo).
6 Refitting is the reverse of removal, but ensure that the anchorages are free to move when the bolts have been tightened to the specified torque setting.

35.1 Front seat belt top anchorage and cover

35.3 Front seat belt bottom anchorage and retractor

35.4 Front seat belt buckle

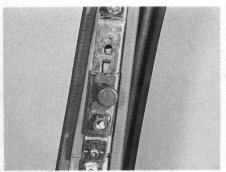

35.5 Front seat belt top anchorage height adjuster

35.8 Remove rear seat base cushion to reach rear seat belt mountings

35.9 Rear seat belt top anchorage and cover

Rear seat belts

7   Remove the rear seat base cushion (see Section 34 of this Chapter.)
8   Unbolt the belt bottom anchorage and buckle from the floor. Note that the centre two-point belt can be unbolted completely (photo).
9   Prise off the plastic cover and unbolt the belt top anchorage (photo).
10   On Saloon models, the retractor can be unbolted from inside the luggage compartment (photo). It will be necessary to remove the rear seat back and parcel shelf to release the belt itself (Sections 33 and 34 of this Chapter).
11   On Hatchback models, the luggage compartment interior trim panels must be removed (see Section 33 of this Chapter) so that the

retractor can be unbolted and the belt removed.
12   Refitting is the reverse of removal, but ensure that the belt anchorages are free to move when the bolts have been tightened to the specified torque setting.

36 Centre console – removal and refitting

1   Park the car on level ground and chock the wheels so that it cannot move when the handbrake is released.
2   Remove the two screws, one at each side, at the console's front end (photo).
3   Lift the panel beneath the handbrake lever at the rear and unclip it. Remove the two screws beneath it (photos).
4   Lift the rear storage compartment cover, withdraw the mat and remove the two screws beneath it (photo).
5   Gently prise up the heated-seat switches (where fitted) and unplug their connectors to disconnect the wiring leads.
6   Gently prise up the finisher surrounding the gear lever gaiter (manual transmission), or gear selector knob (automatic transmission) (photo).
7   Release the handbrake and lift the console at the rear, disconnecting or releasing any electrical wires and manoeuvring the finisher down through its aperture so that the console can be lifted off over the gear lever/gear selector knob and the handbrake lever (photo). On automatic transmission models, the gear selector knob can be released if necessary by removing its two retaining screws (see Chapter 7).
8   Refitting is the reverse of removal.

37 Facia – removal and refitting

1   Disconnect the battery negative lead.
2   Release the rake locking lever and pull the steering column to the

35.10 Rear seat belt retractor – Saloon

36.2 Centre console front retaining screw

36.3A Remove console centre panel ...

36.3B ... to expose mounting screws (arrowed)

36.4 Console rear mounting screws are at bottom of storage compartment (arrowed)

36.6 Releasing gear lever gaiter finisher

36.7 Removing centre console

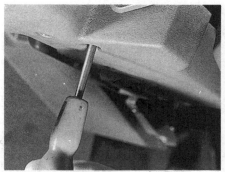
37.2 Removing steering column shroud retaining screw

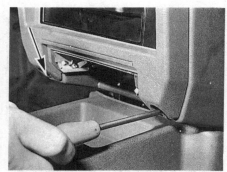
37.7A Radio/heater finisher bottom screws (other arrowed) ...

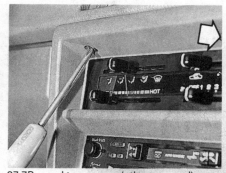
37.7B ... and top screws (other arrowed)

lowest position, then remove the facia lower panel and steering column shrouds as described in Chapter 10, Section 21, paragraphs 2 to 4 (photo).

3   Remove the steering wheel (see Section 10) and withdraw the steering column stalk switches.

4   Remove the instrument panel (see Chapter 12) and release the speedometer cable from its slot.

5   Remove the glovebox lid and front panel (see Section 33 of this Chapter.)

6   Unbolt (but do not remove fully) the bonnet release lever (see Section 9 of this Chapter, paragraphs 3 and 4.)

7   Withdraw the ashtray and remove the four screws (one each side at the bottom, two at the top) which secure the radio/heater finisher. Withdraw the finisher (photos).

8   Remove the radio (see Chapter 12.)

9   Prise off the heater control knobs and withdraw the heater control faceplate, as described in Section 39 of this Chapter, then remove the four screws (two at each end) securing the heater control assembly. There is no need to disturb the control assembly itself but note that the screws themselves are also facia mountings.

10   Remove the three screws securing the ashtray mounting plate, withdraw the plate and disconnect the ashtray illuminating lamp (photos).

11   Unbolt the brackets securing each end of the facia to the car's bodywork (photo).

12   Gently prise up the three defroster grilles along the front edge of the facia top surface and remove the screws securing the facia to the bulkhead (photos).

13   Prise out and disconnect all remaining facia-mounted switches (see Chapter 12.)

14   Remove the fuse panel lid, unscrew the panel's mounting bolts and move it to one side. Unscrew the SMJ (Super Multiple Junction) mounting bolts.

15   Carefully pull the facia away from the bulkhead, releasing any electrical leads or earth connections that retain it. **Do not** use excessive force, it is not necessary and may damage the plastic components. If difficulty is encountered at any point check carefully that all fasteners and other components have been removed as necessary.

37.7C Removing radio/heater finisher

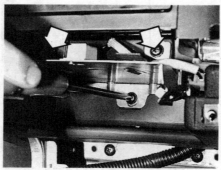

37.10A Ashtray mounting plate screws (upper two arrowed)

37.10B Disconnecting ashtray illuminating lamp

37.11 Facia is supported by a bracket on each side

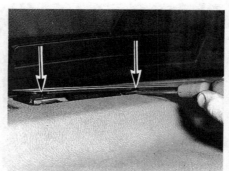

37.12A Prise up defroster grilles at points provided ...

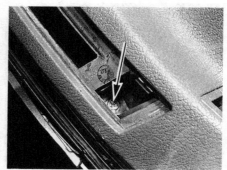

37.12B ... to expose facia mounting bolts

39.5 Removing heater control lever knob

39.6A Removing heater control faceplate screws (other arrowed) ...

39.6B ... to release faceplate

16   Withdraw the facia.
17   The upper crash pad can be removed, if required, from the main facia panel by unscrewing the retaining nuts and bolts.
18   Refitting is the reverse of the removal procedure. Refer, where necessary, to the relevant Sections of this Chapter and of Chapters 10 and 12.

38   Heating and ventilation system – description

The heater is of the type which utilises waste heat from the engine coolant. The coolant is pumped through the matrix in the heater casing where air, force-fed by a radial fan and four-speed motor, disperses the heat into the car's interior.
Fresh air enters the heater or the ventilator ducts through the grille at the rear of the bonnet. Air is extracted from the interior of the car through the exhaust vents on the rear of the body.

The heater/ventilator controls are of lever type, operating through cables to flap valves which deflect the air flowing through the heater both to vary the temperature and to distribute the air between the footwell and defroster outlets.

39   Heater controls – removal, refitting and adjustment

Removal and refitting
1   Disconnect the battery negative lead.
2   Remove the four screws and withdraw the facia lower panel from beneath the steering column.
3   Remove the ashtray and radio/heater finisher (see Section 37 of this Chapter, paragraph 7.)
4   Remove the glovebox lid and front panel as described in Section 33 of this Chapter.
5   Gently pull the knobs from the heater control levers (photo).

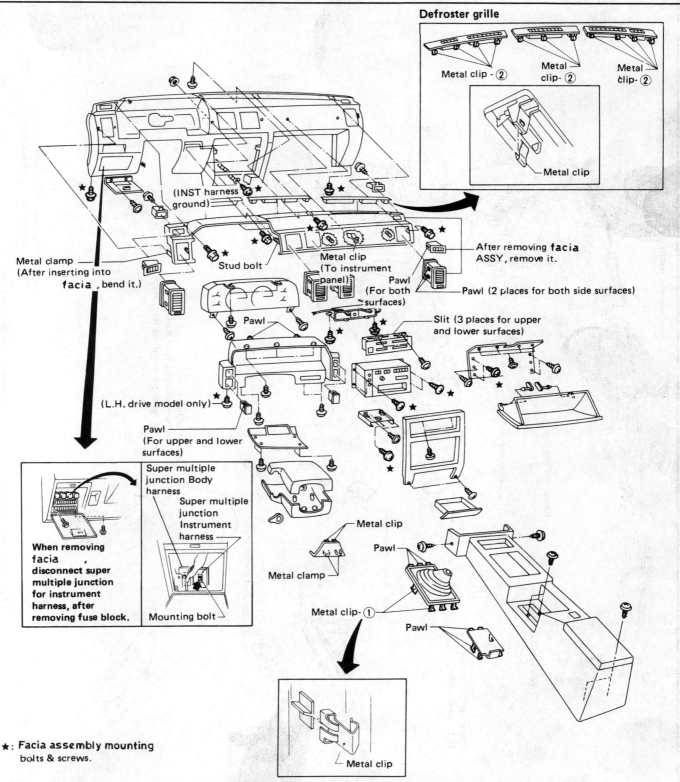

Defroster grille

Metal clip - ②   Metal clip- ②   Metal clip- ②

Metal clip

(INST harness ground)

After removing **facia** ASSY, remove it.

Metal clamp (After inserting into **facia** , bend it.)

Stud bolt

Metal clip (To instrument panel)

Pawl (For both surfaces)

Pawl (2 places for both side surfaces)

Slit (3 places for upper and lower surfaces)

Pawl

(L.H. drive model only)

Pawl (For upper and lower surfaces)

Super multiple junction Body harness

Super multiple junction Instrument harness

When removing facia , disconnect super multiple junction for instrument harness, after removing fuse block.

Mounting bolt

Metal clip

Metal clamp

Metal clip- ①

Pawl

Pawl

Metal clip

★: **Facia assembly mounting** bolts & screws.

Fig. 11.25 Exploded view of the facia – LHD shown (Sec 37)

6   Remove the two retaining screws and withdraw the heater control faceplate (photos).
7   Disconnect the control cables from the heater and intake box by releasing the outer cable clips and prising the inner cable ends from the control lever ends (photo). Release the cables from any ties, insulating tape, etc securing them.
8   Remove the screws securing each end and withdraw the heater

control assembly (photos) until the fan switch wires can be disconnected. Remove the assembly with the cables, noting how they are routed.
9   To disconnect the cables from the control assembly, prise apart the clip ears and withdraw the cable from the clip; the clip ears can be squeezed together to release it (photo).
10   Refitting is the reverse of removal, but adjust the controls and cables as described below.

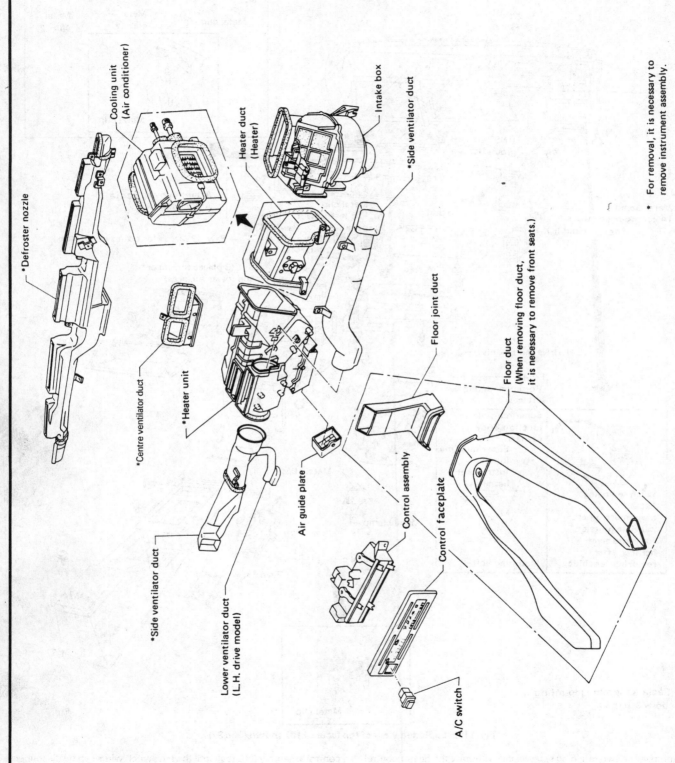

*Defroster nozzle

Cooling unit
(Air conditioner)

Heater duct
(Heater)

Intake box

*Side ventilator duct

*Centre ventilator duct

*Heater unit

*Side ventilator duct

Lower ventilator duct
(L.H. drive model)

Air guide plate

Control assembly

Control faceplate

A/C switch

Floor joint duct

Floor duct
(When removing floor duct,
it is necessary to remove front seats.)

* For removal, it is necessary to
remove instrument assembly.

Fig. 11.26 Heater components and ducting – LHD shown (Secs 38 to 42)

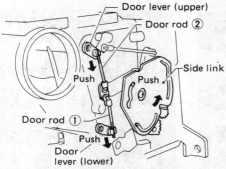

Fig. 11.27 Ventilator door control rod adjustment (Sec 39)

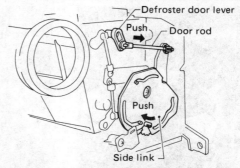

Fig. 11.28 Defroster door control rod adjustment (Sec 39)

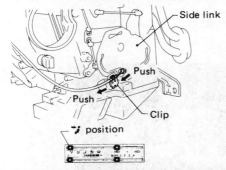

Fig. 11.29 Air control lever cable adjustment (Sec 39)

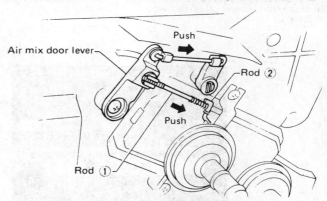

Fig. 11.30 Water cock control rod adjustment (Sec 39)

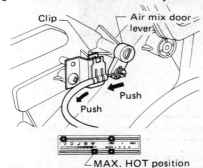

Fig. 11.31 Temperature control lever cable adjustment (Sec 39)

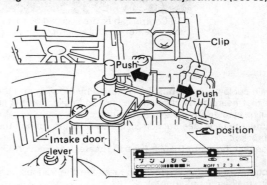

Fig. 11.32 Air intake control lever cable adjustment (Sec 39)

Adjustment

11 First remove the facia lower panel and the glovebox components, as outlined above. Note that access is extremely limited and it would be useful to have a small mirror and a good torch available. Operate the seat adjusters and move both front seats fully rearwards.

12 To adjust the ventilator and defroster door control rods on the heater's right-hand side, first disconnect the air control lever cable from the heater side link (see paragraph 7 above).

13 With reference to Fig. 11.27, disconnect both door rods to the rear of the side link, push both door levers downwards fully and move the side link fully anti-clockwise. Hold the levers and side link in those positions while the rods are re-connected; lower rod first, then the upper rod.

14 With reference to Fig. 11.28, disconnect the defroster door rod above the side link, push the door lever to the front and move the side link fully clockwise. Hold the lever and link in those positions while the rod is re-connected.

15 Connect the air control lever cable to the side link. Move the control lever to the position indicated in Fig. 11.29, push the side link fully clockwise and then push back the cable outer to remove all traces of free play before fastening it with the clip.

16 To adjust the temperature control, first disconnect the cable from the air mix door lever on the heater's left-hand side (see paragraph 7 above).

17 With reference to Fig. 11.30, disconnect the water cock control rod (1) from the air mix door lever. Push the air mix door lever fully in the direction shown and push the control rod until its end just contacts rod

(2); at this point the spring should be compressed by 2 mm (0.08 in). Connect the control rod (1) to the air mix door lever again.

18 Connect the temperature control lever cable to the air mix door lever again, move the temperature control lever to the maximum 'Hot' position and push the air mix door lever fully in the direction shown in Fig. 11.31. Push back the cable outer to remove all traces of free play before fastening it with the clip.

19 To adjust the air intake control lever cable, move the air intake control lever to the 'recirculate' position and push the intake door lever fully in the direction shown in Fig. 11.32, then push back the cable outer to remove all traces of free play before fastening it with the clip (photo).

20 Finally, check that all controls operate smoothly and easily throughout their full range before refitting the heater control faceplate and knobs, the glovebox components, the radio/heater finisher and ashtray and the facia lower panel.

40 Heater unit and matrix – removal and refitting

1 Drain the cooling system (see Chapter 2).

2 Disconnect the heater hoses from their bulkhead unions, noting the arrow marks, and catch any spilt coolant. Note that the heater matrix will

39.7 Air intake control lever cable (A), temperature control lever cable (B), heater fan resistor (C)

39.8A Removing retaining screws at each end ...

39.8B ... to release heater control assembly

39.9 Control cables are secured by metal clips at heater control assembly

39.19 Air intake control lever cable end at intake box

still contain coolant which must be removed by blowing into the feed union (ie that nearest the car's centre line) and collecting the coolant which will be ejected from the return union.

3   Remove the facia (see Section 37 of this Chapter.) Unbolt the facia support bracket.

4   Disconnect the control cables from the heater (see Section 39 of this Chapter.)

5   Unbolting them where necessary, remove the various ventilator ducts from the heater unit (photo).

6   Unbolt the heater unit (photo) and withdraw it, taking care not to spill any remaining coolant on the carpet.

7   If required, the unit's retaining screws can be removed so that it can be dismantled and the matrix can be withdrawn. Note carefully the arrangement of control rods before disconnecting any part of the side linkage.

8   If the heater matrix is leaking, it is best to obtain a new or reconditioned unit. Home repairs are seldom successful. A blocked matrix can sometimes be cleared using a cold water hose and reverse flushing, but avoid the use of searching chemical cleaners.

9   Reassembly is a reversal of removal. Take care not to damage the fins or tubes of the matrix when inserting it into the casing.

10   On refitting, ensure that all heater components are correctly settled on their mountings so that there are no air leaks, then tighten the mountings securely. Adjust the controls as described in Section 39 of this Chapter, then refit the facia as described in Section 37.

11   Connect the heater hoses to the bulkhead unions. The return union is the lower one nearest the car's left-hand side and is connected to the coolant return tube. The feed union (nearest the car's centre line) is connected on early carburettor models to an elbow or T-piece fitting on the rear of the cylinder block. On later carburettor models it is connected to the intake (inlet) manifold. On fuel injection models the feed union is connected to the small metal pipe which passes around the engine's left-hand side from a fitting on the front of the cylinder block (see Chapter 2 for details.)

12   Refill the cooling system as described in Chapter 2.

41   Heater intake box and fan – removal and refitting

1   Disconnect the battery negative lead.

2   Remove the glovebox lid and front panel (see Section 33 of this Chapter.)

3   Disconnect the fan motor wiring and rubber tube (photo).

4   Remove the mounting bolts and withdraw the motor and fan from the base of the intake box (photos).

5   Remove the cover (photo).

6   If necessary, the fan can be removed from the motor shaft by unscrewing the nut (photo). The fan motor resistor is mounted in the connecting heater duct (see photo 39.7).

7   The intake box can be removed by unbolting it from its mountings and bracing straps.

8   Refitting is the reverse of removal.

42   Heater ducts and vents – removal and refitting

1   To remove the ducts concealed behind the facia, the facia must first be removed (see Section 37 of this Chapter.) The ducts can then be unbolted from their mountings and bracing straps and withdrawn (photo).

2   The facia vents can, in theory, be prised out of the facia from the passenger compartment. In practice this was found to be so difficult to do without seriously marking the facia that owners are advised to remove the facia panel first, so that the clips can be released and the vents can be pushed out from behind (photo). Note that the small side window defroster grilles have ducts behind them that are each retained by a single screw.

3   To remove the rear heater ducts, first remove the front seats (Section 34), the centre console (Section 36) and the footwell trim panels and door sill tread panels (Section 33). Remove the facia (Section 37) and

40.5 Unbolt facia support bracket and ventilator ducts to release heater unit

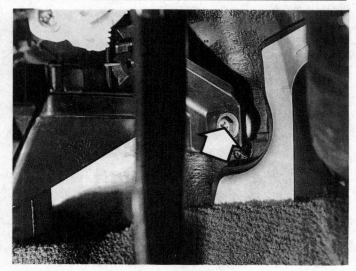

40.6 Heater unit mounting bolt

unbolt the driver's footrest and throttle pedal stop, and the facia support bracket so that the carpets can be folded back sufficiently for the ducts to be withdrawn; they are secured by a single screw at the front.

4   In all cases, refitting is the reverse of removal, referring to the other relevant Sections.

43   Air conditioning system – general information and precautions

1   Air conditioning is installed as standard on Executive models. In conjunction with the heater the system enables any reasonable air temperature to be achieved inside the car. It also reduces the humidity of the incoming air, aiding defogging even when cooling is not required.

2   The refrigeration side of the air conditioning system functions in a similar way to a domestic refrigerator. A compressor, belt-driven from the crankshaft pulley, draws refrigerant in its gaseous state from an evaporator. The compressed refrigerant passes through a condenser where it loses heat and enters its liquid state. After dehydration the refrigerant returns to the evaporator where it absorbs heat from air passing over the evaporator fins. The refrigerant becomes a gas again and the cycle is repeated.

3   Various sub-controls and sensors protect the system against excessive temperature and pressures. Additionally, engine idle speed is increased when the system is in use to compensate for the additional load imposed by the compressor.

Precautions

4   Although the refrigerant is not itself toxic, in the presence of an open

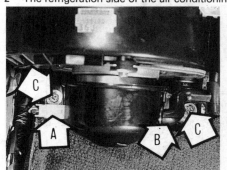

41.3 Fan motor wiring connector plug (A), rubber tube (B), intake box mounting bolts (C)

41.4A Fan motor mounting bolts (arrowed)

41.4B Removing fan motor and fan from intake box

41.5 Removing fan motor cover

41.6 Heater fan retaining nut

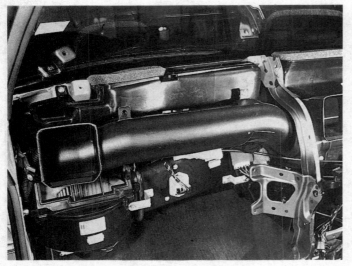

42.1 Heating and ventilator duct layout behind facia

42.2 Facia vents are clipped into place

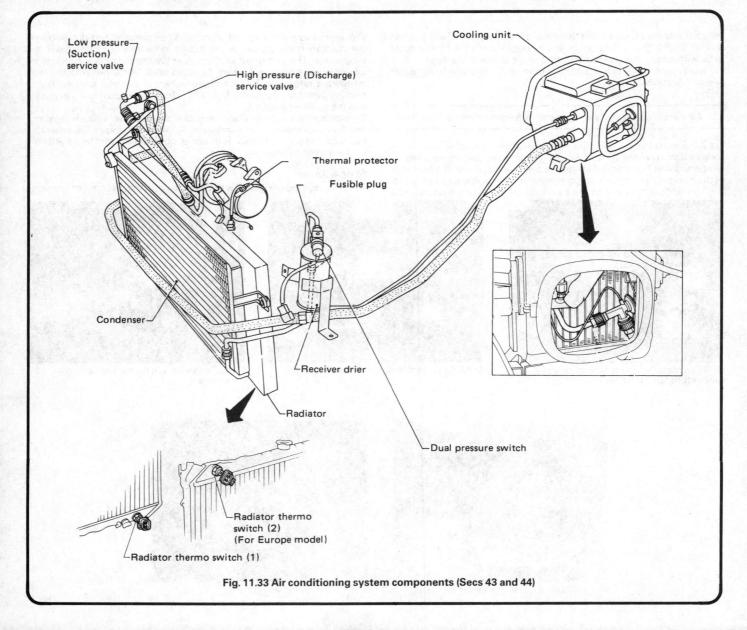

Fig. 11.33 Air conditioning system components (Secs 43 and 44)

flame (or a lighted cigarette) it forms a highly toxic gas. Liquid refrigerant spilled on the skin will cause frostbite. If refrigerant enters the eyes, rinse them with a diluted solution of boric acid and seek medical advice immediately:

5   In view of the above points, and of the need for specialized equipment for evacuating and recharging the system, any work which requires the disconnection of a refrigerant line must be left to a specialist. If, however, it is necessary to remove or disconnect a component as part of some other maintenance or repair procedure, observe the following.

6   Never disconnect any part of the air conditioner refrigerant circuit unless the system has been discharged by a dealer or qualified refrigerant engineer.

7   Where the compressor or condenser obstructs other mechanical operations, such as engine removal, it is permissible to unbolt their mountings and move them to the limit of their flexible hose deflection, but **not** to disconnect the hoses. If there is still insufficient room to carry out the required work, then the system must be discharged before disconnecting and removing the assemblies.

8   The system will, of course, have to be recharged on completion.

9   Do not allow refrigerant lines to be exposed to ambient temperatures above 110°C (230°F) – eg take particular care during welding or paint drying operations.

10   Do not operate the air conditioning system if it is known to be short of refrigerant, or further damage may result.

44 Air conditioning system – maintenance

1   Check the compressor drivebelt's tension and condition at the interval given in *'Routine maintenance'*, proceeding as described in Chapter 2, Section 7.

2   At the same interval it is a good idea to clean the condenser fins. Remove the radiator grille and clean leaves, insects etc, from the fins, using compressed air or a soft brush. Be careful not to damage the condenser by over-vigorous cleaning.

3   Operate the air conditioning system for at least 10 minutes each month, even during cold weather, to keep the seals etc, in good condition.

4   Regularly inspect the refrigerant pipes, hoses and unions for security and good condition.

5   The most common cause of poor cooling is simply a low system refrigerant charge. If a noticeable drop in cool air output occurs, one of the following quick checks will help you determine if the refrigerant level is low.

6   Warm the engine up to normal operating temperature.

7   Move the temperature control knob to the coldest setting and put the fan control knob at the highest setting. Open the doors (to make sure the air conditioning system doesn't cycle off as soon as it cools the passenger compartment).

8   With the compressor engaged – the clutch will make an audible click and the centre of the clutch will rotate – inspect the sight glass. If the refrigerant looks foamy, it's low.

9   If there's no sight glass, feel the inlet and outlet pipes at the compressor. One side should be cold and one hot. If there's no perceptible difference between the two pipes, there's something wrong with the compressor or the system. It might be a low charge – it might be something else.

10   The air conditioning system will lose a proportion of its charge through normal seepage – typically up to 100 g (4 oz) per year – so it is as well to regard periodic recharging as a maintenance operation. Recharging must be done by a Nissan dealer or an air conditioning specialist.

11   The renewal of any of the system's components should also be left to a specialist.

Chapter 12 Electrical system

Contents

Specifications

General

System type	12 volt, negative earth

Battery

Type:

T12 and early T72	Hitachi 55D23L-MF
Late T72	Lucas 065
Capacity	60 Ah

Alternator

Type:

Turbo Executive model	Mitsubishi A2T48292
All other models	Mitsubishi A2T48298 or Lucas/Magneti Marelli A127-72

Rated output:

Misubishi	70 A
Lucas/Magneti Marelli	72 A

Regulated output voltage at 1500 rpm:

Mitsubishi	14.1 to 14.7 volts
Lucas/Magneti Marelli	13.6 to 14.4 volts

Brush minimum length:

Mitsubishi	8 mm (0.32 in)
Lucas/Magneti Marelli	5 mm (0.20 in)

Starter motor

Type:
    1.6 litre models .... Hitachi S114-390A or 392, Mitsubishi M3T3058 or M2T53785, Lucas/Magneti Marelli M78R

    Turbo engine models .... Hitachi S114-393, Mitsubishi M3T33981H or M2T53781
    1.8 and 2.0 litre non-turbo models .... Hitachi S114-391A or 393, Mitsubishi M3T33981 or M2T53781, Lucas/Magneti Marelli M78R

Hitachi S114-390A, 391A:
    Current/voltage .... 60 A maximum at 11.5 volts (no load)
    Commutator minimum diameter .... 32 mm (1.26 in)
    Brush minimum length .... 11 mm (0.43 in)
    Pinion front edge to stop collar clearance ('I', Fig. 12.15) .... 0.3 to 2.5 mm (0.012 to 0.098 in)

Mitsubishi M3T33981, M3T33981H, M3T30581:
    Current/voltage .... 60 A maximum at 11.5 volts (no load)
    Commutator minimum diameter .... 31.4 mm (1.24 in)
    Brush minimum length .... 11.5 mm (0.45 in)
    Pinion front edge to stop collar clearance ('I', Fig. 12.15) .... 0.5 to 2.0 mm (0.020 to 0.079 in)

Hitachi S114-392, 393:
    Current/voltage .... 100 A maximum at 11.5 volts (no load)
    Commutator minimum diameter .... 29 mm (1.14 in)
    Brush minimum length .... 11 mm (0.43 in)
    Difference in height of pinion ('I', Fig. 12.18) .... 0.3 to 1.5 mm (0.012 to 0.059 in)

Mitsubishi M2T53781, M2T53785:
    Current/voltage .... 100 A maximum at 11.5 volts (no load)
    Commutator minimum diameter .... 31.4 mm (1.24 in)
    Brush minimum length .... 11.5 mm (0.45 in)
    Difference in height of pinion ('I', Fig. 12.18) .... 0.5 to 2.0 mm (0.020 to 0.079 in)
    Pinion shaft maximum thrust gap (Fig. 12.21) .... 0.5 mm (0.020 in)

Lucas/Magneti Marelli M78R:
    Current/voltage .... 67 A maximum at 11.5 volts (no load)
    Commutator minimum diameter .... 28.8 mm (1.13 in)
    Brush minimum length .... 3.5 mm (0.14 in)
    Pinion front edge to jump ring clearance ('I', Fig. 12.15) .... 0 to 3.0 mm (0 to 0.12 in)

Wiper and washer system

Recommended fluid .... Clean water and good quality screenwash additive with antifreeze
Wiper blades .... Champion 45 cm (18 in)

Bulbs

Headlamp 60/55W
Front side (clearance) lamp 5W
Direction indicator lamp (front and rear) 21W
Direction indicator side repeater lamp 5W
Stop/tail lamp 21/5W
Tail lamp (where fitted) 5W
Reversing lamp 21W
Rear fog lamp 21W
Number plate lamp 5W
Courtesy lamp (roof) 10W
Map reading lamp 8W
Courtesy stop lamp (door) 3.4W
Luggage compartment lamp:
    Early Saloon models 3.4W
    All other models 5W
Cigarette lighter bulb 1.2W
Instrument panel and warning lamps:
    Charge warning lamp 2W
    Large bulbholders 3.4W
    Small bulbholders 1.4W

Torque wrench settings

	Nm	lbf ft
Alternator pulley nut:		
Mitsubishi	83 to 108	61 to 79.5
Lucas/Magneti Marelli	37.5	27.5
Alternator through-bolts (Mitsubishi)	3.9 to 5.4	3 to 4
Alternator drivebelt adjuster lockbolt	14 to 17	10 to 12.5
Alternator pivot bolts	43 to 58	32 to 43
Starter motor mounting bolts and nut	29 to 39	21.5 to 29
SMJ (Super Multiple Junction) bolts	3 to 5	2 to 4

1 General description

The electrical system is of the 12 volt, negative earth type. Electricity is generated by an alternator, belt-driven from the crankshaft pulley. A lead- acid storage battery provides a reserve of power for use when the demands of the system temporarily exceed the alternator output, and for starting.

The battery negative terminal is connected to 'earth' – vehicle metal – and most electrical system components are wired so that they only receive a positive feed, the current returning via vehicle metal. This means that the component mounting forms part of the circuit. Loose or corroded mountings can therefore cause apparent electrical faults.

Many semiconductor devices are used in the electrical system, both in the 'black boxes' which control vehicle functions and in other components. Semiconductors are sensitive to excessive (or wrong polarity) voltage, and to extremes of heat. Observe the appropriate precautions to avoid damage.

Although some repair procedures are given in this Chapter, sometimes renewal of a well-used item will prove satisfactory. The reader whose interests extend beyond component renewal should obtain a copy of the 'Automobile Electrical Manual', available from the publishers of this book.

Before starting work on the electrical system, read the precautions listed in 'Safety first!' at the beginning of the manual.

2 Electrical system – precautions

1   It is necessary to take extra care when working on the electrical system to avoid damage to semi-conductor devices (diodes and transistors), and avoid risk of personal injury. In addition to the precautions given in Safety first! at the beginning of this manual, observe the following when working on the system.

2   Always remove rings, watches, etc before working on the electrical system. Even with the battery disconnected, capacitive discharge could occur if a component live terminal is earthed through a metal object. This could cause a shock or nasty burn.

3   Do not reverse the battery connections. Components such as the alternator, fuel and ignition control units, or any other having semi-conductor circuitry could be irreparably damaged.

4   If the engine is being started using jump leads and a slave battery, connect the batteries positive to positive and negative to negative. This also applies when connecting a battery charger.

5   Never disconnect the battery terminals, any electrical wiring or any test instruments, when the engine is running.

6   Never use an ohmmeter of the type incorporating a hand-cranked generator for circuit or continuity testing.

3 Routine maintenance

1   Carry out the following procedures at the intervals given in 'Routine maintenance' at the beginning of this manual.

Check the washer fluid level(s) and wipers

2   On early models, the windscreen washer fluid reservoir is located between the battery and the inner wing panel, and the fluid level is visible through the reservoir's translucent casing (photo). On later models, it is located on the engine compartment right-hand side, as described below.

3   The headlamp washer system (where fitted), the tailgate glass washer (Hatchback) and the windscreen washer (later models only) are fed by a fluid reservoir located inside the inner wing panel stiffener. An extended filler neck protrudes upwards in front of the radiator expansion tank. To check the level, plug the filler cap centre vent hole with a finger, unclip the cap and withdraw it, noting the level of fluid in the clear plastic tube (photo).

4   If topping-up is required (photo), it is permissible to use only clean water in summer, though this is best mixed with a screenwash additive for better cleaning and in winter, with methylated spirit or a combined screenwash additive and antifreeze. Follow the manufacturer's instructions for the mixing ratio.

5   Never use strong detergents (washing-up liquids etc) or engine antifreeze in the washer fluid. Not only can they cause smearing of the glass, but they can also damage the car's paintwork.

6   Check the operation of the washers fitted and adjust the jets if necessary, so that the fluid hits the centre of the wiper blade swept area when the car is in motion.

7   When adjusting the position of the washer jets, do not use the jet orifices (ie do not push a pin into the orifice to rotate the jet.)

8   Check the condition of the wiper blades, and if they show signs of deterioration or fail to clean the screen effectively, renew them as described in Section 30. For maximum clarity of vision the windscreen wiper blades should be renewed annually.

Check the alternator drivebelt
9   Refer to Chapter 2, Sections 2 and 7.

Check the operation of all electrical components
10   Check the operation of all the electrical equipment, ie wipers, washers, lights, direction indicators, horn etc. Refer to the appropriate Sections of this Chapter if any of the components are found to be inoperative.

11   Visually check all accessible wiring connectors, harnesses and retaining clips for security, or signs of chafing or damage. Rectify any problems encountered.

4 Battery – maintenance

1   The battery fitted as original equipment is 'maintenance-free', and requires no maintenance apart from having the case kept clean, and the terminals clean and tight.

2   To clean the battery terminals, disconnect them, negative (earth) first (photos). Do not allow any of the material into contact with your skin, eyes, or mouth. Use a wire brush or abrasive paper to clean the terminals. Bad corrosion or 'fungus' should be treated with a solution of bicarbonate of soda, applied with an old toothbrush. Do not let this solution get inside the battery.

3   Coat the battery terminals with petroleum jelly or a proprietary anti-corrosive compound before reconnecting them. Reconnect and tighten the positive (live) lead first, followed by the negative (earth) lead. Do not overtighten.

4   Keep the top of the battery clean and dry. Periodically inspect the

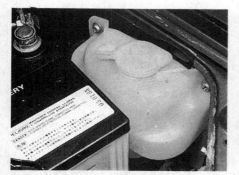
3.2 Windscreen washer fluid reservoir – early models

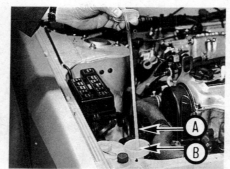
3.3 Checking washer fluid level – later models. 'A' half-full, 'B' quarter-full

3.4 Topping-up washer fluid reservoir

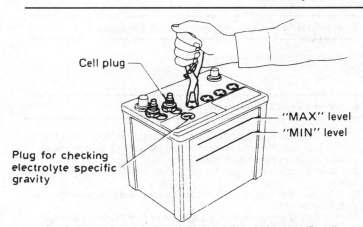

Fig. 12.1 Removing cell cover plugs – Hitachi battery (Sec 4)

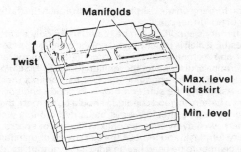

Fig. 12.2 Removing cell cover manifolds – Lucas battery (Sec 4)

battery tray for corrosion, and make good as necessary.

5   In normal use, the electrolyte level of the 'maintenance-free' type of battery should not need topping-up. On the original equipment type, the electrolyte level, visible through the battery's translucent casing, should remain above the 'Min' level line marked on the casing and below the 'Max' level line (Hitachi) or below the bottom edge of the lid skirt (Lucas).

6   If topping-up is required, peel back the adhesive label and unscrew each of the cell cover plugs (Hitachi) or use a $\frac{1}{16}$ in thick metal strip to prise up each of the two manifolds (Lucas). Use only distilled water to top up, then refit the cell cover(s).

7   If a 'traditional' type battery is fitted as a replacement, remove the old cell covers at major service intervals and check that the plate separators in each cell are covered by approximately 6 mm (0.25 in) of electrolyte. If the battery case is translucent, the cell covers need not be removed to check the level. Top up if necessary with distilled or de-ionized water; do not overfill, and mop up any spillage at once.

8   Persistent need for topping-up the battery electrolyte suggests either than the alternator output is excessive, or that the battery is approaching the end of its life.

5   Battery – charging

1   In normal use, the battery should not require charging from an external source unless very heavy use of electrical systems is made over a series of journeys that are too short to allow the charging system to keep pace with the demand. Otherwise, a need for regular recharging points to a fault in the battery or in the charging system.

2   If however, the car is laid up for long periods (in excess of thirty days at a time), the battery will lose approximately 1% of its charge per week. This figure is for an unconnected battery; if the battery is left connected, circuits such as the clock will drain it at a faster rate. To prevent this happening, always disconnect the battery negative lead if the car is to be laid up for a long period. To keep the battery fully charged, it should be given regular 'refresher' charges every six weeks or so. This is especially important on 'maintenance-free' batteries, which will suffer permanent reduction of charge capacity if allowed to become fully discharged.

3   As a simple test of whether the battery needs recharging, disconnect both terminals and use a voltmeter to measure the open circuit voltage across the battery terminals. If the voltage measured is less than 10.5 volts then a permanent reduction in charge capacity will result in 'maintenance-free' type batteries. If the voltage is between 10.5 and 12.1 the battery should be recharged; a fully-charged battery will show a recording of 12.7 volts or more.

4   The only full test of a battery's state of charge is to use an hydrometer. Remove the single plug from the top of the battery (Hitachi) or the manifolds (Lucas) and draw some electrolyte into the hydrometer. Compare the specific gravity readings with the following table, taking into consideration the electrolyte temperature.

Fully discharged	Electrolyte temperature	Fully charged
1.098	38°C (100°F)	1.268
1.102	32°C (90°F)	1.272
1.106	27°C (80°F)	1.276
1.110	21°C (70°F)	1.280
1.114	16°C (60°F)	1.284
1.118	10°C (50°F)	1.288
1.122	4°C (40°F)	1.292
1.126	-1.5°C (30°F)	1.296

If the reading is less than 1.240 the battery requires charging, but if it is less than 1.100 the battery will be completely discharged, with some

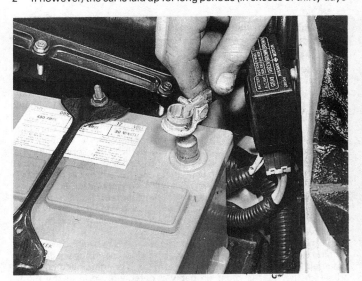

4.2A Battery negative lead and terminal

4.2B Battery positive lead and terminal

sulphation forming on the cell plates. In such a case the battery is almost certainly of no further use.

5   The battery's condition can be tested using only a battery checker or load tester, which is usually found only at specialist battery suppliers. The best approximation of this is to connect a voltmeter across the battery terminals, disconnect the ignition (Chapter 1, Section 25) and to take a reading while operating the starter for (no more than) ten seconds. Assuming the starter motor is in good condition the voltage drop from a battery in good condition should be no more than two volts.

6   Battery charging should always be carried out in a well-ventilated atmosphere, well away from any naked flames or sparks. Disconnect the battery terminals and remove the cell covers or manifolds.

7   If the charger to be used has an adjustable output, set it to no more than 6 amps (ie approximately to the battery's capacity) and charge for 8 to 12 hours (depending on the original state of charge) until the electrolyte specific gravity reading is more than 1.240. As a rough guide, all cells should be effervescing steadily at this point.

8   Domestic battery chargers (up to about 6 amps output) may safely be used overnight without special precautions. Make sure that the charger is set to deliver 12 volts before connecting it. Connect the leads (red or positive to the positive terminal, black or negative to the negative terminal) **before** switching the charger on at the mains.

9   When charging is complete, switch off at the mains **before** disconnecting the charger from the battery. Remember that the battery will be giving off hydrogen gas, which is potentially explosive.

10   Charging at a higher rate should only be carried out under carefully controlled conditions. Very rapid or 'boost' charging should be avoided if possible, as it is liable to cause permanent damage to the battery through overheating.

11   During any sort of charging, battery electrolyte temperature should **never** exceed 60°C (140°F). If the battery becomes hot, or the electrolyte is effervescing vigorously, charging should be stopped.

6   Battery – removal and refitting

1   Disconnect the battery negative (earth) lead.

2   Disconnect the battery positive lead. This may be protected by a plastic cover. Do not allow the spanner to bridge the positive and negative terminals.

3   Release the battery hold-down clamp (photo). Lift out the battery. Keep it upright and be careful not to drop it – it is heavy.

4   Commence refitting by placing the battery in its tray, making sure it is the right way round. Secure it with the hold-down clamp.

5   Clean the battery terminals if necessary (Section 4), then reconnect them. Connect the positive lead first, then the negative lead.

6.3 Unscrewing one of the battery clamp retaining nuts

7   Alternator drivebelt – removal, refitting and adjustment

Refer to Chapter 2, Section 7.

8   Alternator – description and precautions

1   The alternator generates alternating current which is rectified by diodes into direct current which is needed to charge the battery; a voltage regulator controls its output.

2   Main components consists of a stator and a rotor with diode rectifier.

3   The current is generated in the stator windings with the rotor carrying the field.

4   The field brushes carry only a light current and run on slip rings.

5   The alternator is driven by a belt from the crankshaft pulley. A fan is located behind the alternator pulley for cooling purposes.

6   To avoid damage to the alternator semiconductors, and indeed to many other components, the following precautions should be observed.

(a)   *Do not disconnect the battery or the alternator whilst the engine is running*

(b)   *Do not allow the engine to turn the alternator when the latter is not connected*

(c)   *Do not test for output from the alternator by 'flashing' the output lead to earth*

(d)   *Do not use a battery charger of more than 12 volts output, even as a starting aid*

(e)   *Disconnect the battery and the alternator before carrying out electric arc welding on the vehicle*

(f)   *Always observe correct battery polarity*

7   If there are indications that the charging system is malfunctioning in any way, care must be taken when diagnosing faults otherwise damage of a serious and expensive nature may occur to parts which are in fact quite serviceable. The following basic requirements must be observed at all times, therefore, if damage is to be prevented.

8   All alternator systems use a negative earth. Even the simple mistake of connecting the battery the wrong way round could burn out the alternator diodes quickly.

9   Before disconnecting any wires in the system the engine and ignition circuits should be switched off. This will minimise the risk of short-circuits in the system.

10   Do not use test wire connections that could move accidentally and short-circuit against nearby terminals. Short-circuits may not only blow fuses – they can also burn out diodes and transistors.

9   Charging system/alternator – testing on the car

1   In normal use the instrument panel charge warning lamp will illuminate as soon as the ignition is switched on (as a check of its function) and will go out as soon as the engine is started. The lamp should not illuminate while the engine is running (although it may possibly glow dimly if the engine is running at idle speed with a heavy electrical load switched on).

2   If the lamp does not light at all, disconnect the multi-plug connector from the alternator, switch on the ignition and earth the 'L' terminal wire (smaller gauge white/black or white/red). If the lamp lights, then the alternator is faulty (check first the brushes and slip rings). If the lamp does not light, either the bulb is faulty or there is a break in the wire to the alternator. If necessary, renew the bulb as described in Section 24 of this Chapter. On completion, reconnect the alternator.

3   If the lamp does not go out at all, this must be due to a short circuit, most probably in the wire from the bulb to the alternator, but also possibly in the alternator itself.

4   If the lamp goes out, but then lights again while the engine is running (its brightness may vary with engine speed) check first the drivebelt (Chapter 2). If the drivebelt is in good condition and correctly adjusted, the fault is most probably a defective diode in the diode assembly/rectifier pack. The diode assembly/rectifier pack can be

10.2A Disconnecting alternator earth lead (Lucas/Magneti Marelli) ...

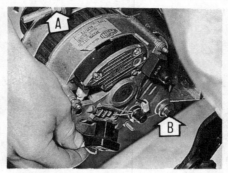

10.2B ... and multi-plug. Note adjuster nut 'A' and pivot bolt 'B'

10.2C Alternator connections – Mitsubishi

10.5A Remove retaining nut to release alternator pulley ...

10.5B ... noting lockwasher

10.5C Mitsubishi alternator – remove pulley, noting shoulder ...

renewed separately, but this requires the careful use of a soldering iron and is best left to an expert.

5   If the lamp functions normally but other symptoms arise which indicate a fault in the charging system, check first that the drivebelt is intact and in good condition and that its tension is correct (Chapter 2). Check the condition and security of the alternator electrical connections and the battery leads.

6   Accurate assessment of alternator output needs special equipment and a degree of skill. A rough idea of whether output is adequate can be gained by using a voltmeter (range 0 to 15 or 0 to 20 volts) as follows.

7   Connect the voltmeter across the battery terminals. Switch on the headlights and note the voltage reading: it should be between 12 and 13 volts.

8   Start the engine and run it at a fast idle (approx 1500 rpm). Read the voltmeter: it should indicate 13 to 14 volts.

9   With the engine still running at a fast idle, switch on as many electrical consumers as possible (heated rear window, heater fan etc). The voltage at the battery should be maintained at 13 to 14 volts. Increase the engine speed slightly if necessary to keep the voltage up.

10   If alternator output is low or zero, check the brushes, as described in Section 11. If the brushes are OK, seek expert advice.

11   Occasionally the condition may arise where the alternator output is excessive (ie 14.5 volts or more). Clues to this condition are constantly blowing bulbs; brightness of lights vary considerably with engine speed; overheating of alternator and battery, possibly with steam or fumes coming from the battery. This condition is almost certainly due to a defective voltage regulator, but expert advice should be sought.

10   Alternator – removal and refitting

1   Disconnect the battery negative lead.

2   Disconnect the alternator wiring. Unscrew the nut and washer to release the earth lead, then pull the multi-plug out of its socket, noting that it is retained by a wire clip on Lucas/Magneti Marelli units (photos).

10.5D ... do not lose metal shield

On Mitsubishi alternators, peel back the rubber cap and unscrew the nut and washer to release the white wire from the extended 'B' terminal (photo).

3   Slacken the alternator pivot bolts and adjuster lockbolt, then unscrew the adjuster nut or bolt until the drivebelt is slack enough to be slipped off the pulley.

4   Remove the pivot bolts and adjuster lockbolt and withdraw the alternator from the engine; do not drop it, as it is fragile.

5   If the alternator is to be renewed and the pulley must be swapped over, clamp the pulley firmly in a vice with padded jaws and unscrew the pulley nut. Take care not to damage the pulley. Withdraw the pulley,

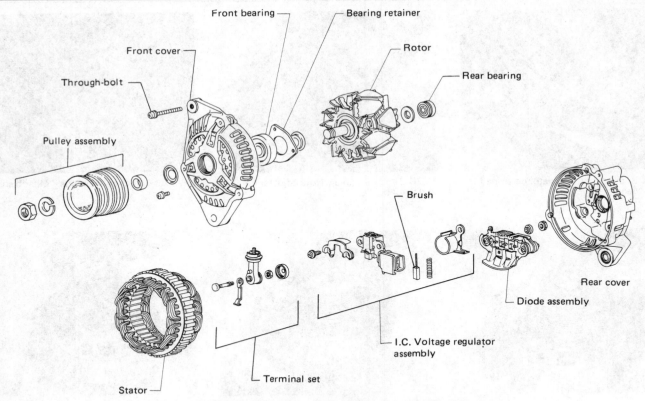

Fig. 12.3 Exploded view of Mitsubishi alternator (Sec 11)

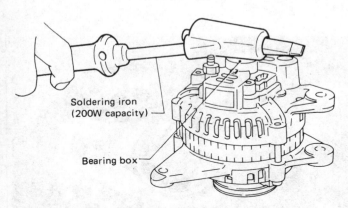

Fig. 12.4 Heating the rear bearing box (Sec 11)

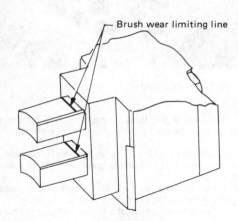

Fig. 12.5 Alternator brush wear limit line (Sec 11)

noting the lockwasher. On Mitsubishi alternators there is a metal shield behind the pulley, against the bearing (photos). On Lucas/Magneti Marelli alternators there is the cooling fan and a spacer. These components must be refitted correctly. Tighten the pulley nut to the specified torque setting.

6   Refitting is the reverse of the removal procedure. Adjust the drive-belt tension as described in Chapter 2 and reconnect the alternator and battery.

11 Alternator brushes and voltage regulator – renewal

Mitsubishi alternator

Note: *There is a possibility that the rear bearing may be damaged during the course of this operation, so ensure that a replacement is available locally before starting work.*

1   Remove the alternator as described in Section 10 of this Chapter.
2   Unscrew the pulley nut and remove the lockwasher, the pulley and the metal shield as described in Section 10.
3   Mark the front and rear covers and stator in relation to each other.
4   Unscrew the through-bolts then remove the front cover from the rotor shaft followed by the metal shield and spacer (photos).
5   Remove the rotor from the rear cover and stator. If difficulty is experienced, heat the bearing box (Fig. 12.4), with a 200 watt soldering iron for 3 or 4 minutes; heat **only** the bearing box and **do not** use any other source of heat (such as a heat gun) or the diode assembly may be damaged.
6   Prise off the cap, unscrew the retaining nut securing the extended terminal 'B' to the rear cover and withdraw the terminal. From inside the stator/rear cover assembly, remove the three retaining screws and withdraw the rear cover from the stator. Withdraw the plastic shield (photos).

11.4A Unscrewing through-bolts – Mitsubishi alternator

11.4B Withdraw front cover ...

11.4C ... inner metal shield ...

11.4D ... and spacer

11.6A Extended terminal 'B' is retained by a single nut

11.6B Separating rear cover from stator assembly

11.6C Withdrawing plastic shield from brush holder ...

11.7 ... to permit checking of brushes

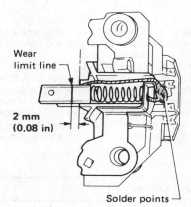

Fig. 12.6 Alignment of brushes on refitting (Sec 11)

7 The brush holder is now accessible and the brush length can be checked for wear (photo). A wear limit line may be incorporated on each brush which corresponds to the minimum brush length given in the Specifications (Fig. 12.5).

8 If the brushes require renewal, remove the insulator to expose the brush leads (photos). Then, with a pair of long-nosed pliers acting as a heat sink, unsolder the leads using the minimum amount of heat. Work quickly so that the heat does not transfer to adjacent components. Renew the brush springs as well as the brushes.

9 Make sure that the new brushes slide freely in their holders, then solder the leads in position with the wear limit lines 2 mm (0.08 in) from the holder (Fig. 12.6).

10 Wipe the slip rings clean with a cloth moistened with methylated spirit – if they are very dirty use fine glass paper to clean them, then wipe with the cloth.

11 Refitting is a reverse of the removal procedure, taking note of the following points.

12 Push the brushes into their holders fully and retain them while

11.8A Remove small plastic insulator ...

11.8B ... to expose brush leads

11.12A Pass a length of wire through hole in rear cover ...

11.12B ... and through holes in brushes and brush holder ...

11.12C ... so that brushes are held clear of slip rings while rotor is refitted

11.17 Unbolting brushbox/regulator assembly – Lucas/Magneti Marelli alternator

11.18 Withdrawing brushbox/regulator – check slip rings (arrowed)

11.19 Measuring brush length – Lucas/Magneti Marelli

reassembling the alternator by inserting a length of soft wire through the special hole in the rear cover (photos).
13 Locate the special half-ring in the rear bearing outer track eccentric groove, so that it protrudes by the minimum amount (Fig. 12.7).
14 Assemble the rear cover to the front cover. Insert and tighten the through-bolts.
15 Pull out the soft wire to allow the brushes to rest on the slip rings.

Lucas/Magneti Marelli alternator
16 The brushes and voltage regulator can be renewed while the alternator is in place on the engine. It is recommended, however, that the alternator is removed (Section 10) for this task to be carried out. Access is much improved, a thorough inspection can be made and there is less risk of foreign matter falling into the alternator. Whichever course is taken, always disconnect the battery negative lead before starting work.
17 Undo the three small screws securing the regulator and brushbox assembly to the rear of the alternator (photo).

18 Tip the assembly upwards at the edge, and withdraw it from its location. Disconnect the wiring terminal and remove the regulator and brushbox from the alternator (photo).
19 Measure the brush length protruding from the brushbox (photo) and renew the brushbox and regulator assembly if the brushes are worn to the minimum length given in the Specifications, or less.
20 Clean the slip rings with a cloth moistened with methylated spirit. If they are badly burnt or damaged, seek expert advice.
21 Refit the brush box and regulator assembly and secure it with the three screws. If the alternator is on the vehicle, reconnect the battery negative lead.

---

12 Alternator – overhaul

1 Due to the specialist knowledge and equipment required to test or repair an alternator, it is recommended that, if the alternator's perfor-

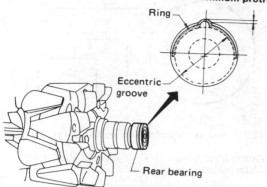

Quantity of protrusion:
Fix ring at the position
of minimum protrusion.

Ring

Eccentric
groove

Rear bearing

Fig. 12.7 Locating rear bearing half-ring on reassembly (Sec 11)

mance is suspect, the car be taken to an automobile electrician who will have the facilities for such work. Because of this recommendation, information given in this manual is limited to the inspection and renewal of the brushes and renewal of the voltage regulator.

2 Before having any repair work carried out **always** check the availability and cost of replacement parts and compare that with the cost of a new or reconditioned unit. Note that a pulley may not be supplied with a

replacement unit.

3 Always check the drivebelt (Chapter 2) and the voltage regulator /brushes (Section 11) before suspecting the alternator itself.

13 Starter motor – testing in the car

1 If the starter motors fails to operate, first check the condition of the battery by switching on the headlamps. If they glow brightly, then gradually dim after a few seconds, the battery is in a discharged condition.

2 If the battery is satisfactory, check the battery terminals, the starter motor main terminal and the engine earth cable for security. Check the terminal connections on the starter solenoid, located on top of the starter motor, for tightness.

3 If the starter still fails to turn, use a voltmeter, or 12 volt test lamp and leads, to ensure that there is battery voltage at the solenoid battery (B) termir.al (containing the cable from the battery positive terminal); remember that this (heavy) lead is always live, so disconnect the battery negative lead before using tools on the solenoid connections.

4 With the ignition switched on and the ignition key in the 'Start' position, check that voltage is reaching the solenoid blade terminal and also the starter main terminal.

5 If there is no voltage reaching the blade terminal, there is a wiring or ignition switch fault. If voltage is available, but the starter does not operate, then the starter or solenoid is likely to be at fault. Refer to Section 15 for details of solenoid checks.

6 Note that it should be possible to hear the solenoid operating if it is

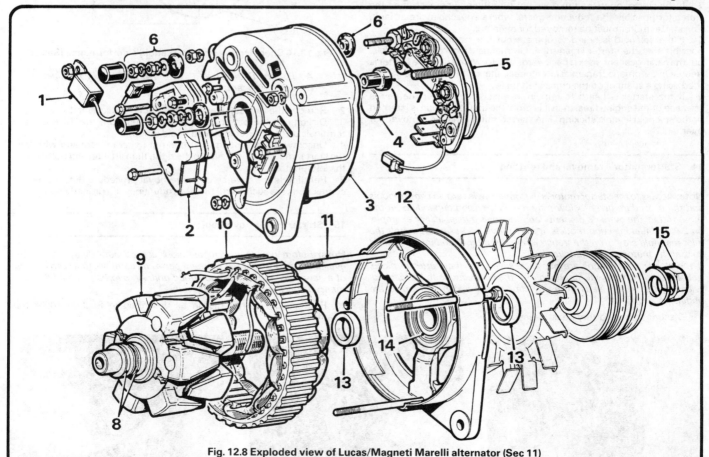

Fig. 12.8 Exploded view of Lucas/Magneti Marelli alternator (Sec 11)

1 Suppression capacitor	5 Rectifier pack	8 Slip rings	13 Spacers
2 Voltage regulator and brushbox assembly	6 Phase terminal attachments and insulating washers	9 Rotor	14 Drive end bearing
3 Slip ring end bracket	7 Main output terminal attachments and insulating washers	10 Stator	15 Pulley nut and washers
4 Slip ring end bearing		11 Through-bolts	
		12 Drive end bracket	

14.3 Disconnecting starter motor solenoid blade terminal – B terminal arrowed

in good condition. If the solenoid is faulty, the starter motor must be removed so that it can be renewed, but note that if the solenoid is heard to 'chatter' (operate repeatedly) it is most likely to be due to a discharged battery.

7   If the starter operates but does not turn the engine over, then the clutch (or possibly the reduction gears, where applicable) are at fault. The starter motor must be removed for overhaul.

8   If the solenoid is heard to operate but the starter does not, it is possible that the starter is jammed. On manual transmission models, put the car in gear and rock it backwards and forwards until the starter is freed. On automatic transmission models, the same procedure can be tried using a spanner on the crankshaft pulley.

9   If the starter is heard to remain in engagement after the key is released or the engine fires, then it is probable that the pinion is jammed or the solenoid lever is sticking. The starter motor must be removed for overhaul.

14   Starter motor – removal and refitting

Note: *Access to the starter motor is extremely awkward on some models and the procedure given below may require revision depending on the motor fitted, the owner's dexterity and the tools available. For example, on 2.0 litre fuel injection models, it may prove necessary to unbolt the inlet manifold stay from the transmission (Chapter 6) and inlet manifold so that the motor can be removed.*

If the starter connections are not accessible with the starter in place, unbolt it and withdraw it far enough for the connections to be reached, releasing the wiring leads from any clips or ties securing them to the engine components.

1   Disconnect the battery negative lead.

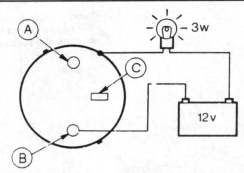

Fig. 12.9 Checking the stator solenoid windings (Sec 15)

A   Battery (B) terminal   C   Switch (S) blade terminal
B   Motor (M) terminal

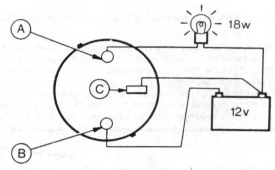

Fig. 12.10 Checking the starter solenoid's performance (Sec 15)

A   Battery (B) terminal   C   Switch (S) blade terminal
B   Motor (M) terminal

2   Remove the air cleaner and/or inlet ducting according to model.

3   Disconnect the battery and switch leads from the 'B' and blade terminals on the starter motor solenoid (photo).

4   Unscrew the mounting bolts and nut (where fitted) and withdraw the starter motor. Move it first to the right, then lift it up and pull it out to the left (photos).

5   Refitting is the reverse of the removal procedure. Ensure that all connections are secure and that the mountings are properly tightened.

15   Starter motor – overhaul

Note: *Before having any repair work carried out, always check the availability and cost of replacement parts and compare that with the cost of a new, exchange or reconditioned unit. An overhaul should be commenced only if it is economically viable.*

1   Remove the starter motor, as described in Section 14 of this Chapter.

14.4A Remove starter motor mounting bolts ...

14.4B ... do not forget bolt(s) on bellhousing ...

14.4C ... to release starter motor

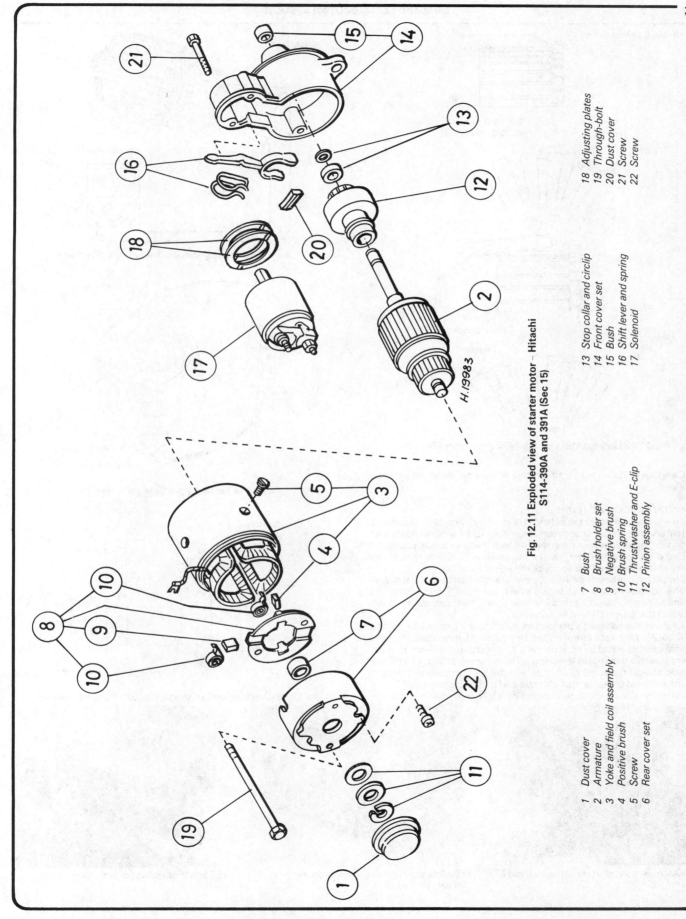

Fig. 12.11 Exploded view of starter motor – Hitachi S114-390A and 391A (Sec 15)

1 Dust cover
2 Armature
3 Yoke and field coil assembly
4 Positive brush
5 Screw
6 Rear cover set
7 Bush
8 Brush holder set
9 Negative brush
10 Brush spring
11 Thrustwasher and E-clip
12 Pinion assembly
13 Stop collar and circlip
14 Front cover set
15 Bush
16 Shift lever and spring
17 Solenoid
18 Adjusting plates
19 Through-bolt
20 Dust cover
21 Screw
22 Screw

H.I9983

Undercut procedures

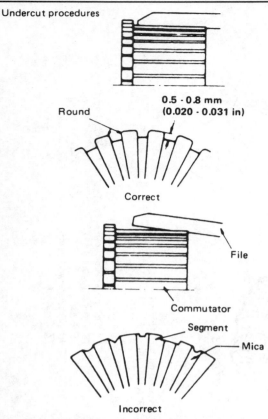

Round

0.5 - 0.8 mm
(0.020 - 0.031 in)

Correct

File

Commutator

Segment

Mica

Incorrect

Fig. 12.12 Undercutting armature commutator (Sec 15)

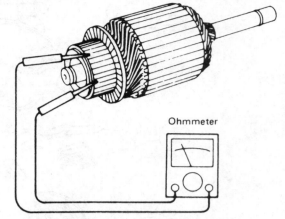

Ohmmeter

Fig. 12.13 Testing armature windings (Sec 15)

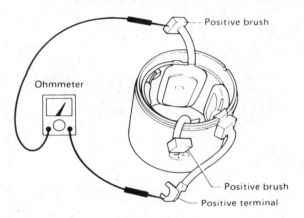

Positive brush

Ohmmeter

Positive brush

Positive terminal

Fig. 12.14 Testing yoke field coils (Sec 15)

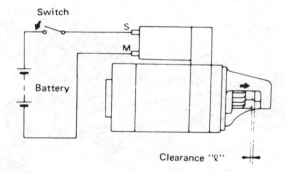

Switch

S

M

Battery

Clearance "ℓ"

Fig. 12.15 Checking pinion-to-stop collar clearance (Sec 15)

2   Clean the unit thoroughly to remove all external dirt, then proceed as follows.

Solenoid check – all types

3   To establish whether the solenoid is at fault or not, first disconnect the battery and motor leads from their solenoid terminal posts and disconnect the switch wire from the solenoid blade terminal (photo).

4   Use either a multimeter (set to the resistance function) or a dry battery and bulb test circuit to check the solenoid as follows.

5   Check that continuity exists between the solenoid blade (S) terminal and the solenoid body, and between the solenoid S and motor (M) terminals. If no continuity exists in either check, then the windings are faulty and the solenoid must be renewed.

6   To check the solenoid's performance, connect a 12 volt battery and an 18 to 21 watt test lamp across the solenoid motor and battery terminals; there should be no continuity. Connect a further lead from the battery positive terminal to the solenoid blade terminal (Fig. 12.10). The solenoid should be heard to operate and the test lamp should light; if not, the solenoid contacts are defective and it must be renewed.

7   To renew the solenoid, disconnect its leads, unscrew the retaining

15.3 Disconnecting starter motor solenoid M terminal

15.7A Starter motor solenoid retaining screws (arrowed)

15.7B Withdrawing solenoid from starter motor

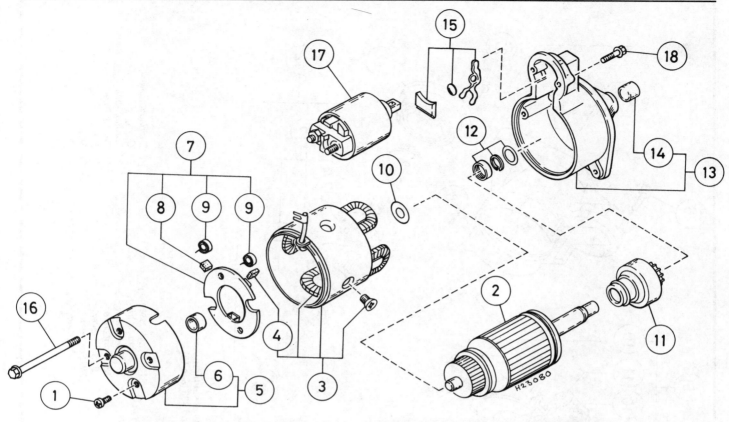

Fig. 12.16 Exploded view of starter motor – Mitsubishi M3T33981, M3T33981H and M3T30581 (Sec 15)

1	Screw	6	Bush
2	Armature	7	Brush holder set
3	Yoke and field coil assembly	8	Negative brush
4	Positive brush	9	Brush spring
5	Rear cover set	10	Thrustwasher set

12	Stop collar, clip and thrustwasher	15	Shift lever set
13	Front cover set	16	Through-bolt
14	Bush	17	Solenoid
		18	Screw

15.8A Refitting shift lever spring – note adjusting plate

15.8B Showing engagement of shift lever with solenoid plunger – typical

15.10 Removing dust cover from rear cover

screws and withdraw it, unhooking it or its plunger from the shift lever end. Note the presence and number of any adjusting plates fitted between the solenoid and the front cover (photos).

8   On refitting, ensure that the correct number of adjusting plates (where applicable) are installed and apply a light smear of grease to all points of contact between the solenoid plunger and shift lever. Refit the solenoid, engaging its plunger with the shift lever and spring and tightening the screws securely (photos).

Hitachi S114-390A and 391A
9   Withdraw the solenoid, as described above.

10   Prise off the dust cover from the rear cover (photo).
11   Prise off the E-clip and remove the thrustwashers (photo).
12   Unscrew the through-bolts, and the screws retaining the brush holder to the rear cover, then withdraw the rear cover (photo).
13   Lift the springs, release the two positive brushes, and withdraw the brush holder from the armature.
14   Withdraw the yoke, armature and shift lever (photo).
15   If the starter drive must be removed, tap the pinion stop collar down the shaft to expose the circlip. Remove the circlip, the stop collar and pull the drive assembly from the armature shaft.
16   Inspect all components for wear and damage and renew as necessary.

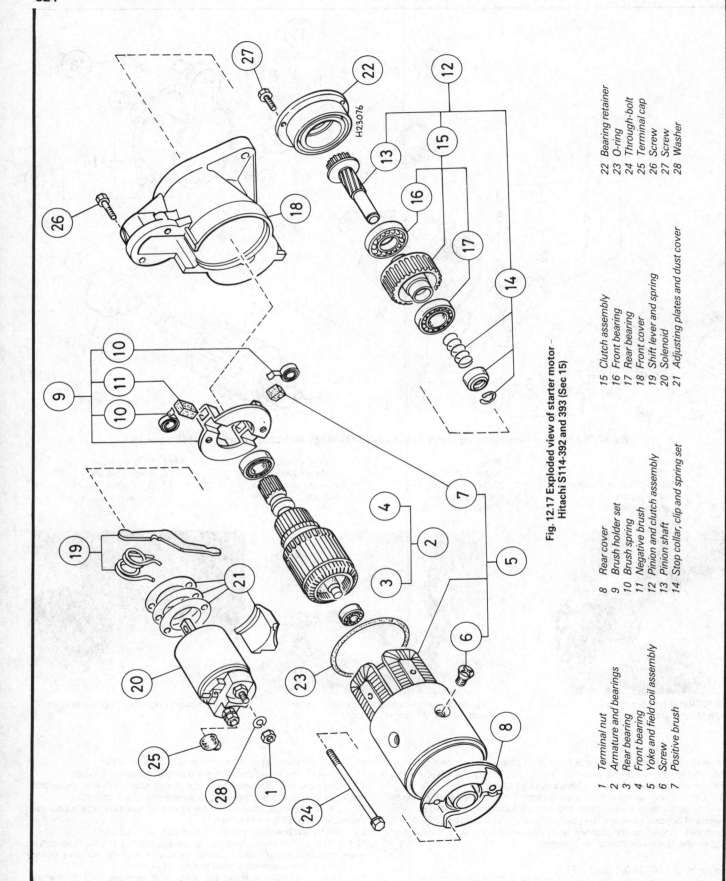

H23076

**Fig. 12.17 Exploded view of starter motor –
Hitachi S114-392 and 393 (Sec 15)**

1 Terminal nut
2 Armature and bearings
3 Rear bearing
4 Front bearing
5 Yoke and field coil assembly
6 Screw
7 Positive brush
8 Rear cover
9 Brush holder set
10 Brush spring
11 Negative brush
12 Pinion and clutch assembly
13 Pinion shaft
14 Stop collar, clip and spring set
15 Clutch assembly
16 Front bearing
17 Rear bearing
18 Front cover
19 Shift lever and spring
20 Solenoid
21 Adjusting plates and dust cover
22 Bearing retainer
23 O-ring
24 Through-bolt
25 Terminal cap
26 Screw
27 Screw
28 Washer

15.11 Prise out E-clip to release armature thrustwashers

15.12 Withdrawing rear cover to expose brushholder

15.14 Shift lever and rubber dust cover

15.30A Unscrew through-bolts to release rear cover – note alignment marks (arrowed)

15.30B Removing rear cover ...

15.31 ... and separating yoke/armature assembly from front cover

15.32A Release positive brushes from brushholder ...

15.32B ... to separate brushholder from yoke

17 If the commutator is discoloured, clean it with a fuel moistened rag or burnish it with fine (No 500 to 600) glasspaper. If the commutator is worn at any point to the specified minimum diameter or less, or if any of

its segments are chipped or damaged, the armature must be renewed.
18 If the mica separators of the commutator are not below the copper segments then they must be undercut as shown in Fig. 12.12 using a hacksaw or other suitable tool.
19 The armature may be tested if an ohmmeter is available by placing the probes on adjacent segments and working round the commutator (Fig. 12.13). If there is no continuity between any pair renew the armature.
20 Now check for insulation between each segment of the commutator in sequence and the armature shaft. Continuity here will indicate the need to renew the armature.
21 Check the brushes for wear. If they have worn down to the specified minimum length or less then they must be renewed. When unsoldering the old brushes and soldering the new ones in place, work quickly and grip the brush lead with a pair of pliers to act as a heat sink and so prevent heat travelling down to the field coil. Take great care not to allow solder to run down the brush lead or its flexibility will be ruined. Ensure that the brushes slide easily in their holders.
22 The field coils can be checked if the ohmmeter is connected

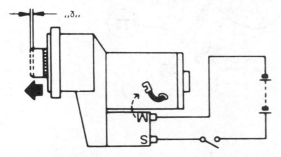

Fig. 12.18 Measuring difference in height of pinion assembly (Sec 15)

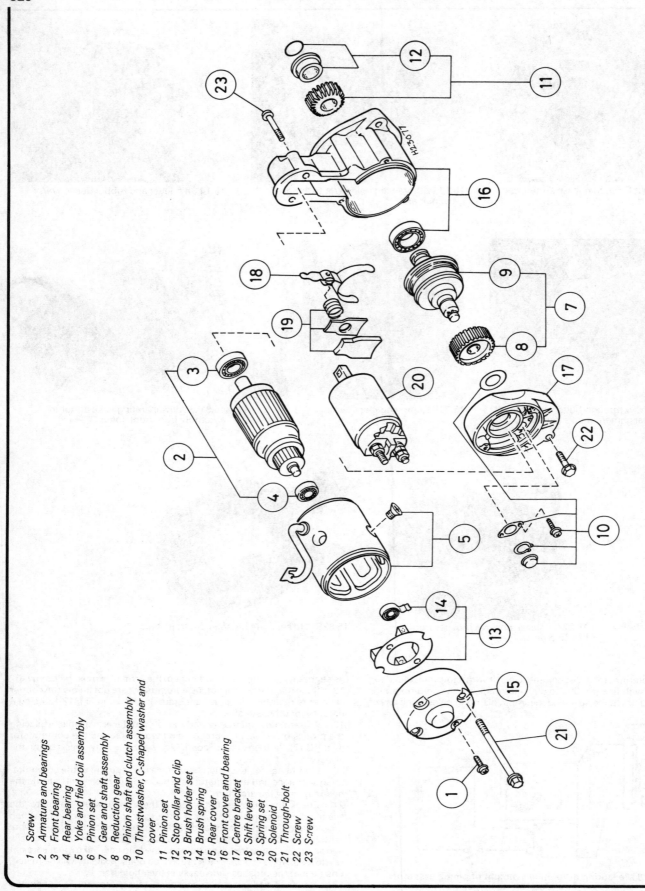

Fig. 12.19 Exploded view of starter motor –
Mitsubishi M2T53781 and M2T53785 (Sec 15)

1   Screw
2   Armature and bearings
3   Front bearing
4   Rear bearing
5   Yoke and field coil assembly
6   Pinion set
7   Gear and shaft assembly
8   Reduction gear
9   Pinion shaft and clutch assembly
10 Thrustwasher, C-shaped washer and
    cover
11 Pinion set
12 Stop collar and clip
13 Brush holder set
14 Brush spring
15 Rear cover
16 Front cover and bearing
17 Centre bracket
18 Shift lever
19 Spring set
20 Solenoid
21 Through-bolt
22 Screw
23 Screw

15.34A Note rubber dust cover between solenoid and front cover

15.34B Withdrawing shift lever with solenoid

15.35A Remove retaining screws (arrowed) ...

15.35B ... to release bearing retainer

15.35C Withdraw clutch and pinion assembly ...

15.35D ... prise out clip from inside stop collar ...

15.35E ... and dismantle assembly

15.36 Measuring brush length

between the (+) terminal of the field coil and a positive brush (Fig. 12.14). If there is no continuity, renew the field coil. This a job best left to your dealer or auto-electrician as a pressure screwdriver will be needed.
23   Now check the insulation between the field coil positive terminal and the yoke. If continuity exists, then the field coils must be renewed.
24   Check that the drive pinion clutch is operating correctly. It should lock when turned against the drive direction and turn smoothly in the reverse direction.
25   Reassembly is a reversal of dismantling. Apply a smear of high melting- point grease to the shift lever and drive pinion friction surfaces, to the armature shaft bushes and to the solenoid plunger.
26   With the starter motor reassembled, but with the motor lead disconnected from the solenoid 'M' terminal, energise the solenoid by connecting a 12 volt supply to the 'S' and 'M' terminals. Check that the clearance between the pinion and stop collar is as specified (Fig. 12.15). If not, change the thickness of the plates fitted between the solenoid and front cover as required. Reconnect the lead to the 'M' terminal on completion.

Mitsubishi M3T33981, M3T33981H and M3T30581
27   These units are very similar to the Hitachi motors described above, the only significant difference being that the armature endfloat-controlling thrustwashers and E-clip are not fitted.
28   Referring to Fig. 12.16, and noting the different information given in Specifications, proceed as described in paragraphs 9 to 26 above.

Hitachi S114-392 and 393
29   Mark the front cover yoke and rear cover in relation to each other.
30   Unscrew the through-bolts and withdraw the rear cover (photos).
31   Separate the yoke, armature and brush holder from the front cover (photo).
32   Disconnect the two positive brushes and remove the brush holder (photos).
33   Lift the armature from the yoke.
34   Remove the shift lever and dust covers (photos).
35   Unbolt the bearing retainer and remove the clutch assembly and shaft from the front cover. Dismantle the assembly, if required, as

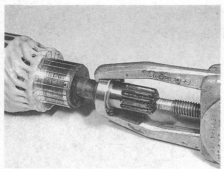

15.37 Drawing off armature front bearing

15.38 Wedging brushes with springs to facilitate reassembly

15.57 Withdraw the commutator end bracket

15.58 Release the rubber grommet (arrowed) and remove brushholder

15.59A Withdraw the yoke

15.59B Disengage the solenoid plunger from the engaging lever

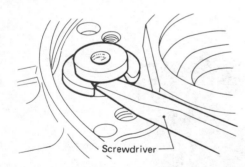

Fig. 12.20 Moving pinion shaft to measure thrust gap (Sec 15)

Screwdriver

described in paragraph 15 above (photos).

36   Check all components as described in paragraphs 16 to 24 above (photo).

37   Note that if the bearings at the front and rear of the armature and pinion clutch assembly are to be renewed, they must be drawn off using a puller (photo). On refitting, use a press (if available), a bench vice with covered jaws or a hammer to drive the new bearing on to the shaft. Apply pressure **only** to the bearing inner race when pressing it into place.

38   Reassembly is the reverse of the dismantling procedure. When refitting the brush holder, use the springs to wedge each brush inside its holder (photo) so that the assembly can be fitted over the commutator. Do not forget to push the brushes into place and engage the springs properly before refitting the yoke and armature to the front cover. Do not forget to lightly grease the various bearing surfaces (refer to paragraph 25).

39   With reference to Fig. 12.18, carry out the procedure described in paragraph 26 above to energise the solenoid. Measure the height of the pinion's front end above the starter motor front cover boss, then pull the pinion out by hand until it is stopped by the clutch assembly contacting the stop collar, and measure again the height of the pinion. If the difference in heights is outside the specified tolerance range, change the

thickness of the adjusting plate(s) until the setting is correct.

Mitsubishi M2T53781 and M2T53785

40   Remove the solenoid as described in paragraph 7 above.

41   Mark the front cover, centre bracket, yoke and rear cover in relation to each other.

42   Unscrew the through-bolts, and the screws securing the brush holder to the rear cover, then withdraw the rear cover.

43   Prise back the springs and slide the positive brushes from the brush holder, then withdraw the brush holder. Note that if any of the brushes are worn to the specified minimum length or less (see paragraph 21 above), the brush holder set must be renewed; only the brush springs are available separately.

44   Separate the yoke and armature from the centre bracket/front cover assembly.

45   Renew the armature bearings, if necessary, as described in paragraph 37 above.

46   Test the field coils, if required, (paragraphs 22 and 23 above).

47   Prise the cover off the pinion shaft rear end or remove the two screws and withdraw the cover (as applicable). Withdraw the C-shaped washer from the shaft-groove, followed by the plain washer (where fitted).

48   Unscrew the retaining screw and separate the centre bracket from the front cover, noting any thrustwashers fitted on the pinion shaft.

49   Prise the clip from the front end of the pinion shaft and withdraw the stop collar, the pinion and (where fitted) the spring.

50   Withdraw the shift lever and the reduction gear and pinion shaft assembly from the front cover.

51   Check all components as described above.

52   Reassembly is the reverse of the dismantling procedure, noting the following points. Apply a light smear of high-melting point grease to the reduction gear and centre bracket bearing surfaces as well as to the points listed in paragraph 25.

53   When reassembling the reduction gear and pinion shaft assembly, refit any thrustwashers found on dismantling, then refit the centre bracket, plain washer and C-shaped washer. Lever the pinion shaft as far as possible to the rear using a screwdriver, then measure the thrust gap

(Figs. 12.20 and 12.21). If the gap is more than that specified, adjust it with thrustwashers.

54   Carry out the procedure described in paragraphs 26 and 39 (see Fig. 12.18) and fit adjusting plates as necessary to adjust the setting to that specified.

55   Hold the brushes by wedging them with the springs when refitting the brush holder (see paragraph 38 above).

Lucas/Magneti Marelli M78R

56   Withdraw the solenoid and its plunger, as described in paragraph 7 above.

57   Undo the two nuts and withdraw the commutator end bracket (photo).

58   Release the rubber grommet from the side of the yoke (photo) and withdraw the brush holder assembly complete with brushes.

59   Withdraw the yoke from the drive end bracket and armature (photos).

60   Lift the armature out of the reduction gearbox, and remove it from the drive end bracket. Recover the armature drivegear from the gearbox (photos).

61   Release the engaging lever pivot and grommet from the drive end bracket, then withdraw the reduction gearbox, engaging lever and drive assembly from the drive end bracket.

62   Using a suitable tubular drift, tap the thrust collar on the end of the pinion shaft towards the pinion, to expose the jump ring. Prise the jump ring out of its groove and slide it off the shaft. Withdraw the thrust collar and drive pinion assembly.

63   With the starter motor completely dismantled, check the condition of the brushes and the tension of the brush springs as described in paragraph 21 above. If any appear excessively worn, or if the tension of any of the springs is suspect, renew the brush holder assembly.

64   Check the condition of the armature, field coils and drive pinion assembly as described in paragraphs 16 to 24 above. Note that the armature and pinion shaft bushes can be renewed separately, if required.

65   Reassembly is the reverse of the dismantling procedure. Apply grease to the drive pinion assembly and pinion shaft, to the reduction

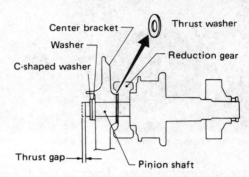

Fig. 12.21 Adjusting thrust gap (Sec 15)

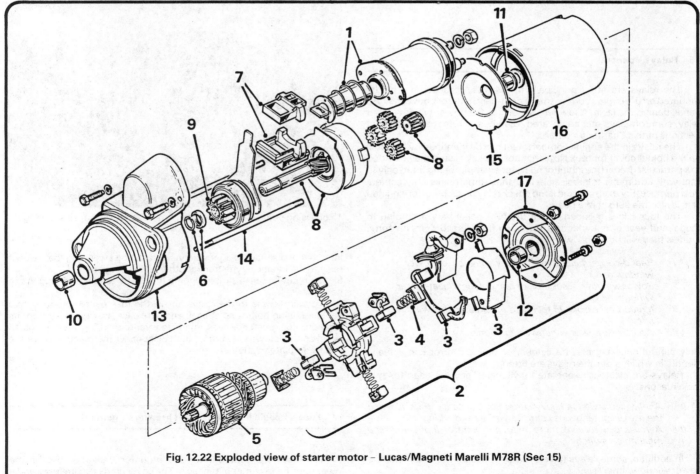

Fig. 12.22 Exploded view of starter motor – Lucas/Magneti Marelli M78R (Sec 15)

1	Solenoid and plunger	5	Armature	9	Drive pinion assembly	14	Through-bolts
2	Commutator end bracket and brush holder assembly	6	Jump ring and thrust collar	10	Bush	15	Intermediate bracket
3	Brush kit	7	Engaging lever pivot and grommet	11	Bush	16	Yoke and field coil assembly
4	Brush spring	8	Pinion shaft and reduction gears	12	Bush	17	Commutator end bracket
				13	Drive end bracket		

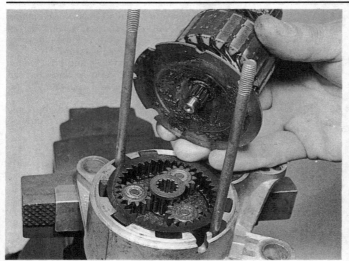

15.60A Remove the armature and intermediate bracket ...

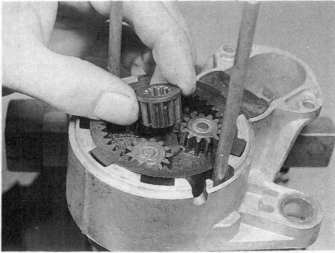

15.60B ... and recover the drivegear

gears and to the armature shaft bushes. Check the pinion/jump ring clearance as described in paragraph 26 above (Fig. 12.15).
66   When refitting the brush holder assembly, carefully compress the brushes one at a time using pointed-nose pliers, tip the holder slightly and ease the brushes over the commutator (photo).

16   Relays – general

1   The relays are fitted principally in two main groups; in a holder mounted on the engine compartment right-hand side, or above the fuse panel, behind the facia. A few relays (such as the power window timer relay, sunroof relays etc) are located elsewhere – refer to the relevant Sections of this Chapter for details.
2   The relays in the engine compartment can be identified by the label on the holder cover (photo). Note that not all relays listed may be fitted to a particular model (the inhibitor relay, for example, being fitted only to cars with automatic transmission) and that some relays may serve a dual purpose. For example, the lamp check relay on carburettor-engined cars is also the auto choke relay.
3   The four relays grouped above the fuse panel vary according to model and year of manufacture. Counting from left to right, on some models they will be as follows:

  1   *Rear defogger/heated rear window, ignition, or power window relay*
  2   *Power window, accessory, or rear defogger/heated rear window relay*
  3   *Ignition, accessory, or rear defogger/heated rear window relay*
  4   *Accessory, power window, or ignition relay*

Only careful checking of wire colours or trial and error can actually identify in which order the relays are fitted.
4   Relays are electrically-operated switches. They are used for two main reasons:

  (a) *A relay can switch a heavy current at a distance, thus allowing the use of lighter gauge control switches and wiring*
  (b) *A relay can receive more than one control input, unlike a mechanical switch*

5   In addition, some relays have a 'timer' function – for example, the power window timer relay.
6   If a circuit or system served by a relay develops a fault, always remember that the problem could be in the relay. Testing is by substitution of a known good unit. Beware of substituting relays which look the same but perform different functions.
7   Most of the relays fitted are one of a standardised series of four types (Fig. 12.23). Due to the terminal configuration they cannot be

15.66 Using pointed-nose pliers to compress brushes against springs

interchanged so fault diagnosis can be eased by swapping the suspect relay for an identical type from another circuit or system.
8   To renew a relay, simply unplug it from its holder and plug in the new one.
9   To gain access to the relays above the fuse panel, undo the two panel retaining bolts, one at each end, and ease the unit away from its location. For greater access, mark the various wiring multi-plugs to avoid confusion when refitting, then disconnect them and remove the panel completely (photos).

17   Fuses, fusible links and circuit breakers – general

Fuses

1   The fuses are located in a panel mounted behind a cover in the lower right-hand corner of the facia. The cover carries spare fuses and a removal tool, while its label gives details of fuse location, circuits protected and current rating (photo).
2   The fuses are of the 'blade' type, and are colour coded to show their current rating. A blown fuse can be recognised by the melted wire link in the middle.
3   To renew a blown fuse, first switch off the circuit concerned. Pull

Type	Outer view	Circuit	Symbols	Case color
1T	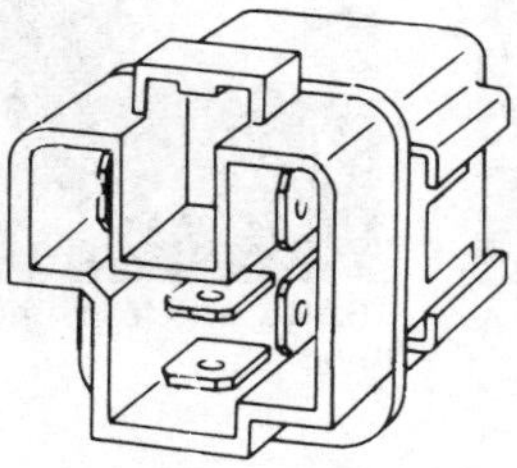	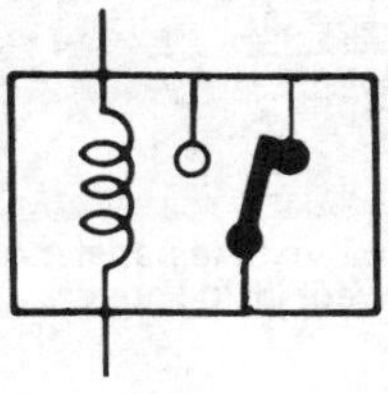		BLACK
1M	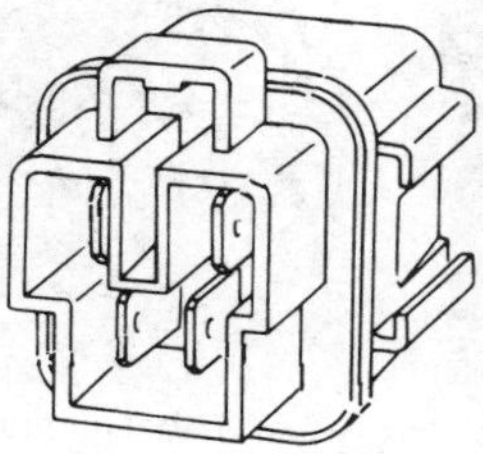	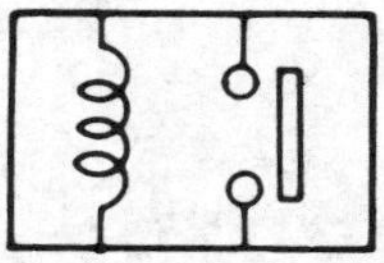	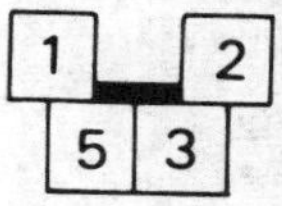	BLUE
2M	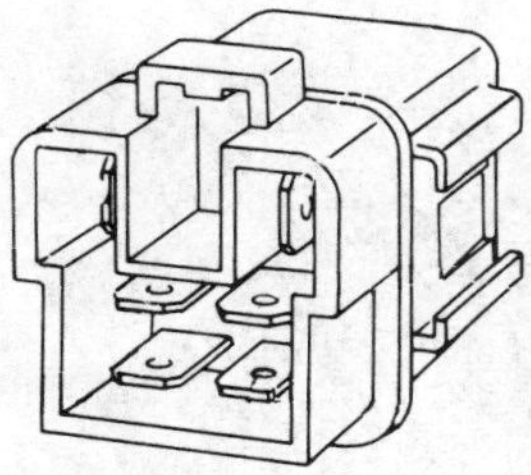	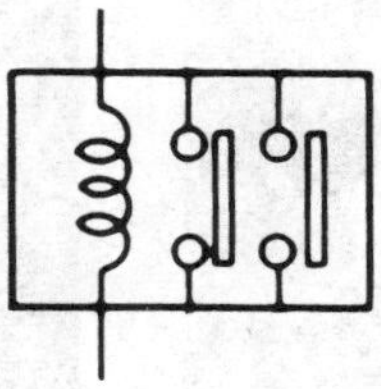	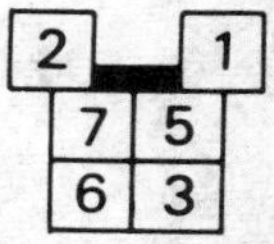	BROWN or Blue
1M·1B	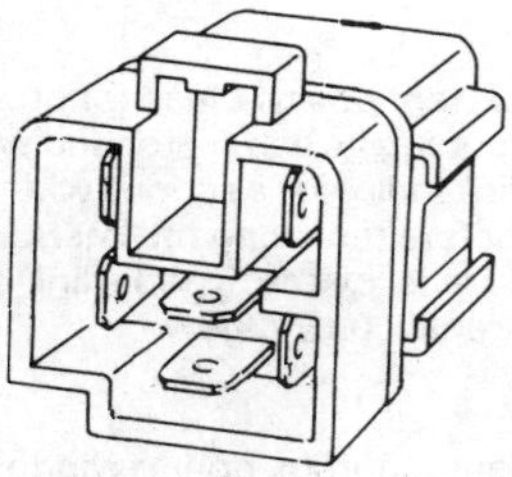	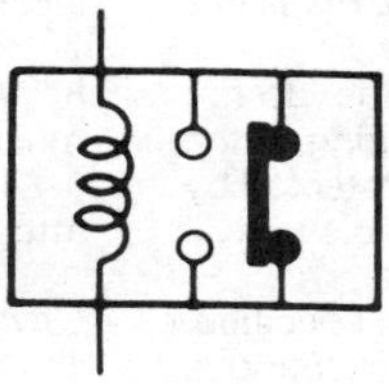		Grey or Blue

Fig. 12.23 Standardised relay identification (Sec 16)

16.2 Use relay holder cover to identify relays actually fitted

16.9A Remove fuse panel mounting screws (one arrowed) inside cover ...

16.9B ... and from underneath to move fuse panel

17.1 Fuse panel cover carries details of circuits protected

17.3 Using the removal tool to withdraw a fuse

17.6A Label on holder cover identifies main fusible links

17.6B Note fusible links in battery positive lead

17.7 Removing a fusible link

the old fuse out of its holder, using the tool provided (photo). Press in a new fuse of the same rating and try the circuit again.

4   If the new fuse blows immediately or within a short time, do not carry on renewing fuses but look for a short-circuit in the wiring to the item(s) protected by the fuse. When more than one item is protected by a single fuse, switching on one item at a time until the fuse blows will help to isolate the defect.

5   Never fit a fuse of a higher rating (current capacity) than specified, and do not bypass fuses with silver foil or strands of wire. Serious damage, including fire, could result. Always replace any spare fuses used, so that a spare fuse of each rating is always available.

Fusible links

6   Some circuits, not ordinarily protected by fuses, are protected by fusible links. These look like ordinary lengths of wire but with very thick insulation. The main links are mounted in a holder on the left-hand inner wing panel, next to the battery, but there may also be additional links

incorporated in the battery positive lead (photos).

7   To renew a link, unplug its connector and withdraw it (photo).

8   A blown fusible link indicates a serious wiring or system fault, which must be diagnosed before renewing the link.

9   Never bind the leads of the fusible link with insulating tape or attempt a makeshift repair, only renew.

Circuit breakers

10   The central locking, sunroof, power window, heated front seat and power support seat circuits are protected by one of two cylindrical circuit breakers located behind the facia, between the steering column and the fuse panel.

11   Normally, the circuit breaker resets itself automatically, so an electrical overload in a circuit breaker protected system will cause the circuit to fail momentarily, then come back on. If the circuit does not come back on, check it immediately. Once the condition is corrected, the circuit breaker will resume its normal function.

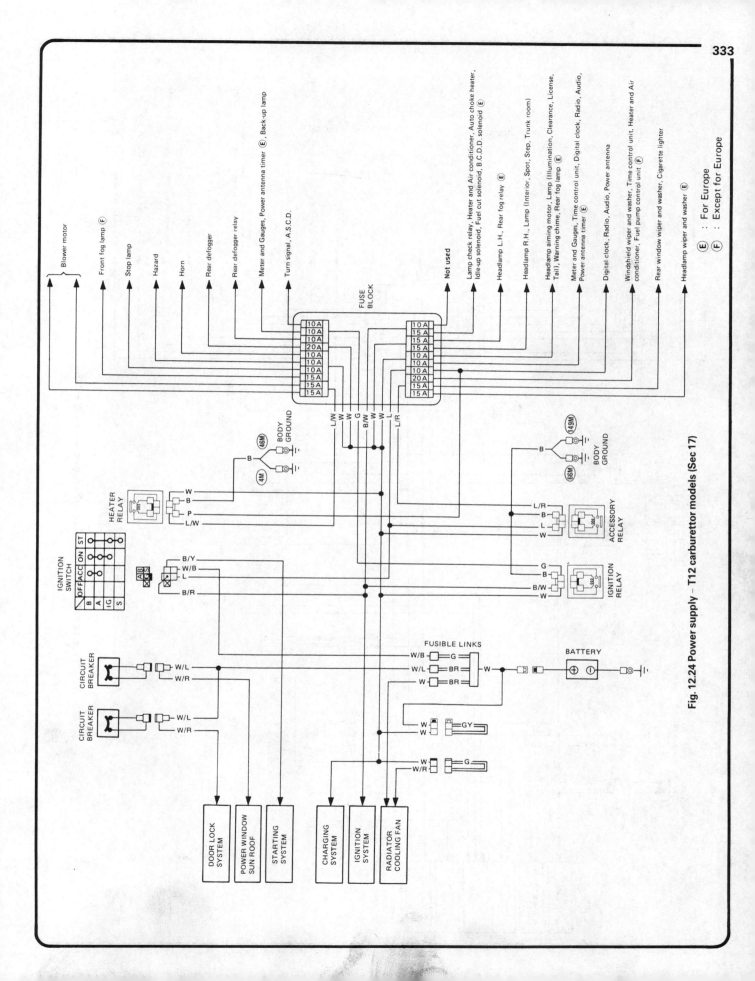

Fig. 12.24 Power supply – T12 carburettor models (Sec 17)

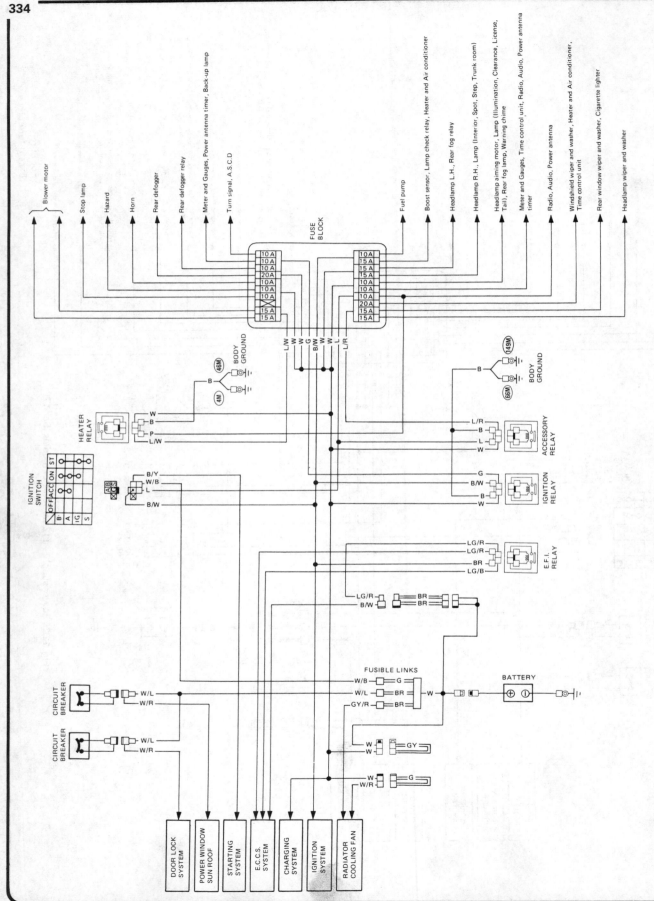

Fig. 12.25 Power supply – T12 turbo engine models (Sec 17)

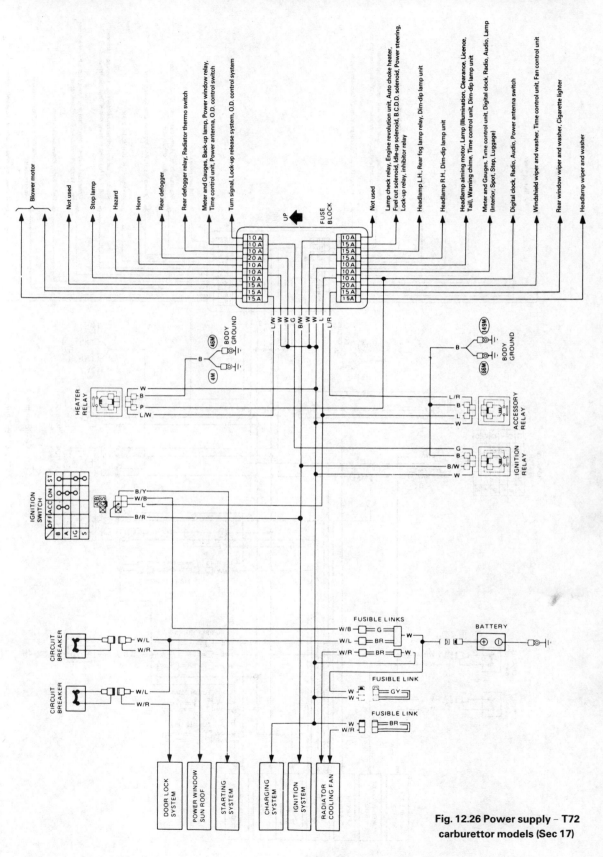

Fig. 12.26 Power supply – T72 carburettor models (Sec 17)

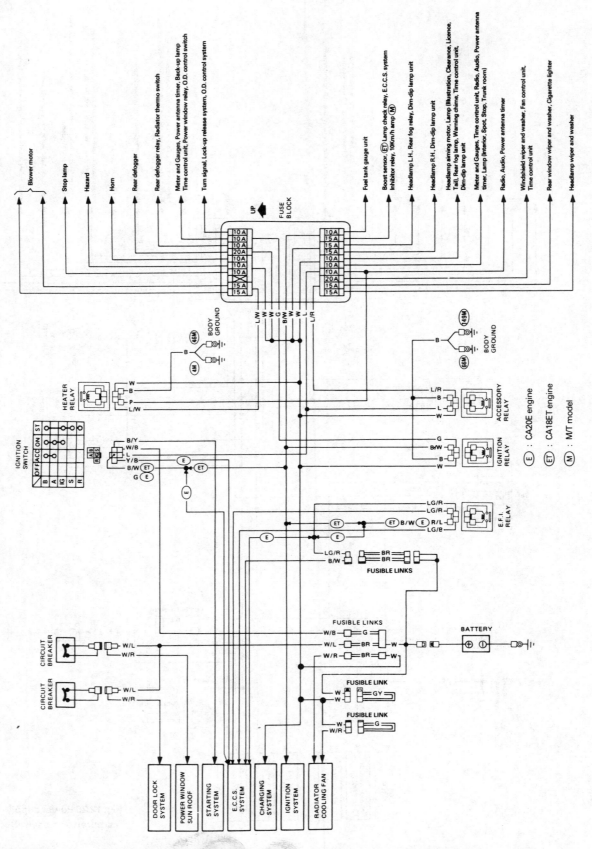

Fig. 12.27 Power supply – T72 turbo and 2.0 litre fuel injection models (Sec 17)

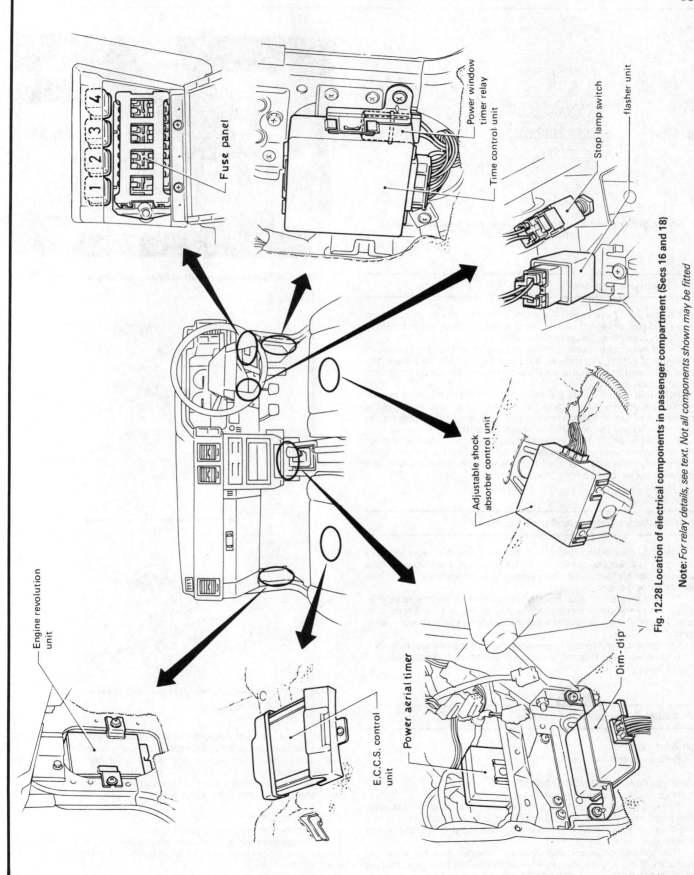

Fig. 12.28 Location of electrical components in passenger compartment (Secs 16 and 18)

Note: For relay details, see text. Not all components shown may be fitted

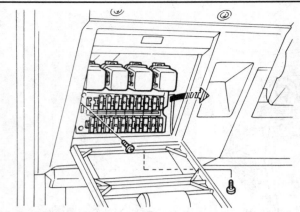

Fig. 12.29 Remove fuse panel mountings and displace panel to reach SMJ (Sec 19)

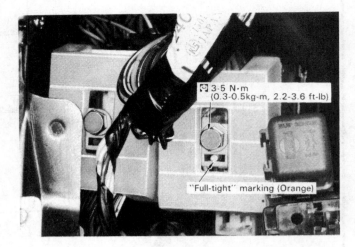

Fig. 12.30 Tightening details of SMJ mounting bolts (Sec 19)

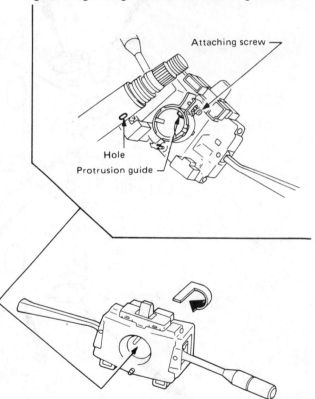

Fig. 12.31 Steering column stalk switch base removal (Sec 19)

18 Control units – general

1   Control units have similar functions to relays, but can accept more inputs and perform more tasks. For the most part they are completely electronic, rather than electro-mechanical.
2   To renew a control unit, remove the seat or interior trim panel, as applicable (Chapter 11), remove the retaining screw(s) to release the units' mounting bracket (and cover), then unplug the wiring connector and withdraw the unit.
3   Note that control units are extremely delicate and must not be knocked, dropped or mishandled. Do not attempt to 'test' them, as the application of uncontrolled current from self-powered testing equipment may destroy the unit's circuit or components.
4   If a control unit is thought to be faulty, the only practical test for private owners (and many dealers) is to substitute a known good component. If the unit is proven faulty it must be renewed, unless a specialist can be found who is prepared to attempt repairs.

19 SMJ (Super Multiple Junction) – general

1   The SMJ referred to at many points in the wiring diagrams is simply a complex junction box for the wiring between the main loom and the sub-wiring looms for the instrument panel/facia components and for the rear body components.
2   To reach the SMJ, unscrew the fuse panel mounting screws (Fig. 12.29), move the panel to one side and unscrew the SMJ mounting bolts. The left-hand half connects the instrument panel/facia sub-wiring loom.
3   On refitting, tighten the bolts carefully until the orange 'Full-tight' marking appears, then tighten to the specified torque setting as required (Fig. 12.30).

20 Switches – removal and refitting

Ignition switch
1   Refer to Chapter 10, Section 21.

Steering column stalk switches
2   Disconnect the battery negative lead.
3   Remove the screws and unclip the steering column bottom shroud. Where applicable, disconnect the ignition switch illuminating bulb's wire. Remove the ignition switch surround and the steering column top shroud.
4   The lighting or wiper and washer switches can be removed separately, but if it is required to remove the switch base, the steering wheel must first be removed (Chapter 10).
5   Disconnect the appropriate wiring, then remove the screws (where

fitted) and withdraw the switch from the base (photos).
6   To remove the switch base, loosen the clamp screw, then push the base down, turn it half a turn, and withdraw it from the top of the steering column (Fig. 12.31).
7   Refitting is a reversal of removal, but make sure that the pip on the base engages the hole in the column.

Facia switches
8   Disconnect the battery negative lead.
9   Prise out the switch. If difficulty is experienced it will be necessary to push the switch from the rear, after removing the instrument panel surround (photos).
10   Disconnect the wiring.
11   Refitting is a reversal of removal.

20.5A Steering column stalk switch mounting screws – early models

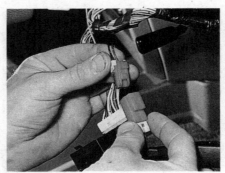

20.5B Disconnecting stalk switch wiring – later models

20.9A Removing a facia switch

20.9B Instrument panel surround switches may need releasing from behind

20.15A Door pillar-mounted courtesy light switch ...

20.15B ... is retained by a single screw

Centre console switches (for heated seats)
12 Removal and refitting is as described in paragraphs 8 to 11 above.

Power support seat switches
13 Both switches are incorporated in a single assembly which is retained to the inside of the seat base by screws. The seat must be removed (Chapter 11) so that the switch's electrical connection and air hoses can be disconnected.
14 Refitting is the reverse of the removal procedure, noting the comments made in Section 42 of this Chapter.

Door pillar switch (for courtesy light)
15 Extract the screw and withdraw the switch (photos).
16 If the leads are to be disconnected from the switch, tape them to the bodywork to prevent them from slipping inside the pillar.
17 It is recommended that petroleum jelly is applied to the switch before fitting, as a means of reducing corrosion.

Luggage compartment lamp switch – Saloon
18 The switch is a plunger type, mounted on the boot lid left-hand hinge.
19 Disconnect the switch wire and withdraw the switch.

Luggage compartment lamp switch – Hatchback
20 The switch is a plunger type, mounted in the bottom edge of the tailgate.
21 To remove the switch, withdraw the tailgate interior trim panel (Chapter 11), disconnect the switch's connector plug and withdraw the switch.

Glovebox lamp switch
22 The switch is a plunger type attached to the lock striker. To remove the switch, disconnect its wires and disengage it from its mounting.

Illuminated driver's door keyhole switch
23 The switch is mounted on the inside of the driver's door outside handle. Refer to Chapter 11, Section 26 for details of removal and refitting.

Map reading lamp switch
24 Unclip the map reading lamp console from the roof, disconnect its wires and withdraw it. The switches are not available separately from the console.

Sunroof switch
25 The switch is removed and refitted as described in paragraph 24 above.

Heater fan switch
26 Refer to Section 40 of this Chapter.

Power window switches
27 Refer to Section 43 of this Chapter.

Central locking switches
28 Refer to Section 34 of this Chapter.

Oil pressure switch
29 Refer to Chapter 1, Sections 16 and 20.

Cooling fan thermostatic switch(es)
30 Refer to Chapter 2, Section 12.

Water temperature switch (automatic transmission)
31 Refer to Chapter 2, Section 12.

Reversing lamp/gear position switch
32 Refer to Chapter 6, Section 6.

Starter inhibitor/reversing lamp switch
33 Refer to Chapter 7, Sections 10 and 11.

21.7 Disconnecting headlamp bulb wiring

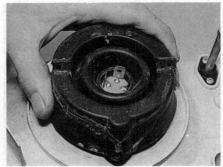

21.8 Pull off the rubber cap ...

21.9 ... release the spring retainer ...

21.10 ... and withdraw the bulb

21.19 Removing front direction indicator lamp lens retaining screw

21.20 Removing front direction indicator lamp bulb

Stop lamp, handbrake lever and master cylinder reservoir switches
34   Refer to Chapter 9, Section 30.

Power-assisted steering pressure switch
35   Refer to Chapter 10, Section 34.

Fig. 12.32 Front side lamp (clearance lamp) bulb renewal (Sec 21)

21   Exterior lamps – bulb renewal

General
1   Whenever a bulb is renewed, note the following points.
2   Remember that if the lamp has only just been in use, the bulb may be extremely hot.
3   Disconnect the battery negative lead before starting work.
4   Always check the bulb contacts and holder, ensuring that there is clean metal-to-metal contact between the bulb and its live and earth. Any corrosion should be cleaned off before a new bulb is fitted.
5   Wherever bayonet-type bulbs are used (direction indicators, rear lamp clusters etc) ensure that the live contact bears firmly against the bulb's contact.
6   Always ensure that a new bulb is of the correct rating and is completely clean before fitting it; this applies particularly to headlamp bulbs (see below).

Headlamp
7   Working in the engine compartment, disconnect the wiring from the rear of the headlamp bulb (photo).
8   Pull off the rubber cap, noting that the drain hole is at the bottom (photo).
9   Unhook and release the spring retainer (photo).
10   Withdraw the bulb (photo).
11   When handling the new bulb, use a tissue or clean cloth to avoid touching the glass with the fingers. If the glass is accidentally touched, wipe it clean using methylated spirit. Moisture and grease from the skin

can cause blackening and rapid failure of the new bulb.
12   Fit the new bulb, aligning its locating tabs with the bulbholder slots.
13   Refit the spring retainer.
14   Refit the rubber cap with the word 'TOP' or triangle mark uppermost.
15   Reconnect the wiring.

Front side lamp (clearance lamp)
16   Twist the bulbholder anti-clockwise a quarter of a turn to release it from the rear of the headlamp unit, outboard of the headlamp bulb (see Fig. 12.32).
17   Pull out the wedge type bulb. If it is a tight fit, push a close-fitting length of tubing over it and extract it that way.
18   Refitting is the reverse of removal.

Front direction indicator lamp
19   Undo the two screws and withdraw the lens or lamp unit, as applicable (photo). Twist the bulbholder anti-clockwise a quarter of a turn to release it from the rear of the lamp unit, where applicable.
20   To remove the bayonet type bulb, press it into its holder, twist

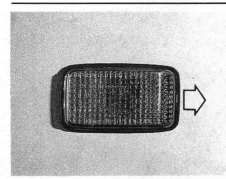

21.22A Push direction indicator side repeater lamp forward ...

21.22B ... to release it from wing

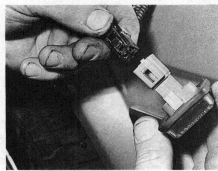

21.22C Disconnect wiring lead ...

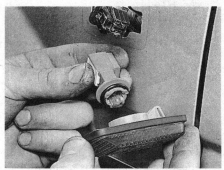

21.23 ... and separate bulbholder from lamp

21.24 Extracting a tight-fitting wedge-type bulb

21.26A Withdrawing rear lamp cluster bulb holder – Saloon models

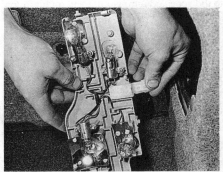

21.26B Disconnect wiring if better access is required

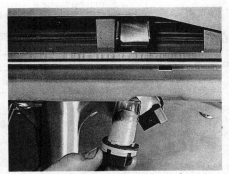

21.31 Removing number plate lamp from boot lid

21.32 Number plate lamp components

anti-clockwise to release and withdraw (photo).

21   Refitting is the reverse of the removal procedure.

Direction indicator side repeater lamp

22   Push the lamp forwards to release its clips, then withdraw it and unplug its wiring connector (photos).

23   Twist the bulbholder anti-clockwise a quarter of a turn and separate it from the lamp (photo).

24   Remove the bulb as described in paragraph 17 above (photo).

Rear lamp cluster

25   Open the boot lid or tailgate and unclip the access panel covering the rear of the cluster.

26   On Saloon models, unclip the bulbholder from the rear of the clamp and withdraw it, disconnecting the wiring connector plug if required (photos).

27   On Hatchback models, twist the bulbholder anti-clockwise a quarter of a turn and withdraw it.

28   All bulbs are of the bayonet type, so remove and refit them as described in paragraph 20 above. On refitting, note that the twin filament stop/tail lamp bulbs have offset pins, so that they can be installed (correctly) only one way.

Number plate lamp

29   On Saloon models, open the boot lid.

30   On Hatchback models, open the tailgate and unclip the access panel covering the rear of the lamp from the tailgate interior trim panel.

31   On all models, unplug the lamp's wiring connector then twist the lamp anti-clockwise a quarter of a turn and withdraw it (photo).

32   Unclip the bulbholder from the lamp (photo). Withdraw the bulb as described in paragraph 17 above.

33   Refitting is the reverse of removal.

22.3 Removing headlamp top mounting bolt

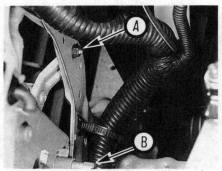

22.4 Headlamp mounting nut 'A', beam adjuster 'B'

22.6A Plastic studs locate headlamp in wing panel

22.6B Withdrawing headlamp from body front panel

22.8 Front direction indicator lamp wiring

22.11 Rear lamp cluster lens is located by brackets and bonded in place

22   Exterior lamps – removal and refitting

Headlamp

1   Disconnect the headlamp and front side lamp bulb wiring.
2   Remove the radiator grille and the trim panel(s) between the radiator grille and the front bumper (see Chapter 11, Section 10).
3   Unscrew the upper mounting bolt (photo).
4   Unscrew the two nuts securing the headlamp brackets to the body front panel (photo).
5   Where fitted, remove the fixing screws to release the headlamp wiper system components from the headlamp.
6   Prising it forwards to release the two studs which locate it in the wing panel, withdraw the headlamp (photos).
7   Refitting is the reverse of removal. Have the beam alignment checked as soon as possible (see Section 23 of this Chapter.)

Front direction indicator lamp

8   Refer to Section 21 of this Chapter. Where the lamps lens and body are separate, the body can be withdrawn from the bumper and the wiring disconnected (photo).

Direction indicator side repeater lamp

9   Refer to Section 21 of this Chapter.

Rear lamp cluster

10   The bulbholder(s) can be removed as described in Section 21 of this Chapter.
11   The rear lamp lenses are bonded to the body rear panel and located by metal brackets secured by nuts (photo).
12   Removal and refitting entail the use of a heat gun to warm up the immediate area to a temperature of just below 60°C (140°F). It will therefore be necessary to remove the luggage compartment interior trim panels (Chapter 11) to gain access to the lens area, and also any electrical wiring, as well as the locating brackets.
13   Warm the edge of the lens until the sealant has softened, then push it out from the inside. Use a suitable solvent to remove all traces of sealant from the lens and body.

14   On refitting, apply a new butyl sealing strip evenly to the lens mating surface, warm it to the specified temperature and refit it to the body aperture. Refit all other disturbed components.

Number plate lamp

15   Refer to Section 21 of this Chapter.

23   Headlamp beam alignment

1   It is recommended that beam alignment be adjusted by a Nissan dealer or similar using optical alignment equipment. In an emergency,

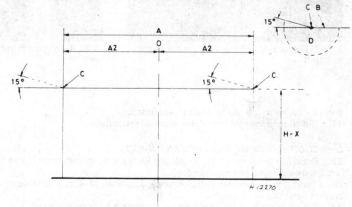

Fig. 12.33 Headlamp beam alignment chart (Sec 23)

A   Distance between headlamp centres
B   Light/dark boundary
C   Dipped beam centre
D   Dipped beam pattern
H   Height from ground to headlamp centre
O   Car's centre line
X   = 53 mm (2.09 in)

24.1A Prising off square-type courtesy lamp lens

24.1B Courtesy lamp uses a festoon-type bulb – retaining screws arrowed

24.3 Unclipping map reading lamp console from roof

24.4 Remove housing to expose bulbs

24.8 Luggage compartment lamp is between boot lid hinges – early Saloon ...

24.10 ... or in side trim panel – Hatchback and later Saloon

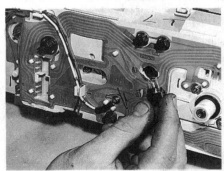

24.13A Instrument panel bulb renewal – note two sizes of bulbholder shown

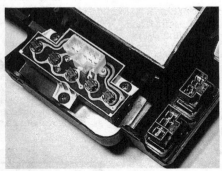

24.13B Instrument panel surround incorporates warning lamp panel

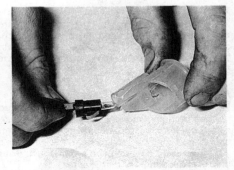

24.19 Cigarette lighter illuminating bulb is inserted in protector

however, the following procedure will produce acceptable results.

2   The car should be normally laden (full fuel tank, driver seated) and the tyre pressures must be correct. Park the car on level ground, approximately 5 metres (16 feet) in front of a flat wall or garage door.

3   Draw a vertical line on the wall or door corresponding to the centre-line of the car. (The position of this line can be determined by marking the centres of the windscreen and rear window with crayon, then viewing the wall or door from the rear of the car).

4   With the centre-line established, construct the other lines shown in Fig. 12.33.

5   Switch the headlights on to dipped beam. Cover one headlight with cloth and adjust the other, using the two adjusters at the rear of the unit, to bring the centre of the beam to the point 'C' on the appropriate side of the alignment chart (photo).

6   Transfer the cloth to the headlight already adjusted, and repeat the adjustment on the other headlight.

7   Have the alignment checked professionally at the first opportunity.

24   Interior lamps – bulb renewal

Courtesy lamp (roof)

1   Remove the lamps lens by twisting it anti-clockwise (round-type) or prising it off (square-type)(photo).

2   Pull the festoon-type bulb from its spring contacts.

Map reading lamp

3   Prise the lamp from the roof (photo).

4   Unclip the housing (photo).

5   Depress and twist the bayonet-type bulb.

Courtesy step lamp (door)

6   Extract the two screws and remove the lens.

7   Pull the wedge-type bulb from its spring contacts.

Luggage compartment lamp (early Saloon)

8   Twist the lens anti-clockwise from the bulbholder (photo).
9   Pull out the wedge-type bulb.

Luggage compartment lamp (Hatchback and later Saloon)

10   Remove the two retaining screws and withdraw the lens, or prise off the lens at its front edge, as applicable (photo).
11   Pull out the wedge-type bulb.

Instrument illumination and warning lamps

12   Remove the instrument panel as described in Section 26.
13   Twist the bulbholder anti-clockwise from the rear of the instrument panel (photos).
14   Pull out the wedge-type bulb. Be very careful to ensure that **exactly** the correct rating of bulb is installed (particularly the charge warning lamp). The three different bulbs used in the instrument panel are matched by three different sizes of bulbholder, to aid identification.

Ignition switch illuminating lamp

15   Remove the screws and unclip the steering column bottom shroud. The lamp's wire can then be disconnected and the assembly can be renewed.

Driver's door keyhole illuminating lamp

16   Refer to Chapter 11, Section 27. The lamp must be renewed as an assembly.

Glovebox lamp

17   Refer to Section 20 of this Chapter. Unless a separate bulb can be obtained, the switch must be renewed.

Cigarette lighter lamp

18   Remove the cigarette lighter as described in Section 28 of this Chapter.
19   Unless a separate bulb can be obtained, the lighter protector must be renewed (photo); note that the bulb rating is not a common type.

Ashtray lamp

20   Referring to Chapter 11, Section 37, remove the ashtray and radio/heater finisher, then remove the three screws and withdraw the ashtray mounting plate. Disconnect the lamp wire.
21   Unless a separate bulb can be obtained, the lamp assembly must be renewed.

Illuminated switches

22   The rear fog lamp, hazard warning, heated seat, adjustable suspension damping and rear defogger/heated rear window switches are all fitted with indicator lamps which are activated when the circuit is operating, or are illuminated when the lights are switched on.
23   In all cases the complete switch must be renewed to cure a faulty bulb (see Section 20 of this Chapter.)

Air conditioning and heater fan switches

24   Refer to Chapter 11, Section 39.

Gear selector panel illumination – automatic transmission

25   Remove the centre console (see Chapter 11, Section 36.)
26   Disconnect the bulb's wire and remove it. The complete assembly must be renewed.

---

25   Interior lamps – removal and refitting

1   Once the lens has been removed, (Section 24) the luggage compartment lamp and door courtesy step lamps can be withdrawn until their wiring can be disconnected.
2   The roof-mounted courtesy lamp is secured by two screws. Remove the lens, (Section 24) undo the screws and withdraw the lamp until the wiring can be disconnected.
3   In all other cases, refer to Section 24.

---

26   Instrument panel and warning lamps – removal and refitting

1   Disconnect the battery negative lead.
2   Release the rake locking lever and move the steering column to the lowest position.
3   Undo the three screws securing the top of the instrument panel surround to the facia hood (photo).
4   Undo the three screws securing the bottom of the surround to the facia – one on the right-hand side (photo) and two on the left.
5   Withdraw the surround until the connector plugs for the switches and warning lamps can be disconnected (photos). Withdraw the surround.
6   Undo the four screws securing the instrument panel – two at the top, two at the bottom (photos).
7   Withdraw the instrument panel until the wiring connector plugs and, where fitted, the econometer hose can be disconnected (photos). Withdraw the panel.
8   The panel assembly can be dismantled to renew the various instruments, clock and gauges by releasing the clips around its edge. Do not forget to remove the clock resetting knob before withdrawing the clock (photos).
9   If the tachometer is faulty, do not forget to check the resistor taped to the wiring loom, just being the left-hand front suspension strut top mounting. Its resistance rating is marked on the unit (photo).
10   On turbo engine models, the boost sensor controls the boost gauge reading (photo).
11   Refitting is the reverse of removal. Ensure that the econometer hose is not trapped and that the speedometer cable engages correctly as the instrument panel is refitted.

---

27   Speedometer cable – removal and refitting

1   Disconnect the battery negative lead.

26.3 Removing instrument panel surround top retaining screws – two of three shown

26.4 Removing instrument panel surround bottom (right-hand) retaining screw

26.5A Withdraw surround until switch and warning lamp wiring ...

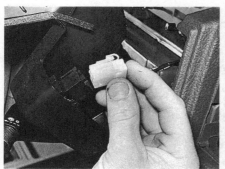

26.5B ... can be disconnected

26.6A Instrument panel top ...

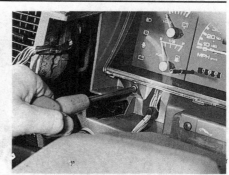

26.6B ... and bottom retaining screw

26.7 Disconnect econometer hose and wiring connector plugs (arrowed) to release panel

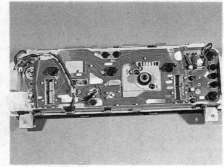

26.8A Instrument panel can be dismantled ...

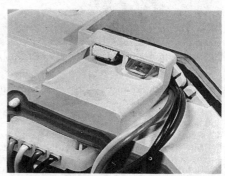

26.8B ... by releasing clips around edge

26.8C Remove resetting knob if clock is to be removed

26.9 Tachometer feed resistor

26.10 Boost sensor is mounted on bulkhead left-hand end – turbo engine models

27.2 Disconnecting speedometer cable from transmission

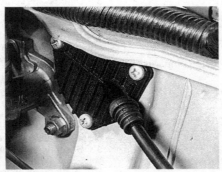

27.3 Cable retainer is secured to bulkhead by three screws

27.5 Cable is retained in facia slot at instrument end

28.3A Cigarette lighter metal centre must be pushed out from behind facia ...

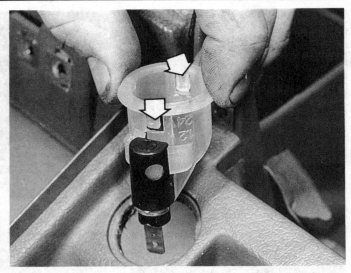

28.3B ... while releasing plastic protector's retainer clips (arrowed)

2   Unscrew the knurled retaining ring and withdraw the speedometer cable from the transmission (photo).
3   Undo the three screws and withdraw the cable retainer from the bulkhead (photo).
4   Remove the instrument panel (Section 26).
5   Move the cable sideways out of its bracket and withdraw it into the engine compartment (photo). It must be renewed as an assembly.
6   Refitting is the reverse of removal. Ensure the cable is routed smoothly with no sharp bends or kinks and that it is secured clear of any other moving components, wiring or control cables.

28   Cigarette lighter – removal and refitting

1   Disconnect the battery negative lead.
2   Remove the facia (Chapter 11, Section 37). It is not possible to release the cigarette lighter retainer clips from in front of the facia without risk of damage, neither is it possible to gain access by removing the radio/heater finisher etc.
3   Using two small screwdrivers, push the plastic retainer clips outwards while pressing out the metal centre from the rear. Withdraw the lighter metal centre and plastic protector, disconnecting the bulb wire, where fitted (photos).
4   Refitting is the reverse of removal.

29   Horns – removal and refitting

1   Unclip and remove the radiator grille if better access is required (Chapter 11).
2   Unbolt the horn(s) from the bracket and disconnect the wiring (photo).
3   Refitting is a reversal of the removal procedure. Check for satisfactory operation before refitting the grille.
4   Note that the horn relay is located in the engine compartment holder (Section 16).

30   Wiper arms and blades – removal and refitting

Headlamp

1   Prise off the plastic covers and unscrew the nut(s) securing the arm assembly to its motor spindle.
2   Disconnect the washer tube and withdraw the arm assembly. If any part of it is faulty or worn, the complete assembly must be renewed.
3   On refitting, check that the blade rests against the two stoppers on

29.2 The horns are mounted behind the radiator grille

the headlamp's lower edge. If not, slacken the two adjusting screws in the lower arm and alter the blade position as required, then re-tighten the screws. Do not overtighten the arm assembly retaining nut(s).

Windscreen

4   Raise the arm assembly away from the windscreen until it locks.
5   Depress the spring clip and slide the blade down the arm until it can be unhooked and withdrawn (photos).
6   If rubber inserts (refills) can be obtained (they are only available for T12 model windscreen wipers as Nissan replacement parts) remove the original, noting how it is clipped into place, then fit the replacement.
7   Refitting is the reverse of removal. Ensure that the blade is securely locked on the arm.
8   Before removing a wiper arm, it is worthwhile sticking a strip of masking tape on the glass against the edge of the wiper blade as a guide to wiper arm setting when refitting. Note also that the arms are different in length. Ensure that identifying marks are made or noted before removal so that the arms are correctly refitted. Open the bonnet for proper access to the arm nuts.
9   Unscrew the nut (photo) and pull the arm assembly from the spindle splines.
10   Refit by reversing the removal operations.
11   Wet the glass and operate the wipers to check their arc of travel. If it is incorrect, remove the arm and move it a spline or two in the required direction.

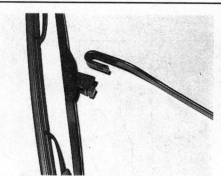

30.5A Depress spring clip and slide blade down arm ...

30.5B ... until it can be unhooked from arm

30.9 Unscrewing wiper arm nut

Tailgate

12   Where the wiper arm assembly is of the single-arm type, removal and refitting of the blade and arm is exactly as described in paragraphs 4 to 11 above. The blade should park at the inner edge of the tailgate glass's black border. Note that on T72 models, the blade is the same as those on the windscreen.

13   Where the wiper arm assembly is of the double-arm type, the blade is removed and refitted as described in paragraphs 4 to 7 above.

14   To remove the double-arm assembly, mark the position of the blade on the screen as described above, prise off the plastic covers and remove the nut and clip securing the assembly to the motor spindle, then withdraw the assembly.

15   On refitting, position the arm so that the blade runs along the inner edge of the tailgate glass's black border. If the blade will not park parallel to the border's edge, slacken the two adjusting screws in the lower arm and alter the blade position as required, then re-tighten the screws. Do not overtighten the arm assembly retaining nut.

31 Wiper motor and linkage – removal and refitting

Headlamp

1   Remove the arm assembly (Section 30). Disconnect the battery negative lead.

2   Remove the radiator grille (Chapter 11).

3   Disconnect the motor wiring connector plug.

4   Remove the screws and nuts, then withdraw the motor and its upper and lower brackets.

5   Refitting is the reverse of removal.

Windscreen

6   Remove the arm assembly (Section 30). Disconnect the battery negative lead.

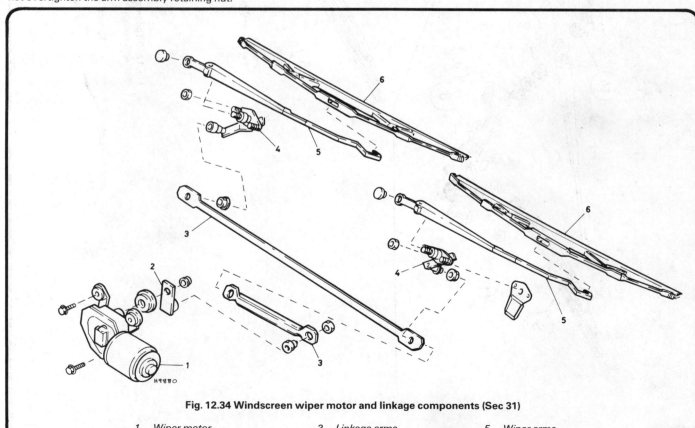

Fig. 12.34 Windscreen wiper motor and linkage components (Sec 31)

1	Wiper motor	3	Linkage arms	5	Wiper arms
2	Crank arm	4	Spindle unit	6	Wiper blades

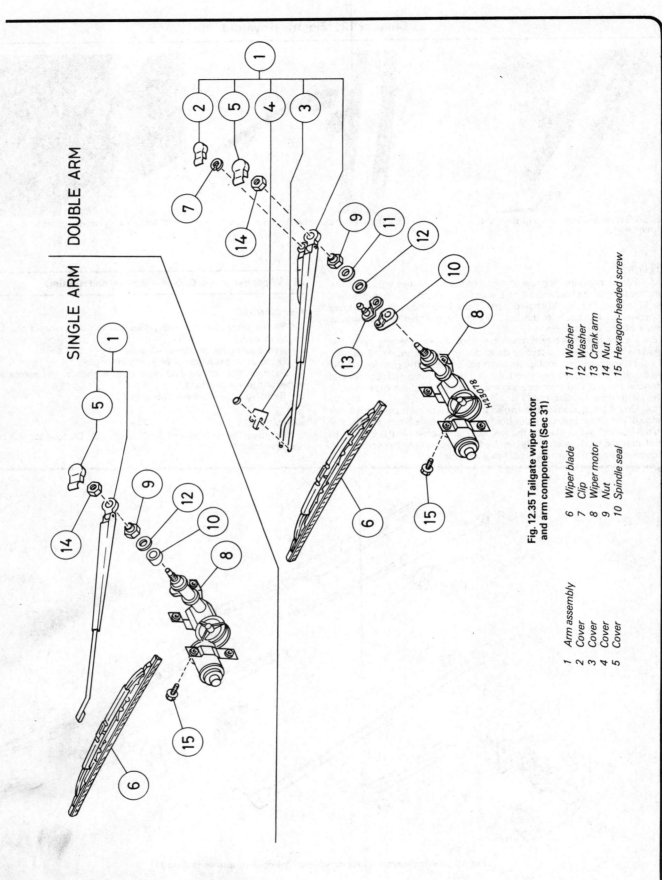

SINGLE ARM | DOUBLE ARM

Fig. 12.35 Tailgate wiper motor and arm components (Sec 31)

1 Arm assembly
2 Cover
3 Cover
4 Cover
5 Cover
6 Wiper blade
7 Clip
8 Wiper motor
9 Nut
10 Spindle seal
11 Washer
12 Washer
13 Crank arm
14 Nut
15 Hexagon-headed screw

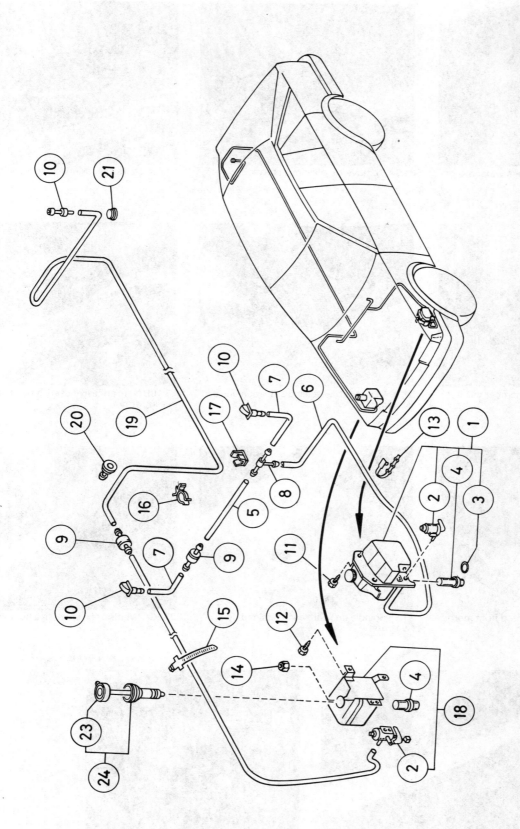

Fig. 12.36 Windscreen/tailgate washer system components – early models (Sec 32)

1	Windscreen washer fluid reservoir	6	Tubing	12	Screw	18	Tailgate washer fluid reservoir
2	Pump motor	7	Tubing	13	Clip	19	Tubing
3	Gasket	8	T-piece	14	Nut	20	Grommet
4	Washer fluid level sensor	9	Check valve	15	Tie	21	Grommet
5	Tubing	10	Washer jet	16	Clip	23	Filler cap/level tube
		11	Screw	17	Clip	24	Filler neck

31.7 Disconnecting windscreen wiper motor wiring

31.8A Remove all retaining screws ...

31.8B ... to release windscreen lower finisher

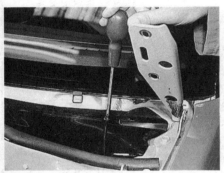

31.9 Removing ventilation chamber grille panel screws

31.10A Bonnet rear sealing strip retaining clip removal

31.10B Note adhesive used at points along sealing strip

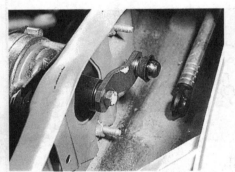

31.11 Linkage arm disconnected from motor crank arm

31.12 Spindle units are each retained by two nuts

31.13A Windscreen lower finisher thin spacers ...

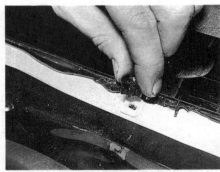

31.13B ... and thick spacers must be placed as described

31.16 Tailgate wiper motor mounting bolts (arrowed)

7   Disconnect the motor wiring (photo). Where applicable, remove the amplifier relay from the motor body.
8   Remove the retaining screws and withdraw the windscreen lower finisher (photos), noting carefully the arrangement of spacers under the finisher.
9   Remove the screws along the rear edge of the ventilation chamber grille panels (photo).
10   Prise up the retaining clips and peel off the bonnet rear sealing strips from the front edge of the grille panels, noting that adhesive or double-sided adhesive tape is also used to secure the strip where necessary (photos). Withdraw the grille panels, noting that butyl sealant may be applied to the edges of the aperture above the wiper motor.
11   To remove the motor, either unbolt the crank arm or disconnect the linkage arm from the crank arm (photo). Unbolt the motor from the bulkhead.
12   To remove the linkage, unscrew the two nuts securing each spindle unit and withdraw the assembly from the ventilation chamber (photo).
13   Refitting is the reverse of the removal procedure. When refitting the windscreen lower finisher, the thin spacers are fitted at the centre screw location and at the two outermost locations, the thick spacers are fitted on each side of the centre screw and the plastic washers are fitted to the remaining locations (photos). Note that the finisher should be tucked under the bodywork at each end.

Tailgate
14   Remove the arm assembly (Section 30). Disconnect the battery negative lead.
15   Remove the tailgate interior trim panel (Chapter 11).
16   Disconnect the motor wiring, unscrew the motor spindle nut on the outside of the tailgate, then unbolt the motor and withdraw it (photo), noting the spindle seal and washer (also the crank arm, on double-arm type assemblies).
17   Refitting is the reverse of the removal procedure.

Windscreen wiper relays
18   Note that the windscreen wiper motor circuit is controlled by a relay in the engine compartment holder (Section 16).
19   On some models, an amplifier relay assembly is clipped to the wiper motor body.

32   Washer system – general

1   Refer to Section 3 of this Chapter for details of reservoir location and maintenance operations.

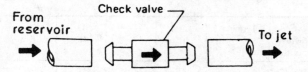

Fig. 12.37 Washer system check valve fitting direction (Sec 32)

2   The pump motor is located in the bottom of the reservoir.
3   A level sensor, which activates the instrument panel warning lamp when the washer fluid falls to a low level, is located in the bottom of the reservoir.
4   No information is available on the removal and refitting of any of the above, except for the early-type windscreen washer reservoir, which can be unbolted from the inner wing panel and raised until the wiring plugs and washer tubing can be disconnected.
5   Note that a non-return check valve is fitted in each circuit to maintain the supply of fluid at the jets. They are located between the T-piece and driver's side jet (windscreen), between the reservoir and the right-hand headlamp (headlamp) and in the washer tubing under the bonnet (tailgate). If the valve is removed, always ensure that it is refitted correctly (Fig. 12.37).

33   Adjustable suspension damping system – general

1   Refer to Chapter 10 for an outline of the system's operation.
2   The electrical circuit consists of the select switch, the control unit, and the four actuators mounted at the top of each suspension strut.
3   The circuit is supplied from the battery via the grey fusible link and the ignition relay to the fuse (actually labelled 'Turn signal/Transmission').
4   The control unit is mounted under the driver's seat which must be removed first to allow access (see Chapter 11, Section 34 for details. Prise up the clip studs to release the plastic cover, then remove the retaining screw(s) to release the unit. Unplug its connector to disconnect the wiring.
5   Each actuator is removed and refitted as described in the relevant Sections of Chapter 10.
6   To remove the switch, prise it carefully out of the facia and disconnect the wiring lead by removing the connector plug.
7   In addition to the switch illuminating bulb which is activated when-

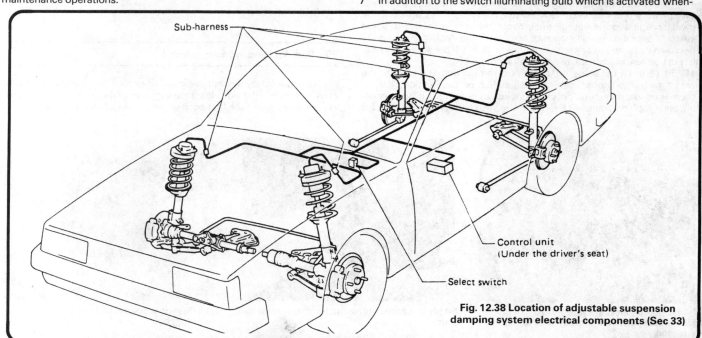

Fig. 12.38 Location of adjustable suspension damping system electrical components (Sec 33)

Switch position	Terminal	C	S	N	F
"S" (Soft)		○——————○			
"N" (Normal)		○———————————○			
"F" (Firm)		○————————————————————○			

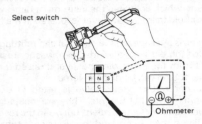

Fig. 12.39 Testing select switch (Sec 33)

ever the lights are switched on, the switch is fitted with three LEDs (Light Emitting Diodes). One of these should light to correspond with the suspension setting selected.

8   The LEDs also fulfil a second role as part of the control unit's self-checking function. If more than one LED are lit at any one time, if all are off, or if any are blinking, check the circuit as follows, having first checked the battery and all connectors.

9   If all LEDs are off, switch off the ignition, change the switch to another setting and switch on the ignition again. If one or two LEDs then light, the switch assembly is faulty and must be renewed. If the LEDs still do not light, first check the fuse, then check the power supply at the control unit as follows.

10   Check for continuity between the harness side (ie with the control unit still connected) of the control unit's terminal 11 (green wire) and earth. If all is well, measure the voltage between the harness side of the unit's terminals 1 and 11 (voltmeter negative probe to terminal 11, positive probe to terminal 1) with the ignition switched on. A reading of full battery voltage should be obtained. If not, check back through the wiring harness until the fault is discovered. If the power supply is correct, the select switch is faulty and must be renewed.

11   If two LEDs light, switch off the ignition and change the select switch to another setting, then switch on the ignition again. If the switch's operation is now normal, check the wiring behind it. If the switch's operation is still incorrect, remove it and check for continuity between its terminals at each position (Fig. 12.39). If the switch is faulty it must be renewed; if not, check carefully the wiring.

12   If all three LEDs are on, switch off the ignition and change the select switch to another setting, then switch on the ignition again. If there is no improvement, check the switch as described in the preceding paragraph and renew it if faulty. If the switch is sound, or if the LED

operation is normal in both the suspension settings, then the fault is in the control unit (see below).

13   If one LED is lit and the other two flash on and off, first switch off the ignition and work carefully through the system checking all connectors for security. If the fault is not corrected when the ignition is switched on again, it is in either the control unit or one of the actuators.

14   If the fault is thought to be in the control unit or one of the actuators, the car should be taken to a Nissan dealer for a thorough test of the system and of these components in particular. If faulty, these units must be renewed.

34   Central locking system – general

1   Refer to Chapter 11, Section 29 for a description of the system's operation.

2   The system comprises the following components.

3   The circuit is fed from the battery via the brown fusible link to a cylindrical circuit-breaker (identical to that fitted to the power window circuit) which is located behind the facia, between the steering column and the fuse panel.

4   The circuit is controlled by the door lock timer, which is mounted behind the footwell right-hand side trim panel and the time control unit (see photo 43.8).

5   The main (number 1) lock/unlock switch is situated in the switch panel mounted in the driver's door armrest. Refer to Chapter 11, Section 33 for details of removal and refitting.

6   The number 2 lock/unlock switch is located in the bottom rear corner of the driver's door and is secured by two bolts. To remove it, remove the door interior trim panel (see Chapter 11, Section 33) and peel back the corner of the polythene condensation barrier. Unbolt the switch and release the clip to disconnect the latch rod from it, then unplug the switch connector and withdraw the switch (photos). Refitting is the reverse of the removal procedure.

7   The number 3 lock/unlock switch is mounted on the driver's door lock barrel and removal and refitting is as described in Chapter 11, Section 27. Note that this switch does not appear to be fitted to cars built after February (T12) or May (T72) 1988.

8   The front passenger door and rear doors are each fitted with an actuator solenoid that is secured by two bolts and connected to the latch by a rod. Removal and refitting is as described in paragraph 6 above (photo).

35   Dim-dip lamp system – general

1   This is a safety system designed to ensure that the car cannot be driven with only the side clearance lamps on. When the lighting control switch is moved to the first position with the ignition switched off, the

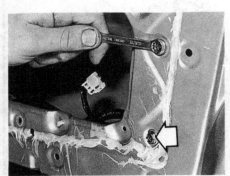

34.6A Central locking system No 2 lock/unlock switch mounting bolts (other arrowed)

34.6B Disconnecting switch wiring connector plug

34.8 Rear door central locking actuator mounting bolts

35.3 Location of dim-dip control unit (later models)

36.4 Location of flasher unit (arrowed)

normal side, tail and instrument illumination lamps are switched on.

2   When the lighting control switch is moved to the first position and the ignition is switched on, the headlamps will operate at reduced power. When the headlamps are switched to their normal on position they will operate at full power.

3   The system is controlled either by a relay (early models) or by a control unit (later models) mounted underneath the radio (photo). It will be necessary to remove the centre console (Chapter 11) to gain access.

36   Direction indicator and hazard warning system – general

1   The direction indicator system consists of the flasher unit, control switch, external and repeater lights and the associated wiring. The hazard warning system shares the same flasher unit.

2   If the direction indicators operate abnormally fast or slowly on one side only, check the bulbs and wiring on that side. Incorrect wattage bulbs, dirty bulbholders and poor earth connections can all cause changes in the flashing rate.

3   If the direction indicators do not work at all, check the fuse before suspecting the flasher unit. If the hazard warning system works but the indicators do not, the flasher unit is almost certainly not faulty.

4   The flasher unit is mounted on a bracket at the bottom of the steering column, next to the stop lamp switch (photo).

5   To renew the unit, undo the four screws and withdraw the facia lower panel from below the steering column, unplug the wiring connector and remove the single retaining screw to release it.

6   Testing is by substitution of a known good unit.

37   Electrically-operated sunroof – general

1   The sunroof operating circuit is fed from the battery via the brown fusible link to the power window circuit-breaker and relay situated behind the facia-mounted fusebox assembly. The sunroof switch is mounted in the map- reading lamp roof console.

2   The circuit's two relays and the motor/limit switch assembly are mounted in the roof, concealed by the headlining and the motor cover.

3   Due to the difficulty of access (see Chapter 11) owners are advised to seek the assistance of a Nissan dealer in the event of failure.

4   Note that if the circuit fails while the roof is open, it may be closed by prising out the blanking plug from the headlining between the switch

37.4 Electrically-operated sunroof can be closed using a screwdriver, if necessary

console and the roof to expose the end of the motor drive shaft. Check that the ignition is switched off then use a screwdriver to press upwards and rotate the shaft clockwise to close the roof (photo).

5   On early models with Japanese-built sunroofs, note that on closing from fully open the roof will stop at approximately 150 mm (6 in) from the fully closed position. The switch must be released and pressed again fully to close the roof. This is a built-in safety feature to avoid fingers being trapped.

38   Electric remote control exterior mirrors – general

1   Some models are fitted with exterior mirrors in which electrically-operated actuators can alter the position of the mirror glass. The adjustment is made by selecting the mirror to be adjusted using a facia-mounted rocker switch, then altering the glass's position as required using the switch's joystick.

2   The actuators are supplied only as part of the mirror assembly. Removal and refitting is described in Section 31 of Chapter 11.

3   The facia switch is removed by prising it out and disconnecting its wiring connector plug (photo).
4   The circuit is fed through the fuse labelled 'Cigarette lighter'.
5   Note that the mirror glass incorporates heater elements which are activated whenever the rear window defogger (heated rear window) is switched on.

39   Heated front seats – general

1   Elements in the base and back cushions (of the front seats only) are activated by individual switches (the front one being for the passenger's seat) mounted in the centre console, and are controlled by thermostatic (one in each back, two in each base cushion).
2   Both switches have 'Hi' and 'Lo' positions according to the temperature required and an illuminating lamp is provided that lights whenever the circuit is switched on.
3   The heating elements, if faulty, must be renewed with the seat trim.
4   The circuit is fed from the power window circuit (see Section 43, paragraphs 6 and 7).
5   The following points should be remembered when using the heated seats:

(a)   *Use the heaters for the minimum time possible and always switch them off before leaving the vehicle. Switch the heaters on only when the engine is running – their consumption is considerable and may flatten the battery if it is not being recharged.*

(b)   *Do not fit seat covers, or cover the seat with blankets, cushions etc – the insulating effect may overheat the system's components.*

(c)   *Do not place anything hard, heavy or sharp on the seat, or pierce the trim with knives, pins etc – the elements may be damaged.*

(d)   *If any liquid is spilled on the seat mop it up immediately and ensure that the seat is dry before switching on the heaters again.*

(e)   *Do not use any strong solvents or petroleum-based cleaners (thinners, benzene, alcohol, gasoline etc) to clean the seat trim.*

40   Heater fan – general

1   The heating and ventilating system's fan is controlled by a switch mounted in the heater control assembly. The fan and its motor are housed in the heater intake box mounted in front of the glovebox.
2   The fan motor is regulated to any one of four speeds by switching in elements of a resistor unit which is mounted in the heater duct between

38.3 Removing electric remote control exterior mirror switch

the intake box and heater unit.
3   Refer to Chapter 11 for details of removal and refitting of all the above components.
4   The heater fan circuit is fed from the battery via the grey fusible link to the heater relay (located in the engine compartment relay holder) and from there to two 15 amp fuses (actually labelled 'Aircon' and 'Blower').

41   Lights-on warning chime – general

1   If the driver's door is opened when the lights are switched on and the ignition switch is in the 'Lock', 'Off' or 'Acc' positions, a two-tone chime will sound as a reminder to prevent the battery being drained while the car is parked.
2   The circuit is fed from the battery via the grey fusible link and a fuse (marked 'Illumi/Clearance').
3   The system is controlled by the time control unit (Section 45).
4   To remove the chime itself, the facia must be removed (Chapter 11). The chime is mounted on the rear of the facia by two screws (photo).

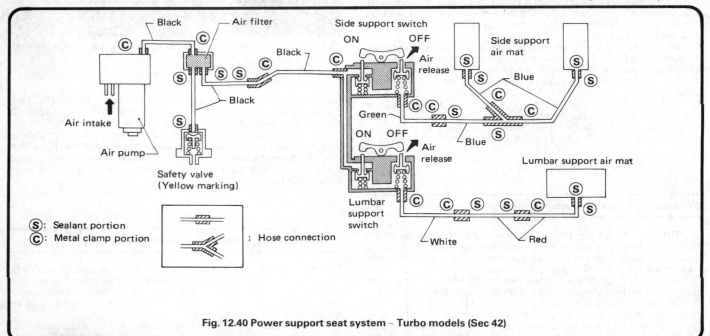

Fig. 12.40 Power support seat system – Turbo models (Sec 42)

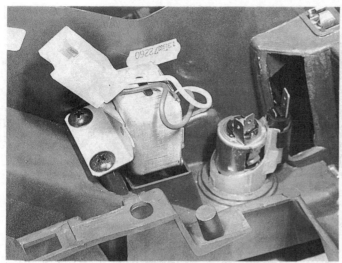

41.4 Lights-on warning chime is mounted behind facia, below cigarette lighter

42.1 Power support seat switches – turbo engine models

5   To test the chime connect it directly to a 12 volt battery, then repeatedly disconnect and connect the positive terminal; if the chime does not sound correctly each time it must be renewed.

42   Power support seat – general

1   The driver's seat only (turbo engine models) is fitted with inflatable air mats in the seat back and side cushions which are pressurised to the required level by an electric air pump mounted under the front of the seat. The pump is activated only when one of the switches is in the 'On' position (photo).
2   To prevent damage, the air pump assembly is fitted with a safety valve and the pump's motor has an auto-reset overload protection device consisting of a circuit-breaker. If the pump stops during operation, stop and wait for at least thirty seconds for the circuit-breaker to reset itself, then start again.
3   The circuit is fed from the power window circuit (see Section 43, paragraphs 6 and 7).
4   If the system is ever disturbed, it is better to disconnect the air hoses where they are joined by metal clamps. If any other connections are disturbed, always apply a suitable sealant on reassembly, to prevent air leaks. Make a careful note of connections before disturbing them, so that hoses can be correctly refitted. Ensure that the pump and air filter are clean, and that none of the air hoses are crushed and that they are correctly routed (see also Fig. 11.22).
5   The following points should be noted when using the power support seat:

(a)   Do not play with the seat for long periods of time when the engine is switched off; current consumption is considerable and may flatten the battery if it is not being recharged.
(b)   Do not operate the switches for more than ten seconds at a time, or the pump may be damaged.

43   Power windows – general

1   Some models are fitted with power windows, in which electric motors fitted to the window regulator assembly in each door are controlled by switches to raise or lower the window glass as required.
2   Each passenger door is fitted with a three-position rocker switch ('Up' to close, 'Down' to open and a neutral centre position) which operates only that door's window glass for as long as the switch is depressed.
3   The main switch is fitted to the driver's door. Apart from the switch controlling the driver's door window (see below), it contains three switches (duplicates of those described above), so that the driver can control all three passenger door windows, and a lock button which can

be depressed to lock the passenger door windows.
4   The driver's door window is controlled by a five-position rocker switch. When pressed lightly ('Up' or 'Down') the switch will operate the window only while pressure is maintained. When the switch is depressed fully ('Up' or 'Down'), it can be released, and the window will move automatically to the fully-up or fully-down position, to be stopped by the amplifier when that position is reached. To stop the window at any point in this mode, press the switch on the opposite side.
5   The time control unit energises the power window timer relay so that if the driver's door is open, the power windows can be operated, by the main switch only, for up to thirty seconds after the ignition switch has been turned to the 'Acc' or 'Off' positions.
6   The circuit is fed from the battery via the brown fusible link to a cylindrical circuit-breaker located behind the facia, between the steering column and the fuse panel.
7   The power window relay is one of the four mounted behind the facia, immediately above the fuse panel. Depending on model, it is either the left-hand relay, the second relay from the left, or the right-hand relay. It is energised from the ignition switch and relay via a fuse (actually labelled 'Meter').
8   The timer relay and time control unit are mounted behind the footwell right-hand side trim panel (photo).
9   The amplifier is mounted behind the driver's door interior trim panel; see Chapter 11, Section 33 for details of panel removal and refitting. Remove the amplifier's single retaining screw and disconnect its wiring at the connector plug (photos).
10   The switches are removed as described in Chapter 11, Section 33.
11   The window regulators are removed and refitted as described in Chapter 11, Section 28. The motors can be unbolted from the regulators and renewed separately.

44   Rear defogger/heated rear window – general

1   All models are equipped with a heated rear window tailgate glass. Heating is achieved by passing current through a resistive grid bonded to the inside of the glass.
2   The heater elements are fragile and the following precautions should be observed:

(a)   Do not allow luggage or other items to rub against the inside surface of the glass
(b)   Do not stick labels over the elements
(c)   Avoid scratching the elements when cleaning with rings on the fingers
(d)   Clean the glass with water and detergent only and rub in the direction of the elements using a soft cloth or chamois

3   Should an element be damaged so that the current is interrupted, a

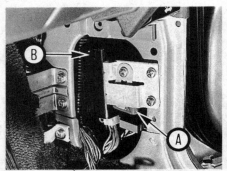

43.8 Power window timer relay 'A', central locking door lock timer 'B'

43.9A Removing power window amplifier retaining screw

43.9B Disconnecting amplifier wiring

repair can be made using one of the conductive silver paints available from motor accessory stores.

4   Note that the system draws a very high current and thus has its own relay, which is one of the four grouped above the fuse panel (Section 16).

5   The circuit is protected by two fuses and is fed from the battery via the grey fusible link.

6   Note that some models have a radio aerial of this type fitted in the rear window/tailgate glass, above the heater element; the same precautions and repair procedures apply.

45   Time control unit (TCU) – general

1   The time control unit is located on the right-hand side of the driver's footwell. Its function is to provide timing for the following items:

(a) *Intermittent wiper control – depending on setting of knob, from 4 to 12 seconds*
(b) *Washer/wiper control – wiper operated together with washer switch*
(c) *Interior lamp – interior lamp fades when driver's door is closed*
(d) *Interior illumination control – depending on setting, brightness adjusted in 16 steps*
(e) *Light warning chime – chime sounds when driver's door opened with light switch on and ignition off*
(f) *Clock – pulse signal emitted to operate clock*
(g) *Power window – if driver's door is open, power windows can be operated by main switch only for up to 30 seconds after ignition is switched off*

2   If the TCU develops a fault, check that the appropriate wiring is intact and correctly fitted. In-depth checking of the TCU should be made by a Nissan dealer or auto electrician with the unit installed in the car.

3   To remove the TCU, first disconnect the battery negative lead.

4   Take note that the TCU incorporates micro-circuitry and for this reason its terminals must never be touched with bare hands.

5   Extract the screws and withdraw the trim panel.

6   Extract the mounting screws, withdraw the TCU, and disconnect the wiring (photo).

7   Refitting is a reversal of removal.

45.6 Time control unit (TCU) is behind footwell right-hand side trim panel

46   Stop/tail lamp bulb failure warning lamp – general

1   The warning lamp operation and details of sensor location are given in Chapter 9, Section 30.

2   If the system fails to operate, check first that the bulbs are of the correct rating, working properly, and properly installed.

3   To test the sensor, remove it from its mounting (photo). It will be necessary to remove the appropriate luggage compartment interior trim panel to reach it (Chapter 11).

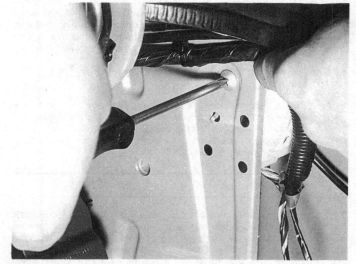

46.3 Removing stop/tail lamp bulb failure warning lamp sensor – Saloon

4   Start the engine and allow it to idle, then check the voltage across the terminals shown in Fig. 12.41. Check first with the brake applied

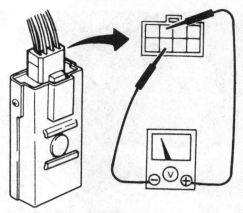

Fig. 12.41 Testing stop/tail lamp bulb failure warning lamp sensor (Sec 46)

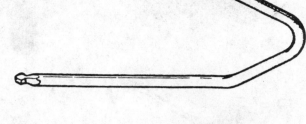

Fig. 12.42 Radio/cassette player DIN extraction tool (Sec 47)

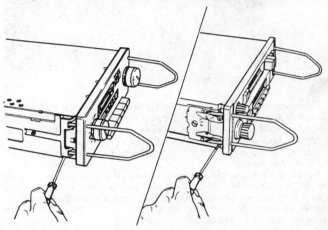

Fig. 12.43 Releasing a DIN extraction tool (Sec 47)

(stop lamp switch on), then with the lighting switch on.
5   The sensor is in good condition if a reading of 12 volts is obtained at each test, with all bulbs in place and of 1 volt with one (or more) bulb removed.
6   If the sensor is faulty it must be renewed.

47 Radio/cassette player – removal and refitting

1   Disconnect the battery negative terminal.
2   According to the type of equipment fitted, the method of removal varies slightly. If there are two small holes vertically in line on each side of the radio faceplate, then the unit has a DIN standard attachment and is removed by inserting two special hooked removal tools into these holes to release the internal catches. These special tools may be purchased from radio accessory outlets, or can be made up from suitable 3 mm (0.12 in) wire rod such as welding rod (Fig. 12.42).
3   Insert the removal tools into the slots until they can be felt to engage with the catches. Now pull the unit forward out of its aperture.
4   Disconnect the electrical connections, making written notes for refitting, and aerial lead at the rear of the radio and push the retaining clips inward to release the removal tools (Fig. 12.43). Remove the unit from the car.
5   To refit, push the radio cassette player back into its aperture until the clips engage.
6   If the radio faceplate does not have holes for removal tools, then the unit is secured in position by screws and must be removed as follows.
7   Remove the ashtray and radio/heater finisher (see Section 37 of Chapter 11.)
8   Undo the securing screws and withdraw the complete assembly (photos).
9   Disconnect the aerial lead. Making written notes to ensure that the wires can be re-connected correctly, disconnect the wires from the rear of the radio/cassette player (photo). Remove the unit from the car.
10   Refitting is the reverse of removal.

11   Note that for radios with manual (ie not electronic) tuning, if either the radio or the aerial have been renewed it will be necessary to re-trim the radio to match the aerial, as follows.
12   Extend the aerial fully, switch on the radio and tune to a weak MW (medium wave) station at around 1000 kHz. Turn to maximum volume.
13   Turn the aerial trimmer screw (a small amount) in either direction until the strongest signal is obtained. On the radio originally fitted, the trimmer screw is on the front face of the unit; for other types of radio, consult the manufacturer's instructions. Electronic units are normally self-trimming.

48 Radio aerial – removal and refitting

Front wing-mounted
1   Raise the front of the car and remove the roadwheel, mudflap (where fitted), anti-chipping protector strip and wheel arch liner from inside the front wing (Chapter 11).

47.8A Remove radio/heater finisher panel to expose radio mounting screws

47.8B Withdrawing radio/cassette player unit

47.9 Make written notes of wiring connections before disconnecting wires

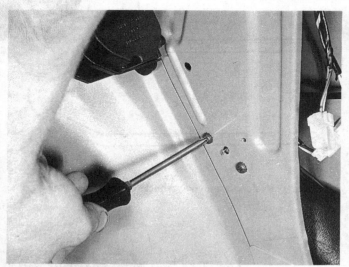

48.11 Power aerial securing screws – Saloon

48.14 Location of power aerial timer – typical

2   Disconnect the aerial lead and, where fitted, the aerial motor electrical leads. Pull the aerial (and wiring) through into the wing.
3   Undo the screw(s) securing the aerial under the wing, then unscrew the retaining nut above the wing panel.
4   Noting the cap above the wing and the spanner beneath, withdraw the aerial from the car.
5   Refitting is the reverse of removal. Ensure that there is clean metal-to-metal contact between the aerial base and the underside of the wing panel. Apply a smear of petroleum jelly or similar to the bare metal to prevent corrosion. Note that in some cases it may be necessary to re-trim the radio to match the aerial (Section 47).

Windscreen pillar-mounted
6   Disconnect the aerial lead from the rear of the radio (Section 47).
7   Undo the retaining screws and withdraw the aerial from the outside of the pillar, disconnecting the drain tubes.
8   Withdraw the aerial, removing the facia and interior trim panels as necessary (Chapter 11) to permit the removal of the aerial lead.
9   Refitting is the reverse of removal (see paragraph 5 above).

Rear wing-mounted
10   Remove the luggage compartment interior trim panels as necessary to reach the aerial mountings (Chapter 11, Section 33).
11   Noting that there is a drain tube connected to the bottom of the aerial, remove and refit the aerial as described in paragraphs 2 to 5 above (photo).

Rear window/tailgate glass-mounted
12   On some models an additional aerial is bonded to the rear window/tailgate glass. Refer to Section 44 of this Chapter for details.

Power aerial timer
13   On some models the aerial retracts automatically when the ignition is switched off, and then extends when the ignition is switched on again (if the aerial Up/Down switch has not been disturbed). On other models the aerial extends automatically when the radio is switched on and retracts either when the radio, or the ignition is switched off.
14   This function is controlled by the aerial timer which is mounted either on the aerial itself (rear wing-mounted aerials only) or underneath the radio (photo). In the latter case, either the radio or the centre console must be removed to gain access to the unit. Refer to Section 47 of this Chapter or to Chapter 11, Section 36, as necessary.

---

49   Loudspeakers – removal and refitting

Front door
1   Remove the door interior trim panel (Chapter 11).
2   Undo the retaining screws (photo).
3   Withdraw the loudspeaker and disconnect its wiring (photo).
4   Refitting is the reverse of removal.

Parcel shelf
5   Carefully prise up the speaker cover to release the four retaining clips.
6   On Hatchback models, disconnect the wiring and withdraw the assembly (photo).
7   On Saloon models, remove the retaining screws and nuts to release the loudspeakers and their base. Disconnect the wiring and withdraw the assembly (photo).
8   Refitting is the reverse of removal.

49.2 Front loudspeakers are retained by screws

49.3 Disconnecting loudspeaker wiring

49.6 Removing rear loudspeaker assembly – Hatchback

49.7 Rear loudspeaker assembly – Saloon

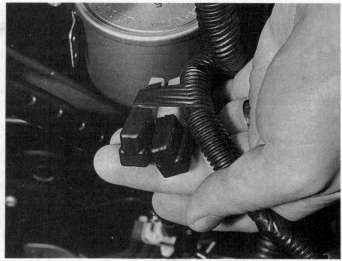

50.7 Note diodes taped to wiring harness

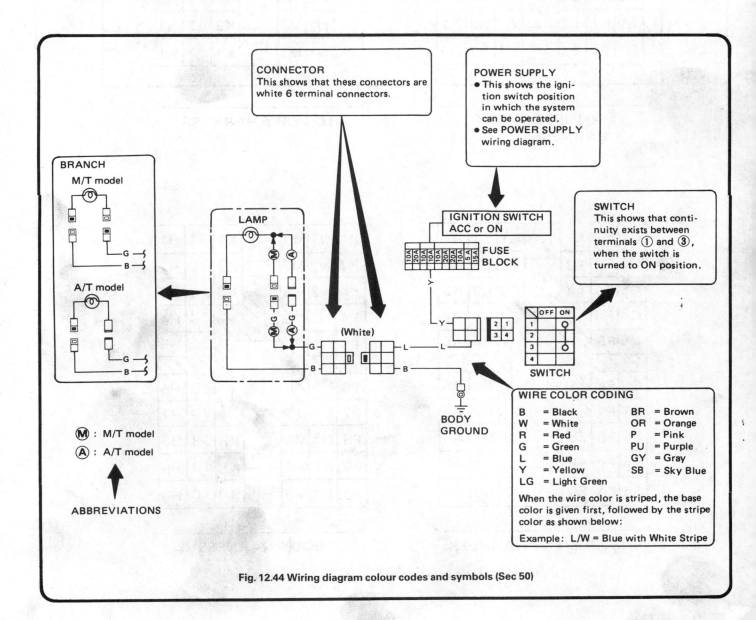

CONNECTOR
This shows that these connectors are white 6 terminal connectors.

POWER SUPPLY
● This shows the ignition switch position in which the system can be operated.
● See POWER SUPPLY wiring diagram.

SWITCH
This shows that continuity exists between terminals ① and ③, when the switch is turned to ON position.

BRANCH
M/T model
A/T model

LAMP

IGNITION SWITCH
ACC or ON

FUSE BLOCK

(White)

BODY GROUND

SWITCH

Ⓜ : M/T model
Ⓐ : A/T model

ABBREVIATIONS

WIRE COLOR CODING

B = Black	BR = Brown
W = White	OR = Orange
R = Red	P = Pink
G = Green	PU = Purple
L = Blue	GY = Gray
Y = Yellow	SB = Sky Blue
LG = Light Green	

When the wire color is striped, the base color is given first, followed by the stripe color as shown below:

Example: L/W = Blue with White Stripe

Fig. 12.44 Wiring diagram colour codes and symbols (Sec 50)

MAIN HARNESS

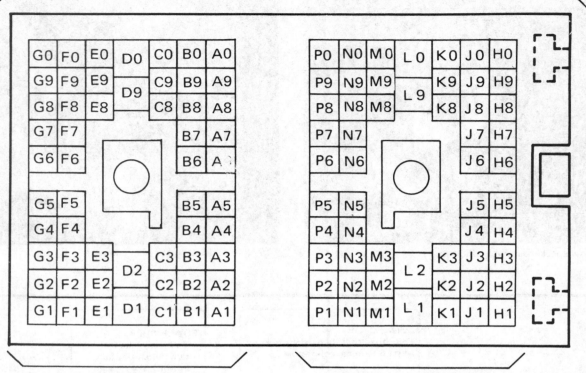

TO INSTRUMENT HARNESS

TO BODY HARNESS

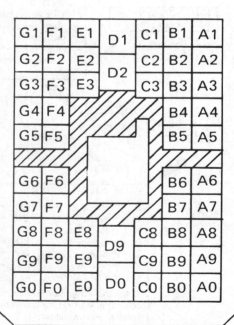

INSTRUMENT HARNESS

BODY HARNESS

Fig. 12.45 SMJ (Super Multiple Junction) connections (Sec 50)

50   Wiring diagrams – explanatory notes

1   Since it isn't possible to include all wiring diagrams for every year covered by this manual, the following diagrams are those that are typical and most commonly needed.

2   Note that many of the diagrams contain references to circuits, components or features not applicable to UK models; all such references should be ignored.

3   Fig. 12.44 shows the colour-coding used and explains the symbols most commonly employed.

4   Switch and relay contacts are drawn to illustrate whether they are normally closed or normally open.

5   Multi-pin connector plugs are drawn using the locking tab/guide as a reference point; black locking tabs/guides indicate a male connector, white ones a female connector. In most cases, connections are drawn from the terminal side (TS) ie. as though the connector had been unplugged. In a few cases, the connections are drawn from the harness side (HS); these are identified by a double line drawn around the connector.

6   SMJ (Super Multiple Junction) connections are shown in Fig. 12.45 (see Section 19 of this Chapter.)

7   Some small components, such as diodes, will be found taped to the wiring harness itself (photo).

51   Fault diagnosis – electrical system

Symptom	Reason(s)
No voltage at starter motor	Battery discharged Battery defective internally Battery terminals loose or earth lead not securely attached to body Loose or broken connections in starter motor circuit Starter motor switch or solenoid faulty
Voltage at starter motor – faulty motor	Starter brushes badly worn, sticking, or brush wires loose Commutator dirty, worn or burnt Starter motor armature faulty Field coils earthed
Electrical defects	Battery in discharged condition Starter brushes badly worn, sticking, or brush wires loose Loose wires in starter motor circuit
Starter motor noisy or rough in engagement	Pinion or flywheel gear teeth broken or worn Starter motor retaining bolts loose
Alternator not charging	Drivebelt loose and slipping, or broken Brushes worn, sticking, broken or dirty Brush springs weak or broken
Battery will not hold charge for more than a few days	Battery defective internally Electrolyte level too low or electrolyte too weak due to leakage Plate separators no longer fully effective Battery plates severely sulphated Drivebelt slipping Battery terminal connections loose or corroded Alternator not charging properly Short in lighting circuit causing continual battery drain Integral regulator unit not working correctly
Ignition light fails to go out, battery runs flat in a few days	Drivebelt loose and slipping, or broken Alternator faulty

Failure of individual electrical equipment to function correctly is dealt with below

Symptom	Reason(s)
Fuel gauge gives no reading (refer also to Chapter 3)	Fuel tank empty! Electric cable between tank sender unit and gauge earthed or loose Fuel gauge case not earthed Fuel gauge supply cable interrupted Fuel gauge unit broken
Fuel gauge registers full all the time	Electric cable between tank unit and gauge broken or disconnected
Horn operates all the time	Horn push either earthed or stuck down Horn cable to horn push earthed
Horn fails to operate	Blown fuse Cable or cable connection loose, broken or disconnected Horn has an internal fault

Symptom	Reason(s)
Horn emits intermittent or unsatisfactory noise	Cable connections loose Horn incorrectly adjusted
Lights do not come on	If engine not running, battery discharged Light bulb filament burnt out or bulbs broken Wire connections loose, disconnected or broken Light switch shorting or otherwise faulty Fusible link melted
Lights come on but fade out	If engine not running, battery discharged
Lights give very poor illumination	Lamp glasses dirty Reflector tarnished or dirty Lamps badly out of adjustment Incorrect bulb with too low wattage fitted Existing bulbs old and badly discoloured
Lights work erratically, flashing on and off especially over bumps	Battery terminals or earth connections loose Lights not earthing properly Contacts in light switch faulty
Wiper motor fails to work	Blown fuse Wire connections loose, disconnected or broken Brushes badly worn Armature worn or faulty Field coils faulty
Wiper motor works very slowly and takes excessive current	Commutator dirty, greasy or burnt Drive to spindles too bent or unlubricated Drive spindle binding or damaged Armature bearings dry or unaligned Armature badly worn or faulty
Wiper motor works slowly and takes little current	Brushes badly worn Commutators dirty, greasy or burnt Armature badly worn or faulty
Wiper motor works but wiper blades remain static	Linkage disengaged or faulty Drive spindle damaged or worn Wiper motor gearbox parts badly worn
Heated rear window not operating	Blown fuse Broken filament Faulty relay

Note: *This Section is not intended to be an exhaustive guide to fault diagnosis, but summarises the more common faults which may be encountered during a car's life. Consult a dealer for more specific advice.*

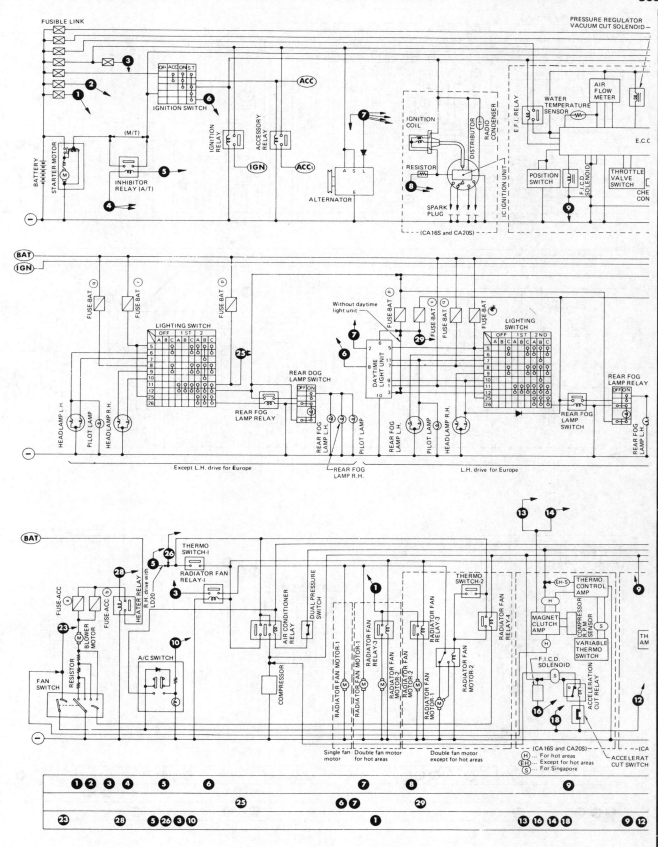

Fig. 12.46 Schematic wiring diagram (all T12 models)

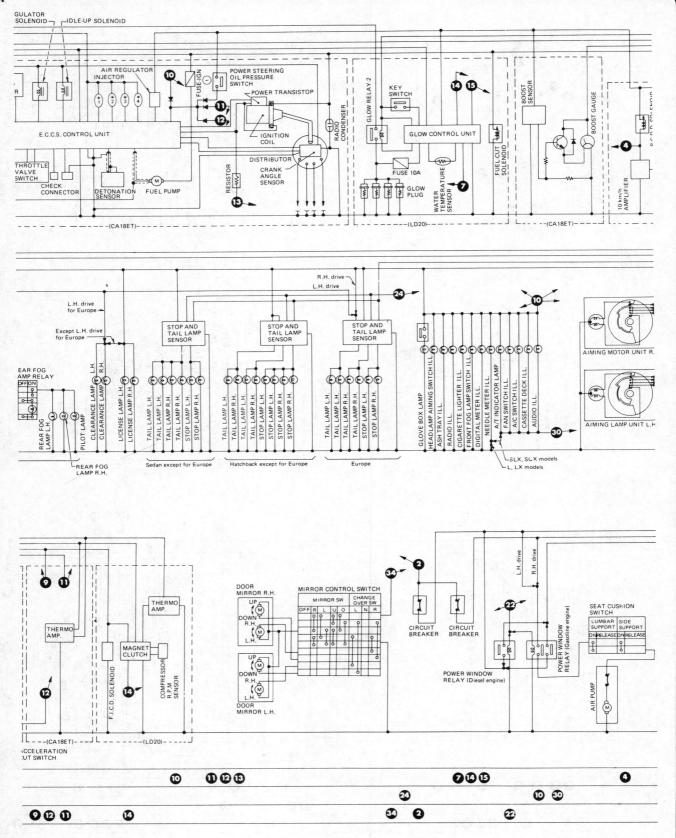

Fig. 12.46 Schematic wiring diagram (all T12 models) (continued)

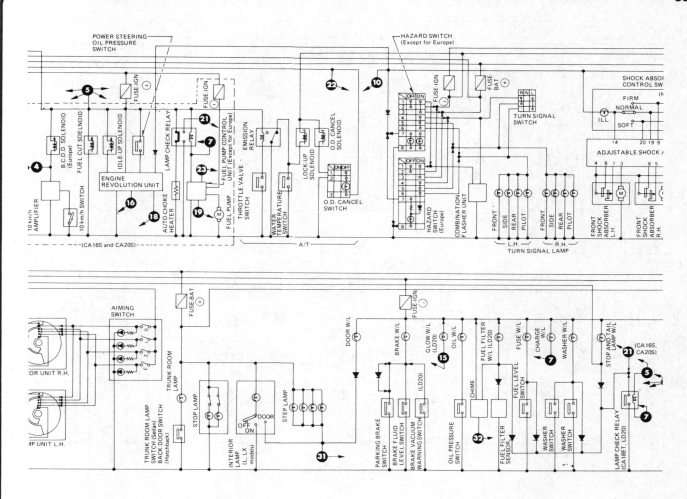

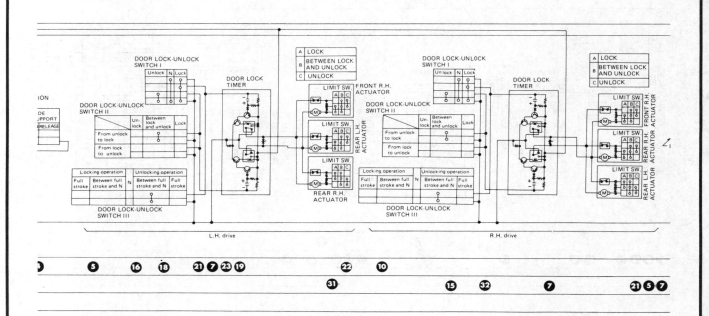

Fig. 12.46 Schematic wiring diagram (all T12 models) (continued)

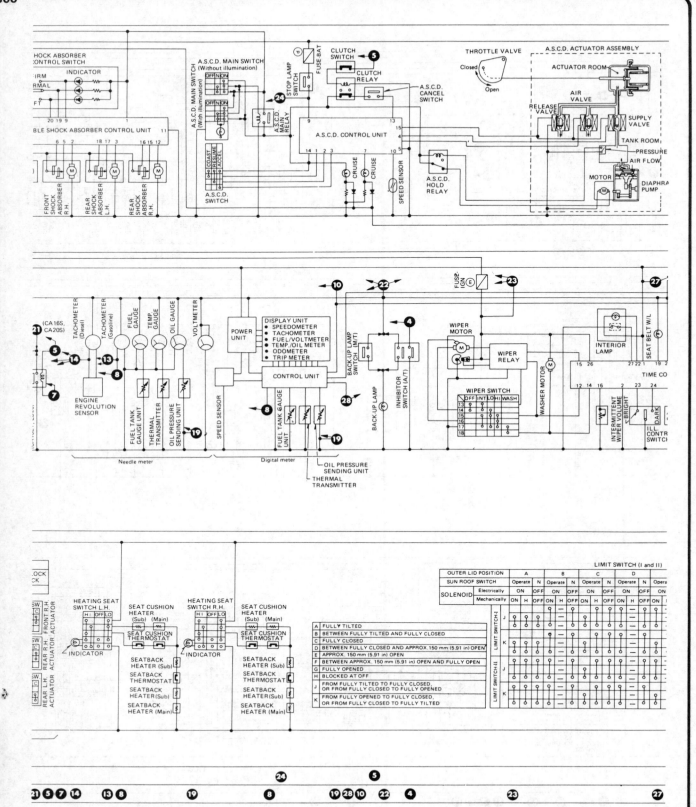

Fig. 12.46 Schematic wiring diagram (all T12 models) (continued)

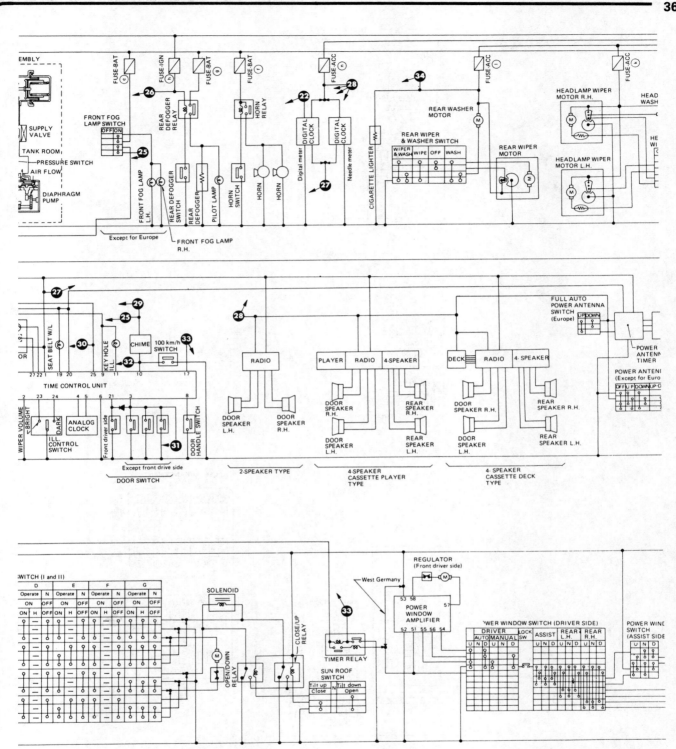

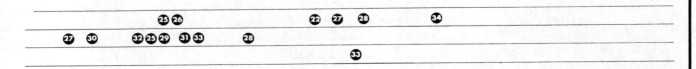

Fig. 12.46 Schematic wiring diagram (all T12) models (continued)

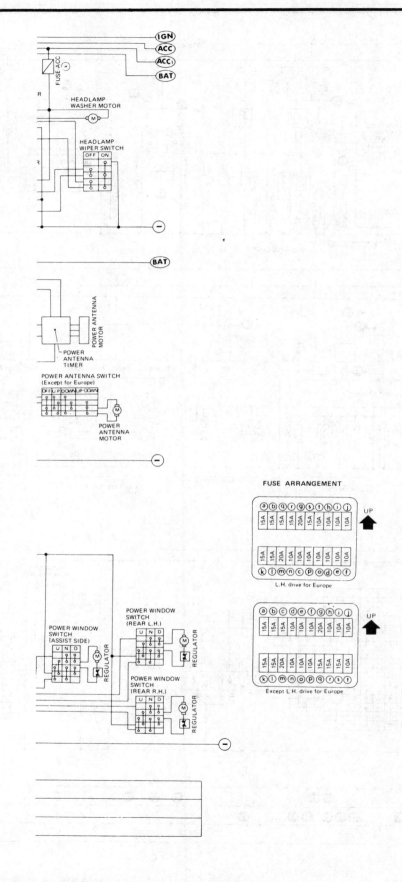

Fig. 12.46 Schematic wiring diagram (all T12 models) (continued)

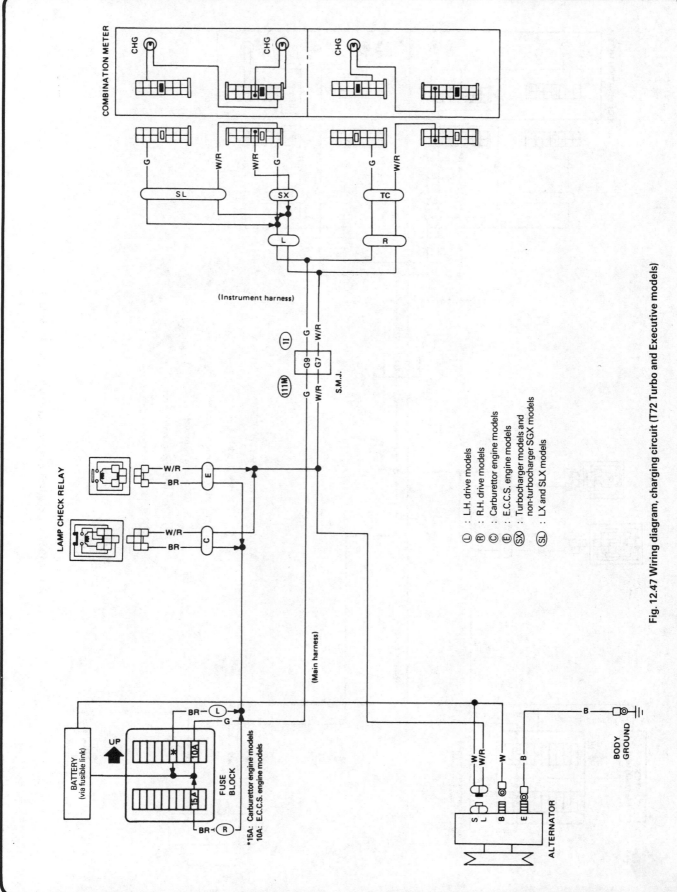

Fig. 12.47 Wiring diagram, charging circuit (T72 Turbo and Executive models)

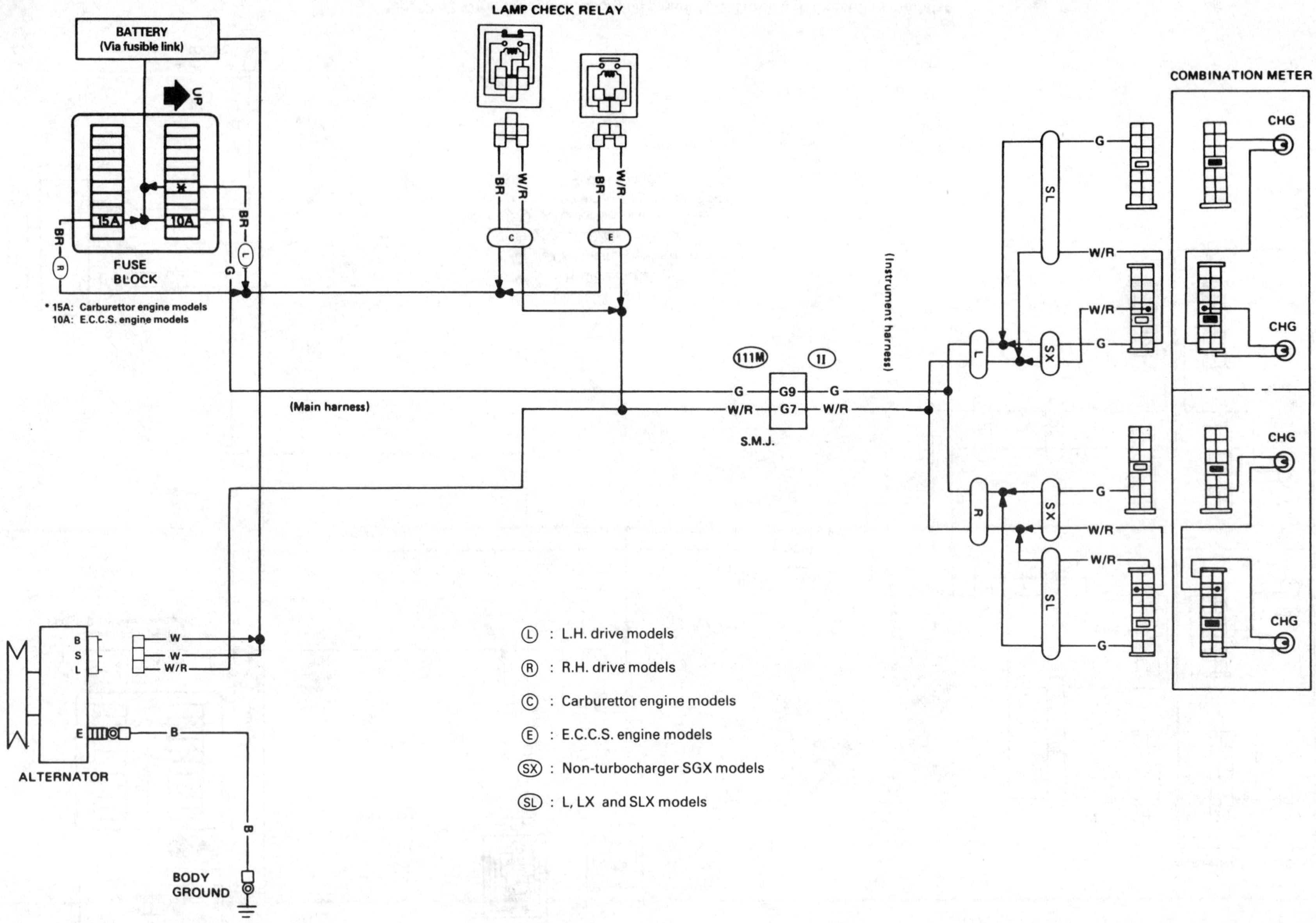

Fig. 12.48 Wiring diagram, charging circuit (all other T72 models)

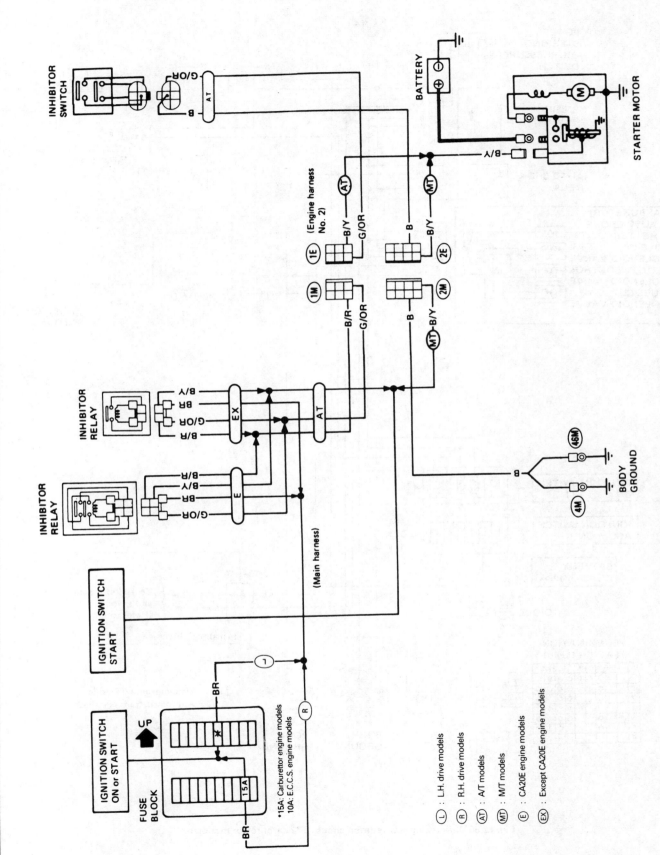

Fig. 12.49 Wiring diagram, starting circuit (all T72 models)

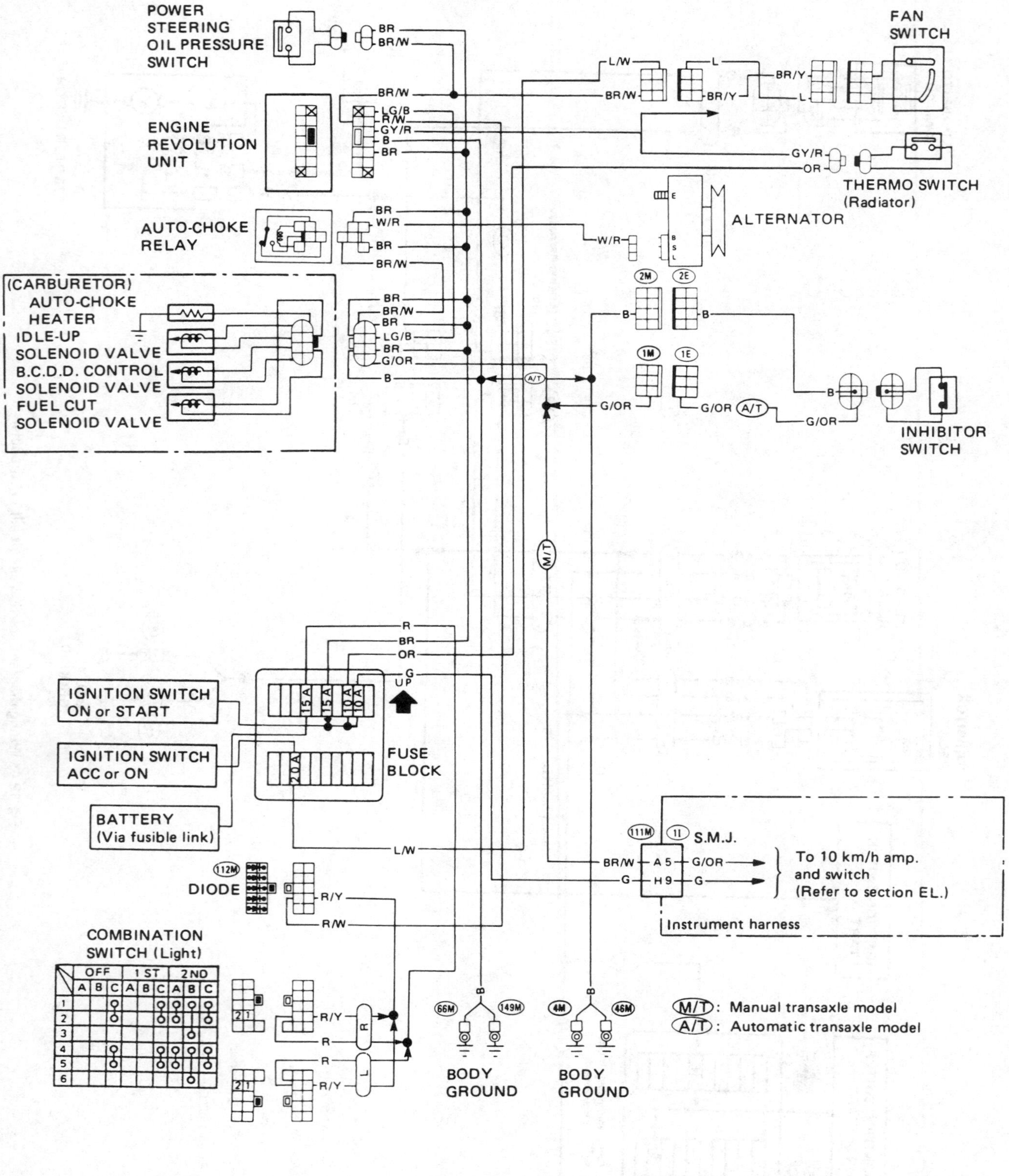

Fig. 12.50 Wiring diagram, ignition circuit (T72 carburettor models)

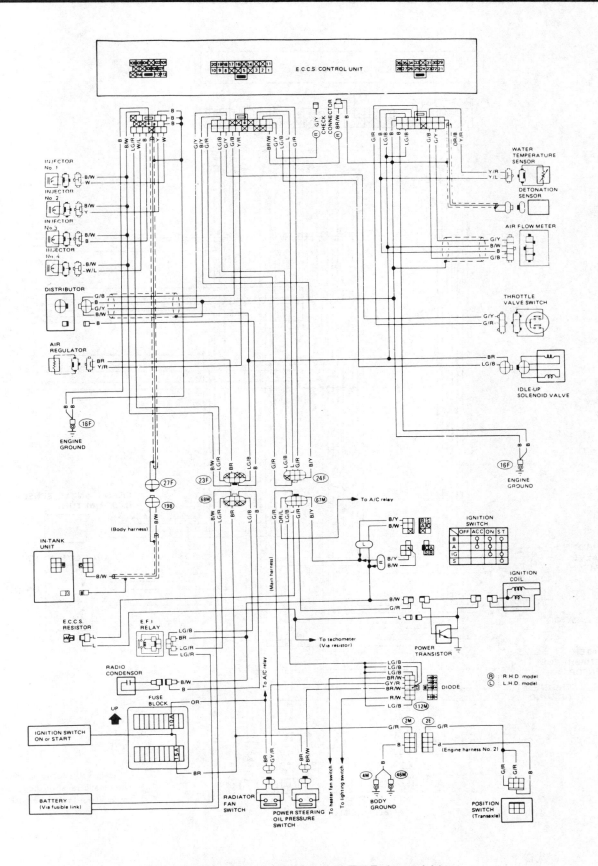

Fig. 12.51 Wiring diagram, ECCS system (T72 Turbo models)

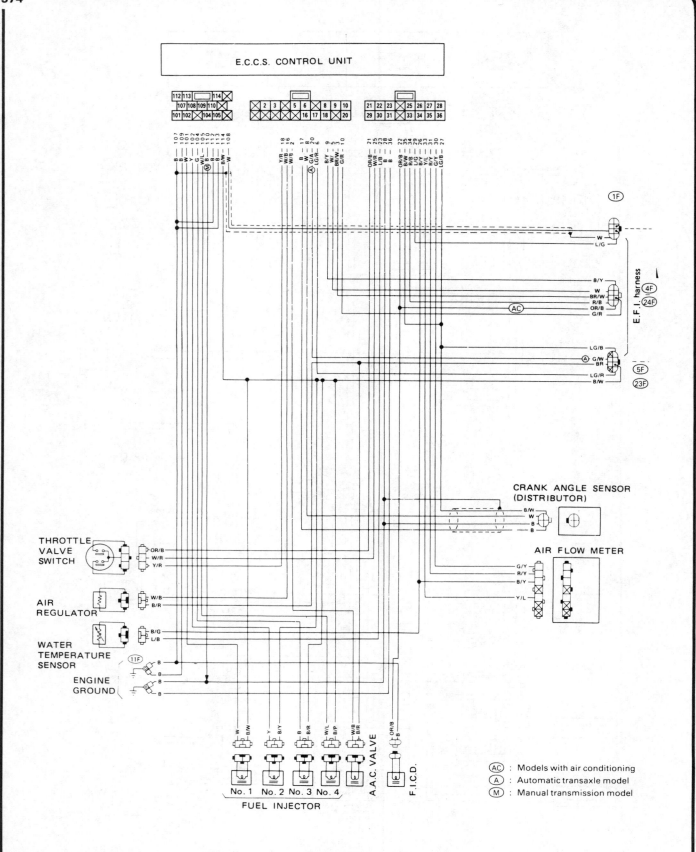

Fig. 12.52 Wiring diagram, ECCS system (T72 2.0 litre fuel injection models)

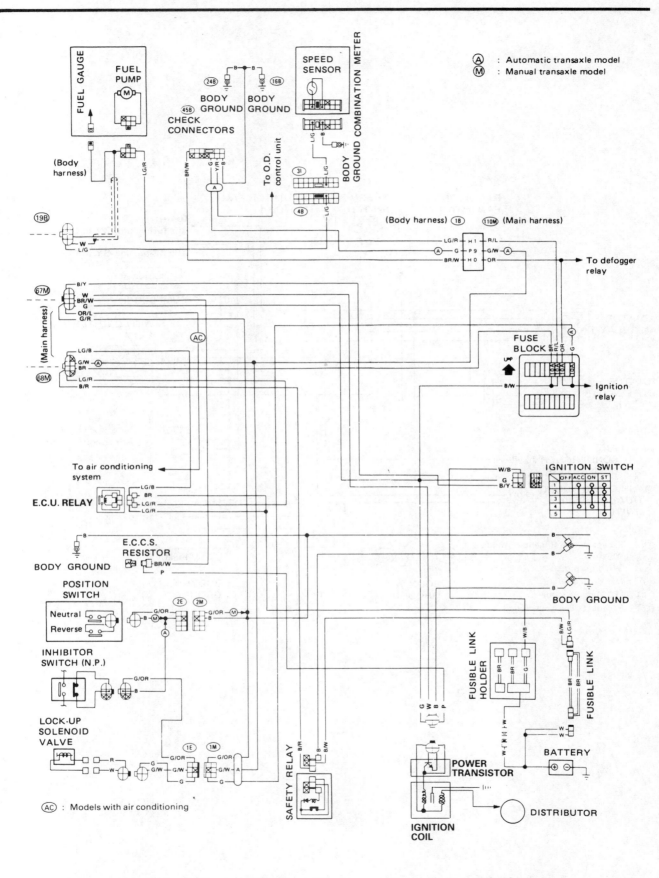

Fig. 12.52 Wiring diagram, ECCS system (T72 2.0 litre fuel injection models) (continued)

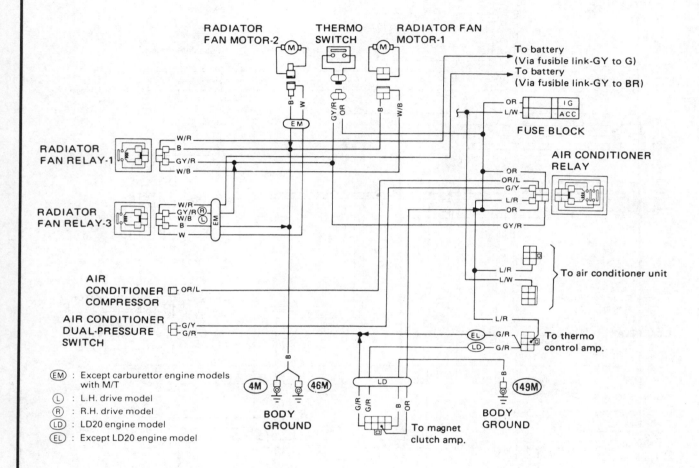

Fig.12.53 Wiring diagram, cooling system (T72 models with air conditioning)

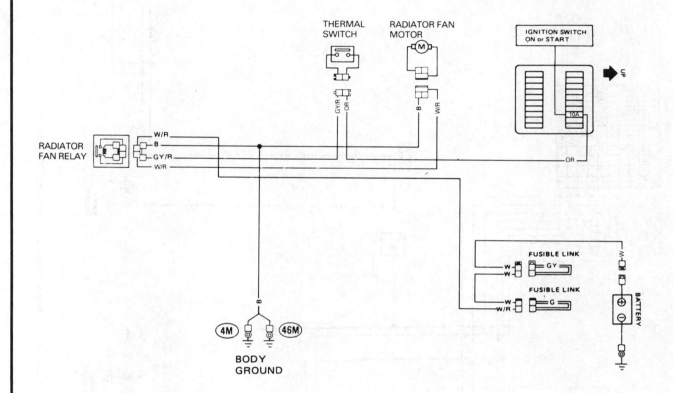

Fig. 12.54 Wiring diagram, cooling system (T72 models without air conditioning)

R.H. DRIVE (WITH DIM-DIP)

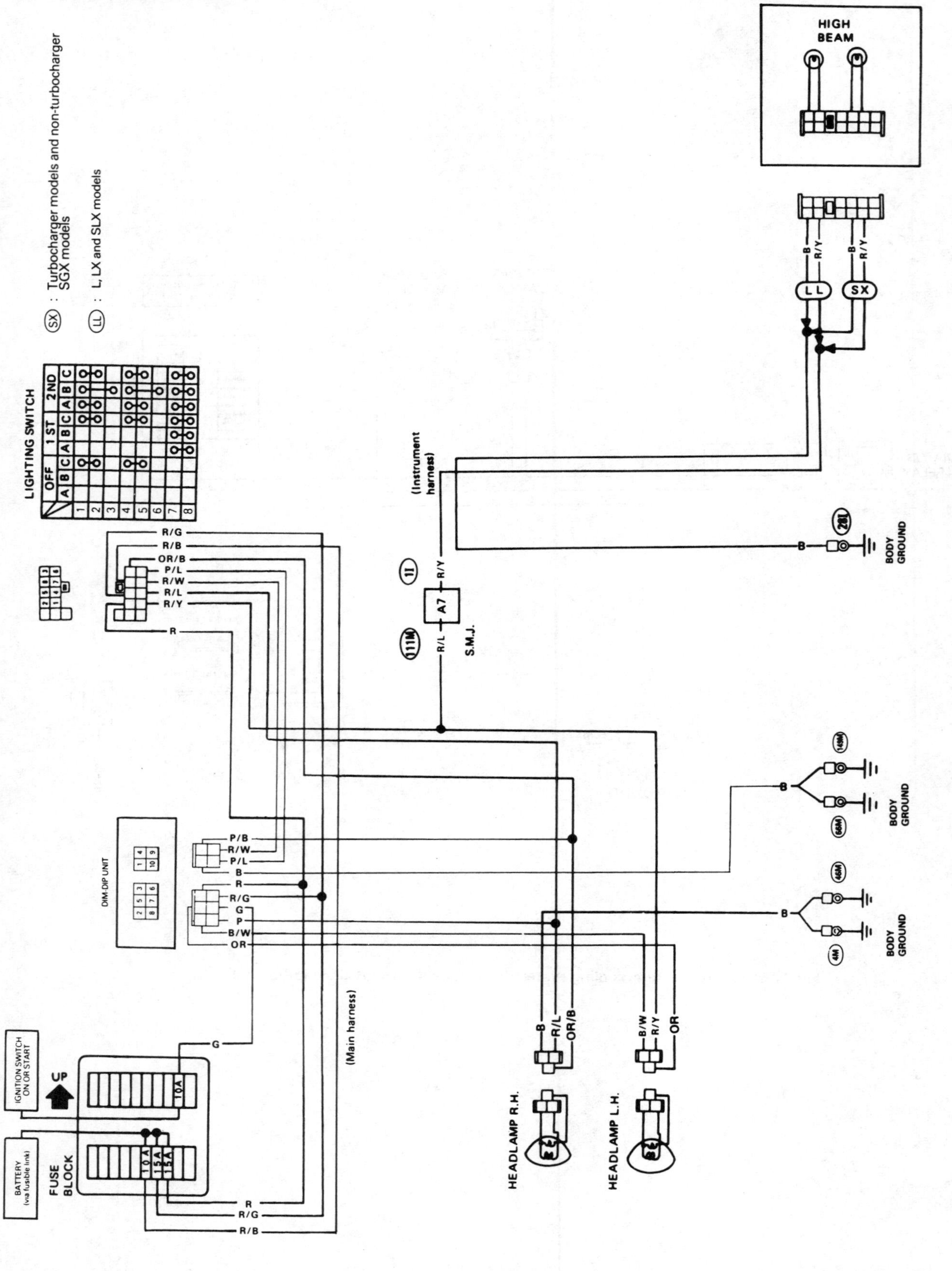

Fig. 12.55 Wiring diagram, headlamp circuit (all T72 models)

HATCHBACK MODEL
(With stop & tail lamp sensor)

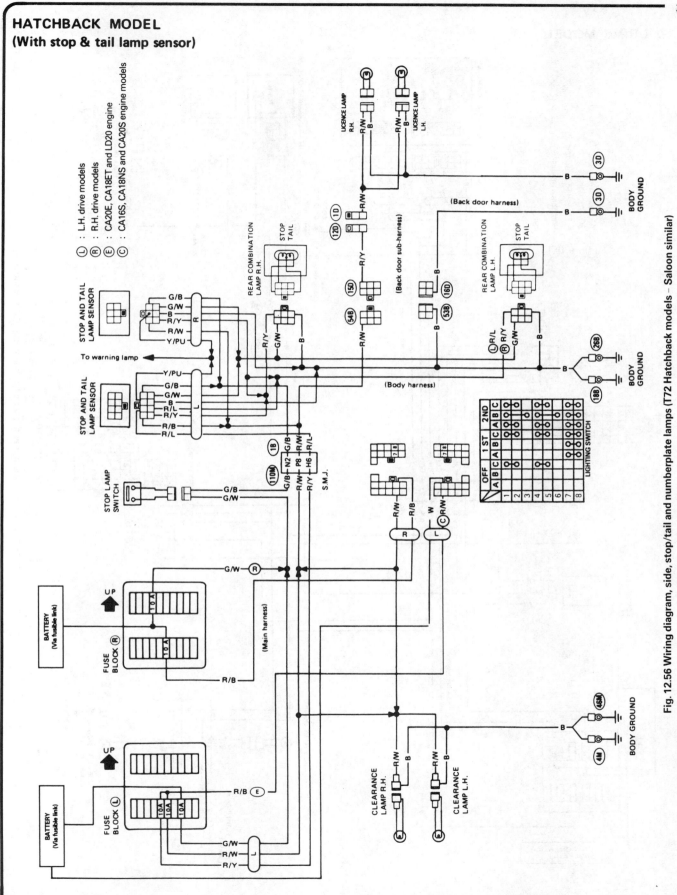

Fig. 12.56 Wiring diagram, side, stop/tail and numberplate lamps (T72 Hatchback models – Saloon similar)

R.H. DRIVE MODEL

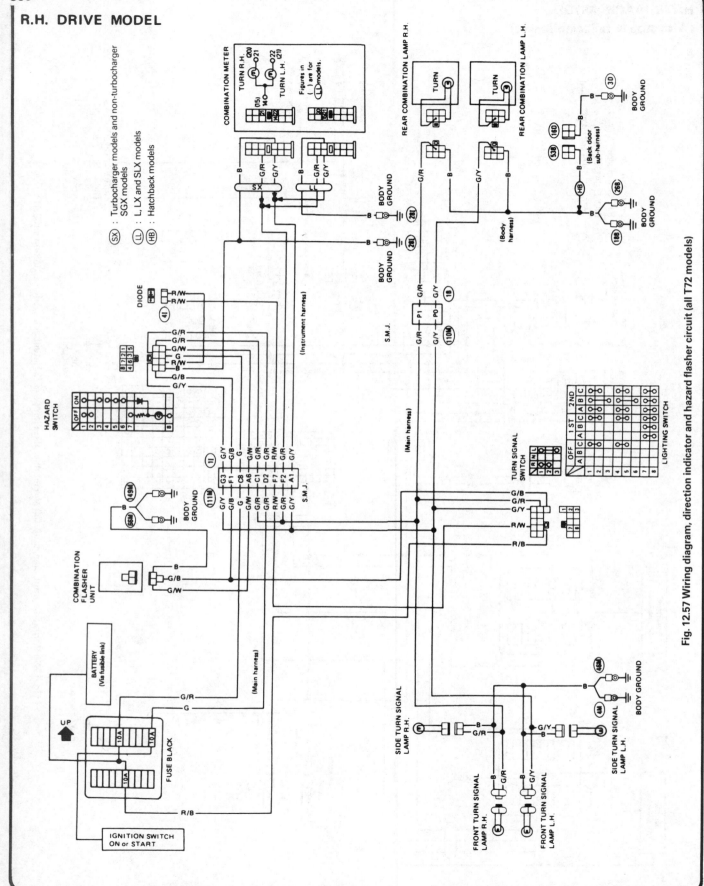

Fig. 12.57 Wiring diagram, direction indicator and hazard flasher circuit (all T72 models)

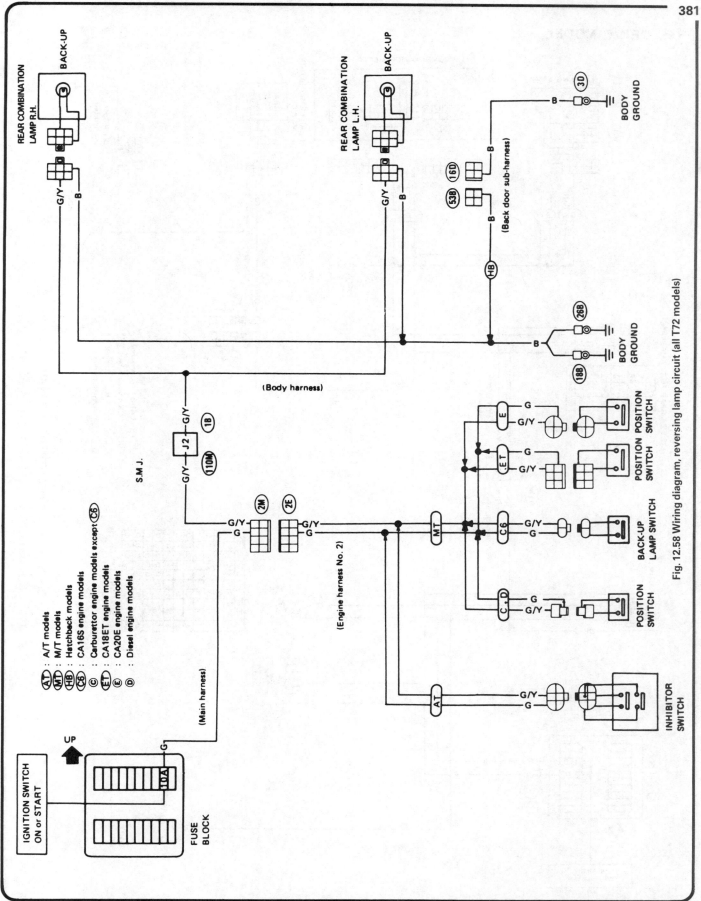

Fig. 12.58 Wiring diagram, reversing lamp circuit (all T72 models)

R.H. DRIVE MODEL

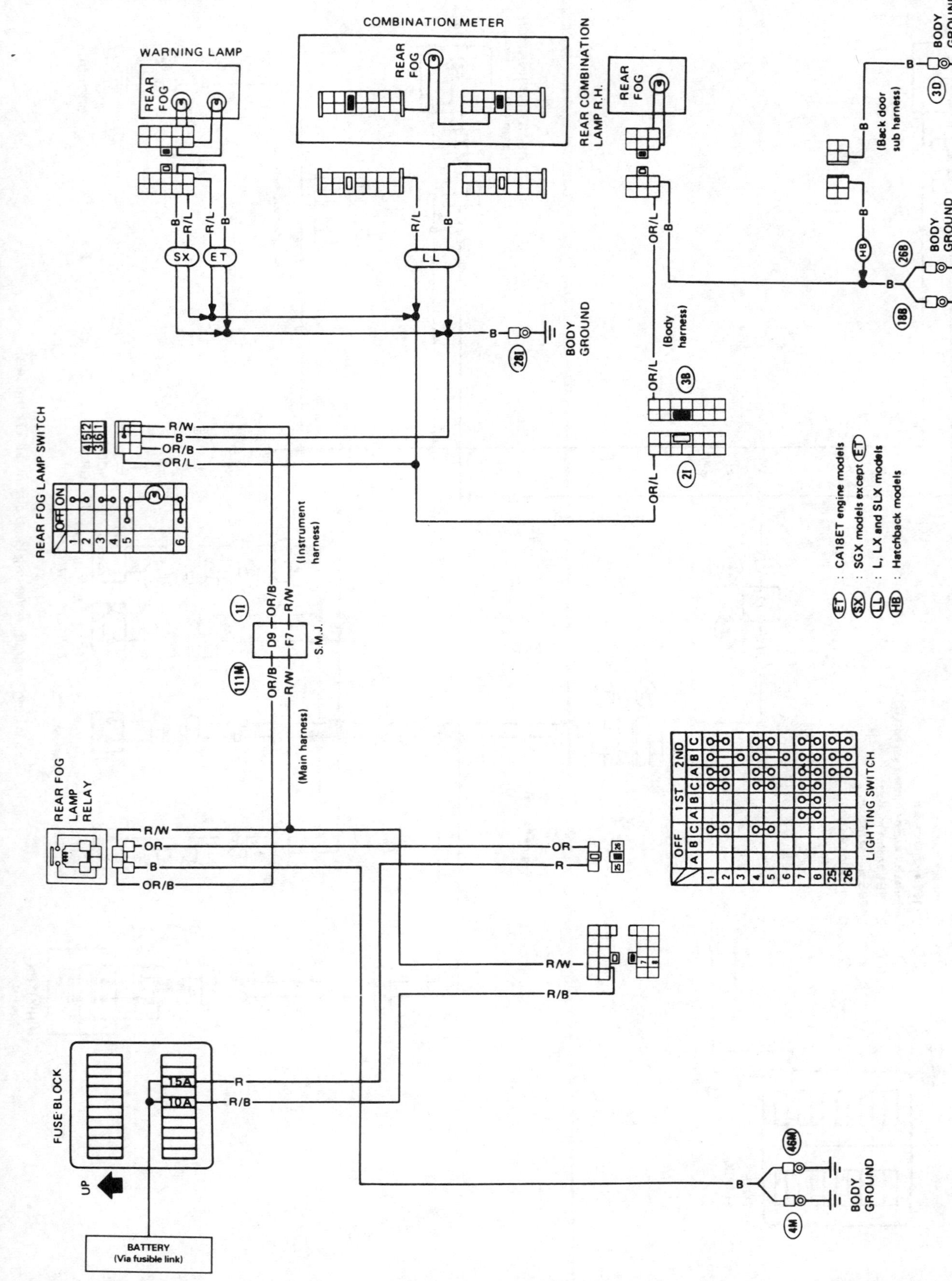

Fig. 12.59 Wiring diagram, rear fog lamp circuit (all T72 models)

R.H. DRIVE MODEL

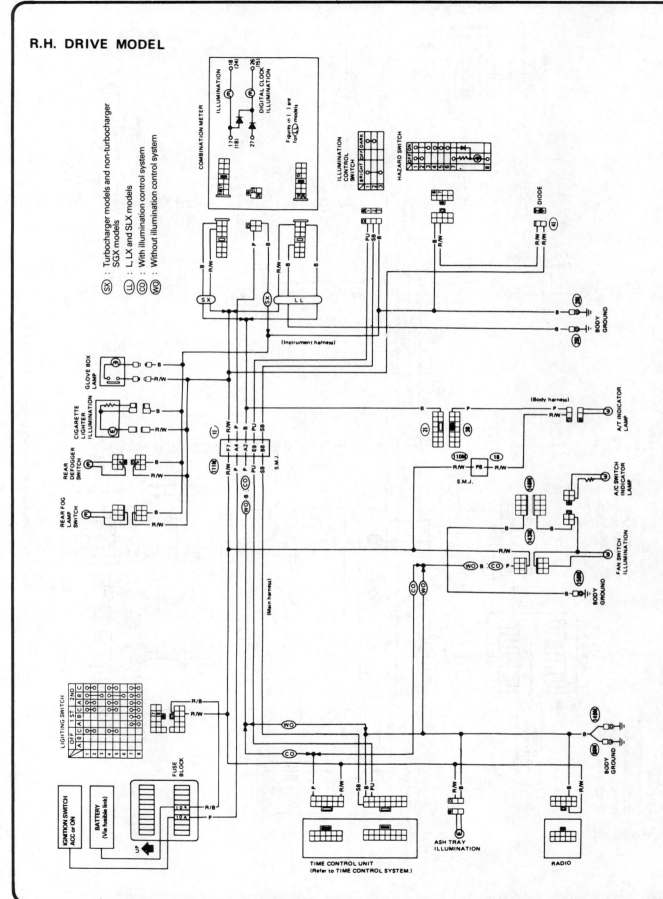

Fig. 12.60 Wiring diagram, illuminated interior fittings (all T72 models)

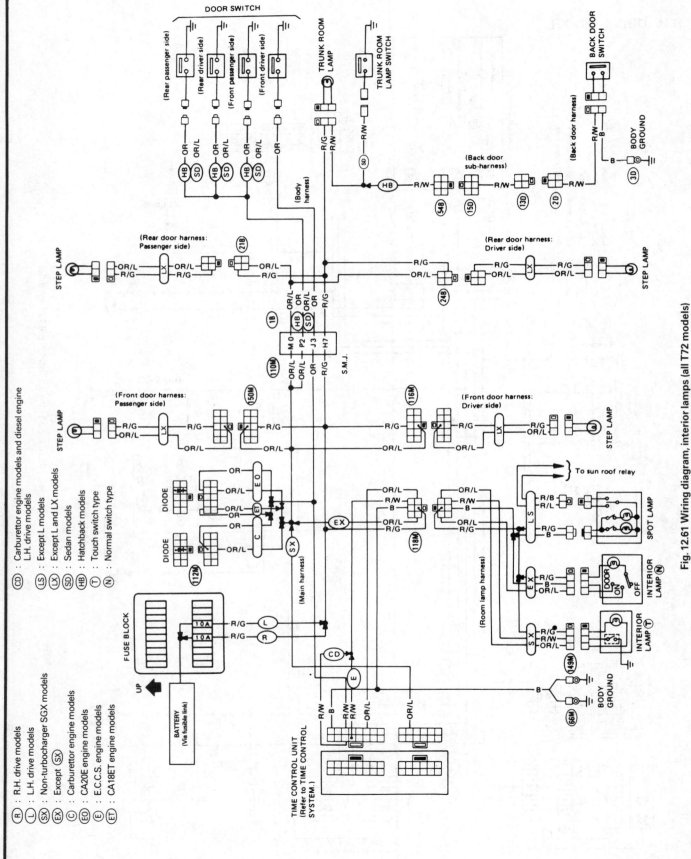

Fig. 12.61 Wiring diagram, interior lamps (all T72 models)

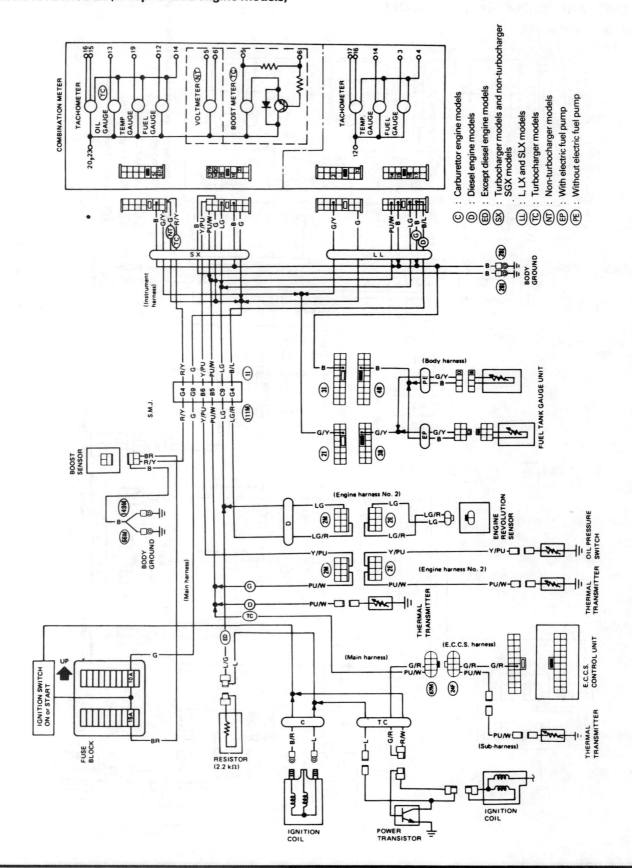

Fig. 12.62 Wiring diagram, instrument panel (all T72 models except 2.0 litre fuel injection engine)

CA18ET AND CA20E ENGINE MODEL
(L.H. drive model)

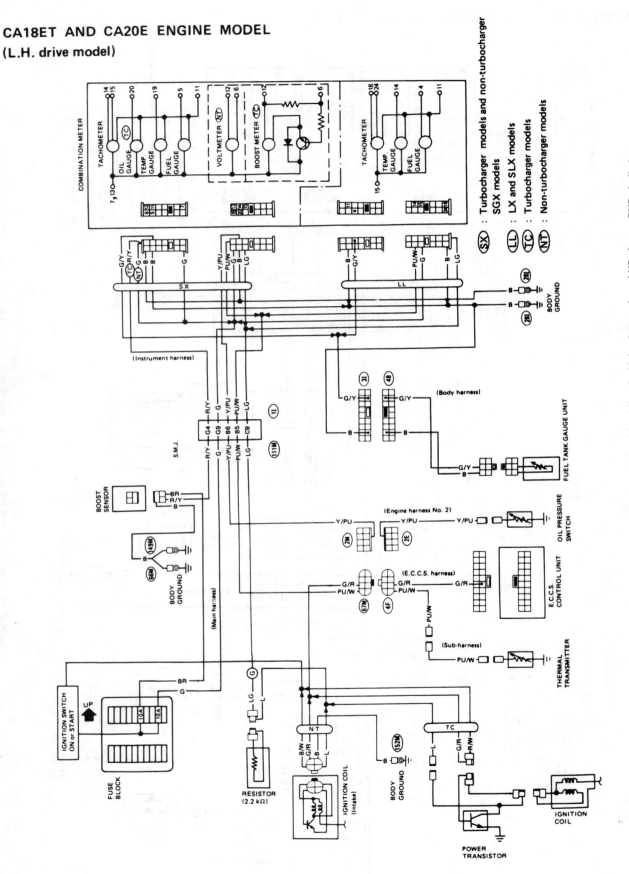

Fig. 12.63 Wiring diagram, instrument panel (T72 models with 2.0 litre fuel injection engine – LHD shown, RHD similar)

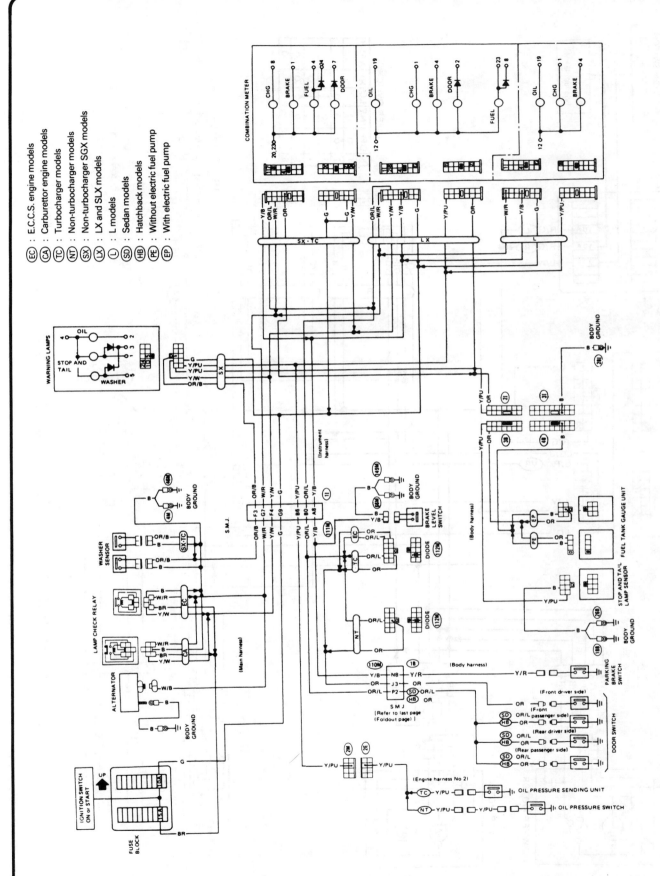

Fig. 12.64 Wiring diagram, warning lamps (all T72 models)

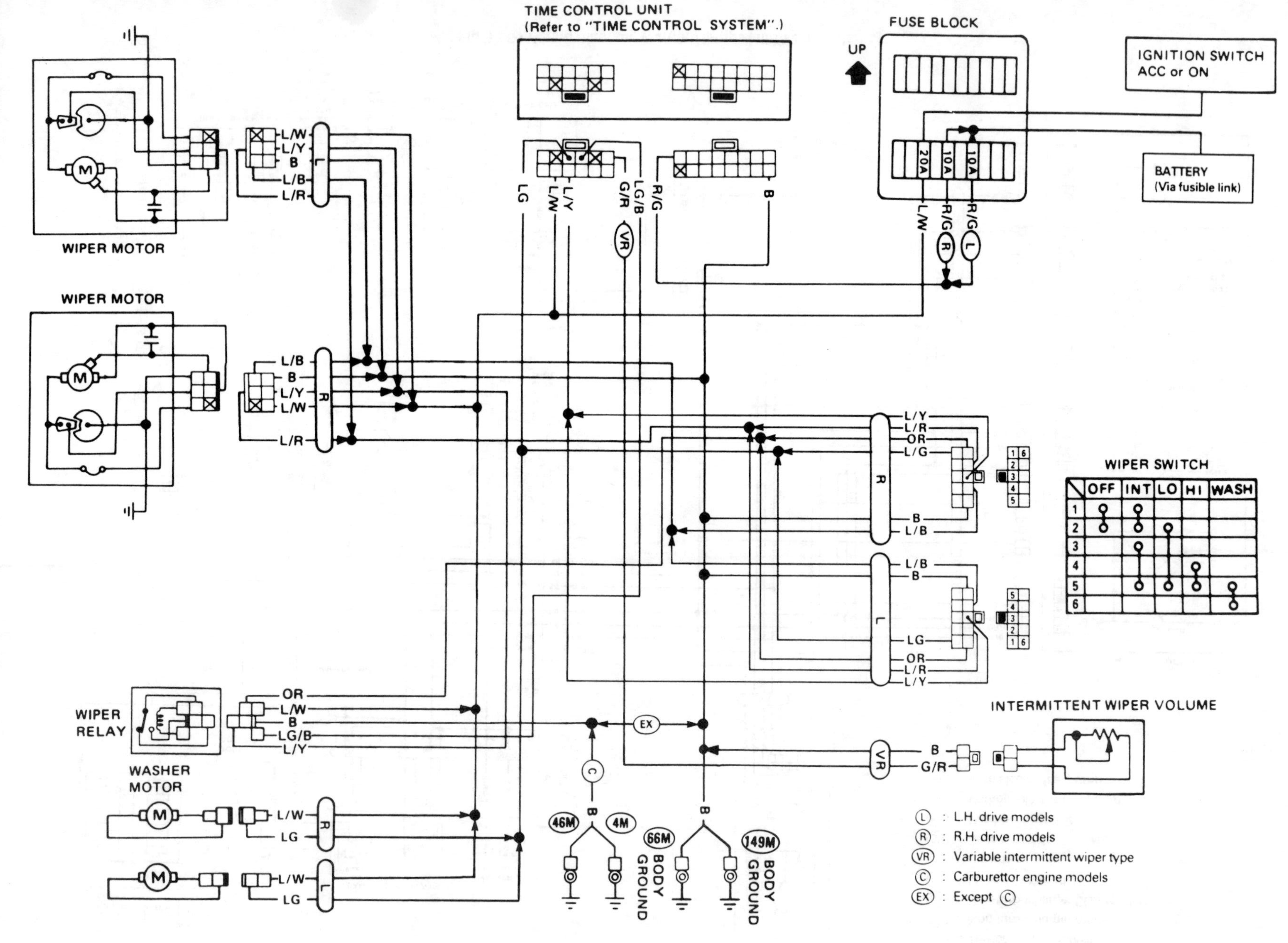

Fig. 12.65 Wiring diagram, windscreen wiper and washer (all T72 models)

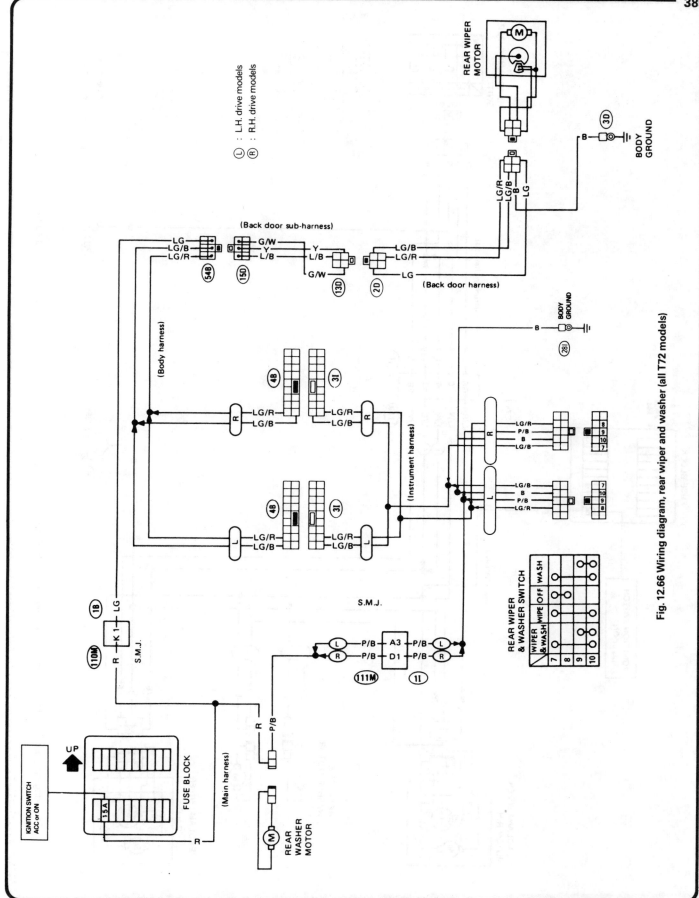

Fig. 12.66 Wiring diagram, rear wiper and washer (all T72 models)

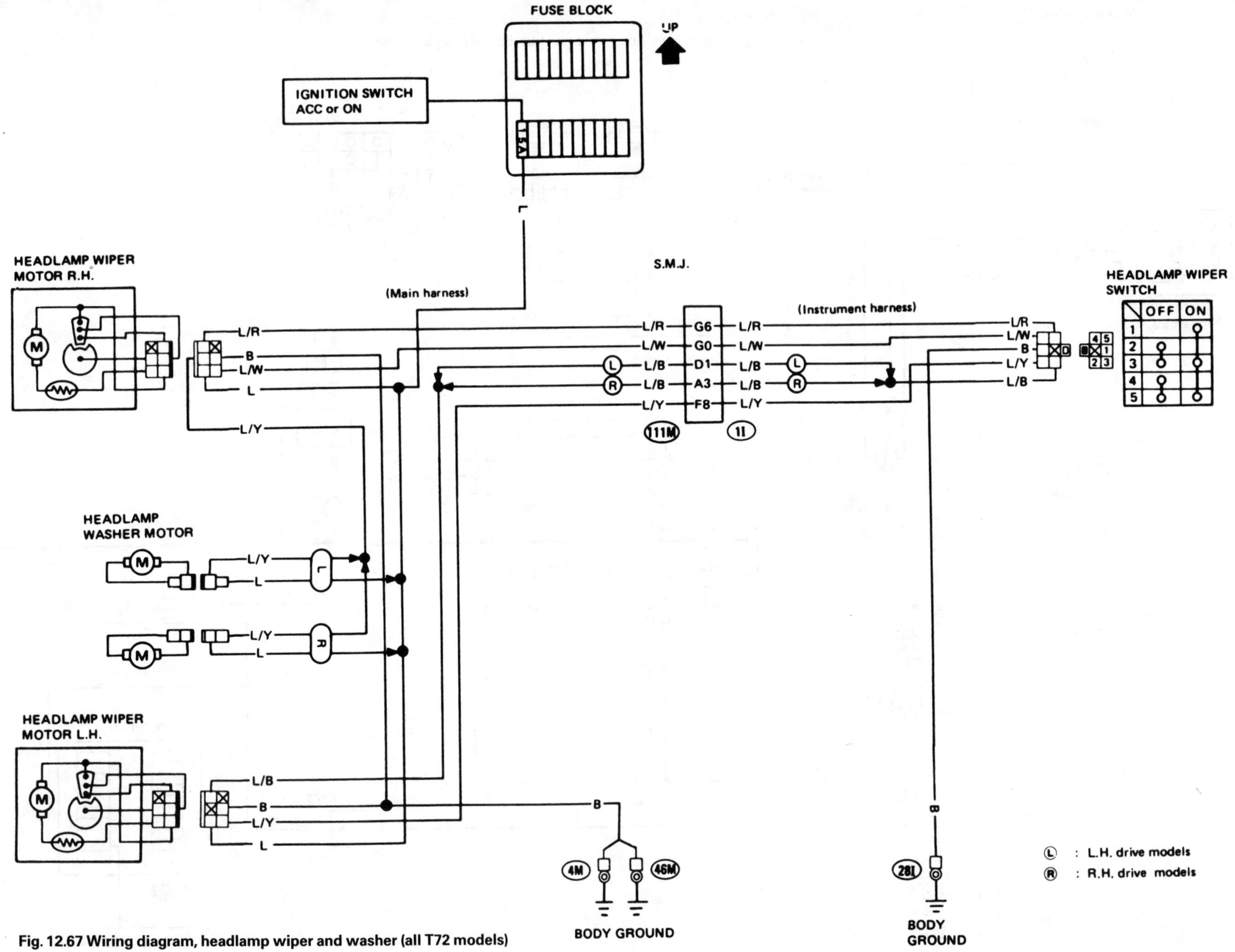

Fig. 12.67 Wiring diagram, headlamp wiper and washer (all T72 models)

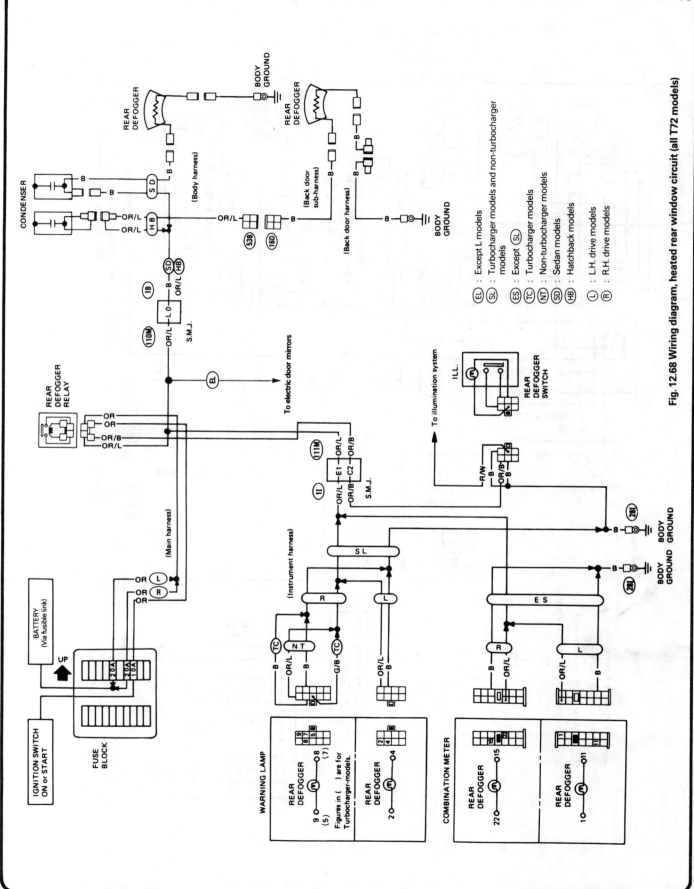

Fig. 12.68 Wiring diagram, heated rear window circuit (all T72 models)

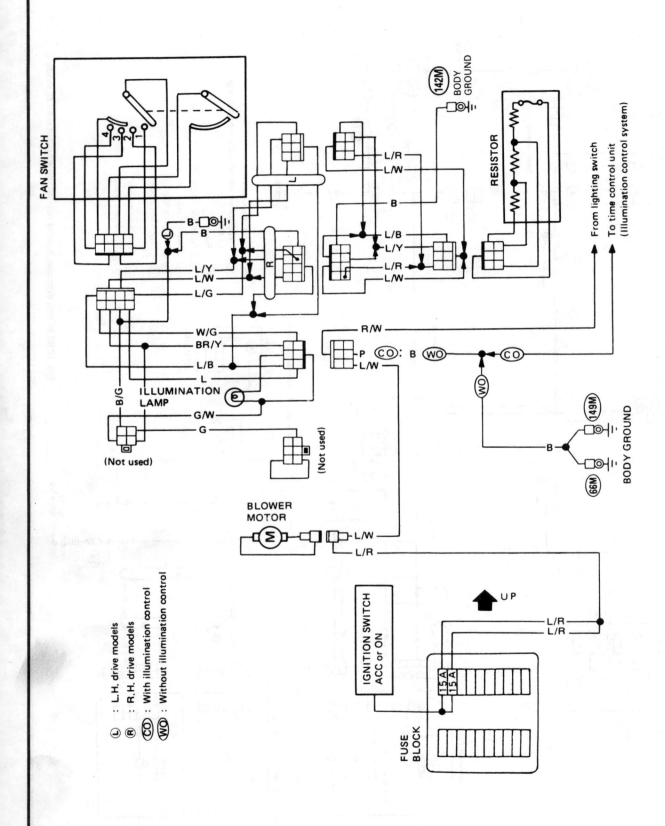

Fig. 12.69 Wiring diagram, heater circuit (all T72 models)

CA ENGINE (Non-turbocharged) MODEL

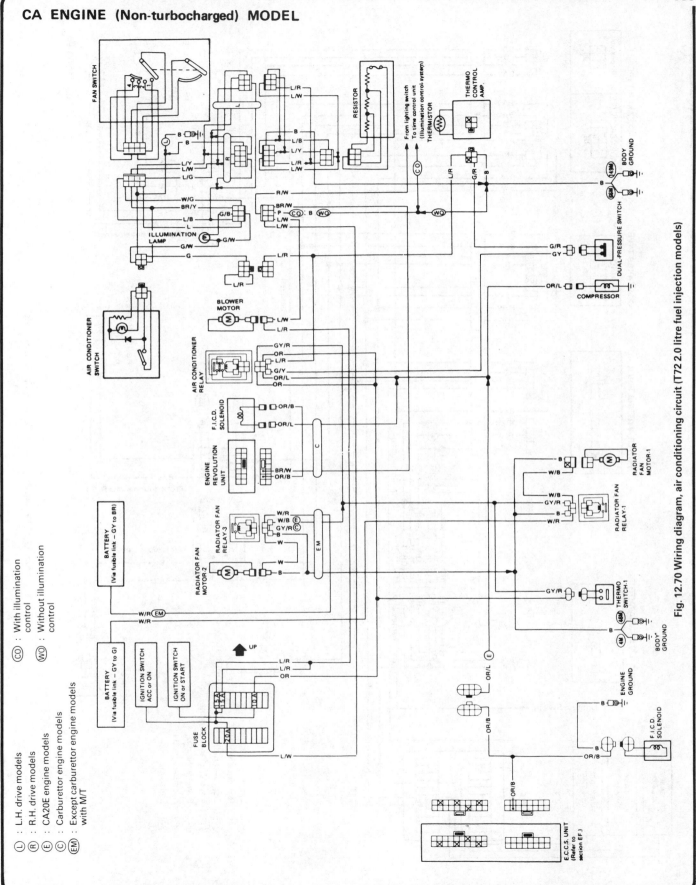

Fig. 12.70 Wiring diagram, air conditioning circuit (T72 2.0 litre fuel injection models)

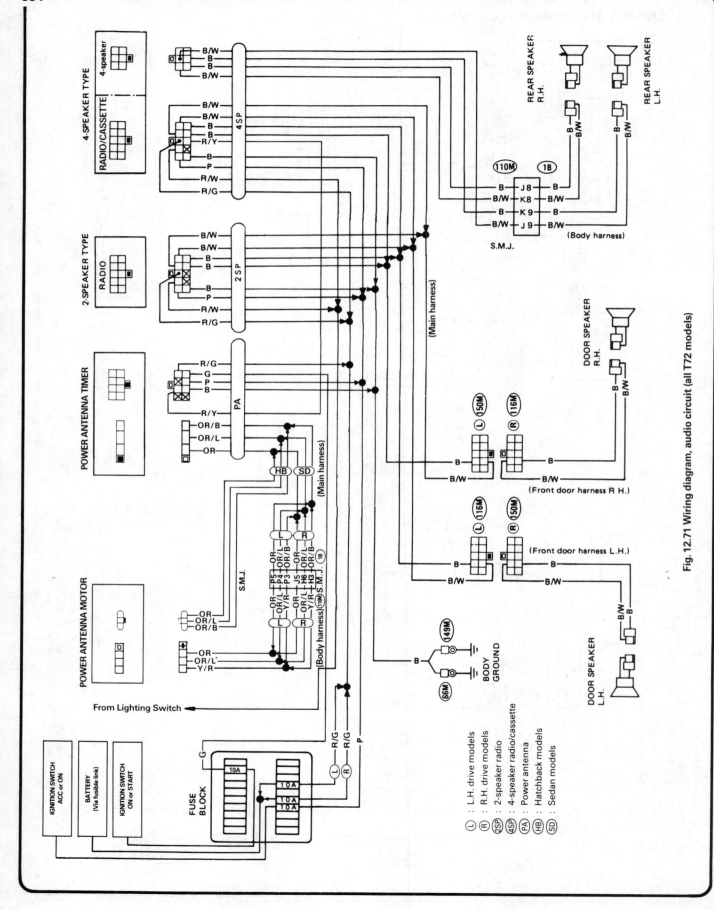

Fig. 12.71 Wiring diagram, audio circuit (all T72 models)

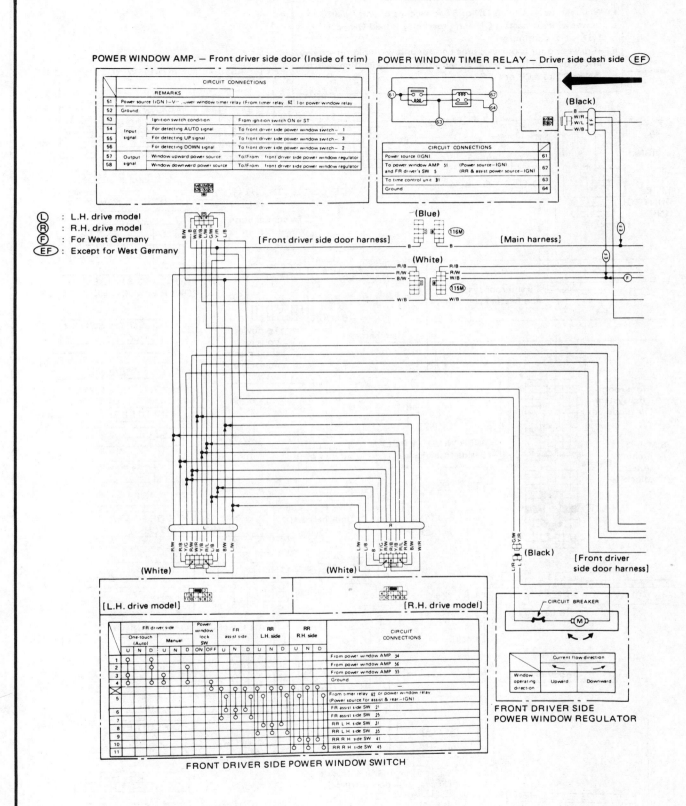

POWER WINDOW AMP. — Front driver side door (Inside of trim)

		CIRCUIT CONNECTIONS	
		REMARKS	
51		Power source (IGN) — Via power window timer relay (From timer relay 62) or power window relay	
52		Ground	
53	Input signal	Ignition switch condition	From ignition switch ON or ST
54		For detecting AUTO signal	To front driver side power window switch— 1
55		For detecting UP signal	To front driver side power window switch— 3
56		For detecting DOWN signal	To front driver side power window switch— 2
57	Output signal	Window upward power source	To/From front driver side power window regulator
58		Window downward power source	To/From front driver side power window regulator

POWER WINDOW TIMER RELAY — Driver side dash side (EF)

	CIRCUIT CONNECTIONS		
Power source (IGN)			61
To power window AMP 51	(Power source–IGN)		62
and FR driver's SW 5	(RR & assist power source–IGN)		
To time control unit 31			63
Ground			64

(Black)

(L) : L.H. drive model
(R) : R.H. drive model
(F) : For West Germany
(EF) : Except for West Germany

(Blue)

[Front driver side door harness]

[Main harness]

(White)

[L.H. drive model]

[R.H. drive model]

(Black)

[Front driver side door harness]

CIRCUIT BREAKER

Window operating direction	Current flow direction	
	Upward	Downward

FRONT DRIVER SIDE POWER WINDOW REGULATOR

	FR driver side				Power window lock SW		FR assist side			RR L.H. side			RR R.H. side			CIRCUIT CONNECTIONS
	One-touch (Auto)		Manual														
	U	N	D	U	N	D	ON	OFF	U	N	D	U	N	D	U	N	D	
1	O			O														From power window AMP 54
2			O			O												From power window AMP 56
3		O	O		O	O												From power window AMP 55
4	⊠		O	O		O												Ground
5							O		O	O	O	O	O	O	O	O	O	From timer relay 62 or power window relay (Power source for assist & rear–IGN)
6									O	O								FR assist side SW 21
7										O	O							FR assist side SW 25
8												O	O					RR L.H. side SW 31
9													O	O				RR L.H. side SW 35
10															O	O		RR R.H. side SW 41
11																O	O	RR R.H. side SW 45

FRONT DRIVER SIDE POWER WINDOW SWITCH

Fig. 12.72 Wiring diagram, power window circuit (all T72 models)

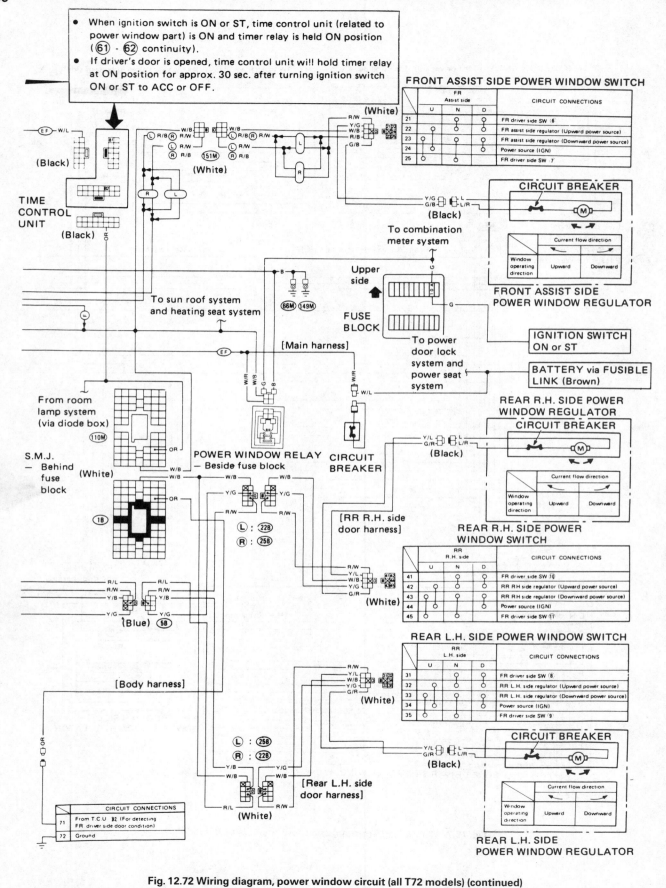

Fig. 12.72 Wiring diagram, power window circuit (all T72 models) (continued)

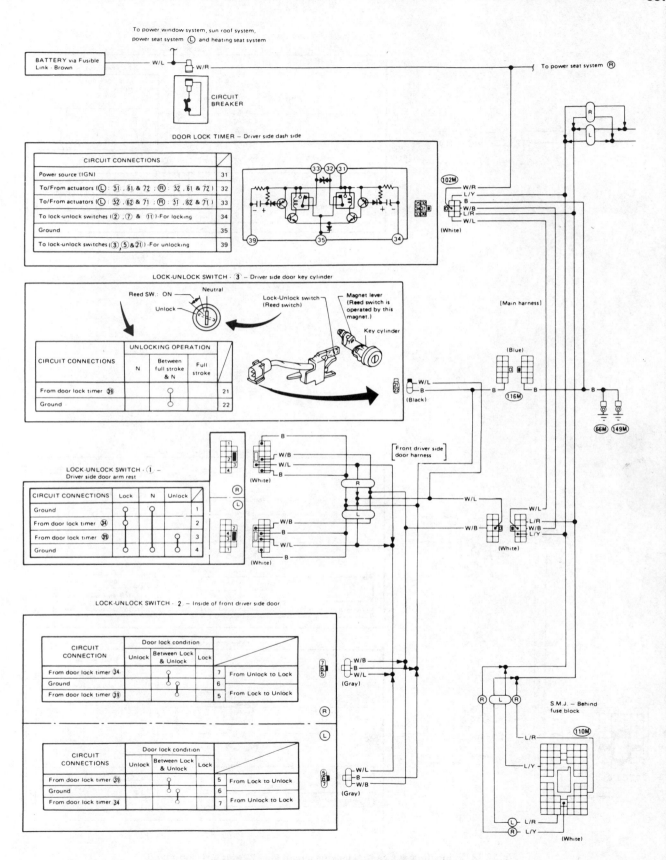

Fig. 12.73 Wiring diagram, central locking circuit (all T72 models)

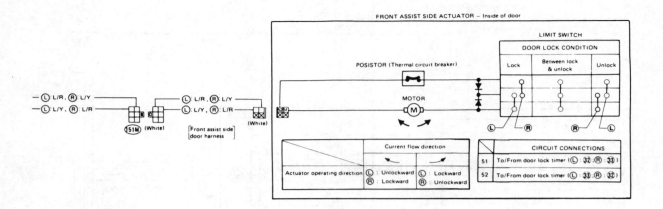

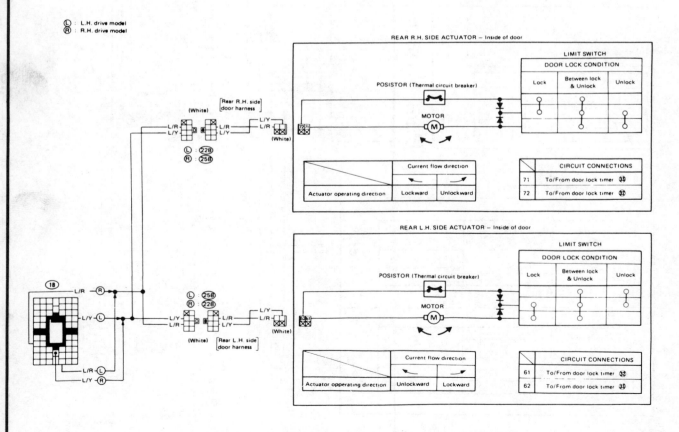

Fig. 12.73 Wiring diagram, central locking circuit (all T72 models) (continued)

Index